JOURNEYS IN SCIENCE

James A. Shymansky   Nancy Romance   Larry D. Yore

Macmillan Publishing Company
New York

Collier Macmillan Publishers
London

Acknowledgments

Artists Claudia Barazi; Bookmakers, Inc./David Wenzel; Publishers' Graphics/Jean Helmer, James Watling; Philip Veloric/ Michael Adams, Suzanne Clee; John Walter and Associates/Larry Mikec/Joel Snyder / *Cover Photo* Clyde H. Smith/ Peter Arnold, Inc. (continued on page 256)

AUTHORS

Dr. James A. Shymansky
Professor of Science Education
University of Iowa
Iowa City, Iowa

Dr. Nancy Romance
Former Science Supervisor
Broward County Schools
Fort Lauderdale, Florida

Dr. Larry D. Yore
Professor of Science Education
University of Victoria
Victoria, British Columbia

CONTRIBUTING AUTHOR

Peter Beugger
Principal
School District 44
North Vancouver, British Columbia

READING CONSULTANT

Dr. Diane L. Schallert
Associate Professor
Department of Educational Psychology
University of Texas
Austin, Texas

SKILLS CONSULTANT

Dr. Michael J. Padilla
Professor
Department of Science Education
University of Georgia
Athens, Georgia

REVIEWER-CONSULTANTS

Joanne Brenneis
Springview Elementary
Miami, Florida

Virginia D. Clark
Principal
Lakeview Elementary
Solon, Iowa

Michele Cox
Onalaska Elementary
Onalaska, Washington

Robbie Currie
Key Elementary
Jackson, Mississippi

Phyllis Dailey
Clinical Supervisor of
 Primary Teachers
Rochester Public Schools and
 Winona State University
Rochester, Minnesota

Shirley DiRado
Pacoima Elementary
Pacoima, California

Dr. James D. Edoff
Director of Curriculum and Instruction
Fitzgerald Public Schools
Warren, Michigan

Sister Patricia Gannon, SND
Associate Director of Curriculum
Diocesan Education Office
Cleveland, Ohio

Dr. Charles LaRue
Elementary Science Coordinator
Montgomery County Public Schools
Rockville, Maryland

Mark C. Schulz
Apostles Lutheran School
Melrose Park, Illinois

Georgeanne Sherrill
Assistant Principal
Una Elementary
Nashville, Tennessee

Fred Stewart
Supervisor of Science
Neshaminy School District
Langhorne, Pennsylvania

Brenda Stokes
West Pensacola Elementary
Pensacola, Florida

Althenia Storr
Lopez Elementary
Seffner, Florida

Sister M. Francis Regis Trojano, C.S.J.
Vice-Principal
St. Theresa School
West Roxbury, Massachusetts
Former Superintendent of Schools
Diocese of Memphis, Tennessee

Anne Tyler
Principal
Boones Mill Elementary
Boones Mill, Virginia

Dr. Barbara Valerious
Ralph Metcalf Magnet School
Chicago, Illinois

Dianne Vann
Science Supervisor
Henry County Schools
Collinsville, Virginia

INTERDISCIPLINARY REVIEWERS

Dr. Beverly Armento (Social Studies)
Associate Professor
Social Studies Education
Georgia State University
Atlanta, Georgia

Dr. Susan Fein (Language Arts)
School District of Pennsylvania
District 5 Educational Service Center
Philadelphia, Pennsylvania

Dr. Alan Kapczynski (Language Arts)
Director of Instructional Service
Ridley School District
Folsom, Pennsylvania

Dr. Cathy Petrosky (Gifted)
Gifted and Talented Coordinator
Cincinnati City Schools
Cincinnati, Ohio

Patricia Schwartz (Mathematics)
Mathematics Consultant
Elmhurst, Illinois

David Sommerfeld (Health & Safety)
Supervisor, Elementary Health
 and Physical Education
Ysleta Independent School District
El Paso, Texas

Macmillan Publishing Company
866 Third Avenue
New York, New York 10022
Collier Macmillan Canada, Inc.

Printed in the United States of America

Pupil Edition: ISBN 0-8445-5302-6

9 8 7 6 5

CONTENTS

Unit 2   The World's Oceans   44

Unit 4   Measuring All Around You   112

Unit 6 Foods and You 178

Unit 7 Environments 206

Look at the pictures. Why are the children wearing raincoats and carrying umbrellas? What helped the children to guess what kind of weather was coming?

This is a unit about weather. As you study this unit, you will learn how people find out about weather. You will learn why weather is important to people.

What Is Weather?

What was the air like when you came to school this morning? Was the air warm or cold? Was the air wet or dry? Was the air moving or still?

When you tell about the air, you are telling about the weather. Weather is what the air outside is like each day.

Our Weather		
	Morning	Afternoon
Monday		
Tuesday		
Wednesday		
Thursday		
Friday		
Saturday		
Sunday		
Monday		
Tuesday		
Wednesday		
Thursday		
Friday		
Saturday		
Sunday		

What is the weather outside?

What to Do

1. Make a chart like the one in the picture.

2. Observe the weather outside twice a day. Record your observations on the chart.

3. At the end of two weeks, look at your chart.

What kind of weather occurred most often?
On what days did the weather change?
Did one kind of weather usually follow another?

Different Kinds of Weather   There are many kinds of weather. Look at the pictures. Each one shows a different kind of weather. Does either picture show the kind of weather you are having today?

Tell about the kind of weather you see in each picture. What kind of conditions did you tell about? What clothes would you wear if you were in each of these places? What kind of games could you play?

The weather in a place might change often. The weather might be cloudy and cool one day and sunny and warm the next. How has the weather where you live changed this week?

THINKING

Sometimes the weather can change quickly. The boys in the picture are swimming. What should they do if they see a storm coming?

Temperature

Do you know what the temperature outside is today? When you know the temperature of the air, you know how warm or how cold the air is.

Air temperature is measured with a thermometer. When the air gets warmer, the liquid in a thermometer goes up. When the air gets cooler, the liquid in a thermometer goes down. What temperature does the thermometer in the picture show?

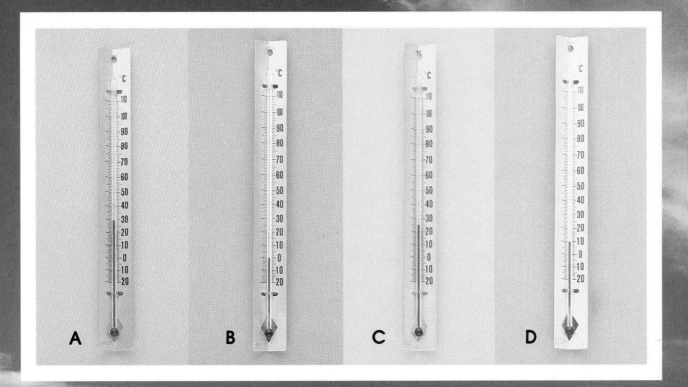

Look at the thermometers in the picture. Some show warm temperatures. Some show cool temperatures.

Divide a sheet of paper into four parts. Label the parts A, B, C, and D. Look at thermometer A. Does it show a warm temperature or a cool temperature? In box A, draw a picture of yourself having fun outside on a day with a temperature like the one shown on thermometer A. Then draw pictures for the temperatures on thermometers B, C, and D.

Wind

Wind is moving air. Wind can bring changes in the weather. Sometimes the wind blows slowly. A slow wind, called a breeze, can make you feel cooler.

Sometimes the wind blows fast. Usually, the wind blows faster when rain is coming. During a storm, the wind blows very fast.

Look outside. Is the wind blowing fast or slowly? How can you tell?

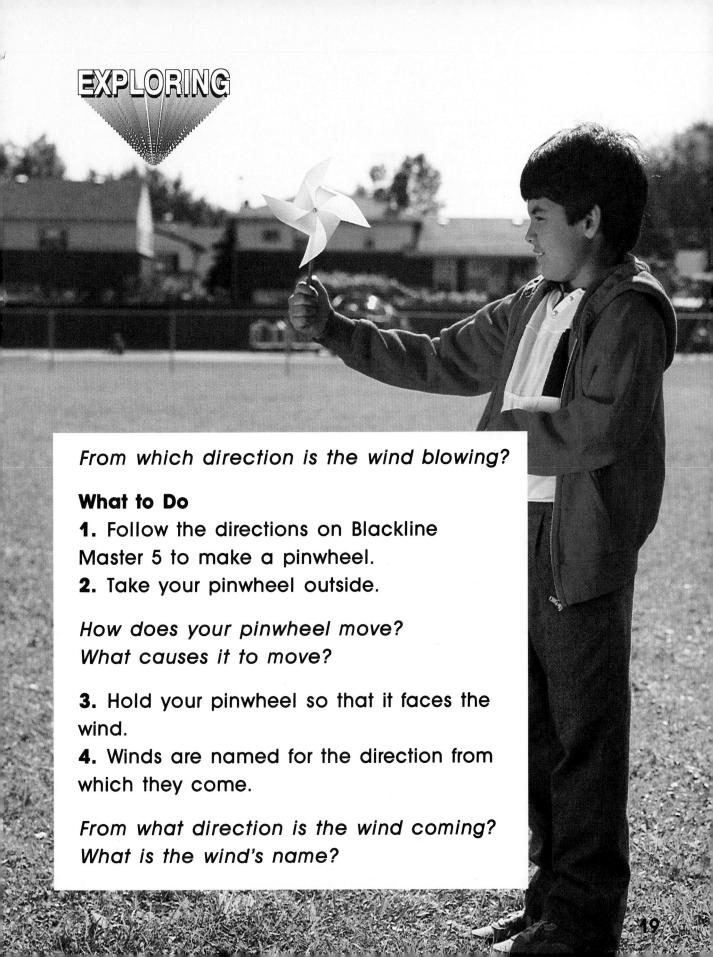

EXPLORING

From which direction is the wind blowing?

What to Do

1. Follow the directions on Blackline Master 5 to make a pinwheel.
2. Take your pinwheel outside.

How does your pinwheel move?
What causes it to move?

3. Hold your pinwheel so that it faces the wind.
4. Winds are named for the direction from which they come.

From what direction is the wind coming?
What is the wind's name?

Measuring Wind People use tools to help them find out about the wind. The object shown in the picture on the left turns when the wind blows on it. It is used to measure how fast the wind is blowing.

The picture on the right shows a weather vane. When the wind blows, the weather vane turns and points into the wind. The weather vane shows the direction from which the wind is blowing. You name the wind by this direction.

Fair-Weather Clouds

Water in the form of a gas is in the air. When this water collects around bits of dust in the air, it forms clouds.

There are many shapes of clouds. These shapes may even look like people or animals. What are some of the shapes of clouds you have seen?

Looking at Clouds   People can sometimes tell what the weather will be by looking at clouds. Look at the picture of clouds on this page. These very large clouds are white and fluffy. Usually, these clouds mean that the weather will be fair. Fair weather is clear and sunny. Most of the time, these clouds form in the afternoon and disappear in the evening.

The clouds shown on this page look like feathers or curls. They are very high in the sky where it is very cold. Because it is so cold, the water in the clouds freezes and becomes tiny bits of ice. These clouds often mean that the fair weather will change.

Storm Clouds

Look at the picture of clouds on this page. These clouds are very dark and close to the earth. They cover the sky so that you cannot see the sun. These clouds usually mean that stormy weather is coming soon. It may rain or snow.

Look at the sky. What kind of clouds do you see? What kind of weather may be coming? Draw a picture of the clouds and write down what you think the weather will be like tomorrow.

Tomorrow, observe the weather to see if your prediction matches the weather. How did the clouds help you to predict what the weather would be?

Rain and Snow

Clouds contain small drops of water. Sometimes these drops come together to make bigger drops. If these drops are large enough, the drops will fall to the ground as rain.

In some places, it rains often. Other places have very little rain and are very dry. Does it rain often where you live? During what time of the year does it rain most? Where are some dry parts of our country?

Sometimes the water drops in clouds become very cold. The water drops freeze, forming ice crystals. The tiny ice crystals fall to the ground as snowflakes.

THINKING

During what kind of weather does snow usually fall? Why do you think this is so?

How much water is in snow?

What to Do

1. Put a large glassful of snow into a jar.

2. Mark the jar to show how much space the snow takes up.

3. Let the snow melt.

4. Mark the jar to show how much space the water takes up.

Which took up more space, the snow or the water? How can you tell?

5. Pour the water back into the glass.

Does the water fill the glass? What part of the glass does the water take up?

Thunderstorms

During the summer, storms often occur when there are large, dark clouds in the sky. These storms are called thunderstorms. They bring rain, strong winds, lightning, and thunder.

Lightning is a bright flash of light in the sky. It forms in a thundercloud.

Thunder is a loud sound that happens during thunderstorms. Thunder is caused by the lightning as it passes through the air.

THINKING

How would you describe lightning and thunder? How do they make you feel?

Storm Safety   Thunderstorms are very powerful. Lightning can harm houses. Sometimes people are killed by lightning.

People can do certain things to be safe during a thunderstorm.

Do not stand under a tree.

Do not stay on or near water.

Do not stay by open windows or doors.

Do not use the telephone.

Stay inside a building or a car.

The person in the picture is going back to the shore. Why?

Hurricanes

Sometimes very strong storms called hurricanes form over the ocean. Hurricanes bring heavy rains and strong winds. The winds in a hurricane blow in a circle. Look at the picture of the storm. Which way are the winds blowing?

The middle of the swirling clouds is called the eye of the storm. This is a very calm place. The wind is almost still and there is very little rain. Where is the eye of the storm shown in the picture?

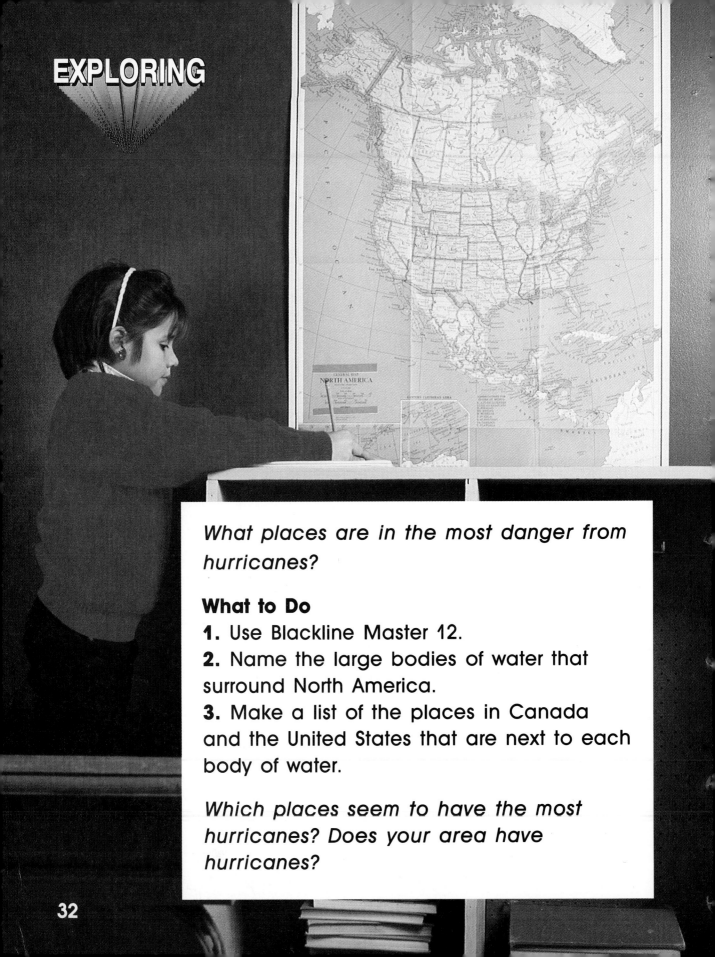

What places are in the most danger from hurricanes?

What to Do

1. Use Blackline Master 12.

2. Name the large bodies of water that surround North America.

3. Make a list of the places in Canada and the United States that are next to each body of water.

Which places seem to have the most hurricanes? Does your area have hurricanes?

Hurricane Damage   Hurricanes may move from the ocean to the land. The winds of a hurricane can damage trees and buildings. The heavy rains can cause streets and buildings to flood.

Weather forecasters tell people that a hurricane is coming. People then have time to protect themselves and their property. What can people do to protect their property?

SEARCHING

Hurricanes are given the names of people. What names have been used for hurricanes?

Tornadoes

A tornado is a kind of windstorm. It forms over land. A tornado looks like a large funnel-shaped cloud. The winds in a tornado blow in a circle.

Tornadoes may only last for a few minutes, but they are the most powerful of all storms. Tornadoes usually destroy everything in their path. Tornadoes can lift and move cars, houses, and trees.

SEARCHING

Where in North America do most tornadoes occur?

    Tornadoes happen very quickly. There is little time to tell people that a tornado is coming. For this reason it is hard for people to protect themselves from a tornado.

    If people know a tornado is coming, they can do several things to protect themselves. People can seek shelter in a basement. They can also stay away from windows and doors.

Weather and the Seasons

You have learned that weather changes from day to day. Weather also changes with the seasons.

Look at the pictures. They show summer weather. During summer, most days are sunny. The weather in most places is warm. Most thunderstorms occur during the summer.

In fall the weather begins to get cooler. Many places have rainy weather. In some places, leaves change color. Hurricanes are most likely to occur during late summer and early fall.

THINKING

How does the weather in fall affect living things?

Winter and Spring   These pictures show winter weather. Winter is the coldest season. In some places the weather during winter is very cold. Snow falls and the water in lakes and ponds freezes.

Other places do not have snow during winter. These places may just have cool weather. Other places have rain. What is the winter weather like where you live?

During spring, the weather becomes warmer. The snow and the ice melt. Some places have much rain. Tornadoes are most likely to occur during spring.

SEARCHING

Think about the kind of weather the place where you live has during the summer, fall, winter, and spring. Find out about a place that has different kinds of weather during the seasons.

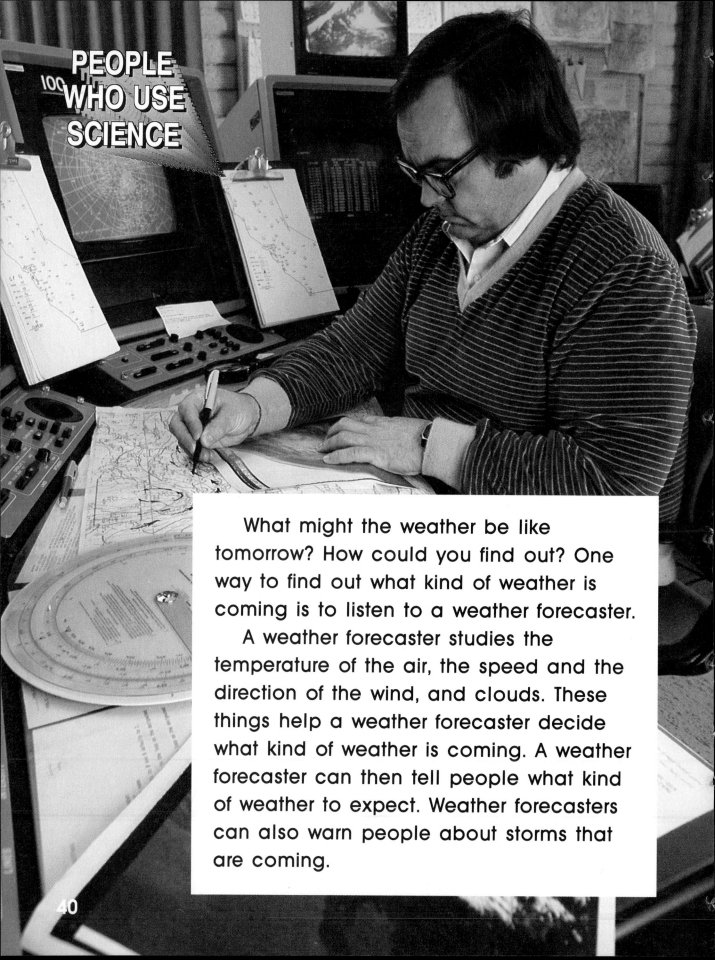

What might the weather be like tomorrow? How could you find out? One way to find out what kind of weather is coming is to listen to a weather forecaster.

A weather forecaster studies the temperature of the air, the speed and the direction of the wind, and clouds. These things help a weather forecaster decide what kind of weather is coming. A weather forecaster can then tell people what kind of weather to expect. Weather forecasters can also warn people about storms that are coming.

Journey Highlights

Weather is what the air outside is like each day.

Temperature tells how warm or cold the air is. A thermometer is used to measure temperature.

Wind is moving air. As the air moves, it can bring changes in weather.

Water in the air can form clouds.

Thunderstorms, hurricanes, and tornadoes are storms. People must do certain things to be safe during storms.

The weather changes with the seasons.

Journey Wrap-up

Science Words

Match each picture with the word it shows. You will not use all the words.

e 1.

g 2.

c 3.

b 4.

5.

a. temperature   **d.** fall   **g.** lightning

b. wind   **e.** tornado   **h.** cloud

c. winter   **f.** thunder   **i.** hurricane

Using What You Have Learned

What kind of weather is coming? Use the words *fair* or *stormy*.

stormy   *fair*   *fair*   *stormy*

1.   **2.**   **3.**   **4.**

Tell what way the wind is blowing from in each picture. How can you tell?

5.   **6.**

Things to Do

1. Draw a poster showing how to be safe during a storm. Explain the poster to your classmates.

2. Listen to a weather report on the TV or the radio each day for a week. Write down the type of weather that is predicted for the next day. The next day, check the weather. Is the weather forecast always correct? Why do you think this is so?

Much of the earth is covered by water. Most of this water is in the oceans. Oceans are the largest bodies of water on the earth.

Many things live in the ocean. People depend on the ocean for food and for other things.

How do people explore the ocean?

Water, Water Everywhere

Look at the picture of our world on the right. What can you tell about our planet from this picture? What are the large blue areas?

The pupils below are looking at a globe. How is it like our world?

Almost all the water on the earth is in the oceans and seas. Where do you find other water on the earth?

SEARCHING

How many oceans does the earth have? What are the names of the oceans? Which ocean is the largest?

EXPLORING

How is salt water different from water on land?

What to Do

1. Fill two jars with the same amount of water.

2. Add salt to one jar, a teaspoonful at a time, until no more salt will dissolve.

3. Gently place a hard-boiled egg in each jar. Describe what happens.

4. Remove the eggs and place an ice cube in each jar. Describe what happens.

5. Fill in the chart on Blackline Master 2.

Salt Water   The water in the oceans is different from the water you drink. The water in the oceans is salty. Ocean water is called salt water. The water on land is not salty.

SEARCHING

Put some salt on a piece of colored paper. Look at the salt carefully with a magnifier. Pour salt into a glass of water. What happens to the salt? Keep adding salt. What do you think will happen?

When salt disappears in water, we say that the salt dissolves. The salt disappears when it is dissolved, but it is still there.

The Water Cycle

How do you feel when the sun shines on you? What happens to wet clothes hanging on a clothesline on a sunny day?

The sun shines on the oceans of the earth. It warms the water. As the water gets warm, some of the tiny droplets of water move very fast. The droplets move so fast that they bounce up into the air.

Clouds   You have learned that water droplets
in the air mix with dust to make clouds. When
this happens, the water in the air changes
back to liquid water.

Winds push the clouds across the sky. What
happens to clouds when they cannot hold any
more water? The water falls to the earth as
rain, snow, sleet, or hail.

Look at the diagram. The pattern of water rising into the sky and falling back to the earth is called the water cycle. The water cycle happens over and over. What parts of the water cycle can you see?

The water cycle keeps providing fresh water for lakes and rivers. The rivers take water from the land back to the ocean. Where did the land get its water?

The clouds bring water

Water goes back into the air

Water returns to the ocean

THINKING

Every drop of water that was on the earth a long time ago is still on the earth today. Why is this so?

Waves, Currents, and Tides

Have you ever watched the water in a lake, a sea, or an ocean? If you have, then you know that the water is never still.

Water in lakes, seas, and oceans moves as waves. Waves are movements on the surface of the water. Most waves are caused by the wind.

SEARCHING

Try to make some waves. Fill a cake pan with water. Use a straw to blow at the water. What happens to the surface of the water? How could you make bigger waves?

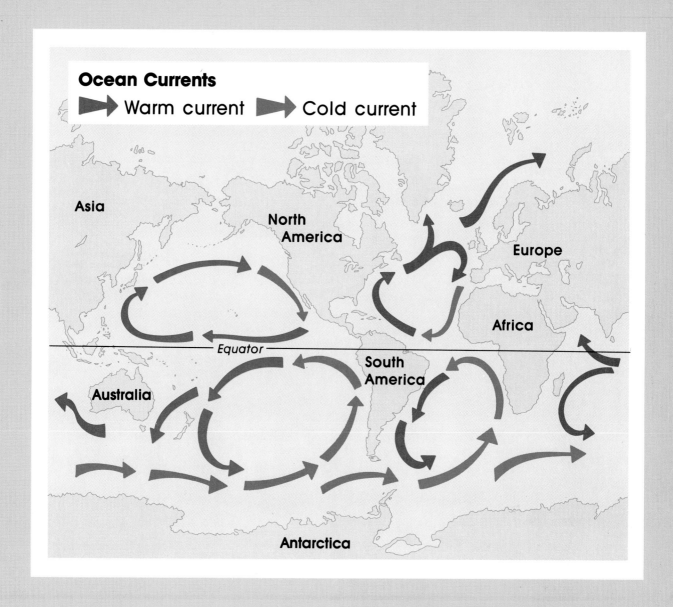

Ocean Currents
Warm current   Cold current

Asia

North
America

Europe

Africa

Equator

South
America

Australia

Antarctica

Ocean water also moves in currents. A
current is a stream of water flowing through
the ocean.

Some currents in the ocean are cold. Some
are warm. Look at the map on this page.
Where do the cold currents come from? Where
do the warm currents come from?

Tides   Tides are a special kind of movement of water in the oceans. Tides are the rise and fall of the level of the ocean. This happens twice a day.

At low tide, the water along the seashore is very shallow. At high tide, the water along the seashore is deep. Which picture shows low tide? Which picture shows high tide?

THINKING

Find out what happens to the living things along the shore at each tide.

Getting to the Bottom of It

Have you ever been to a beach near the ocean? If so, what happens as you walk directly out into the water?

The land under the water slopes downward away from the shore. The land keeps sloping downward to the bottom of the ocean.

The Ocean Bottom   Imagine that you are in a submarine at the bottom of the ocean. Close your eyes and think about your new place. Suppose you were to look out the window. What would you expect to see?

The bottom of the ocean has mountains, plains, and valleys. Some of the mountains are volcanoes. Many kinds of animals live on or near the bottom of the ocean.

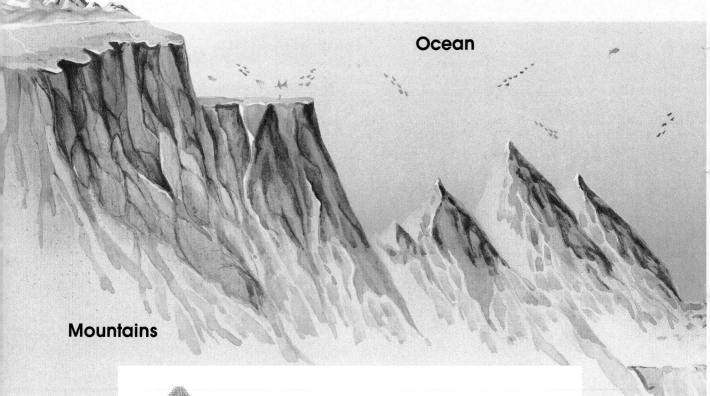

Land

Ocean

Mountains

THINKING

How is the bottom of the ocean like the land on which we live?

The bottom of the ocean is covered in many places with loose sand and gravel. There are layers of thick mud called ooze in other places. Some of the mud has dead things in it. All of this material is called sediment.

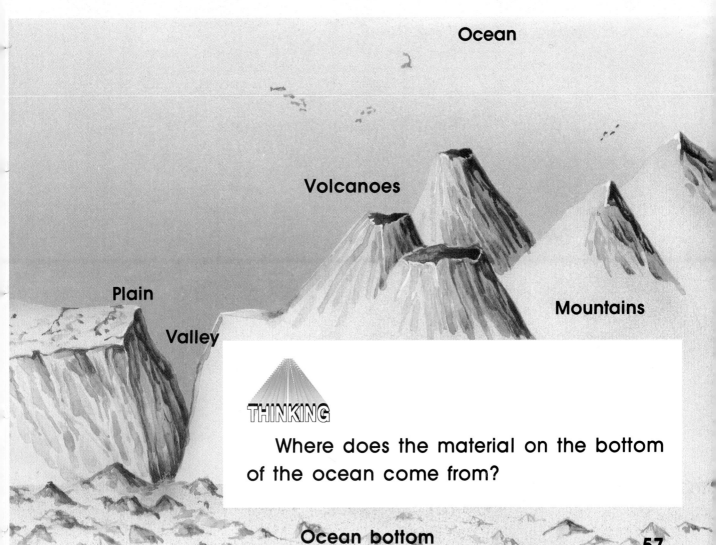

Ocean

Volcanoes

Plain

Valley

Mountains

THINKING

Where does the material on the bottom of the ocean come from?

Ocean bottom

EXPLORING

How does sediment build up on the bottom of the ocean?

What to Do

1. Fill a jar half full of water.

2. Add a handful of sand and some pebbles. Then cover the jar.

3. Shake the jar and lay it on its side.

4. Draw a picture of what you see after you shake the jar.

What happens to the sand in the jar? How is this like what happens in the ocean?

Animals in the Ocean

Ocean animals have special ways to protect themselves. Some ocean animals live in heavy shells. Others can change color to look just like the things around them. How would changing color help protect an animal?

Ocean animals have special ways to catch their food. Corals and sponges catch their food when water carrying smaller living things moves through their body.

How might an octopus, a shark, and a starfish each catch their food?

Ocean Animals Need One Another Some ocean animals need other animals. The sea anemone and fish are ocean animals. How do they need each other?

SEARCHING

Look at the pictures of ocean animals in this lesson. Which animals have shells? Which ones have fins and gills? Which animals have tentacles? Collect other pictures of ocean animals. Divide the pictures into groups. Tell how the animals in each group are alike. Tell how the animals are different.

Needs of Living Things in the Ocean

The ocean has millions of living things. Some are plants or are like plants. Some are animals or are like animals. Many of the living things in the ocean are so small that they can be seen only with a microscope.

Small animals eat the small plants. Larger animals eat the smaller living things. All of these living things in the ocean depend on one another for food.

Ocean Food Chain

THINKING

What foods from the ocean do people depend on?

Needs of Ocean Plants   All living things on land or in water have the same needs. What do living things need?

The plants living in the ocean need sunlight. They use the sun's energy to grow. Why do you think most ocean plants grow where the water is not too deep?

Living things need oxygen. Do you think there is oxygen in the ocean? Why or why not?

EXPLORING

How do living things in the ocean get oxygen?

What to Do

1. Place a small water plant in the bottom of a large beaker that is full of water.

2. Cover the plant with a glass funnel. **CAUTION: Be careful when using materials made of glass.**

3. Fill a test tube with water. Place it upside down over the funnel.

4. Put the beaker in the sunlight. Watch the water in the test tube.

What causes the bubbles in the water?
What do the bubbles mean?
Where does the oxygen come from?

63

Algae in the Ocean

The ocean has many kinds of algae. Some algae float in the water. Others attach themselves to rocks.

Most algae grow near the shore. Others grow in deep water that is clear enough for sunlight to reach them. Why is sunlight important to the algae?

THINKING

Describe the algae in the pictures on these two pages. How are algae in the ocean like plants on land? How are they different?

Some algae provide food for fish. Other algae, such as seaweeds, provide food for people. Seaweeds are also used to make medicine and skin-care products.

Algae are very important in the ocean. They make oxygen needed by other living things in the ocean.

THINKING

Without algae there would be no life in the ocean. Why is this so?

Exploring the Ocean

Some people explore the ocean for fun. The people in this picture are snorkeling. A snorkel is a special tube that swimmers breathe through.

Scuba divers explore the ocean, too. They have special air tanks to help them breathe. Scuba divers can go underwater to see the many things in the ocean. How is scuba diving different from snorkeling?

THINKING

What problems do underwater explorers face?

An oceanographer is a scientist who explores the ocean. Oceanographers want to know more about the living and nonliving things in the ocean. They need special tools to explore the ocean. What are the scientists in these pictures using? How can these things help them learn more about the ocean?

Ocean Engineers   Some oceanographers do special work. They are engineers. They design the equipment that others use. This equipment helps scientists learn more about the underwater world. Perhaps someday people will live in an underwater city.

SEARCHING

What do you think an underwater city would look like? Draw a picture of an underwater city. Write a story to tell how people could live there.

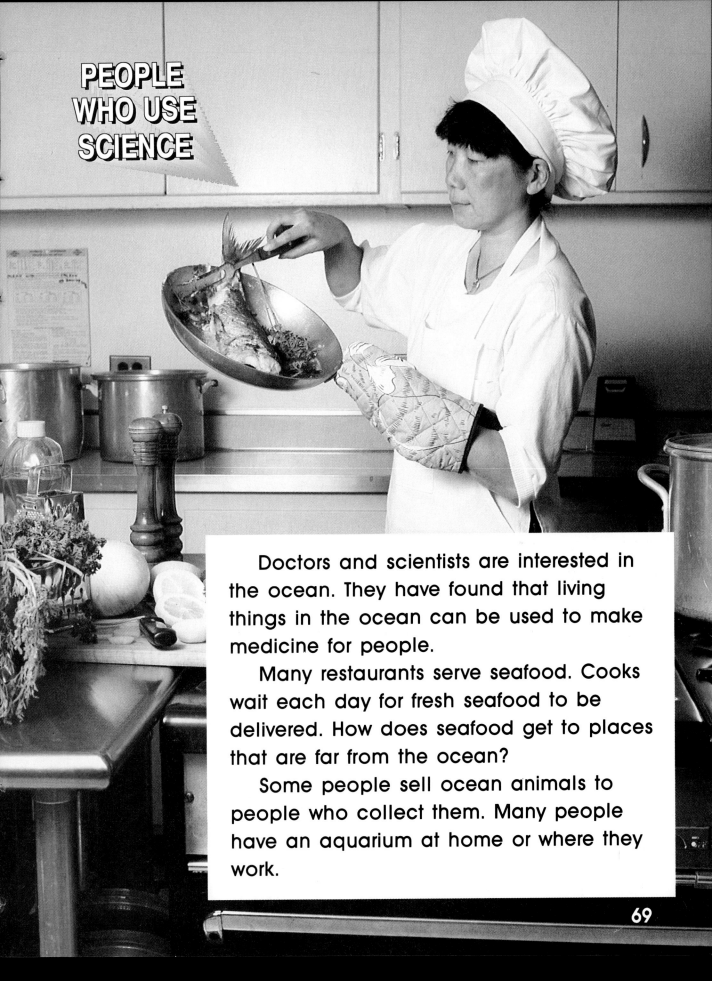

PEOPLE WHO USE SCIENCE

Doctors and scientists are interested in the ocean. They have found that living things in the ocean can be used to make medicine for people.

Many restaurants serve seafood. Cooks wait each day for fresh seafood to be delivered. How does seafood get to places that are far from the ocean?

Some people sell ocean animals to people who collect them. Many people have an aquarium at home or where they work.

Using the Ocean

People use the ocean in many ways. Some people spend their vacation at the seashore. What kinds of things can you do there?

People also get food from the ocean. Seaweed is used in some kinds of ice cream and in other creamy foods. What foods that you eat come from the ocean?

Some people earn their living from the ocean. How do the people in these pictures use the ocean?

The ocean has many minerals that people need. Two of the minerals are salt and gold. How do you think the minerals got into the ocean?

Scientists have found ways to get some minerals from the water. They are still working to find ways to remove other minerals. Scientists are also exploring ways to mine the bottom of the ocean.

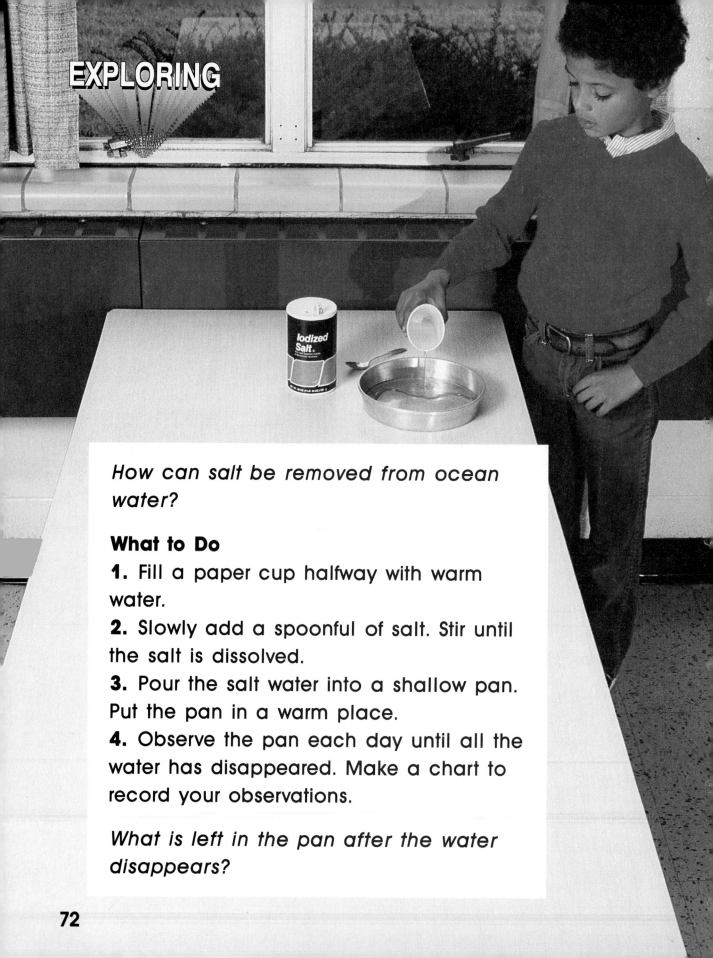

How can salt be removed from ocean water?

What to Do

1. Fill a paper cup halfway with warm water.

2. Slowly add a spoonful of salt. Stir until the salt is dissolved.

3. Pour the salt water into a shallow pan. Put the pan in a warm place.

4. Observe the pan each day until all the water has disappeared. Make a chart to record your observations.

What is left in the pan after the water disappears?

Protecting the Ocean

For a long time, people thought that they could not really harm the ocean. They used the ocean like a dump. They believed the ocean was too large and too deep to be harmed by people. Today people know differently.

Sewer water from some cities is pumped into the ocean. This water can harm plants and animals living in the ocean. Garbage and trash are dumped into the ocean. How can this harm the ocean and its living things?

Oil Slicks   People may also harm the ocean by accident. Oil is carried on large ships called tankers. Sometimes the ships spill the oil they are carrying. The oil floats along the top of the water. This is called an oil slick. Why are oil slicks harmful?

SEARCHING

Find out more about oil slicks. What happens to beaches? What happens to fish and birds? How can people help?

Journey Highlights

Much of the earth's surface is covered by oceans.

The water in the ocean is different from the water on land.

Water comes from the ocean and returns to it. This is called the water cycle.

Water in the ocean moves in waves, currents, and tides.

The ocean floor has mountains and valleys.

People use many things from the ocean.

People must protect the ocean.

Journey Wrap-up

Science Words

Write the word or words in ( ) that best complete the sentences.

1. Oceans are large bodies of water that cover (much, little) of the earth's surface.

2. The tides are the rise and fall of the level of the ocean that happens (once, twice) a day.

3. Material that settles on the ocean floor is (sediment, living).

4. Some kinds of algae are small, green living things in the ocean that (make their own food, eat other living things).

5. (Astronomers, Oceanographers) are scientists who study the ocean.

Using What You Have Learned

1. Tell how each of the pictures shows a way that people use the ocean.

A

B

C

D

2. Tell how each of these ocean animals gets its food.

Things to Do

1. Make a model of the ocean floor in a box. Fill the bottom of the box with clay. Use the clay to make mountains, valleys, and other land shapes. Use toothpick flags to name each part of the model. Cover the box with plastic wrap.

2. Make a poster of the underwater world. First collect pictures of ocean animals and algae. Then arrange the pictures on a poster. Color the background to look like the ocean. Label each living thing. Paste the pictures in place.

Unit 3 Forces in Action

Look at the pictures on these pages. A force is pulling or pushing in each picture you see. What are these forces?

Forces are in action all around you. What forces do you know about?

Using Magnets

Have you ever used a magnet? A magnet attracts some objects. It pulls these objects to itself. What are the children picking up with magnets?

A magnet cannot attract everything. It attracts one car. It does not attract the other car. Why not? What are the cars made of?

Find some objects like those on this page. Which ones do you think a magnet will attract?

Now hold a magnet near each object. Which objects did the magnet attract?

What kinds of metal does a magnet attract?

What to Do

1. Get some metal objects. Use paper clips, scissors, coins, and other such things.

2. Find out if a magnet attracts each object.

3. Look for other objects made of iron and steel.

Does the magnet always attract iron and steel objects? How can you find out?

Special Stones   The first magnets were special stones discovered by chance. Maybe they were discovered like this: Someone laid an iron object on the ground. Later, the object was picked up. A stone was sticking to the iron! The stone seemed to stick there by magic!

Today people know that the stone was not magic. They know that some stones act like magnets. People do not use these stones much anymore. They have learned how to make their own magnets.

Kinds of Magnets

Many magnets are made of iron and steel.
They come in many shapes and sizes. What
kinds of magnets do you see in the picture?

Electromagnets are made magnetic by electricity. When the electricity is on, the electromagnet works. It can pick up pieces of iron. What happens when the electricity is off?

THINKING

Why are electromagnets better than other magnets for some jobs?

Uses of Magnets

Magnets are used in many ways. You may have magnets working for you at home.

Ed.
CAll Bill
At NooN

Groceries
bread
milk
lettuce

Check Mail
before 11:00
on Sat,

SEARCHING

How do magnets on a refrigerator help people?

What does a magnet on an electric can opener do?

How can a magnet help you find a lost pin?

How have you used magnets at home?

MIXED SIZES
PEAS

Poles of a Magnet   A bar magnet is not strong all over. It is strongest at its two ends. These ends are called the poles of the magnet. All kinds of magnets have poles. Are the poles of your magnet marked? How are they marked?

SEARCHING

Lay a bar magnet on your desk. Place three paper clips on top of the magnet as in the picture. Try to pick up each paper clip. Where is the magnet strongest?

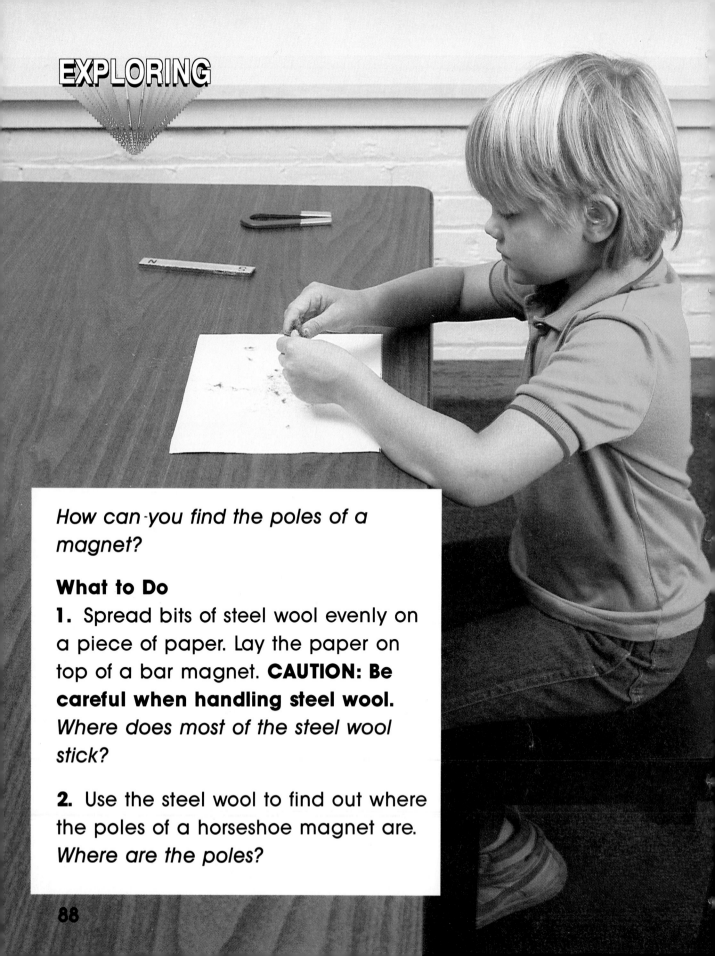

How can you find the poles of a magnet?

What to Do

1. Spread bits of steel wool evenly on a piece of paper. Lay the paper on top of a bar magnet. **CAUTION: Be careful when handling steel wool.** *Where does most of the steel wool stick?*

2. Use the steel wool to find out where the poles of a horseshoe magnet are. *Where are the poles?*

A Pair of Magnets

The poles of many magnets are marked with an **N** and an **S**. **N** stands for "north-seeking pole." **S** stands for "south-seeking pole."

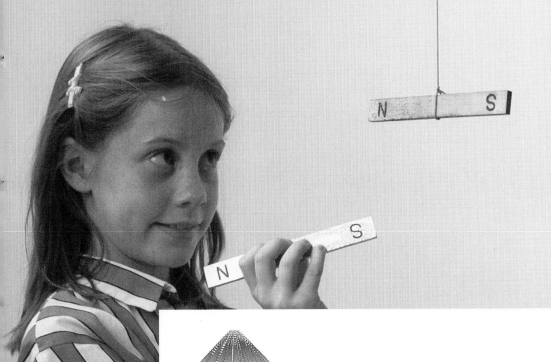

SEARCHING

Hang a magnet as in the picture. What happens when you bring another magnet close to it?

Try to bring two **S** poles together. Then try to bring two **N** poles together. Try to bring an **N** pole and an **S** pole together. Which time did the magnets attract each other? When did they push each other away?

EXPLORING

Can a magnet attract things without touching them?

What to Do

1. Place a magnet under a piece of cardboard.

2. Put paper clips on top of the cardboard.

What happens?

3. Try putting other things between the magnet and the paper clips. Try paper, cloth, plastic, and wood.

Which of these does the magnet pull through?

Finding North

People on ships need to know which way
they are sailing. They use a magnet to find
north. The magnet is the needle of a compass.
The needle always points north.

SEARCHING

A magnet can help people find their
way. To find out how, hang a bar magnet
on a string. Where does the **N** pole of the
magnet point? Now you know where north
is. Where is south?

Try other bar magnets. Where does the
N pole always point?

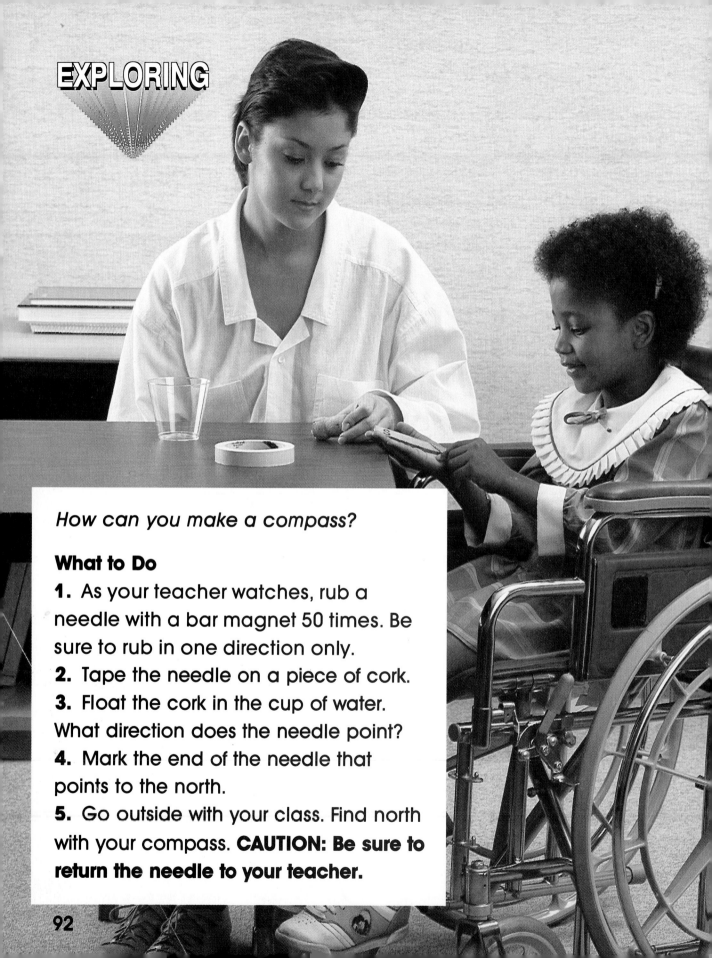

How can you make a compass?

What to Do

1. As your teacher watches, rub a needle with a bar magnet 50 times. Be sure to rub in one direction only.

2. Tape the needle on a piece of cork.

3. Float the cork in the cup of water. What direction does the needle point?

4. Mark the end of the needle that points to the north.

5. Go outside with your class. Find north with your compass. **CAUTION: Be sure to return the needle to your teacher.**

Making Sounds

Hold your hands on your throat. Whisper. Talk. Hum. What do you feel happening in your throat? Now clap your hands.

Each sound seems different. A sound may be high or low. It may also be loud or soft. But the sounds are alike in a way. You use a force of moving air to make each sound. The force makes something move back and forth, or vibrate. What vibrates when you talk or hum? What vibrates when you clap your hands?

How can you make sounds?

What to Do

1. Hold one end of a ruler on a table.

2. Pull down on the free end and let it go.

Does the ruler make a sound? Why?

3. Move the ruler so that more of it is on the table. Pull down on the free end of the ruler and let it go.

How did the sound change?

Hearing Sounds

Make a sound. You made the air in your throat and around you vibrate. The air vibrated parts inside your ear, too. The vibrating parts in your ear helped you hear the sound.

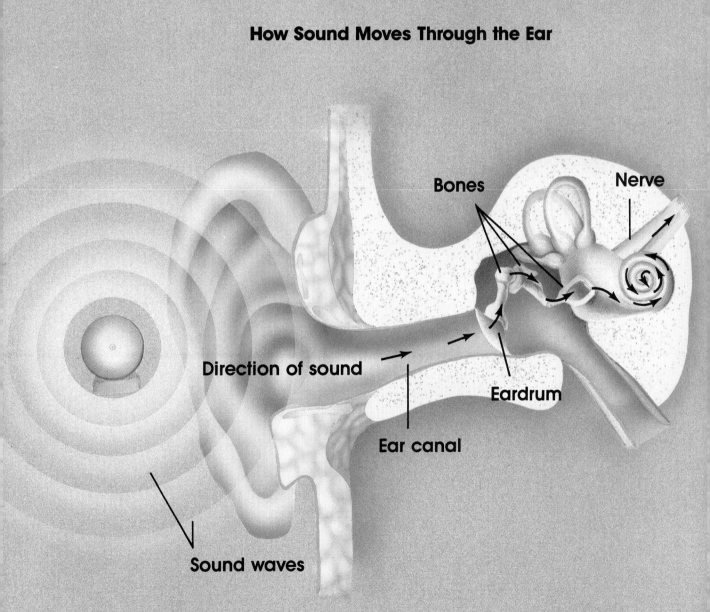

How Sound Moves Through the Ear

Bones

Nerve

Direction of sound

Eardrum

Ear canal

Sound waves

Does sound travel best in air, in water, or in wood?

What to Do

1. Hold a plastic bag of water against one of your ears. Cover your other ear with your hand. Have someone hold a ticking clock against the bag of water. Listen.

2. Keep the clock in the same place. Remove the bag of water. Listen.

3. Place a block of wood between your ear and the clock. Listen.

Did you hear the clock best through the air, the water, or the wood?

EXPLORING

How can you make a telephone?

What to Do

1. Poke a hole in the bottom of a paper cup. Have a friend poke a hole in the bottom of another paper cup.

2. Push one end of a long piece of thin string through the hole in your cup. Tape the end of the string inside the cup.

3. Have your friend tape the other end of the string inside his or her cup. Pull the string tight. Talk into your cup.

What carried the sound to your friend's ear?

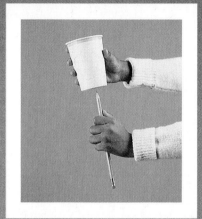

PEOPLE
WHO USE
SCIENCE

Sounds of Music

Some sounds are high. Other sounds are low. A high sound is one with a high pitch. A low sound has a low pitch.

THINKING

Look at the pictures. Which of the instruments make high sounds? Which ones make low sounds?

How can you change the pitch of a sound?

What to Do

1. Stretch a rubber band over a strong box. Place a pencil across the middle of the box, under the rubber band. Pluck the rubber band and listen to the sound.
2. Move the pencil toward one end of the box. Pluck the shorter part of the rubber band and listen. Pluck the longer part of the rubber band and listen.

What happened to the pitch?

EXPLORING

How can you use bottles to make music?

What to Do

1. Pour water to a different level in each of six identical bottles.

2. Make sounds by blowing through a straw over the openings of the bottles.

Which bottle makes the highest sound?
Which makes the lowest sound?
Why are the sounds different?

3. Put the bottles in order, from lowest pitch to highest.

4. Play a song on your bottles.

Some Strong Forces

There are many forces in nature. One of these forces is the wind. You cannot see the wind. But you can see what it does. The wind turns windmills and pushes sailboats. Its force helps people do work. When has the wind helped you?

Sometimes winds are very strong. Strong winds can cause much damage. What kinds of damage can winds cause?

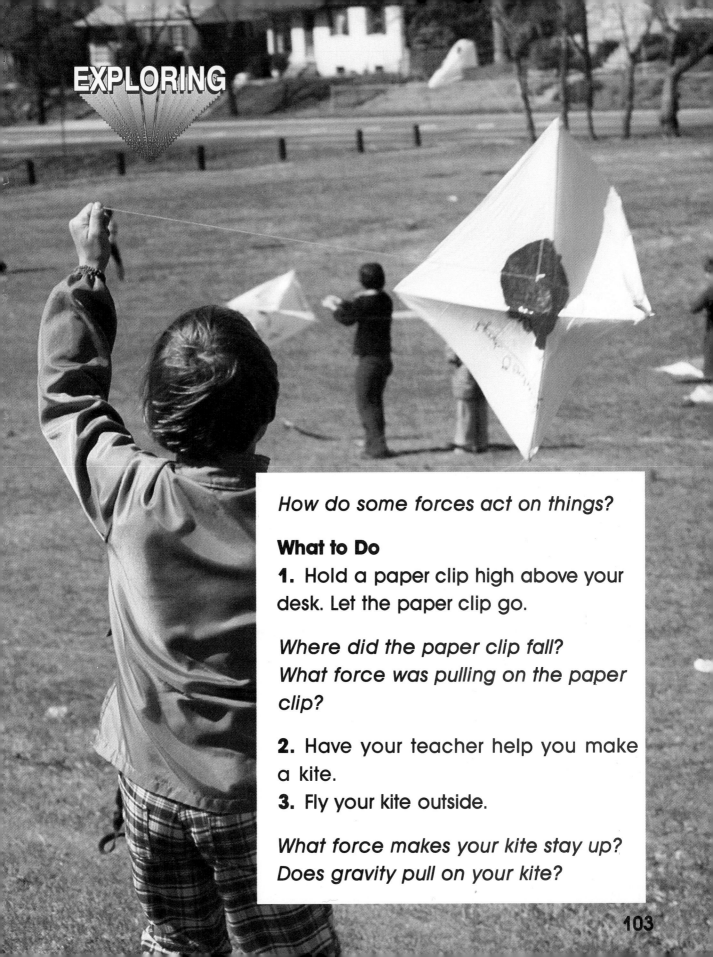

EXPLORING

How do some forces act on things?

What to Do

1. Hold a paper clip high above your desk. Let the paper clip go.

Where did the paper clip fall?
What force was pulling on the paper clip?

2. Have your teacher help you make a kite.

3. Fly your kite outside.

What force makes your kite stay up?
Does gravity pull on your kite?

Look at the sky divers in the picture. They cannot stay up in the air. A force is pulling them to the earth. The force is called gravity.

Gravity pulls on the water in a river. It forces the water to move downhill. Moving water is a force that pushes on things.

Sinking and Floating

Look at the picture. People are throwing pennies into a lily pond. Each person makes a wish before her penny sinks to the bottom. Why do you think the pennies sink?

Notice that some things float on the water. What keeps these things from sinking?

What is pushing them up?

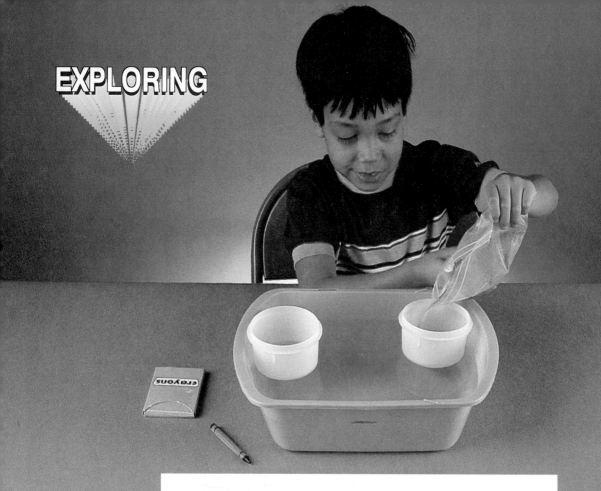

EXPLORING

Why do some things float?

What to Do

1. Pour some water into a pan. Use a crayon to mark how high the water is.
2. Get two plastic dishes of the same size. Put the dishes in the water. Mark how high the water is now.

What happened to the water?
What happened to the dishes? Why?

3. Pour sand into one of the dishes.

Does the water still push the dish up?
How could you make the dish sink?

You can feel water pushing things up. It makes things float. Why might this happen?

A boat placed in water pushes some water aside. Then the water pushes to get back where it was. It pushes the boat up.

What if you put something heavy in a boat? Do you think the boat will still push water aside? Will the water push to get back where it was?

Look at the picture below. Why does one of the boats sink? What two forces are working in the water?

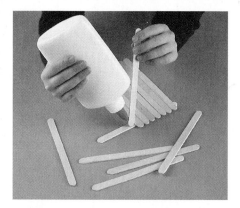

What kind of boat can hold the most weight without sinking?

What to Do

1. Use some clay to make a boat that floats in a pan of water.

2. Make the same size boat from foil.

3. Build a raft from sticks. Make it the same size as the other boats.

4. Put iron washers in each boat and on the raft until each one almost sinks.

How many washers can each model hold without sinking?

Journey Highlights

A magnet attracts iron and steel objects.

The strongest parts of a magnet are called poles. Two magnets may attract each other or may push each other away.

The **N** pole of a hanging magnet points north; the needle (magnet) of a compass points to the north.

Sounds are made when something vibrates.

Sound travels through solids, liquids, and gases.

You can change the pitch and the loudness of a sound.

Gravity is a force that pulls things to the earth.

When the force of water pushing up on an object is greater than the force of gravity, the object will float.

Journey Wrap-up

Science Words

Choose a word to complete each sentence.

attract   float   poles

gravity   north   vibrate

1. The force of _gravity_ pulls things to the earth.

2. You make a sound when you cause air to _vibrate_

3. The needle of a compass always points to the _North_

4. Some objects _flot_ because water pushes up on them.

5. Magnets _attract_ iron and steel objects.

6. The strongest parts of a magnet are the _poles_

Using What You Have Learned

1. Which will float?

110

Match each force with one picture only.

2. rushing water   5. wind
3. gravity   6. magnet attracting
4. vibrating air   7. water pushing up

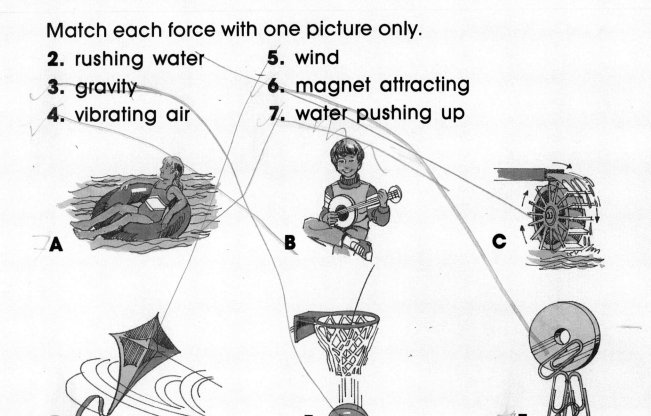

A   B   C

D   E   F

8. Suppose you spilled a box of pins on the lawn. How could you pick the pins up without missing any?

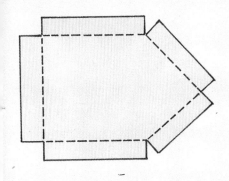

Things to Do

Cut out a boat like the one pictured here. Fold the paper and tape the corners. Tape a paper clip under your boat. Use a magnet to pull your boat in the water.

Have races with your friends.

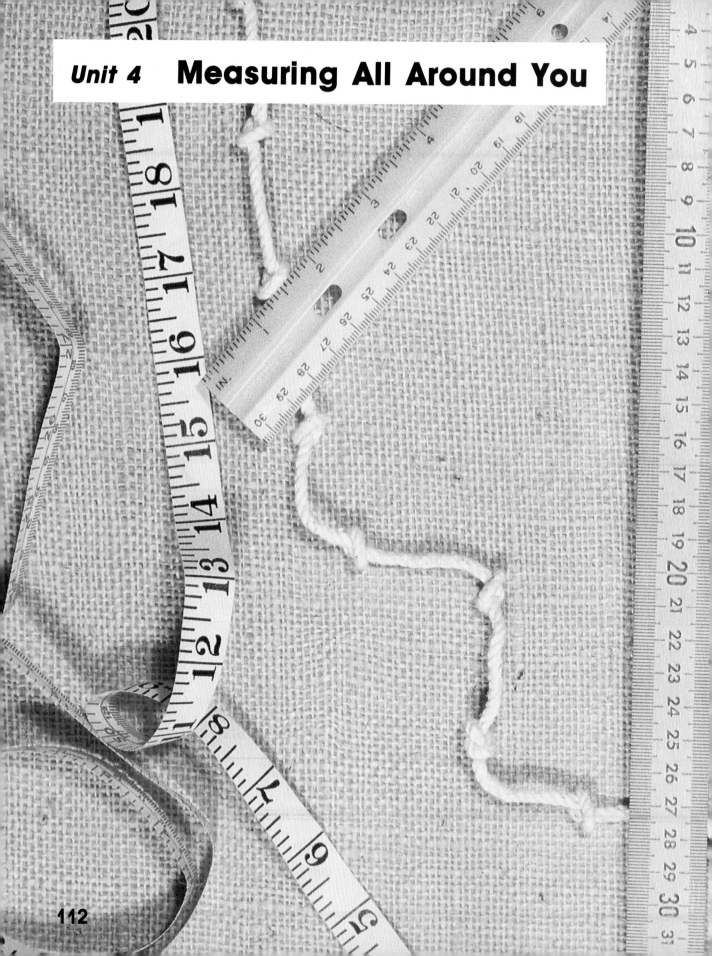

These buses are very big. Which bus is bigger? To find out, you could count how many windows there are on each bus. Or you could measure how long each bus is. How else could you measure the buses?

Measuring for Size

Think of the people in your family. How are they alike? How are they different? Probably everyone in your family is different in size. Who is the tallest person in your family? Who is the shortest? How can you tell?

Sometimes it is easy to tell if someone is taller. At other times you have to measure to find out.

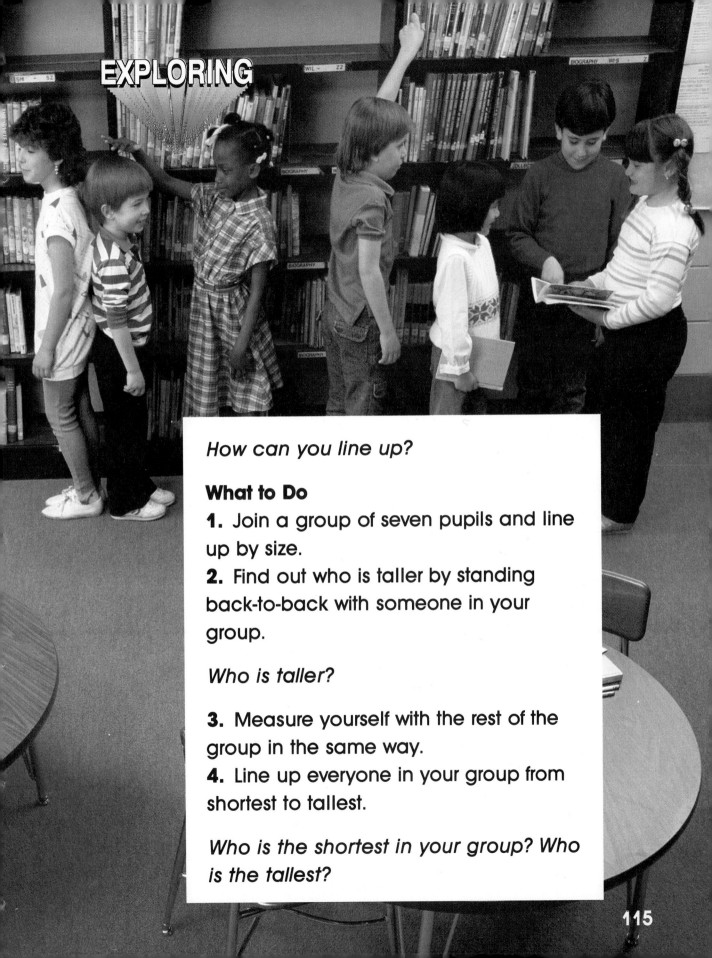

How can you line up?

What to Do
1. Join a group of seven pupils and line up by size.
2. Find out who is taller by standing back-to-back with someone in your group.

Who is taller?

3. Measure yourself with the rest of the group in the same way.
4. Line up everyone in your group from shortest to tallest.

Who is the shortest in your group? Who is the tallest?

Units of Measure

You know how to find out if you or your friend is taller. But how can you measure other things—like your book? You need something to measure with. It helps if what you use has a straight edge.

Suppose you decide to use paper clips to measure with. Each paper clip will be a unit of measure. How many paper clips placed end to end are as long as your book?

What can you use as a unit to measure your desk?

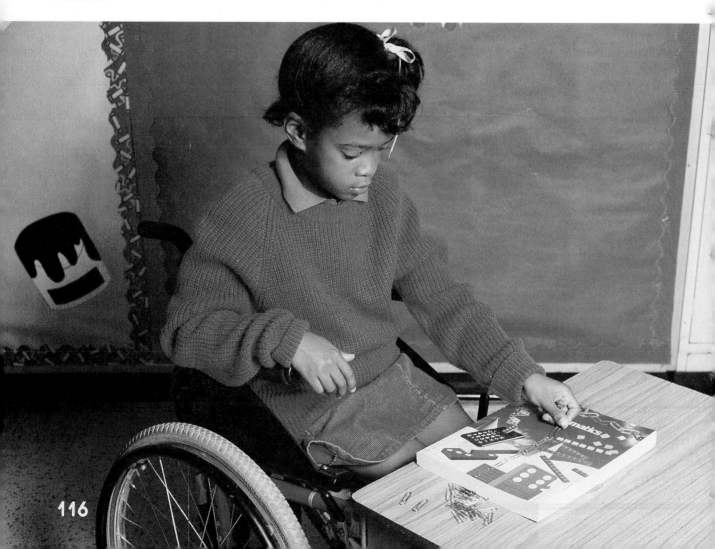

How can you make a measuring tape?

What to Do

1. Cut a piece of paper into five strips as wide as your ruler.

2. Color each strip a different color. Each colored strip is a unit of measure.

3. Tape the colored strips together end-to-end.

4. Use your measuring tape to measure your desk.

How many units long is your desk?
How many units wide is your desk?
How many units high is your desk?

Comparing Volume

Suppose you want to cook some rice. You know that you need water and rice. The box says, "Boil 1 cup of water. Add 1 cup of rice." The cup is used to measure how much.

You fill the space inside the cup. The cup holds the same measure of water every time. The cup holds the same measure of rice every time. How does a cup of water compare with a cup of rice?

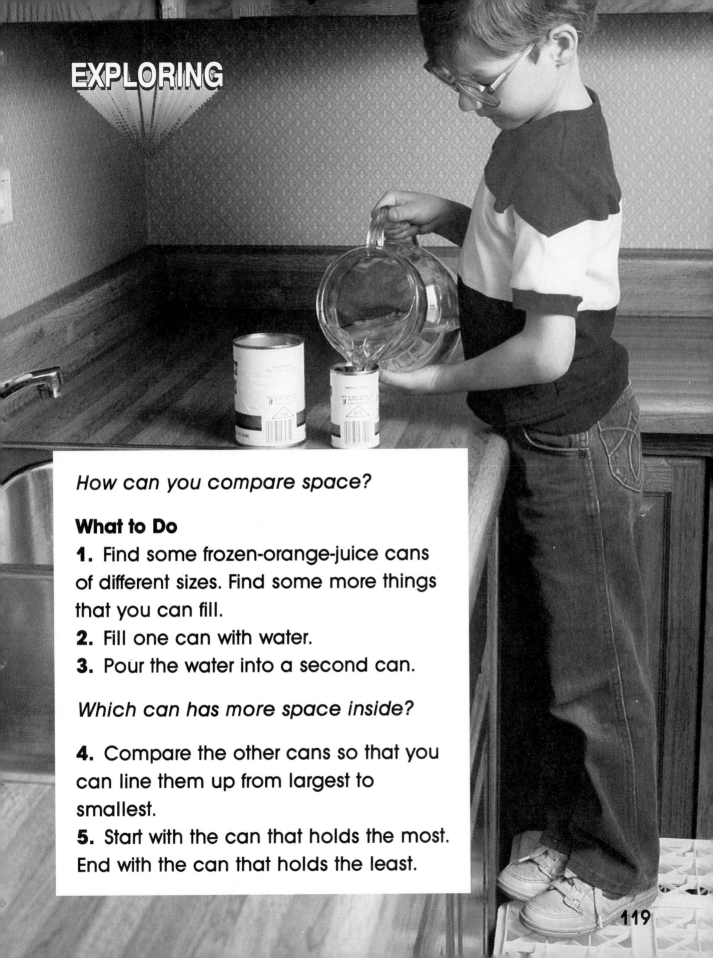

How can you compare space?

What to Do

1. Find some frozen-orange-juice cans of different sizes. Find some more things that you can fill.

2. Fill one can with water.

3. Pour the water into a second can.

Which can has more space inside?

4. Compare the other cans so that you can line them up from largest to smallest.

5. Start with the can that holds the most. End with the can that holds the least.

Finding Volume

Suppose you have some fish in a fishbowl. Your family wants more space for your fish. They ask you to measure the space inside an old aquarium. What if you try using a measuring cup as a unit of measure?

You discover that it takes 80 cups of water to fill the aquarium. Your family is pleased. They knew that the fishbowl held only 40 cups. So the aquarium has twice the space.

Volume is a measure of how much something holds, or of how much space something takes.

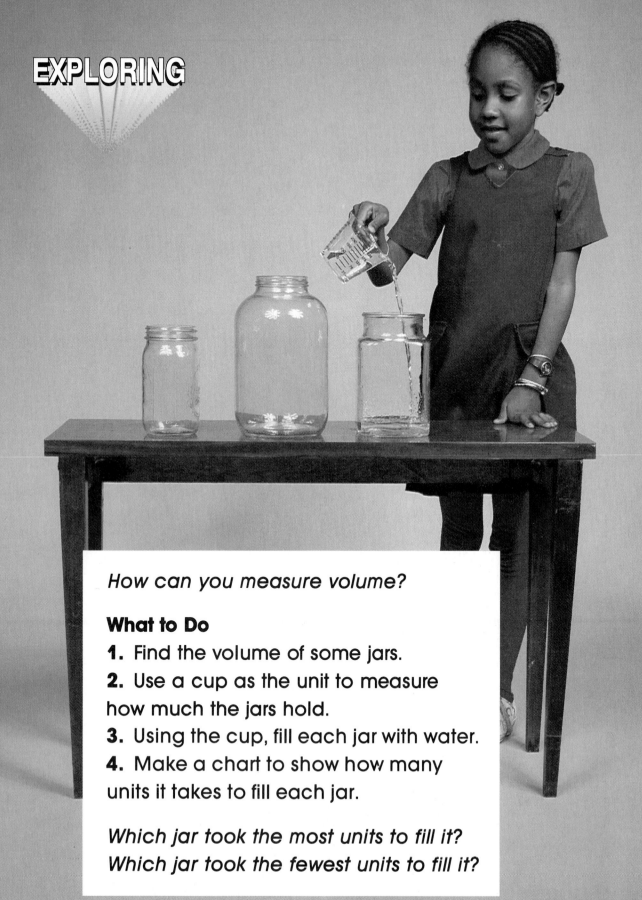

EXPLORING

How can you measure volume?

What to Do
1. Find the volume of some jars.
2. Use a cup as the unit to measure how much the jars hold.
3. Using the cup, fill each jar with water.
4. Make a chart to show how many units it takes to fill each jar.

Which jar took the most units to fill it?
Which jar took the fewest units to fill it?

Measuring How Heavy

Jeff says his toy is heavier than Sandy's toy. Sandy is not sure. How can they find out which toy is heavier?

Sandy and Jeff place the toys in their hands first. Sandy's toy seems heavier. To make sure, they use a balance. Jeff puts his toy on one side. Sandy puts her toy on the other side. Whose toy is heavier?

How can you make a balance?

What to Do

1. Make a balance. Use a board and a small block as in the picture.

2. Try to balance objects found in your classroom.

Do any two objects balance each other?
Which objects weigh more?
Which objects weigh less?
How can you tell?

3. Make a chart to show what you find out.

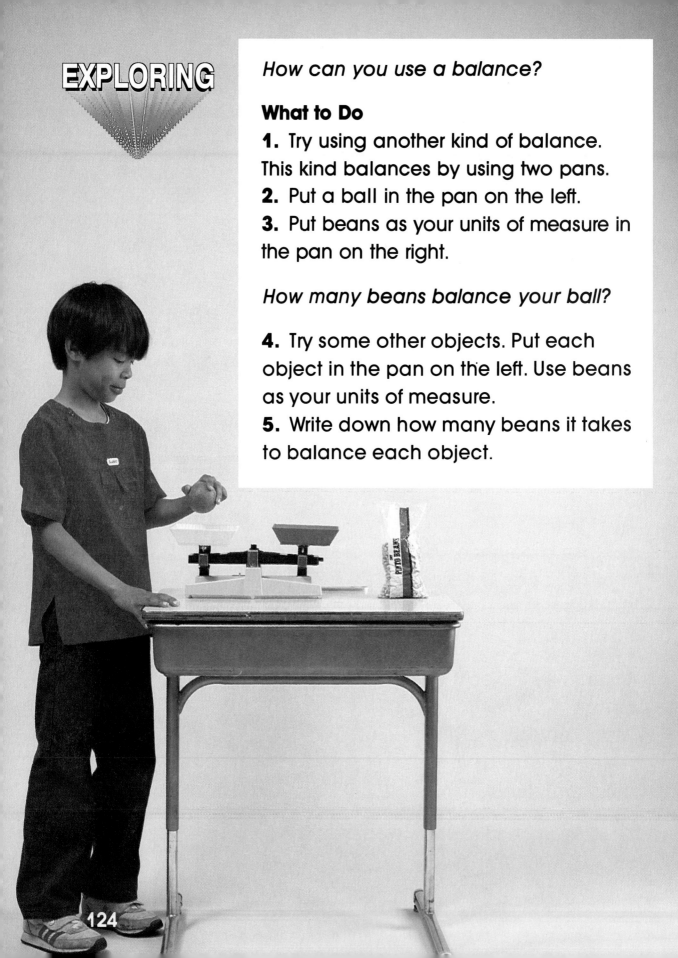

EXPLORING

How can you use a balance?

What to Do

1. Try using another kind of balance. This kind balances by using two pans.

2. Put a ball in the pan on the left.

3. Put beans as your units of measure in the pan on the right.

How many beans balance your ball?

4. Try some other objects. Put each object in the pan on the left. Use beans as your units of measure.

5. Write down how many beans it takes to balance each object.

Using a Balance

Now Jeff is using beans to balance his toy. How many beans do you think the toy will equal? A bean can be a unit of measure.

Sandy wants to balance her toy with beans. How many beans do you think she will need?

Standard Units

Sandy and Jeff want to measure how far it is across the room. They decide to count the number of steps it takes to cross the room. Sandy steps first. She counts 40 steps. Then Jeff tries. He counts 37 steps. The number of steps for Sandy and for Jeff is different. Why?

Then Jeff and Sandy cut a piece of string to measure with. Jeff measures 28 string units across the room. Sandy also measures 28 string units. Because the strings are the same size, the string is called a standard unit.

SEARCHING

Later, Sandy talked to her friend on the telephone.

"Our room is 28 string units across," said Sandy.

"How long is that?" asked her friend.

Sandy did not know how to answer. What could Sandy do to let her friend know how long her string unit was?

PEOPLE WHO USE SCIENCE

Some people have to measure every day. Builders measure many things. They have to make every room the right size.

Butchers weigh the meat they sell. They want to give you what you pay for.

Clothes designers measure the lengths of dresses and suits. They measure how much cloth to use.

What workers have you seen measuring things?

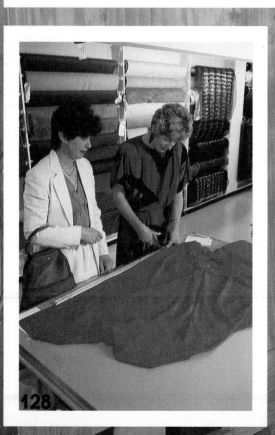

Different Standards

The first leaders of this country held many meetings. They talked about which units of measure to use. They decided to use units that were standard in England. People called these units English units of measure.

People in some other countries began using different standard units. These were called metric units of measure. Today, scientists in this country use metric units of measure.

Units of Length

You measure how long something is to find its length. Some English units for length are the inch, the foot, and the yard. What things are sold by these lengths?

The picture at right shows a small ruler. Each number stands for an inch.

How many inches does this ruler show?

A ruler usually measures 12 inches.

A 12-inch ruler is 1 foot long.

A yard is 3 feet long.

16'

SEARCHING

Where can you find English units for length being used?

What things might be measured in English units of length in a food store, in a hardware store, and in a clothing store? What things might be measured in English units of length in a school and in a home?

Using Metric Units

Some metric units for length are the millimeter, the centimeter, and the meter. The picture at right shows a metric ruler.

Each number marks off a centimeter. How many centimeters does this ruler show?

Each small line marks off a millimeter. How many millimeters are in a centimeter?

A meter is a large unit of measure. There are 100 centimeters in a meter.

Measure your book in centimeters. Measure the room in meters.

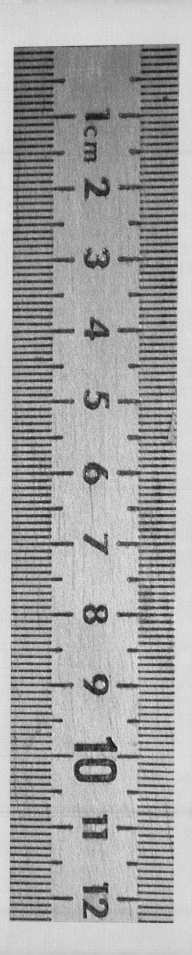

EXPLORING

How can you use a string to measure?

What to Do

1. Use Blackline Master 12 to make a meter tape, or use a meterstick. Cut a string the length of a meter. **CAUTION: Be careful when using scissors.**

2. Measure around your waist with the string.

3. Make a mark on the string where the end of the string touches it.

4. Lay the string on the meter tape.

5. Read the number nearest the mark on the string.
How many centimeters around is your waist?

6. Measure other things with the string.

Units of Volume

Volume is how much space something takes up. People need to know about volume to buy milk or gasoline.

The quart and the gallon are two English units of volume.

What is sold by the quart? By the gallon?

The milliliter and the liter are two metric units of volume.

What is sold by the liter?

SEARCHING

Look at the chart below. The first column lists some units of volume. The second column lists each unit of volume in a short way.

Unit Name	Short Name
quart	qt
gallon	gal
milliliter	mL
liter	L

Look at the labels below. Some of the labels show the units of volume the short way. Read the unit of volume on each label.

APPLE JUICE

NO SUGAR ADDED

775

NET 32 FL. OZ. (1 QT.) .946 L

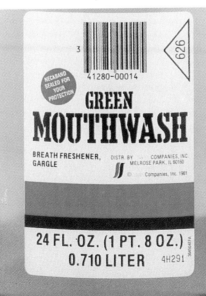

3

626

41280-00014

NECKBAND SEALED FOR YOUR PROTECTION

GREEN MOUTHWASH

BREATH FRESHENER, GARGLE

DISTR. BY ___ COMPANIES, INC. MELROSE PARK, IL 60160

Companies, Inc. 1981

24 FL. OZ. (1 PT. 8 OZ.)
0.710 LITER   4H291

GLASS CLEANER

32 FL OZ (1 QT) 946 mL

135

EXPLORING

What units are used for measuring?

What to Do

1. Ask an adult to help you. Collect labels from bottles, jars, and cartons.

2. Read each label to find out what unit or units of volume are used.

3. Make a chart like the one shown below.

4. Write your findings on the chart.

Product	English Units	Metric Units
milk	gal	L
liquid soap	qt	mL or L

Units of Weight and Mass

Your family uses standard units for weighing things. They buy meat by the pound. Many fruits and vegetables are sold by the pound. An ounce is much less than a pound. The pound and the ounce are English units of weight. The picture shows a pound of butter and an ounce of butter.

Many foods are also shown in metric units. Breakfast food is often shown in grams. A kilogram is 1 000 grams. Look at breakfast foods to see how many grams they are.

1 pound

1 ounce

What standard units are used on food labels?

What to Do

1. Read the short forms for the following units.

English Units of Weight
pound (lb)   ounce (oz)

Metric Units of Mass
gram (g)   kilogram (kg)

2. Look at food labels that show these units.

3. Find out whether the food shows English units, metric units, or both.

4. List the units of each food with the short form of the unit.

Guessing in Metric Units

Guess the length of these things in metric units.

Guess the volume of these things in metric units.

Guess how many kilograms or grams these things are.

How tall are you in meters? How many kilograms are you?

How can you learn to use metric units of measure?

What to Do

1. Make a play store with pictures of things to sell.

2. First put out the things you sell by length.

3. Next put out what you sell by volume.

4. Then put out what you sell by mass.

5. Have your friends ask for each object.

6. Someone who uses the right metric unit of measure may buy the product.

Journey Highlights

You can measure by comparing.

Units are used to measure how long, how much, and how heavy things are.

Length is a measure of how long something is.

Volume is a measure of how much space something takes up.

A balance can be used to compare weight.

A standard unit is the same for everybody.

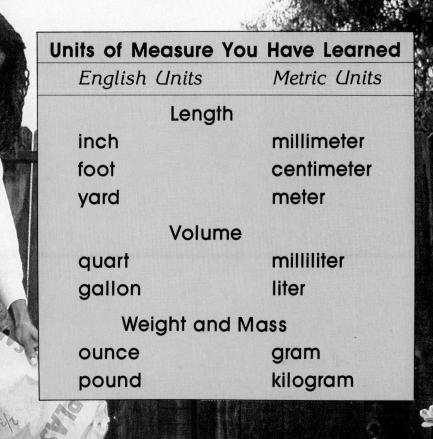

Units of Measure You Have Learned	
English Units	*Metric Units*
Length	
inch	millimeter
foot	centimeter
yard	meter
Volume	
quart	milliliter
gallon	liter
Weight and Mass	
ounce	gram
pound	kilogram

Journey Wrap-up

Science Words

Tell if the units are English units or metric units.
1. quart
2. foot
3. gram
4. milliliter
5. meter
6. pound
7. liter
8. kilogram

Using What You Have Learned

Tell which is the smaller unit in each pair below.
1. pound – ounce
2. inch – foot
3. meter – centimeter
4. gram – kilogram
5. liter – milliliter
6. quart – gallon

Which unit of measure on the right is
<u>not</u> used when people buy the item on the
left?

7. milk   **a.** quart
              b. liter
              c. meter

8. rice   **a.** inch
              b. pound
              c. kilogram

9. cloth   **a.** yard
              b. gram
              c. meter

Things to Do

1. You are told to measure your room. Use
a meterstick to find out the size of your
room.

2. What is heavier — a ball or an apple? Use
a balance to find out.

Unit 5   Growing Seeds

What is the child in the picture doing? Have you ever done this? What happened to the old flower when you blew on it?

What is each fluffy part that floated away? What do you think happened to these fluffy things?

Planting Seeds

Seeds need certain things to help them grow. They need water and warmth to start growing. Soon the seeds will germinate, or start to grow. Then they need other things. They need water, warmth, air, light, and soil to keep growing.

The picture on this page shows how to plant seeds in a garden box. What is put in the bottom of the box? Where do the seeds go? What do the seeds need to help them grow?

How can you plant your own seeds?

What to Do

1. Write your name on the cups.

2. Punch a hole in the bottom of each cup.

3. Put small rocks in the cups.

4. Put some soil over the rocks.

5. Put a seed in each cup.

6. Cover the seeds with more soil.

7. Water your seeds.

What kind of plants do you think will grow from your seeds?
How can you find out?

What Seeds Need   You need to make sure that your seeds have what they need to grow. Seeds need water and warmth to start growing. Water your seeds twice a week. How can you provide warmth for your seeds?

THINKING

What other things might your seeds need to grow into healthy plants?

How Are Seeds Different and Alike?

Seeds are different in many ways. They are of different colors and of different sizes. Some seeds are round and others are flat. Some seeds are rough and some are smooth. Seeds also travel in different ways.

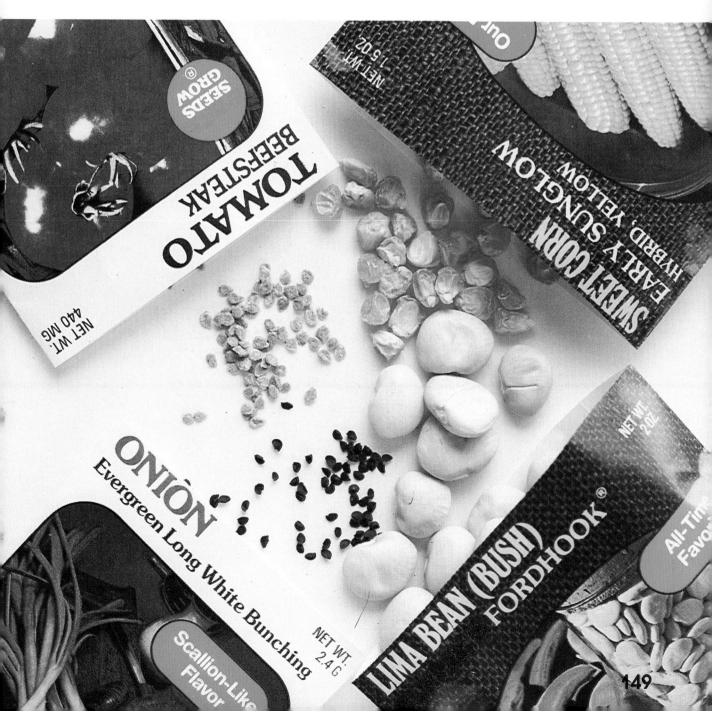

SEARCHING

Collect different kinds of seeds. Put the seeds into groups. Tell how the seeds in each group are alike.

How Seeds Are Alike   Seeds are alike in some ways. All seeds have certain parts that are the same. They need certain things to help them grow.

What is inside a seed?

What to Do

1. Cut open some soaked seeds.

CAUTION: Be careful when using a knife.

2. Find the seed coat, the embryo, and the food supply.

3. Tape these parts on a piece of paper.

4. Label each part.

How are your seeds different?
How are they alike?

Parts of Seeds

All seeds have some parts that are alike. They all have a seed coat, a baby plant, and a food supply.

The seed coat is a covering for the seed. It protects the inside of the seed. It keeps the seed from losing water. It also protects the seed from injury and disease. How is a seed coat like your skin?

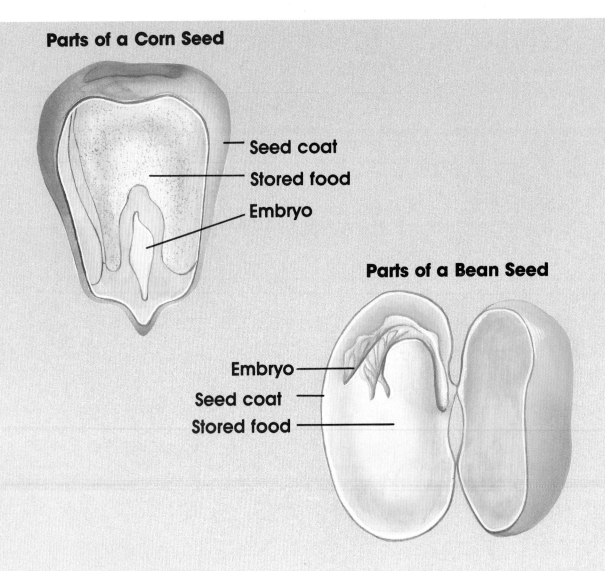

Parts of a Corn Seed

— Seed coat
— Stored food
— Embryo

Parts of a Bean Seed

Embryo———
Seed coat———
Stored food———

Food supply

Embryo

The baby plant is called an embryo. The
embryo is the start of a new plant.

An embryo needs food to grow. But it
cannot make its own food. A seed has a food
supply for the embryo. The embryo uses the
stored food.

Sources of Food   Some seeds have one source of food. Other seeds have two sources of food.

Look at the drawings on this page. Which shows a seed that has one source of food? Which shows a seed that has two sources of food? How can you tell?

THINKING

Can you tell by looking at the outside of a seed whether it has one source of food or two sources of food? How could you find out?

154

How do seeds germinate?

What to Do

1. Fold the paper towel like the one in the picture.

2. Tape the seeds to the paper towel.

3. Roll up the paper towel with the seeds inside and put it into the jar. **CAUTION: Be careful when using glass jars.**

4. Add enough water to fill 3 centimeters of the jar.

5. Look at the seeds after three days.

What has happened to the seeds?
What helped the seeds begin to grow?

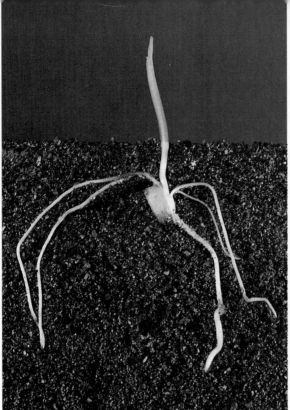

How Seeds Start to Grow

Seeds germinate, or begin to grow, when they have water and warmth. The embryo is the part of the seed that grows. The embryo uses the food supply inside the seed.

When you can begin to see the parts of the plant, the embryo is beginning to grow. The stem and leaves grow up toward the light. The root grows down toward the water.

THINKING

Can a seed be tricked into growing the wrong way? Check the results from the "Exploring" on page 155.

What happens to seeds when they get no water?

What to Do

1. Put six seeds into an empty jar.
2. Put the other seeds into another jar.
3. Put some wet paper towels into the second jar. Keep the towels moist.
4. Watch the seeds for a few days.

What happened to the seeds in each jar? What happens to seeds when they get no water?

Under the Soil   Most of the time, seeds grow under soil. You cannot see what is happening. How can you tell if a seed has germinated?

Not all seeds will germinate. Not all germinated seeds will grow into plants.

THINKING

What would happen if all the dandelion seeds in a park germinated? What would happen if every germinated dandelion seed grew into a flowering dandelion?

Growing Plants

A young plant is called a seedling.
Seedlings need many things to keep growing.
They need water, warmth, air, light, and soil.

The seedling grows up through the soil. It
spreads its green leaves. The green leaves
make food for the new plant.

Rate of Plant Growth   A plant grows at different rates during its lifetime. Sometimes the plant grows very fast. At other times, it grows more slowly.

An embryo grows slowly. A seedling grows fastest. An adult plant grows slowly.

Do people grow at different rates during their lifetime? When do people grow the fastest? When do they stop growing?

Check the record of your plant's growth. Is your plant growing slowly or fast? Check the record of your plant's growth each week for the next 2 weeks. At what rate is your plant growing now?

The Life Cycle of Plants

Plants grow like other living things do. As they grow, they begin to look more like their parents.

A seed grows into a seedling. A seedling becomes an adult plant. The adult plant makes more seeds.

This pattern of growth is called a life cycle. A life cycle happens over and over. What parts of the life cycle of your plants have you seen?

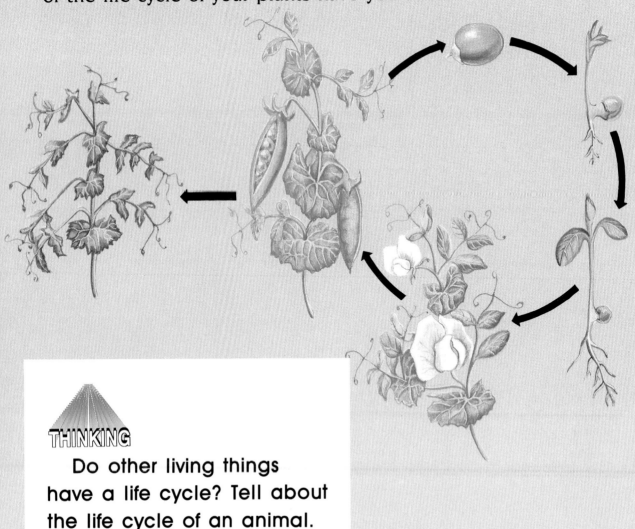

THINKING

Do other living things have a life cycle? Tell about the life cycle of an animal.

162

The life cycles of some plants are different from those of other plants. Write a story about the life cycle of the apple tree in the pictures on this page.

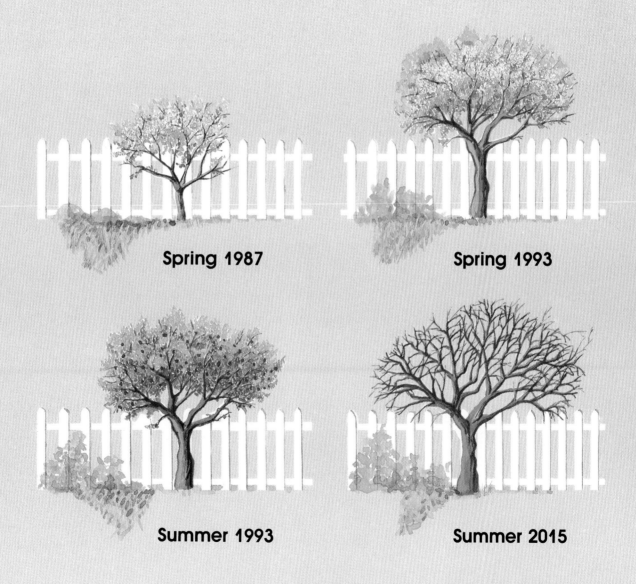

Spring 1987

Spring 1993

Summer 1993

Summer 2015

Where Do Seeds Come From?

Seeds are formed on adult plants. Adult plants form different numbers of seeds. Some form only a few seeds. Others form many seeds.

Some adult plants have fruit. Other adult plants have cones. The fruit or the cones are the parts of the plant that form seeds.

SEARCHING

Which of the pictures on this page show plants that have fruit? Which show plants that have cones?

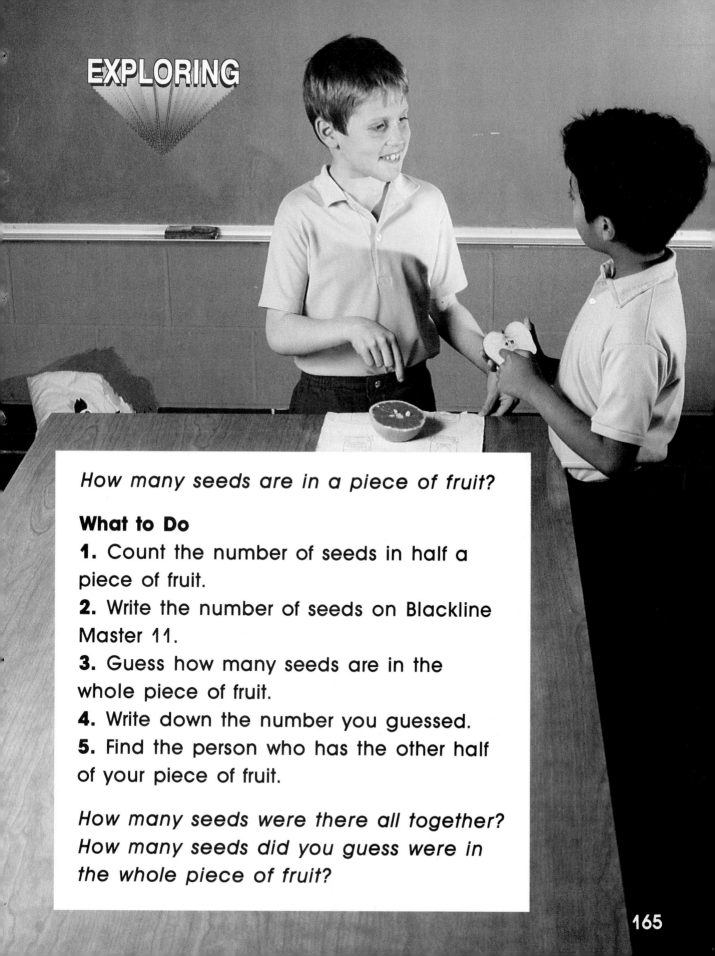

EXPLORING

How many seeds are in a piece of fruit?

What to Do

1. Count the number of seeds in half a piece of fruit.

2. Write the number of seeds on Blackline Master 11.

3. Guess how many seeds are in the whole piece of fruit.

4. Write down the number you guessed.

5. Find the person who has the other half of your piece of fruit.

How many seeds were there all together? How many seeds did you guess were in the whole piece of fruit?

Seeds and a Plant's Life Cycle   The life cycle of a plant starts with a seed. The seed grows into an adult plant. The adult plant will be like the plant the seed came from. The adult plant forms more seeds. Then the cycle starts again.

THINKING

Why are seeds important to the life cycle of a plant?

Foresters are people who take care of forests. They make sure that there are enough trees for people and animals to use. How do people use trees? Why do animals need trees?

Foresters work with seeds. Foresters select certain adult plants for seeds. The biggest and strongest trees are usually selected. Sometimes they plant tree seeds in a nursery. The seeds grow into seedlings. Then the foresters use a special tool to put the seedlings in the ground.

Foresters also cut trees to be used for wood and other things. But they do not cut all the adult trees. How do adult trees make it possible for new trees to grow?

How Do Seeds Travel?

People and animals help seeds travel.
Sometimes people buy seeds in a store.
Sometimes they gather seeds from plants.
People take these seeds to new places to
plant them. Sometimes people and animals
carry seeds and do not know it.

THINKING

How are the people and animals in
these pictures carrying seeds? Do they
know they are carrying seeds? What
helped these seeds catch a free ride?

Seeds are food for many animals. Animals may take the seeds to different places to eat them. Animals sometimes store seeds that have hard coats. Birds sometimes drop seeds. Crows drop seeds to break them open. Some birds eat whole seeds. What might happen to seeds that are dropped by birds?

How Wind and Water Help Wind and water help seeds travel. Some seeds have coverings that look like sails. These seeds can be moved by the wind. Some seeds have coverings that look like wings. How do you think these seeds travel?

The shape and weight of seeds and their coverings help seeds travel. Seeds with round coverings can roll. Seeds with light coverings can float on water.

Which of the things in these pictures can roll? Which can travel on the wind?

SEARCHING

Find out how a dandelion seed, a milkweed seed, and a maple seed travel.

How Do People Use Seeds?

The most important use of seeds is to grow new plants. But people use seeds for other things, too.

People use seeds for food. The seeds of plants such as corn and rice are used for food. These seeds are used in making bread and cereal. Beans, peas, and peanuts are other seeds used for food.

Not all seeds can be used for food. Some seeds are poison. How can you find out if a seed is poison?

How can you make food from seeds?

What to Do

1. Put two cups of peanuts in a blender.
CAUTION: Do not put your hands in the blender.
2. Put the lid on the blender.
3. Blend the peanuts at high speed until smooth.
4. Put some of the food on a cracker and taste it.

What kind of food did you make?
What other foods that are made from seeds can you think of?

Other Uses of Seeds People use seeds to make things. Soap and medicine can be made from seeds. Coconuts are used to make soap. Castor beans are used to make medicine.

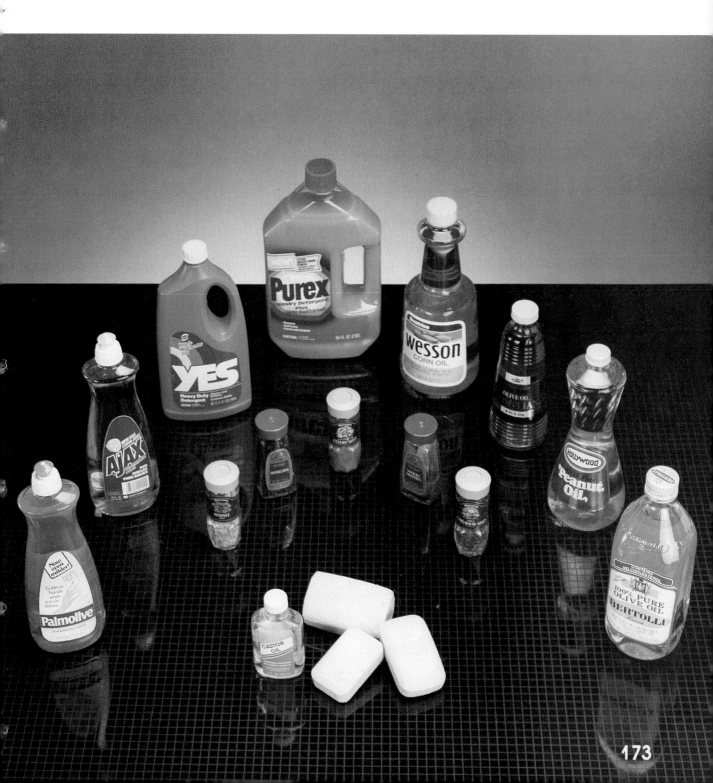

Oil From Seeds   People use some seeds to make oil. They use the oil from sunflower seeds, peanuts, and corn for cooking. Some spices come from seeds. Seeds are also used to make drinks, such as cocoa.

SEARCHING

Find a bottle of cooking oil. Read the label. What kinds of seeds were used to make the oil? Collect labels of other foods made from seeds.

INGREDIENTS: *PARTIALLY HYDRO-GENATED SOYBEAN OIL.*

NUTRITION INFORMATION PER PORTION:
PORTION SIZE . . . . 1 TBSP (14g)
PORTIONS PER CONTAINER. 93
CALORIES 130
PROTEIN 0g
CARBOHYDRATE 0g
FAT* 14g
    % OF CALORIES FROM FAT. . . . 100
    POLYUNSATURATED 5g
    SATURATED 2g
CHOLESTEROL   (0 mg per 100g) 0 mg
SODIUM. . . . . 0 mg

Journey Highlights

Seeds are parts of plants.

Seeds have a seed coat, an embryo, and a food supply.

The life cycle of a plant is seed, seedling, and adult plant.

Adult plants form seeds. Seeds are formed in fruits and cones.

People, animals, wind, and water help seeds travel.

People use seeds to grow new plants. They also use seeds for food, for cooking, and for making things.

Journey Wrap-up

Science Words

Find the words in your book that will complete the sentences.

1. The parts of a plant from which new plants grow are ____.

2. A baby plant is called an ____.

3. A ____ protects the inside of a seed.

4. Seeds need water and warmth before they will ____, or start to grow.

5. A young plant is called a ____.

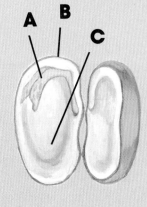

Using What You Have Learned

1. Match each part of the seed with its picture.

seed coat   embryo   food supply

2. Tell which seeds have germinated.

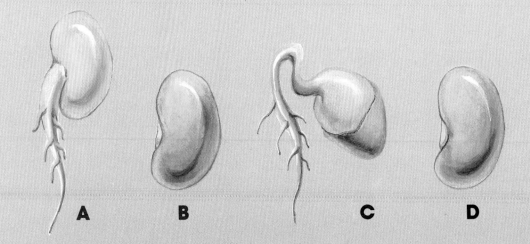

3. Arrange these pictures so that they show the life cycle of seeds and plants.

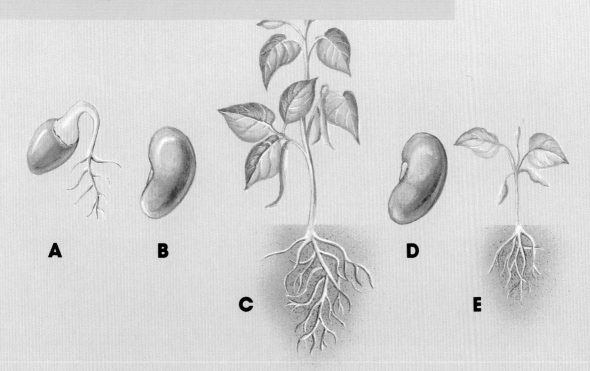

A   B   D

C   E

Things to Do

1. Get a large sponge. Cut the sponge into the shape of a mountain or an animal. Wet the sponge slightly. Cover it with grass seeds. Put the sponge in a shallow pan of water. Watch what happens.

2. Make a seed mosaic. Draw the outline of a picture on a piece of tagboard. Glue seeds to the tagboard to fill in the outline. Use colorful seeds of different sizes and shapes.

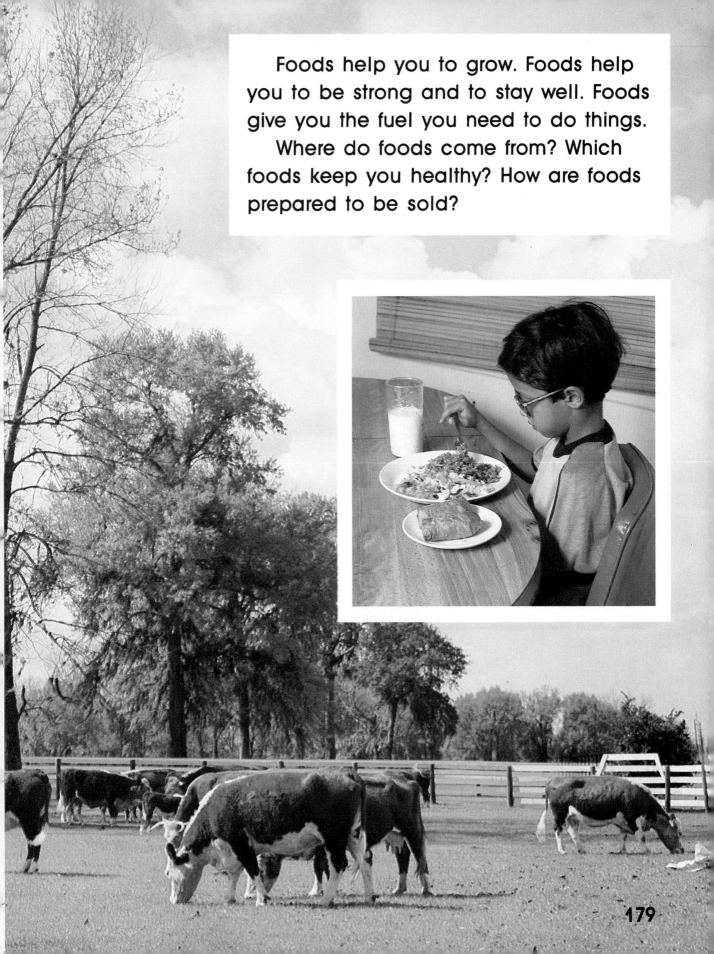

Foods help you to grow. Foods help you to be strong and to stay well. Foods give you the fuel you need to do things.

Where do foods come from? Which foods keep you healthy? How are foods prepared to be sold?

Where Foods Come From

You eat many foods every day. Where do the foods you eat come from?

Some foods come from animals. Meat comes from animals. Eggs and milk also come from animals.

Other foods come from plants grown on farms or in people's gardens.

What foods from plants do you eat?

What foods from animals do you eat?

Have you ever helped make hamburgers? Hamburgers are made from beef. Beef comes from cattle. Cattle spend many hours every day eating grass and corn. Grass and corn help the cattle to grow. What other foods come from cattle?

Pigs and sheep are also raised for food. What other animals are raised for food?

THINKING

What name is given to meat that comes from cattle? From pigs? From sheep?

Food From Water Animals

Have you ever eaten tuna fish? Tuna live in the sea, or ocean. People eat other animals from the sea. People eat shellfish, like clams. Tuna, shellfish, and other sea animals used for food are called seafood.

Not all water animals live in the sea. Some live in freshwater lakes and rivers. Fresh water is not salty like seawater.

What foods from water animals have you eaten?

What foods come from animals?

What to Do

1. Make a chart.

2. On the chart, paste pictures of animals in a column.

3. Next to the picture of each animal, paste pictures of the foods that come from that animal.

Do more of the foods that you eat come from water animals or from farm animals?

How could you find out?

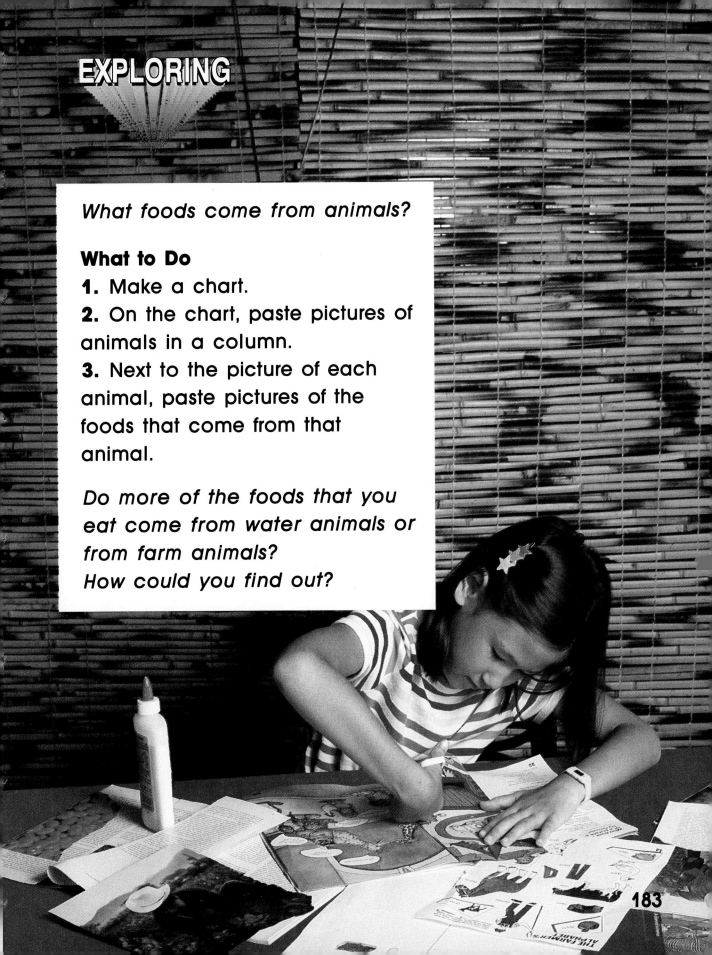

Plants: The Real Food Factory

Have you eaten bread, rice, carrots, or apples? These are some foods from plants. Plants are different from animals. Plants make their own food. They make much of the food you eat. Plants use water and air to make the food they need. They also use sunlight. The green coloring in plants helps them make food.

Why do plants need food?

SEARCHING

Find out what foods are made from wheat.

1. At the top of a large piece of paper, write "Foods Made From Wheat."

2. Think about the foods you eat.

3. Look at the labels on foods.

4. Draw pictures of foods that are made from wheat.

What foods did you draw?

Where Do Plants Store Their Food?

The food plants make is stored in different plant parts. Some plants, such as carrots, store food in their roots. Other plants, such as cabbages, store food in their leaves. Still other plants, such as asparagus, store food in their stems. Plants even store food in their flowers, fruits, and seeds.

What seeds do you eat?

What fruits do you eat?

What are some foods that are flowers?

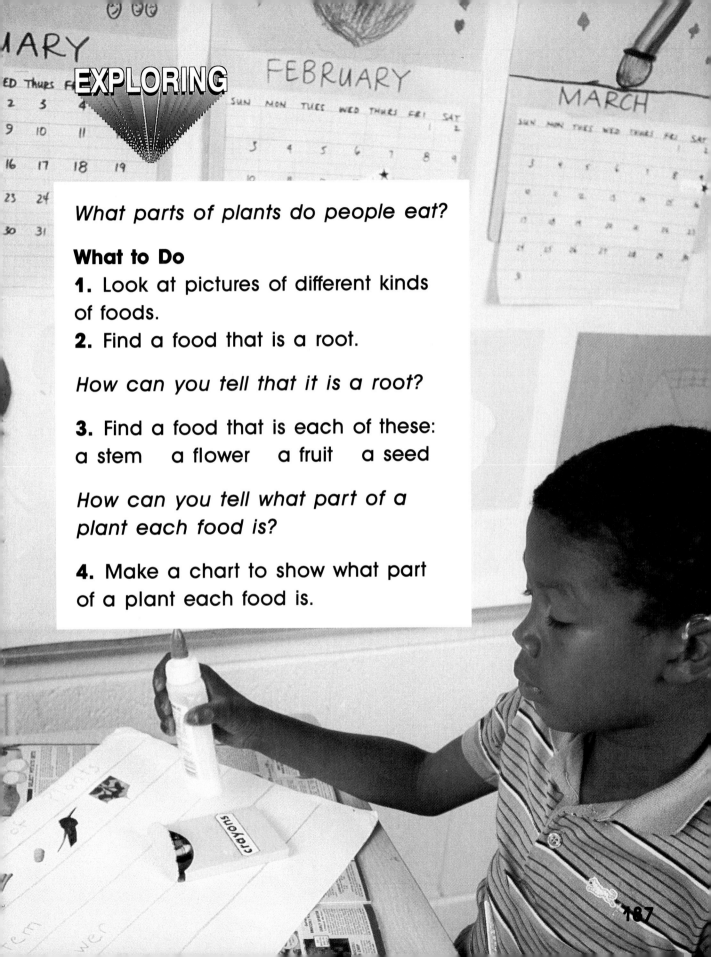

What parts of plants do people eat?

What to Do

1. Look at pictures of different kinds of foods.

2. Find a food that is a root.

How can you tell that it is a root?

3. Find a food that is each of these:

a stem   a flower   a fruit   a seed

How can you tell what part of a plant each food is?

4. Make a chart to show what part of a plant each food is.

Food Chains

Look at the pictures on this page. They show a food chain. The apple tree stores food in its fruit. Name this fruit. A worm feeds on this fruit. What feeds on the worm that fed on the apple? A fox feeds on the bird that fed on the worm that fed on the apple. Why do you think this is called a food chain?

Food Chains and People   Find the food chain in these pictures and in this story.

Farmer Loma is growing corn. Joseph Loma feeds the corn to the chickens. Carla Loma eats chicken for dinner.

THINKING

What would happen if one part of the food chain shown on this page were taken out?

189

Foods for Good Health

Some foods are made of the same kinds of things. They help your body in the same way. They belong to the same food group.

You will learn about four food groups. One food group is the milk group. Milk is a food that you need every day. Cheese and yogurt are other foods in the milk group. Foods in the milk group help you to have strong bones and teeth.

What are other foods in the milk group?

Foods for Healthy Eyes and Skin   Another group of foods is the vegetable-fruit group. Spinach and potatoes are two vegetables in this group. Oranges and apples are two fruits in this group.

Foods in the vegetable-fruit group help you to have healthy skin and eyes. Foods in the vegetable-fruit group help your body heal cuts. Which foods in the vegetable-fruit group have you eaten today?

191

Foods for Strength

Every day you should eat foods from the bread-cereal group. The foods in this group are made from the seeds of certain plants, called grains. Wheat, rice, corn, and oats are grains. The cereal you eat is made from grains. The bread you eat is also made from grains.

The foods in the bread-cereal group give you strength to do many things. What foods in the bread-cereal group do you eat?

Foods That Help You Grow   The meat group is another group of foods. Chicken and ground beef belong to this group. Ham and pork are in this group. Fish also belongs to the meat group.

Some foods that are not meats belong to the meat group. Eggs, beans, and nuts belong to the meat group.

The foods in the meat group help you to grow and to be strong. What foods in the meat group do you like to eat?

Eating Wisely

Sometimes people eat foods that are not good for them. They may eat foods that have a lot of sugar in them. Sugar sticks to their teeth. Sugar helps make holes, or cavities, in their teeth. How can you tell which foods have lots of sugar?

Which foods shown on this page would
make a healthful snack?

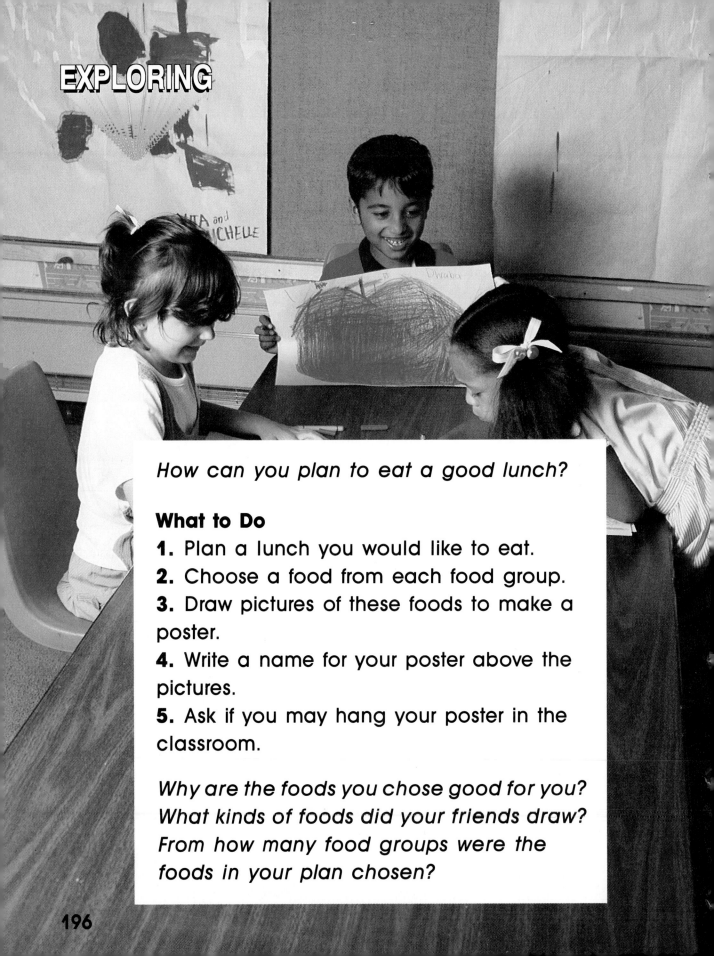

How can you plan to eat a good lunch?

What to Do

1. Plan a lunch you would like to eat.

2. Choose a food from each food group.

3. Draw pictures of these foods to make a poster.

4. Write a name for your poster above the pictures.

5. Ask if you may hang your poster in the classroom.

Why are the foods you chose good for you?
What kinds of foods did your friends draw?
From how many food groups were the foods in your plan chosen?

Food From Other Countries

Most people like to eat different kinds of food. Do you like to eat tacos? Do you like to eat egg rolls? The ideas for many kinds of foods have come from other countries.

The people in this country like to eat foods from all over the world. They call these foods ethnic foods. What is your favorite ethnic food? Why do people from different countries eat what they do?

5

How can I make my favorite ethnic food?

What to Do

1. Think about your favorite ethnic food.

2. Bring a recipe for this food to school.

3. Tell your class how to make your favorite ethnic food.

4. Make a book of your class's recipes.

5. Try to make some of these foods.

What did you learn about foods from other countries?

How Do Foods Get to Food Stores?

Some people grow their own food. But most people depend on others to grow their food. Farmers use their farmland to grow food for other people.

A farmer sometimes sells food to a company. People at the company prepare the food to be sold in food stores.

Why do farmers grow food for other people?

Preparing Foods for Stores   At a food company, people get foods ready to be sold in stores. They cut the foods and clean them. Sometimes they cook or freeze the foods. How does freezing help a food?

The people who prepare foods weigh the foods. They put the foods in boxes, bags, jars, or cans. Trucks and trains carry the foods to your food store. Where does your family buy the foods you like to eat?

SEARCHING

Find out how foods are sorted in a store.

1. Visit a food store.

2. Find out where fresh vegetables and fruits are kept.

3. Find out where eggs and milk are kept.

4. Find out where meats are kept.

5. Find out where frozen dinners, juices, and vegetables are kept.

6. Find out where canned foods and dry foods in boxes are kept.

Why are eggs and milk kept in a cold place?

Why are some foods frozen?

Why are canned foods and dry foods not kept in cold places?

Fred Jones raises cows. He has to milk the cows every morning and evening.

The Reyes family raises corn. They make sure the corn is good to eat.

Mary Barnes prepares foods to be sold in stores. She freezes foods to keep them safe.

Lorna Ali is a food-store manager. She makes sure the food your family needs is ready to buy.

Kumi Sato owns a restaurant. She serves foods your family likes.

What other people work with food?

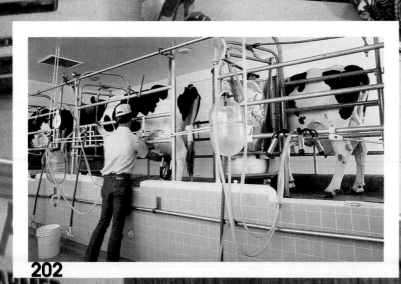

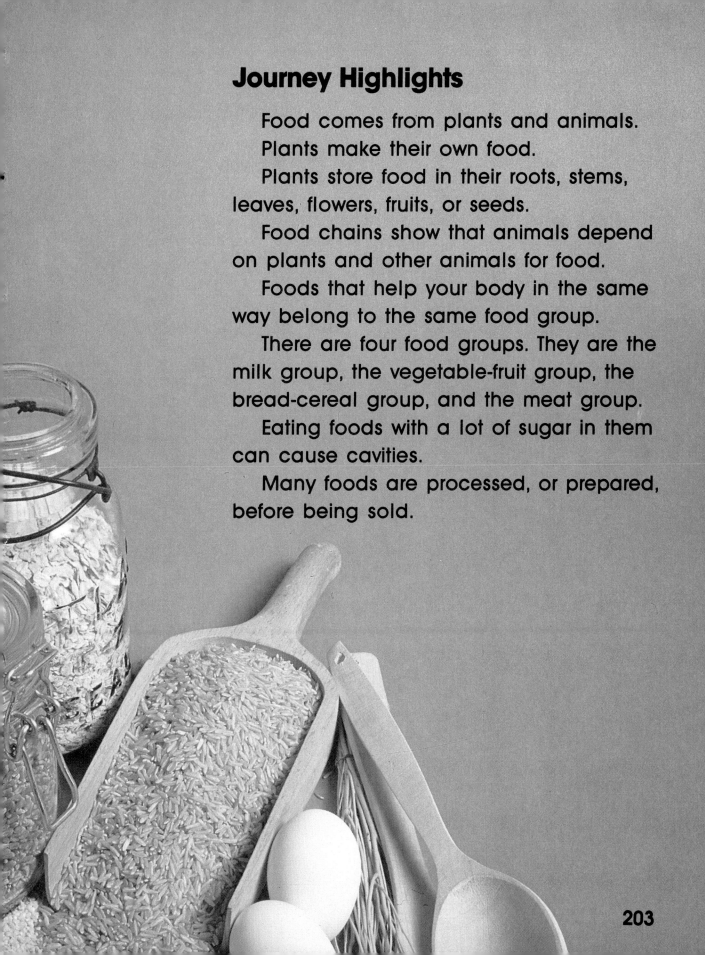

Journey Highlights

Food comes from plants and animals.

Plants make their own food.

Plants store food in their roots, stems, leaves, flowers, fruits, or seeds.

Food chains show that animals depend on plants and other animals for food.

Foods that help your body in the same way belong to the same food group.

There are four food groups. They are the milk group, the vegetable-fruit group, the bread-cereal group, and the meat group.

Eating foods with a lot of sugar in them can cause cavities.

Many foods are processed, or prepared, before being sold.

Journey Wrap-up

Science Words

The underlined word or group of words in each sentence makes the sentence wrong. Use a word or group of words from the list to make each sentence correct. You will not use all the words.

animals   ethnic foods   flowers
food chains   meat   milk
plants   seafood   sugar
roots

[handwritten: animals]
1. Farmers raise <u>plants</u> for meat.

[handwritten: sea food]
2. Food from sea animals is called <u>ethnic food.</u>

[handwritten: plants]
3. Sunlight helps <u>animals</u> make their own food.

[handwritten: roots]
4. Carrots store food in their <u>stems</u>.

[handwritten: milk]
5. Foods in the <u>meat</u> group help you have strong bones.

[handwritten: meat]
6. Fish and chicken belong to the <u>milk</u> group.

7. Cavities can be caused by eating too much <u>seafood</u>. *sugar*

8. Foods from other countries are called *ethnic food* <u>food chains</u>.

Using What You Have Learned

1. What do plants use to make food?

2. How do animals get their food?

3. What parts of plants do you eat?

4. What are the four food groups?

5. How is food prepared for sale?

Things to Do

Draw a food chain made up of four living things.

Unit 7 Environments

Suppose you lived on an island like the one in the picture. How would you get food? What kind of house would you live in? What kind of games would you play?

207

What Is an Environment?

The children in these pictures live in two different places.

What is the weather like in each place? What are the people like? What plants and animals might live in each place?

Everything around each group of children makes up their environment. Weather, soil, people, plants, and animals are all parts of the environment of a place.

EXPLORING

What is your environment like?

What to Do

1. Draw a picture of your environment.

2. Show the important places in your environment.

3. Show what the weather is like.

4. Put in some people who are important in your environment.

5. Add some plants and animals that live in your environment.

6. Name your picture.

7. Hang your picture of your environment at school or at home for others to see.

Plant and Animal Environments

An evergreen tree can grow in a cold place. It can grow on the side of a mountain.

A palm tree can grow in a hot place. It can grow in sandy soil. How is the environment of the evergreen tree different from the environment of the palm tree?

A polar bear and an alligator live in different environments. How are their environments different?

What can a polar bear find to eat in its environment?

What can an alligator find to eat in its environment?

What other things are important in the environments of these two animals?

THINKING

Do you think the polar bear and the alligator could trade places? Why or why not?

Homes and Habitats

The place where you live in your environment is your home. Many of your needs are taken care of in your home.

What are some of your needs?

Who takes care of your needs at home?

Other people in your environment also take care of your needs. They help you to be healthy. They keep you safe. Who are the people in your environment that take care of your needs?

How do you help people in your environment?

Plant and Animal Habitats   The place where a plant or an animal lives in its environment is called a habitat. A frog's habitat is a pond.

What food can a frog find in its habitat? Where can a frog hide in a pond? What other plants and animals live in a pond habitat?

How do some living things in the pond help other living things?

SEARCHING

Match each animal with its habitat.
Tell a story about each habitat.

Food Chains

All living things need food to live. Food helps living things to grow.

Plants make their own food. Animals have to look for food in their habitat.

Animals such as cows depend on plants for food. They are plant eaters.

Animals such as tigers depend on other animals for food. They are meat eaters.

Other animals, such as bears, eat both plants and animals.

The pictures on this page show a food chain. A food chain shows what some animals in a habitat eat. A plant is always at the beginning of a food chain.

Which animal in the food chain eats plants? Which animals in the food chain eat other animals?

THINKING

What would happen if there were no plants in this food chain?

What food chains can be found in a forest?

What to Do

1. Think about a food chain that can be found in a forest.

2. Write the names of four living things in this food chain. (Write each name on a different card.)

3. Ask a friend what each animal in your food chain eats.

4. Tell what each animal in your friend's food chain eats.

How are the food chains alike?
How are the food chains different?

PEOPLE
WHO USE
SCIENCE

Living Things Around You

People share their environment with plants and animals. How can people help the living things in their environment?

How are you important to the living things in your environment?

SEARCHING

What plants and animals live in your environment? Make a list of their habitats. Find out what each of these places is like.

EXPLORING

How can you learn about habitats?

What to Do

1. Choose a quiet place in the school yard. A place with grass and some plants will do.

2. Mark a circle with some string. Inside the circle, there is a little habitat.

3. Find out all you can about the habitat.

What things make up the habitat?
What plants can you find?
What animals are in the habitat?
What food chains are found in the habitat?

4. Tell your class about the habitat.

Adapting to Environments

There are many kinds of environments in the world. Some environments are on land. Others are in water. Some environments are hot, and others are cold. Some have much food, and others have little food.

The living things in an environment are adapted to that environment. That is, they are suited to live in the environment.

How is a penguin adapted to a cold environment?

SEARCHING

Are the animals in the pictures below adapted to the environments in which they are shown? Why or why not? If an animal is not adapted to the environment shown, tell what environment it is adapted to.

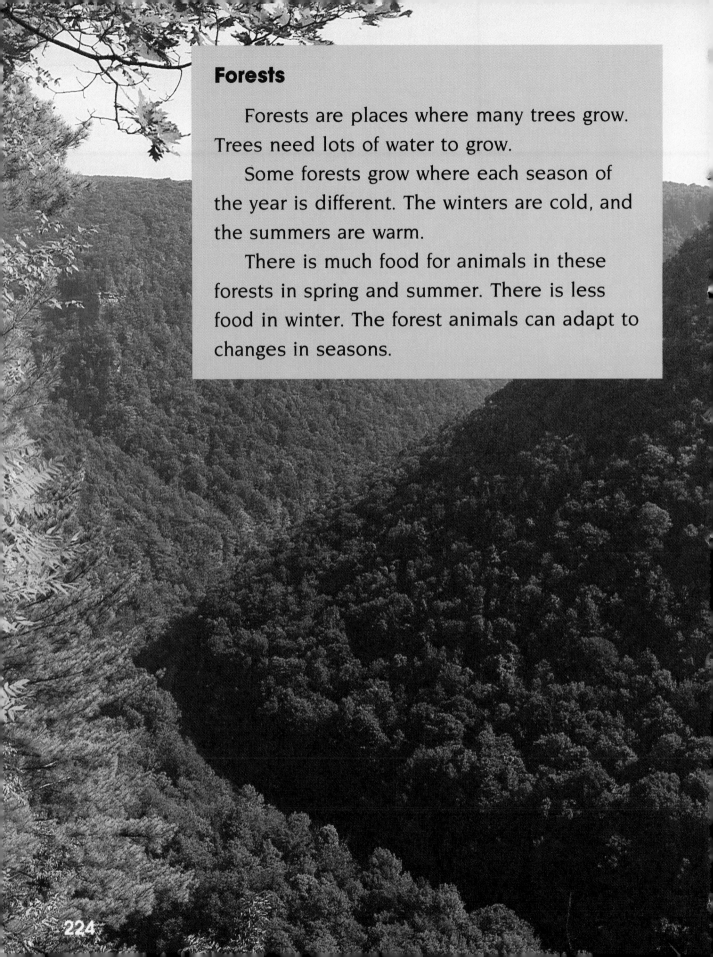

Forests

Forests are places where many trees grow. Trees need lots of water to grow.

Some forests grow where each season of the year is different. The winters are cold, and the summers are warm.

There is much food for animals in these forests in spring and summer. There is less food in winter. The forest animals can adapt to changes in seasons.

THINKING

How do some forest animals adapt to the cold winter?

Some forests grow where it is hot and wet all year. Plants grow well in these forests. Why do the plants grow well?

Many animal habitats in these forests are in the trees. How are some animals adapted to moving among the trees?

Deserts

Deserts are another kind of environment. Deserts are very dry because they get little rainfall. Some plants and animals are adapted to a desert environment.

To help them live in the desert, some plants have long roots. Other desert plants store water in their thick stems. How do long roots and thick stems help desert plants?

How do desert animals get water? How do these animals stay cool?

Kangaroo rat

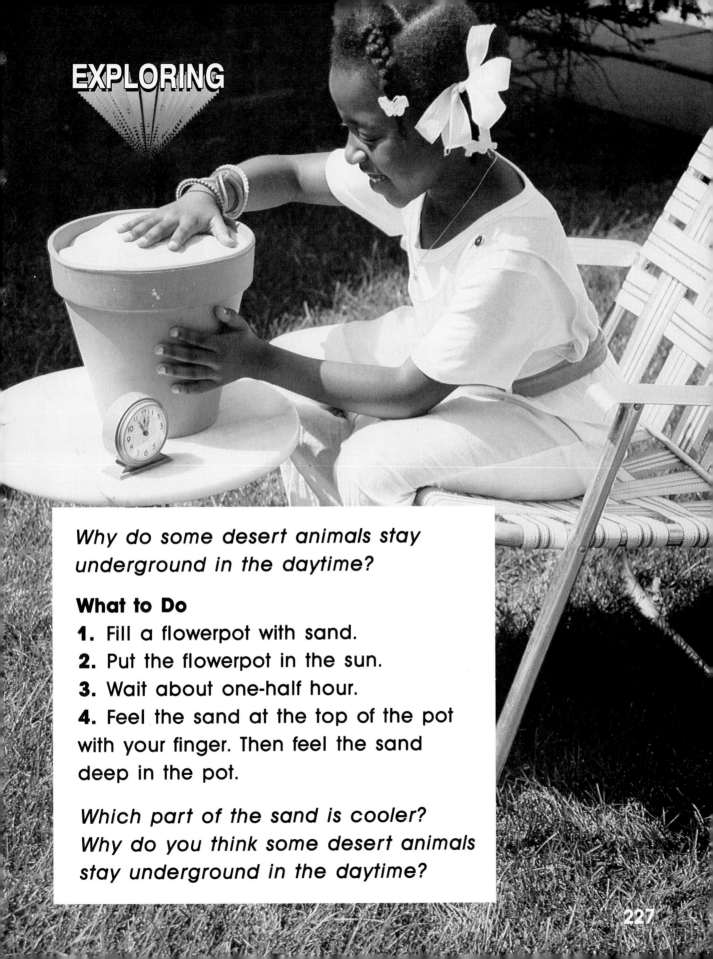

EXPLORING

Why do some desert animals stay underground in the daytime?

What to Do

1. Fill a flowerpot with sand.
2. Put the flowerpot in the sun.
3. Wait about one-half hour.
4. Feel the sand at the top of the pot with your finger. Then feel the sand deep in the pot.

Which part of the sand is cooler? Why do you think some desert animals stay underground in the daytime?

Water Habitats

Oceans are large bodies of water. All the water in an ocean is salty.

Many living things are found in an ocean. Some very small living things float in large groups near the surface. These living things are called plankton. Many animals in the ocean feed on plankton.

Have you ever been to the seashore? The seashore is where the ocean and the land meet.

SEARCHING

Most living things in the ocean stay near the ocean's surface. Find out why. Also find out how seabirds get their food.

What are some things that live at the seashore? How are these things adapted to living at the seashore?

Do living things at the seashore live in water or on land? Explain your answer.

Fresh Water Habitats   The water in ponds, lakes, and rivers is not salty. It is fresh water. Many plant and animal habitats are found in ponds and lakes.

Look at the picture of a pond. To what food chains do the living things in the picture belong?

How do some pond animals move about?

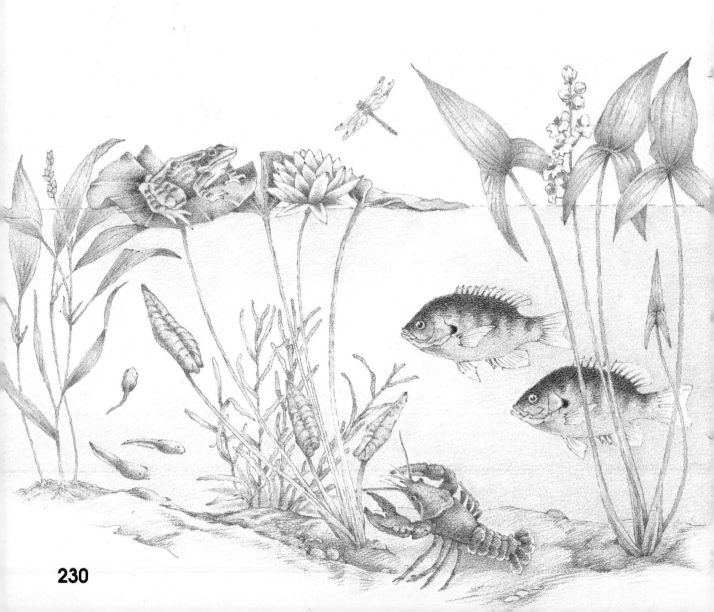

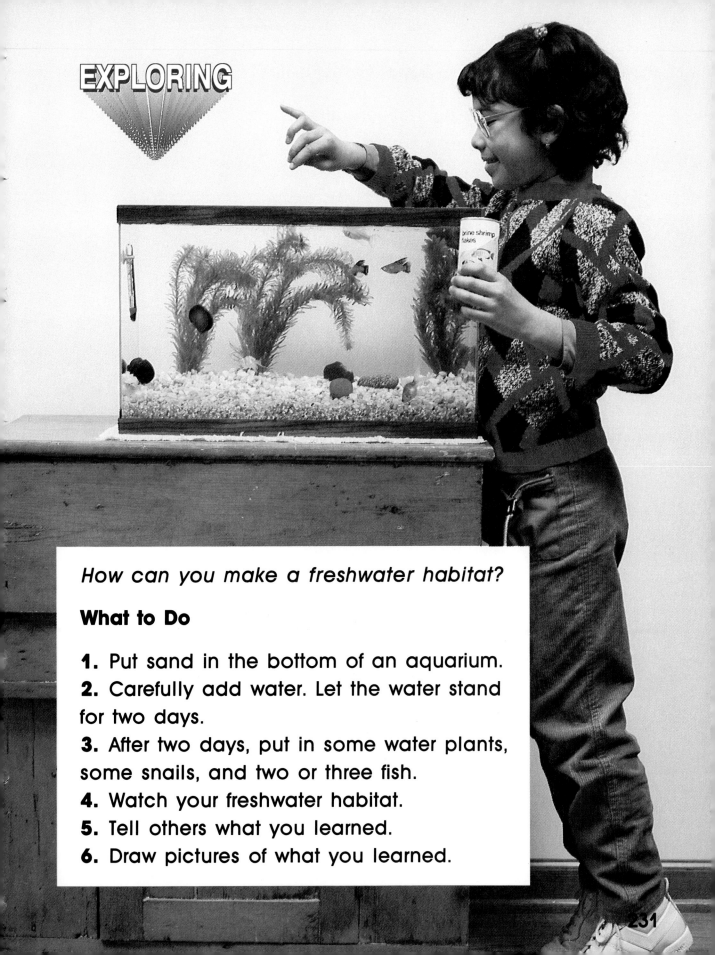

How can you make a freshwater habitat?

What to Do

1. Put sand in the bottom of an aquarium.

2. Carefully add water. Let the water stand for two days.

3. After two days, put in some water plants, some snails, and two or three fish.

4. Watch your freshwater habitat.

5. Tell others what you learned.

6. Draw pictures of what you learned.

Changes in Environments

Environments and habitats are always changing. You can count on some changes, like the change of seasons. These changes take place every year.

Look at the pictures of a park environment in spring and in winter. How does the park change from spring to winter?

Some environments and habitats change slowly. How is the field in the picture changing?

Some environments and habitats change quickly. What do these changes do to the habitats and to the living things in them?

233

SEARCHING

Notice what things have changed in your environment. Tell if the changes happened because of the change of seasons. Tell if the changes were slow changes or quick changes. Tell how people can help their environment.

People sometimes change environments and habitats. Some changes are helpful. Other changes are harmful.

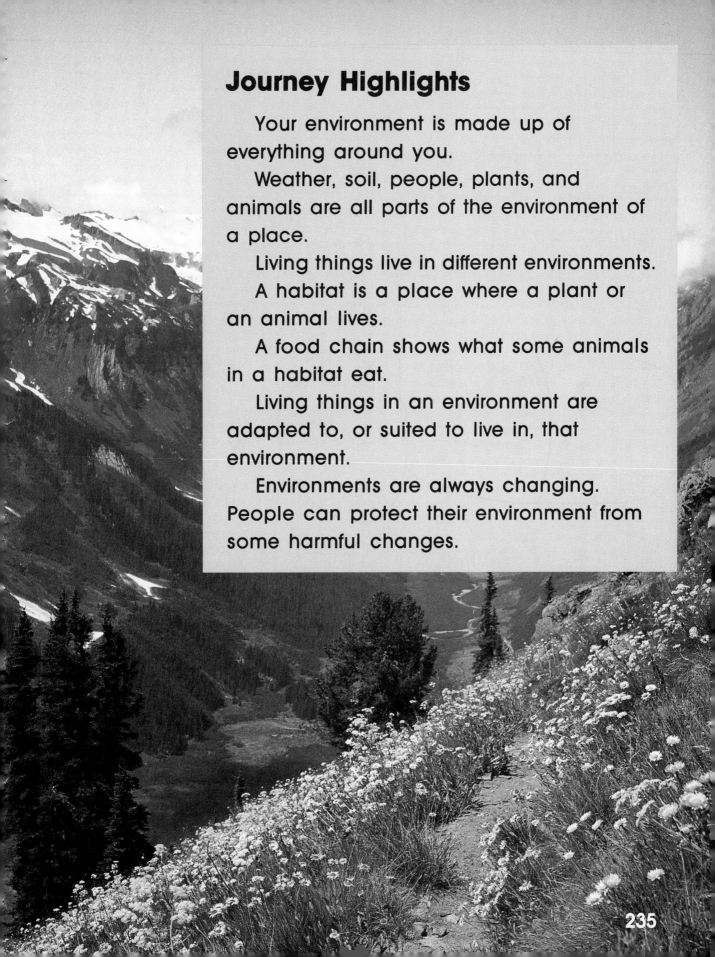

Journey Highlights

Your environment is made up of everything around you.

Weather, soil, people, plants, and animals are all parts of the environment of a place.

Living things live in different environments.

A habitat is a place where a plant or an animal lives.

A food chain shows what some animals in a habitat eat.

Living things in an environment are adapted to, or suited to live in, that environment.

Environments are always changing. People can protect their environment from some harmful changes.

Journey Wrap-up

Science Words

1. Which of these are part of your environment?

2. Match the name of each environment with its picture.

forest   pond   ocean   desert

B   *desert*

A   *pond*

forest   C

D   *ocean*

Using What You Have Learned

1. Find a habitat for each of these animals.

caterpillar   cow   kangaroo rat   fish

A   **B**   **C**   **D**

2. Put this food chain in order. Tell what each animal in the food chain eats.

Things to Do

1. Get a large clear-plastic jar. Make a habitat for a small plant. You might also put a ladybug in the jar. Watch what happens in the habitat.

2. Make a poster that shows how people can protect their environment from some harmful changes.

Table of Metric Measures

Length

millimeter (mm)
1 centimeter (cm) = 10 millimeters
1 meter (m) = 1 000 millimeters
            100 centimeters

Volume

milliliter (mL)
1 liter (L) = 1 000 milliliters

Mass

milligram (mg)
1 gram (g) = 1 000 milligrams
1 kilogram (kg) = 1 000 grams

Temperature

Water freezes at 0 degrees Celsius (0°C).
Normal room temperature is about 22 degrees
Celsius (22°C).
Water boils at 100 degrees Celsius (100°C).

Safety in the Science Classroom

Science can be fun. But you need to stay safe in the science classroom. Here are a few safety rules.

Never touch or use broken glass.

Never taste or smell anything unless your teacher says you may.

Smell things this way.

Tell your teacher about accidents right away.

Ask your teacher before you touch a plant or an animal. Wash your hands afterwards.

Using Science Tools

Here are some science tools that you use to measure.

A **metric ruler** or **meterstick** measures length in centimeters (cm) and millimeters (mm).

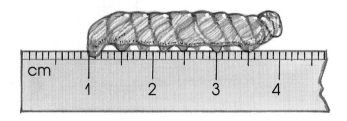

The insect is **3** centimeters long.

A **balance** can compare weight.

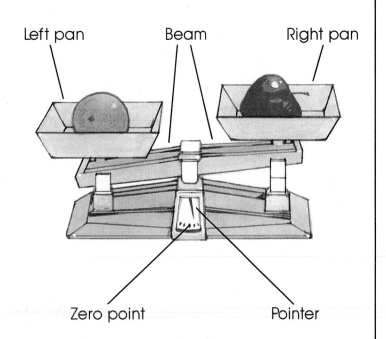

Left pan Beam Right pan

Zero point Pointer

The orange weighs more than the apple.

A **Celsius thermometer** measures temperature in degrees Celsius (°C).

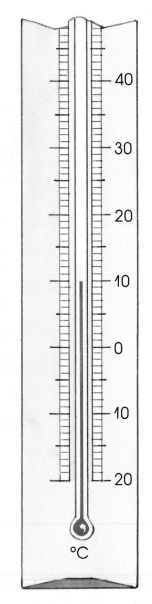

40

30

20

10

0

10

20

°C

The air temperature is 10 degrees Celsius.

Glossary

attract

Magnets **attract** matter such as pieces of steel.

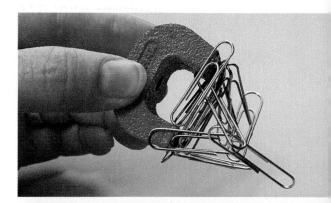

balance

A **balance** can be used to see if an apple is heavier than an orange.

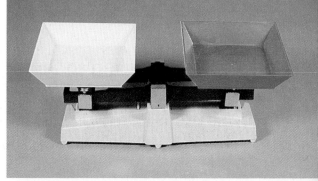

bread

People use **bread** to make sandwiches.

centimeter

A fly is about one **centimeter** long.

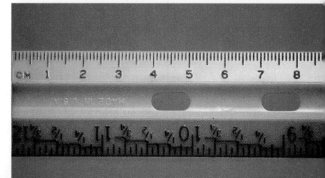

cereal

People eat **cereal** for breakfast.

cloud

A **cloud** is formed by water and bits of dust in the air.

compass

A **compass** is used to find directions.

cone

A pine tree forms its seeds in **cones.**

crystal

A snowflake is made up of tiny ice **crystals.**

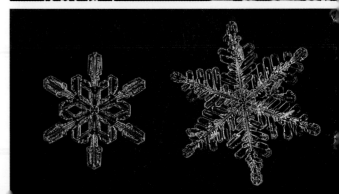

current

A **current** is a moving stream of water.

desert

A **desert** is a dry place.

embryo

The start of a new plant is called an **embryo.**

environment

Your **environment** is everything around you.

float

A cork will **float** in water.

fluid ounce

Liquids are measured in **fluid ounces.**

food chain

You are part of many **food chains.**

food group

Eggs belong to the meat **food group.**

food supply

Every seed has a **food supply** for its plant embryo.

foot

A 12-inch ruler is 1 **foot** long.

forest

A **forest** has many trees and other living things.

fruit

The **fruit** forms the seeds of a plant.

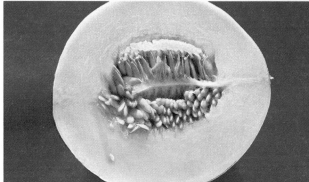

gallon

Milk is often sold by the **gallon.**

habitat

The place where an animal lives is its **habitat.**

hurricane

A **hurricane** is a powerful windstorm usually with heavy rains.

inch

An English unit of length is the **inch.**

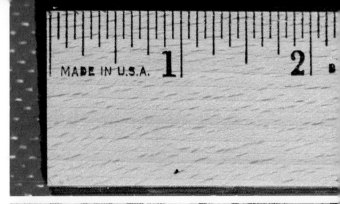

leaf

Leaves make a plant's food.

length

The scientist measured the **length** of the alligator.

life cycle

Seed, seedling, and adult plant are parts of the **life cycle** of a plant.

lightning

Lightning is often seen during a thunderstorm.

liter

You can buy soda pop in a 2-**liter** bottle.

magnet

Magnets are made in many sizes and shapes.

meat

Hamburger and chicken are **meats.**

meter

A metric unit used to measure length is the **meter.**

millimeter

Very tiny things can be measured in **millimeters.**

ocean

An **ocean** is one kind of environment.

plankton

Many animals in the ocean feed on **plankton.**

plants

Some of our food comes from **plants.**

quart

Some of the liquids we buy come in **quart** containers.

rain

Rain is drops of water that fall from clouds.

root

Beets are plant **roots** that people eat.

seafood

Tuna, clams, and shrimps are **seafoods.**

seashore

A **seashore** is the environment for many small animals.

season

A **season** is one of the four parts of a year.

sediment

Sand, gravel, and mud on the bottom of the ocean are called **sediment.**

seed

A **seed** can grow into a new plant.

seed coat

A **seed coat** covers a seed.

seedling

A young plant is called a **seedling**.

snorkel

People can breathe through a **snorkel** while swimming.

snow

Snow is tiny ice crystals that fall from clouds.

stem

The **stem** is part of a plant.

tacos

Tacos are an ethnic food.

thermometer

A **thermometer** measures temperature.

thunderstorm

Rain, wind, thunder, and lightning occur during **thunderstorms.**

tide

Tides are the rise and the fall of the level of the ocean.

tornado

A **tornado** looks like a funnel-shaped cloud.

vegetable

Peas, beans, and carrots are **vegetables.**

vibrate

Sounds are made when the strings of a guitar **vibrate.**

volume

The **volume** of a container is how much it can hold.

water cycle

The **water cycle** provides fresh water for rivers and lakes.

wave
Waves are movements on the surface of water.

weather
Weather is the condition of the air around you.

weather vane
A **weather vane** points to the direction from which the wind is blowing.

wind
Wind is moving air.

yard
The table is a **yard** in length.

Index

Photography Acknowledgments

Peter Arnold Inc.: A.G.E. Fotostock, 109; Laura Dwight, 248 (D), 252 (D); W.H. Hodge, 249 (A); John R. MacGregor, 242 (D); Ray Pfortner, 253 (C) / Artstreet: 14 (inset), 232; Bob Glaze, 246 (A) / Mary Lue Baer: 250 (B) / Tom Bean: 22 / Berg & Associates: 141, 221; Margaret C. Berg, 202 (inset); Jennings Keele, 199; Michael Plack, 195 (doughnuts); Kirk Schlea, 241 (D) / Jim Bradshaw: 213 (right) / Walter Chandoha: 18, 24, 186 (inset), 246 (D), 250 (C), 251 (A) / Click/Chicago, Ltd.: 78–79, 99 (tuba), 180 (inset); Frank A. Cezus, 85; Frank Rockerby, 26 (inset); Martin Rogers, 55; Brian Seed, 98 (top left); Dave Woodward, 59 / Bruce Coleman: Jane Burton, 59 (octopus); Robert Carr, 64 (top right); R.C. Sefton, 44; John Shaw, 27 (inset) / Ed Cooper: 252 (E) / Cyr Color Photo Agency: 36, 99 (drum), 171 (right); Lee Lemelin, 191 (left) / Larry Day: 168, 243 (C) / Marvin L. Dembinsky, Jr.: 45, 50, 131 (inset) / Leo de Wys Inc.: Everett Johnson, 252 (A); J.P. Nacivet, 2–3; Schroefer, 41 / Joseph A. DiChello, Jr.: 38 (top left), 78 (inset), 93, 233 (bottom right) / DRK Photo: 226; Tom Bean, 70, 219 (top); J. Brandenburg, 221; D. Cavagnaro, 219 (bottom), 246 (B); John Gerlach, 164 (pinecones); Stephen J. Krasemann, 166, 211 (left), 215 (sheep), 216 (inset); Wayne Lankinen, 215 (bird) / Don & Pat Valenti: 166 (seeds), 170 (inset), 190 (inset), 195, 244 (C) / William Ferguson: 168 (seeds on sock) / FPG: 129; Dennis Hallinan, 10 (inset); Hallinan, 248 (E); J. McNee, 98 (top right); K. Ober, 182 (inset); Stan Osolinski, 17; Clyde Smith, 30; Michael Stoklos, 29; Renaud Thomas, 14; Tom Tracy, 134 (left); A. Uptis, 20 (right); U.S. Department of Agriculture, 233 (bottom left); L. West, 99; Willinger, 15 / Tony Freeman: 84 / Frost Publishing Group, Ltd.: Bonaire Tourist Board, 8–9 / Gamma-Liaison: Hoagland, 74 / Grant Heilman: 54, 164 (lemons), 184, 215 (fish), 224, 228 (left), 234; John Colwell, 164 (pea pods); Isaac Geib, 189 (left); Larry Le Fever, 164 (pepper); Barry L. Runk, 153, 156 (left & center), 191 (right), 192, 193; Runk/Schoenberger, 156 (right), 217 (top & bottom left) / Robert Holland: 66 / Ronald Holle: 33 / Ed Hoppe Photography: 17 (insets), 86, 135 / Michael J. Hruby: 28 (inset), 201, 241 (B), 244 (A), 245 (C), 251 (C), 253 (E) / IMAGERY: 120; Sandy Gregg, 130 (inset), 147–148, 161, 231 / Tom Ives: 215 / Rodney C. Jones: 105 / Wolfgang Kaehler: 70 (inset), 225 (bottom), 249 (C) / Ginny Karp: 146 / Kenji Kerins: 19, 28, 46, 58, 63, 88, 89, 92, 94, 96, 97, 100, 106, 107, 108, 115, 117, 122, 123, 124, 125, 126, 127, 136, 138, 139, 150, 155, 157, 173 / Bob Keys: 243 (E) / Rubin Klass: 250 (D) / Dwight R. Kuhn: 244 (D) / Don Lansu: 16 / J. Scott Lawrence: 242 (A) / Neil G. McDaniel: 59 (crab), 67 (inset) / Bill Means: 194 (top) / Laurence Migdale: 11 (inset), 40, / Norma Morrison: 128, 247 (D) / Tom Myers: 128 (top right), 253 (D) / NASA: 46 (inset) / National Center for Atmospheric Research: 23 / OPC: John Lei, 249 (B) / Thomas M. Pantages: 134 (right), 229, 247 (A), 247 (C), 247 (E), / Connie and P.C. Peri: 80, 81, 82, 87, 90, 91, 114, 121, 185, 187, 197 / Phillips Photo Illustrators: 208 (right) / Photo Network: 213 (left) / Photo Researchers: Chesher, 68 / Photri: 34, 103, 144–145, 246 (E), 248 (A); B. Kulik, 149; Novak, 36 (inset); Leonard Lee Rue III, 245 (D) / James H. Pickerell: 190, 249 (D) / Doug Plummer: 128 (bottom left) / Positive Images: Jerry Howard, 12, 37 / Carl Purcell: 245 (E), 250 (E), 251 (D) / Kay Reese & Associates: Ray Ellis, 181, 194 (bottom), 195 (celery); H. Armstrong Roberts, 27, 37 (inset), 39, 49, 71, 73, 104 (top), 131, 145 (inset), 158, 170, 180, 203, 206–207, 210, 216, 228 (right); Camerique, 4–5, 52, 178–179, 204–205, 252 (C); J. Gleiter, 195 (oranges); Koene, 243 (B); P. Kresan, 253 (B); R. Krubner, 253 (A); D. Logan, 160 (inset); D. Muench, 160; M. Thonig, 245 (A) / Root Resources: 168 (burrs); James Black, 104 (bottom); Louise K. Broman, 26; Kitty Kohout, 214, 250 (A); Russel A. Kriete, 21; Lia Munson, 35; Mary A. Root, 166 (seedling), 241 (A), 242 (C) / James P. Rowan: 182 / Will & Angie Rumpf: 102, 242 (B), 251 (B) / John Running: 20 (left), 31 / Kjell B. Sandved: 248 (B) / Ron Sanford Photo: 200 / Bob Sample: 65 (inset) / Shostal: 62 / Tom Sistak: 244 (E) / Slots: Jacqueline Durand, 243 (D) / Elliot V. Smith: 171 (left) / Gordon E. Smith: 241 (C) / R. Hamilton Smith: 6–7, 159 (right), 243 (A) / Southern Light: 98 (bottom left and right); Bohdan Hrynewych, 212 (inset) / Bob and Ira Spring: 233, 234 (inset), 235 / Tom Stack & Associates: 64 (center), 75; Terry Ashley, 64–65; Brian Parker, 217 (top right); Carl Roessler, 60; Don & Pat Valenti, 217 (bottom right) / Stock Boston: Judy Canty, 38 (top right); Bela Kalman, 38; John Running, 202 / Taurus: Alec Duncan, 212; Cliff Fairfield, 10–11; Marty Meitner, 186; Alfred Owczarak, 167; Doug Wallin, 67 / Samuel Teicher: 33 (inset), 35 (inset) 247 (B), / Mary Elenz Tranter: 13, 25, 32, 47, 48, 69, 72, 101, 112–113, 116, 118, 119, 130, 132, 133, 137, 140, 142–143, 151, 165, 172, 174, 178 (inset), 179 (inset), 183, 189 (bottom right), 196, 198, 209, 227 / Valan Photos: Kennon Cooke, 79 (inset); Pam Hickman, 39 (inset); Albert Kuhnigk, 175; Dennis Roy, 208 (left); Dennis W. Schmidt, 226 (inset); Wayne Shields, 189 (top right); Val Whelan, 248 (C); Alan W. Wilkinson, 184 (inset) / Visuals Unlimited: 210 (inset); Frank T. Aubrey, 222; Kathleen Blanchard, 214 (inset); Albert Copley, 245 (B); Dr. John D. Cunningham, 219 (center); Kirtley, 169; Robert F. Myers, 249 (E); David Newman, 159 (left); Kirtley Perkins, 246 (C); Tom J. Ulrich, 244 (B); Richard C. Walters, 242 (E); William J. Weber, 169 (inset), 211 (right), 225 (top), 251 (E); Weyerhaeuser Co.: 167 (inset)

FIRST CANADIAN EDITION

media/ impact

AN INTRODUCTION TO MASS MEDIA

SHIRLEY BIAGI
CALIFORNIA STATE UNIVERSITY, SACRAMENTO

CRAIG MCKIE
CARLETON UNIVERSITY

I(T)P Nelson

an International Thomson Publishing company

Toronto • Albany • Bonn • Boston • Cincinnati • Detroit • London • Madrid • Melbourne
Mexico City • New York • Pacific Grove • Paris • San Francisco • Singapore • Tokyo • Washington

I⟨T⟩P® International Thomson Publishing

The ITP logo is a trademark under licence

www.thomson.com

Published in 1999 by

I⟨T⟩P® Nelson

A division of Thomson Canada Limited

1120 Birchmount Road

Scarborough, Ontario M1K 5G4

www.nelson.com

Canadian Cataloguing in Publication Data

Biagi, Shirley

 Media impact : an introduction to mass media

1st Canadian ed.
Includes bibliographical references and index.
ISBN 0-17-616628-9

1. Mass media. I. McKie, C. (Craig), 1944– . II. Title.

P90.B54 1999   302.23   C98-932991-7

Director, Higher Education	Michael Young
Acquisitions Editor	Jessica Mosher
Project Editor	Evan Turner
Managing Production Editor	Tracy Bordian
Managing Production Coordinator	Brad Horning
Marketing Manager	Kevin Smulan
Art Director	Sylvia Vander Schee
Cover and Interior Design	Fizz Design
Senior Composition Analyst	Daryn DeWalt
Input Operator	June Reynolds

Printed and bound in Canada

1 2 3 4 (BG) 02 01 00 99

ABOUT THE AUTHORS

SHIRLEY BIAGI is a professor in the Department of Communication Studies at California State University, Sacramento. She is the author of several communications text books besides *Media/Impact*, including *Media/Reader: Perspectives on Mass Media Industries, Effects and Issues*; and *Interviews That Work: A Practical Guide for Journalists*. She is co-author, with Marilyn Kern-Foxworth of Texas A&M University, of *Facing Difference: Race, Gender and Mass Media*, published by Pine Forge Press. She also is editor of the national media history quarterly *American Journalism*, published by the American Journalism Historians Association.

She has served as guest faculty for the Poynter Institute, the American Press Institute, the National Writers Workshop, the California Newspaper Publishers Association, and the Southern Newspaper Publishers Association. She also has been a project interviewer for the Washington (DC) Press Club Foundation's Women in Journalism Oral History Project, which completed 57 oral histories of female pioneers in journalism. Her international experience includes guest lecture appointments at El Ahram Press Institute in Cairo, Egypt, and Queensland University in Brisbane, Australia.

CRAIG McKIE is an associate professor in the Department of Sociology and Anthropology at Carleton University in Ottawa. He is the author of *The Internet Toolkit* and *Using the Web for Social Research* and was for six years editor-in-chief of *Canadian Social Trends*, Statistics Canada's social statistical quarterly.

Professor McKie is best known for his Web site, *Research Resources for the Social Sciences* (www.socsciresearch.com), a social science metasite housed in Toronto and mirrored by UNESCO in Paris. He has been a visiting professor at the University of Waterloo and at Salford University in Manchester, England, and taught in the Department of Sociology at the University of Western Ontario for a number of years. He lives in British Columbia and commutes to Ottawa for academic terms. His living arrangements give meaning to the words of encryption technology expert Bruce Schneier: "On the Internet, there is no such thing as place."

BRIEF Contents

DETAILED Contents

Chapter 4

Chapter 5

Chapter 9

NEW MEDIA, ON-LINE MEDIA,
AND THE WEB   192

Chapter 10

ADVERTISING   216

Chapter 12

Chapter 13

Chapter 15

ETHICS   308

Chapter 16

A GLOBAL MEDIA MARKETPLACE   328

PREFACE

Emerging technology, media globalization, concentration of media ownership in the hands of a few, new ethical challenges ... with so many changes in our society, it's an exciting time for you to study the media.

Canada has a rich tradition of media studies, beginning with Harold Innis's *Empire and Communications* (1950), a groundbreaking insight into the importance of communications in creating and maintaining historic empires, and continuing with Marshall McLuhan's *The Gutenberg Galaxy* (1963) and *Understanding Media: The Extensions of Man* (1964). In addition, Canadians have shaped media formats around the world through technological advances and new approaches to broadcasting, such as Moses Znaimer's innovative use of mobile, live television cameras at CITY-TV in Toronto, and the development of new cartoon animation techniques at Nelvana Ltd. of Toronto.

As national borders decline in importance, we need to understand the media in the context of trends that have swept the Western world in the last few decades. Such trends have undermined the ability of nation states such as Canada to sustain and foster indigenous culture and to resist being overwhelmed by the "world monoculture" of the sprawling U.S. news and entertainment industry.

The Canadian media have developed in a constant state of tension with the U.S. and British media, whose dominance has made it difficult to assert and sustain a unique Canadian cultural perspective. Today, the strained Canadian–U.S. relationship, complete with borrowing in both directions, is nowhere more obvious than in the Canadian content rules for radio broadcasting. On April 10, 1998, the Canadian Radio-Television and Telecommunications Commission (CRTC) announced that effective January 3, 1999, the Canadian music quota will be 35 percent all day, every day. This increase was the first since a 25 percent quota was imposed in 1971. National cultural practices and traditions have come under tremendous pressure from increased globalization both in business and on the World Wide Web. Nevertheless, nation states still have the ability to insist on performance standards should they wish to do so.

Canada and the United States are now tightly tied in a common commercial arrangement involving all of the media of mass communications. Although the Free Trade Agreement (FTA) and its successor, the North American Free Trade Agreement (NAFTA), specifically exempted the cultural industries at Canada's request, the entanglement of the two nations' institutions continues to grow stronger. It has become routine to see Canadians in leading roles in the U.S. media, including network television news and entertainment programs, motion pictures, newspapers, magazines, and animation companies. Likewise, U.S. content is pervasive in all aspects of Canadian media today. Some may lament this connectedness as meaning a loss of national opportunity and distinctiveness for Canada; others may celebrate the new possibilities. Whatever your response, it is necessary to acknowledge and understand the new reality. We hope *Media/Impact* will help you do this.

You will find many features designed to help you develop a critical, informed perspective on the wealth of information in *Media/Impact*. Each element will enhance your conceptual and practical understanding of the dynamics of the media, their convergence with information technologies, and the effects on our society.

ACKNOWLEDGMENTS

We would like to thank those people who took the time to review drafts of the manuscript and made this a better book: Paul Altallah, Carleton University; Madeleine Hard, University College of the Fraser Valley; David Spencer, University of Western Ontario; and Gregory S. Yellard, University of Saskatchewan.

1 YOU IN THE NEW INFORMATION AGE

> WHO WILL RIDE THE NEXT AVALANCHE OF BITS ON THE INFORMATION SUPERHIGHWAY—AND WHO WILL BE BURIED UNDER IT?
>
> *George Gilder, futurist*

What's Ahead

- Understanding the Communication Process
- Taking Advantage of the Information Superhighway
- How the New Communications Network Will Function
- How the New Communications Network Is Different
- Five Challenges for the New Network
- When Will the New Communications Network Happen?
- Understanding the Information Age
- Understanding the Mass Media Industries: Three Key Themes

Imagine an electronic device that's as easy to use as the telephone, with pictures and sound, offering a massive choice of information, entertainment, and services. You can use this appliance to—

◎ Watch your favourite program when you want to see it

◎ See a first-run movie and have an on-screen dialogue with your favourite movie producer about her latest movie release

◎ Order food to be delivered from a local restaurant

◎ Play the newest video game with opponents on another continent

◎ Conduct research for a term paper

◎ Make airline reservations

◎ Check your bank balance and make routine payments electronically

◎ Transfer funds from your savings account to your chequing account

◎ Chat with relatives on an audio connection free of direct charges

With all of these services, you decide what time you want to use them.

Futurists are calling this new machine an "information appliance," a "network computer" (NC), or a "teleputer," a fusion of *television*, *telephone*, and *computer* technology. This machine would be one of the central elements in what has been called the information superhighway. "The teleputer will end the [current] decade not as a luxury but as an indispensable appliance," says futurist George Gilder.[1]

The information superhighway, in fact, will be more like an intricate, interlocked, webbed network of many different types of communications systems. This network will be connected to each home, school, library, and business, creating a complex, universal pathway for high-speed communication.

The information superhighway is receiving a great deal of attention today because governments have placed communications on the public agenda. More than ten years ago, U.S. Vice President Al Gore (then a U.S. senator) coined the term *information highway*. Since then, the road has been upgraded to a *super*highway.

Today, the term *information superhighway* is used to describe an interconnected communications system using broadcast, telephone, satellite, cable, and computer technologies to connect everyone in Canada (and eventually around the world) to a variety of services. The government of Canada, through Industry Canada, the **Canadian Radio/Television and Telecommunications Commission (CRTC)**; and Canarie Inc., is working to install the new, high-speed infrastructure for the Internet. Ideally, this communications system would be affordable and accessible to everyone, such as through free terminals located in public libraries. The issue, as futurist George Gilder phrased it, is, "Who will ride the next avalanche of bits on the information superhighway—and who will be buried under it?"[2]

Understanding the Communication Process

To understand the information superhighway, you first need to understand the process of communication. Communication is the act of sending ideas and attitudes from one person or group of persons to another. Writing and talking are only two of the many ways human beings communicate. We also communicate when we gesture, move our bodies, and roll our eyes.

Three terms that scholars use to describe how people communicate are *intrapersonal communication, interpersonal communication*, and *mass communication*. Each communication situation involves different numbers of people in specific ways.

If you are in a grocery store and you silently discuss with yourself whether to buy a package of chocolate chip cookies, you are using what scholars call *intrapersonal communication*: communication within one person.

To communicate with one another, people use many of the five senses—sight, hearing, touch, smell, and taste. Scholars call this direct sharing of experience between two people *interpersonal communication*.

Mass communication is communication from one person or group of persons through a transmitting device (a medium) to large audiences or markets. In *Media/Impact* you will study mass communication.

Figure 1.1 describes the process of mass communication, using five simple terms: *sender, message, receiver, channel*, and *feedback*.

Imagine that you're standing directly in front of someone and you say, "I like your hat." In this simple communication, you are the sender, the message is "I like your hat," and the person in front of you is the receiver (or audience). This example of interpersonal communication involves the sender, the message, and the receiver.

Figure 1.1

Elements of Mass Communication

The process of mass communication: A sender (source) puts a message on a channel, which is the medium that delivers the message to the receiver. Feedback occurs when the receiver responds, and that response changes subsequent messages from the source.

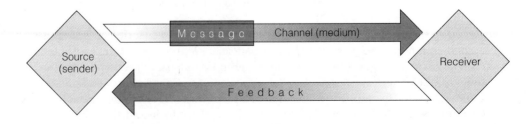

In mass communication, the **sender** (or **source**) puts the message on what is called a **channel**. The sender (source) could be your local cable TV company, for example. The channel delivers the *message*. The channel could be the cable line that hooks into the back of your TV set. A **medium** is the means by which a message reaches an audience. (The plural of the word *medium* is *media*; when scholars discuss more than one medium they refer to **media**.) Your television set is the medium that delivers the message simultaneously to you (and to many other people).

Feedback occurs when the receivers process the message and send a response back to the sender (source). Consider this simple example: the cable TV company (sender/source) sends an advertisement for pizza (the message) over the cable (channel) into your TV set (medium). If you (the receiver) use the controls on your interactive TV set to order a pizza, the order you place will ultimately bring you a pizza (feedback). This entire loop between sender and receiver, and the resulting response (feedback) of the receiver to the sender, describes the process of mass communication.

Broadly defined, mass communication today shares three characteristics:

1. A message is sent out using some form of mass media (such as the Internet, newspapers, or television).

2. The message is delivered rapidly.

3. The message reaches large groups of different kinds of people simultaneously or within a short period of time.[3]

Thus, a telephone conversation between two people would not qualify as mass communication, but a message from the prime minister, broadcast simultaneously by all of the television networks, would qualify.

Mass media deliver messages to large numbers of people at once. The businesses that produce the mass media—newspapers, magazines, radio, television, movies, recordings, the Internet, and books—are mass media industries.

Taking Advantage of the Information Superhighway

The economics of the communications industries make the information superhighway an important issue for all Canadians. All of the industries involved in building and maintaining this interconnected network—broadcast, cable, telephone, computer, software, satellite, and consumer electronics industries—want a piece of the billions of dollars that such a project ultimately will cost us all. Leaders of the media industries believe that Canada is ideally positioned to be the first to develop such a network because many Canadians already have most of the tools that such a system needs. Indeed, Canada has for many years been the most heavily "cabled" country in the world, as a result of the long distances between Canadian urban communities.

As Table 1.1 indicates, nearly all of the households in the Canada have colour televisions and telephones, about three-quarters are connected to cable, and about a third have personal computers. Because Canadian telecommunications facilities are already among the best in the world, people in the media industries believe that it would be logical—and ultimately very profitable—for the media industries in this country to develop the technology to package and deliver information worldwide.

Table 1.1

Electronics Equipment in Canadian Households, May 1997	
Percentage of Canadian Households with:	
Telephones	98.6
One	24.1
Two	37.2
Three or more	37.3
Cell phones	18.6
Radios	98.7
One	17.6
Two	25.2
Three or more	55.9
Colour televisions	98.7
One	46.8
Two or more	51.9
Cable television	73.7
VCRs	84.7
One	64.4
Two or more	20.3
Camcorders	17.7
Cassette or tape recorders	82.0
CD players	58.1
Home computers	36.0
Modem	21.5
Internet	13.0

Source: Adapted from *Household Facilities and Equipment 1997*, Catalogue No. 64-202-XPD, Text Table II, pp. 20–21. Reprinted with permission from Statistics Canada.

One-Way versus Two-Way Communication

The classic model of mass communication (see page 4 and Figure 1.1) describes a process that begins with a sender (or source), who puts a message on a channel (a medium), which delivers the message to the receiver. This model can be described as the equivalent of a one-way road: communication travels directly from sender to receiver. The information highway, as envisioned today, begins in the same way. The channel will carry information and entertainment (messages) from many different sources (senders) to many different people (receivers).

The messages that return from the receiver to the sender are sometimes called *feedback*. On this new information highway, messages and feedback can occur almost instantaneously. The sender and the receiver can communicate with each other at the same time.

To accomplish this, today's delivery system must develop from a communications system that works like an ordinary television (sending messages and programming one-way from the sender to the receiver) to a two-way system that can send and receive messages simultaneously and that works more like a combination television and computer. This is why some futurists have called the new machine a *teleputer*.

"Dumb" versus "Smart" Communications

The television set is a "dumb" appliance; it can only deliver programming. You can change the channel to receive different programs, but you can't talk back to the people who send the programming to your television set to tell them when you'd like to see a particular program. You can't watch something when you want to watch it, unless you remember ahead of time to tape the program on your VCR. You also can't add anything to the programs on your TV. You can't add commentary about sports programs or replace a bad movie with a good one. This type of mass communication—in which the programs are sent to you on an established schedule and you are a passive receiver (or a couch potato)—is *one-way*.

As communications devices, however, telephones are smarter. When you talk on the telephone, the person on the other end of the conversation can listen to you and talk back right away (in the case of a teleconference, this can involve several people at the same time). This ability to let you talk back—to receive as well as to transmit messages—makes the telephone **interactive**. Telephone communications are *two-way*.

THE GUY WHO TOOK A WRONG TURN OFF THE ELECTRONIC SUPERHIGHWAY AND WOUND UP IN A MICROWAVE OVEN IN DAVENPORT, IOWA

Telephone communication uses a system of rapidly digitized information. When you talk, the telephone system uses electronic signals to transform your voice into a series of digits—ones and zeroes—and then reassembles these digits into an exact reproduction of your voice on the other end of the line. This method of storing and transmitting data is called **digital**.

Like telephone communications, computers also operate using digitized information and are interactive. Written words, audio, and video are translated and stored as *bits*. These bits can easily be transmitted, using two-way communication. This is the reason that someone can, for instance, dial up the Internet on a computer and receive and send information. To dial up the Internet, someone uses a device called a *modem* (short for modulator/demodulator), which connects the computer to a telephone line, making two-way communication possible. Consumers can also connect to the Internet via high-speed ISDN telephone lines or through the cable TV system using the WAVE utility, provided by Rogers Communications, as well as through other cable systems provided by the @HOME facility. Unlike television and telephones, computers can store information for future use. This ability to store information makes the computer different from broadcast, cable, and telephone communications. "Nearly all of the relevant activity is in the computer industry rather than the television industry," says futurist George Gilder. "In the information economy, the best opportunities stem from the exponential rise in the power of computers and computer networks."[4]

How the New Communications Network Will Function

The communications network of the future will combine different elements from each of these industries. Today, the broadcast industry can produce content and deliver one-way communication by microwave broadcast; the cable industry can deliver one-way communication, and very limited two-way communication, by underground (or overhead) cable; the telephone companies can efficiently deliver digital two-way communication using fibre optics, cellular telephone, or PCS technology; and the computer industry can create digital storage capability. The network of the future must combine all of these elements: content, two-way digital communication, and digital storage. Figure 1.2 shows how this communications network of the future would work.

Figure 1.2

The New Communications Network

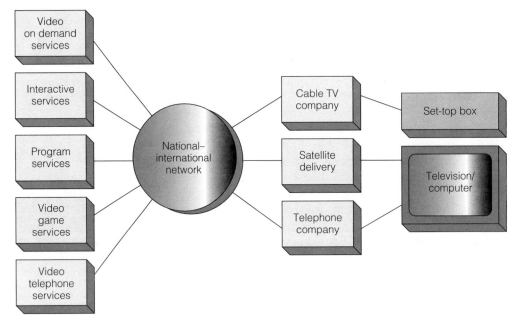

The Receiver (You, the Subscriber)

The network begins with you, the receiver/subscriber. You will choose which services you want. Using a device similar to either today's remote control or a computer mouse, you will turn on your television/computer. A **set-top box** sitting on top of your television/computer will be your electronic link to the new communications network. The screen will show you a menu of services, much like a computer menu, including—

◎ An on-line edition of your local newspaper

◎ A listing of programs by category (comedy, dramas, specials, and so on)

◎ A national video news service

◎ A worldwide video news service

◎ A library database research service

◎ A sports video and information service

◎ A family and lifestyle video and information service

◎ A travel video and information service

◎ A shopping video and information service

◎ A music video and information service

◎ An on-line game site

◎ A listing of bulletin board discussion groups by topic

◎ A video telephone message service, with video messages from the day's callers

◎ A first-run movie service

By clicking your remote control mouse, you could glance through the offerings of each service and then make your choices. Your television/computer could show several screens at once, so that you might choose to use several services at the same time, each in a different frame on the screen. Using video multiplexing for instance, you might check your bank balance while you watch a hockey game or check your video phone messages while you read the news headlines.

The software in the set-top box could also track your usage, detailing the charges for the services you choose, though there is great resistance to this pay-per-use model. Consumers tend to favour unlimited use for a set fee. As with today's TV cable and telephone services, there would probably be a basic fee, and additional charges would be added for premium services.

Many of these services exist now, either on the World Wide Web (through newspapers, TV listings, and limited TV and radio rebroadcast), in information services delivered through unused television broadcast transmission capacity in the blanking interval (the British Ceefax system), or through add-ons to the telephone system (the French Minitel system). It is now possible to pack up to 20 TV channels onto your computer monitor screen using the ATI All-in-Wonder video card connected to cable TV.

The Channel (Cable, Telephone, and Satellite Companies)

Cable, telephone, or satellite companies will deliver the new services. These companies may choose to offer only specific services; they might package some services together (local, national, and international news services, for example); or they may offer an unlimited menu of all services available and let you make the choices.

As now envisioned, the cable, telephone, and satellite companies would compete for business in each city. Customers will choose which type of service they want, based on each company's offerings and pricing. Some services will be billed as pay-per-view (for example, there might be a $5 charge to view a first-run movie, as there is now in most Canadian urban areas) or per minute (for example, to use a library database for research). Billing for these services would arrive monthly, or the company could bill the amount directly to your chequing account or credit card.

The cable, telephone, and satellite companies will be connected to the program services by a national and international network or by a satellite system. This network and the satellite systems are already in place today through the long-distance carrier networks, such as Stentor, AT&T, and Sprint, and through satellite services, such as USSB. The domestic long-distance networks could appear as a basic fee on your television/computer bill; international services would be an additional cost. The **Internet**, an international web of computer networks, could remain a free service, or it might become a low-fee backbone of the new network, available to anyone with a television/computer and a cable or telephone hook-up.

IMPACT

Technology   *THE DAWN OF TECHNOMANIA*

By Nathan Myhrvold

It is easy to get caught up in tech-nomania. Those who are most deeply involved with technology want to know more, those who fear it want reassurance, and those who see an opportunity—financial or other—don't want to miss out. *It's gonna change everything. It's gonna be here next Thursday. Watch out or you'll be left behind!*

Even newspaper gossip columns have become technomaniacal. Suddenly, the geeks who used to ace the math exam are the barons of the information age. If "The Graduate" were to be remade for the late nineties, the single word of advice imparted to Benjamin would be "information."

Such, in any case, is the pop-ular notion, although in the short run it is hopelessly exaggerated. A lot of guys with tool belts will have to shinny up a lot of phone poles before digital television or high-speed Internet gets to your home. Someday, Internet firms will be a major force in the economy. Indeed, someday they will even—dare I predict it!—make a profit. But it will take years before the aggregate sales volume of the Internet industry measures up to that of, say, the pantyhose industry.

In some ways, every attribute of technomania has a parallel in the industromania of a hundred years ago. By 1897, large factories

had sprouted, creating the notion of "going to work" in urban areas. Previously, cities had been centers of commerce which served the primary source of wealth—the agrarian countryside. Now they became the centers of both popu-lation and power. This caused other shifts, as organized labor started to take hold, and a political transformation followed.

Inventions emerged from everywhere—typewriter in 1874, the telephone in 1876, the internal-combustion engine and the phonograph in 1877, electric lights in 1880, the zipper in 1891, and radio in 1895 ... Few imagined that the industrial revolution would continue at the same pace for sixty years more ...

The twilight of the twentieth century is driven by a mixture of technology and resources very like that which drove nineteenth-cen-tury America. This time, it is silicon and software rather than oil and steel. Instead of transcontinental railroads, we have a global com-munication infrastructure that links us as the railroads did, but at the speed of light. And, once again, this change is being driven by people from around the world, making possible an unprecedented level of economic growth. Workers may start out sewing Nikes, but chip plants and more diverse

enterprises will eventually follow. In the nineteenth century, you had to cross an ocean to find economic opportunity, freedom from repres-sion, or a respite from famine. The pioneers of the twenty-first century can stay put—their diaspora is to cyberspace.

Still, we may not be able to gauge the real impact of the infor-mation revolution for fifty or sixty years more. Consider our cities, which in many cases have been transformed into artifacts of indus-trialization. Will large numbers of people begin to telecommute and, in that way, return to a pastoral America? Or will the cities somehow become even more nec-essary to our lives? Technomania, like its industrial equivalent in 1897, is a reminder that all this lies just beyond our knowing. What has happened already is bound to be very small in comparison to what lies ahead.

The New Yorker, *10/20–27/97, pp. 236–237. Used by permission.*

The Sender (Program Services)

Program services will provide—

1. video on demand, such as movies

2. interactive services, such as banking, shopping, chat rooms, on-line news-papers, and information research services

Satellite companies such as Direct TV are competing with cable and telephone companies to deliver services to consumers.

Gamma Liaison/Pablo Bartholomew

3. video telephone services

4. program services (comedies, game shows, soaps, and sports)

5. video game services

Today's broadcast networks and cable channels would become program services, so that you might subscribe to the CBC and Global but not CTV, for example. The cable channels, such as MuchMusic, Newsworld, and CTV News1, would provide programming much as they do now, and you could select the program services you wanted. You might also want to add local stations from other areas, such as CITY-TV from Toronto or VTV from Vancouver.

The Message (Content)

All print, audio, and video that is digitized into bits becomes **content** for a digitized communications system. In this future of networked, rapid, digitized communications, any digitized textbook, novel, movie, magazine article, or news story, for example, qualifies as content.

Information and entertainment that has already been produced, stored, and digitized will become the first content. Companies that hold the copyrights on information and entertainment will be able to market the content they own as products quickly and easily because they won't have to purchase the rights to digitize the content.

Media companies that already produce content, such as newspaper publishers, book publishers, TV program producers, and movie producers, are busy creating more "inventory" so they will be ready for the on-line world when it comes. "Movie companies have been increasing production," says the *Wall Street Journal*, "because there is a general feeling that as 'content providers' they will be big winners in the coming age of the information super-highway."[5]

As information and entertainment products are digitized, they will become available in many different formats as quickly as they can be created. For example, a music video of Disney songs could be made available on-line as soon as the new Disney movie is released; a news organization could create a

Computers are already changing how Canadian kids learn.

CP Picture Archive (Ron Bull)

background story on a well-known musician, complete with video and sound, and make it available on-line during the musician's worldwide concert tour; or a publisher could assemble excerpts and photos from a new book, along with an interview with the author, and make it available on the communications network as the book hits bookstores. Inexpensive CD-ROM writers for home computers can be used to custom make music CDs with downloadable files from the Web.

How the New Communications Network Is Different

Two-way communication on the network makes it possible to receive and send information. You can decide to produce a screenplay, put an ad for your screenplay on a bulletin board, and respond to anyone who wants to see your produced screenplay. Viewers might pay you a fee to receive the video and audio, or you could create a mystery roundtable, with authors from different parts of the world contributing to the screenplay. Then you could produce the screenplay for the network, complete with music that you could distribute through an on-line music network.

Computer networks "free individuals from the shackles of corporate bureaucracy and geography and allow them to collaborate and exchange ideas with the best colleague anywhere in the world," says futurist George Gilder. "Computer networks give every hacker the creative potential of a factory tycoon of the industrial [turn-of-the-century] era and the communications power of a TV magnate of the broadcasting era."[6]

In an interconnected world, the speed and convenience of the network could redefine the mass media industries and erase all previous notions of how mass communication should work.

IMPACT

on You

TALES OUT OF SCHOOL

By Joe Chidley

In this excerpt from his article in Maclean's, Joe Chidley reveals that the Internet makes cheating in school easier than ever.

Thank you for choosing writemyessay.com

At writemyessay.com, we are confident that you will receive the highest quality custom paper available anywhere. Our expert writers are all college graduates and all have an emphasis in writing. Their expertise will help you in further understanding your assignment and completing it with a high grade.—from the Web site of Write My Essay term-paper service, which charges $20 (U.S.) for the first page, $10 for each additional page, and accepts major credit cards.

Business is good for Kenny Sahr—booming, in fact. And why not? When he launched his new Web site last year, the Houston-based entrepreneur knew he had tapped into a gold mine. "One day, it just hit me that no one had done this yet," says Sahr, 26. The idea was simple: post university essays on the World Wide Web—a veritable treasure trove of other people's ideas and words—to inspire and inform students around the world. A year and [a] half after launching his site, School Sucks, Sahr claims it attracts 5,000 to 6,000 Web-surfers a day, with as much as 20 per cent from Canada. He has already launched another site in Hebrew. Within 16 months, he estimates, the service will be available in 15 languages. As for what surfers *do* with the more than 25,000 essays on the site, Sahr—who makes most of his money selling ad space to video-

game companies, publishers and other youth-oriented retailers—insists that 99 per cent of them "are using School Sucks for decent purposes." Sure, he concedes, a handful of college students have been caught printing up the essays and handling them in as their own. "But they don't belong in school anyway," Sahr adds. "The universities should thank me for helping them find these people."

Not likely. And university professors and officials would question Sahr's assertion that "School Sucks is not about plagarism"—or that it merely provides an independent research tool. But Sahr is right about one thing: it didn't take the Internet to bring academic dishonesty to lecture halls and exam rooms. Cheating has been around for as long as organized education. And according to both students and university officials, the traditional forms of academic dishonesty—crib notes, stand-ins for exams, and so on—still have their loyal practitioners.

In the plugged-in Nineties, essay-writing services—once the denizens of college-town back alleys and benighted basements—are digitized, sophisticated, and just a mouse-click away. Dozens of them—and most are American—are now available to Canadian students on the Internet. Some, like School Sucks and the Evil House of Cheat, make papers available at no cost, but usually require students to upload their own papers before they are given full access to the essay database. The majority of services, however, expect money for their product. Prices vary: Professor Korn, operated out of Brooklyn, N.Y., advertises rates, "as low as $5 a page," while others demand fees of

$35 per page. "It's kind of tempting, because if you're in a rush you can just order an essay up," says Stacey Brown, 21, a fourth-year history/native studies major at Brandon University in Manitoba. "But your conscience says no, I have to just write the paper."

Universities, of course, take the threat very seriously. In late October, Boston University launched an unprecedented lawsuit against several Internet-based essay mills in the United States, charging them in federal court with wire fraud, mail fraud, racketeering and violating a Massachusetts law that bans the sale of term papers. The case, legal experts say, is a touchstone for the future of essay-writing services on the Internet.

But in the past, shutting down such companies has proven problematic. The services' standard defence is that the essays are intended as research tools. And most of the Internet mills post dire warnings about the consequences of plagiarism. Sahr has an entire Web page on his service devoted to telling students why they should not hand in School Sucks essays. "The essays are free, so students should know their professors also have access to them," he says. Prof. Mark Webber has heard such arguments before. Essay services "always say they're not doing anything wrong," says Webber, co-director of the Canadian Centre for German and European Studies at York. "But it's very clear to anyone who's talked to these people, or to the students who hire them, that they know damned well what they're doing."

Maclean's, *November 24, 1997, 76–79. Reprinted with permission.*

Creating the Network

The information highway promises to make all of these services, and many more, available to everyone at an affordable price, in the same way that telephone service today is accessible to almost everybody.

The Information Highway Advisory Council, established by Industry Canada to advise the government on the shape of the new telecommunications structure, stated in its final report several elements required for the information highway:

◎ *advanced networks*—infrastructure and applications development encouraging private and public sector partnerships that would further the roll-out of advanced networking and related applications development

◎ *Canadian content*—developing and implementing a stronger, broader and more integrated strategy to reinvigorate the cultural dialogue essential to Canadian unity

◎ *access*—providing dialogue and advice to government on the changing nature of universal access in an information society, including the definition of essential services

◎ *lifelong learning*—providing a forum for governments, educators and the technology community to consider issues whose resolution is necessary to making lifelong learning "a key design element of the Information Highway"

◎ *standards*—promoting the development, diffusion and adoption of standards for open networks and connectivity and continuously charting the "standards road map for the Information Highway"

◎ *government as a model user*—encouraging government departments and agencies to become model users of the Information Highway, both for internal administration and for the delivery of services to the public

◎ *performance indicators*—defining and measuring the key economic and social indicators of Canada's progress as a knowledge society, and providing for appropriate benchmarking against international developments.[7]

Government Regulation

The issue of what can legally be transmitted on the Internet is controversial. In the history of audio and video communication, governments have always played a regulatory role. However, the technical means to regulate the content of the World Wide Web do not yet exist, and the degree of security afforded electronic transactions must reflect a delicate balance between the interests of consumers, who value total confidentiality, and law enforcers, who advocate legal surveillance of telecommunications traffic.

Canadian courts have long held that distributors, as well as authors, must be held responsible for any material that violates the Criminal Code of Canada. This interpretation has, for instance, allowed bookstore owners to be prosecuted for distributing obscene books. How this policy might work in a case involving an Internet service provider in Canada is another matter. The fact is that all Internet service providers provide customers with access to obscene material on the World Wide Web. It is unclear whether there is any way that providers could cease making this material available and stay in business, as the nature of Web publication is to provide unfiltered access to any and all resources.

In 1996, the U.S. Congress passed the Telecommunications Act. Part of that legislation was the Communications Decency Act (CDA), which outlined certain constraints on content on the Internet even though the Internet is a borderless, international communications medium. As soon as the Act passed, civil liberties organizations challenged the law, and in 1997 the U.S. Supreme Court upheld the concept that the government should not control content on the Internet. (See Chapter 14.)

Even if a country passed legislation to control content on the World Wide Web, it could not regulate content stored in other countries, which can be freely retrieved from anywhere in the world. Failing an international agreement, it is improbable that any significant restrictions can be placed on the free flow of ideas, words, pictures, and sounds through the World Wide Web on the Internet, however offensive this material may be. The situation is further complicated by the fact that people can use software to encrypt their files and e-mail for transmission; thus, governments cannot identify senders and receivers of files.

Copyrights for Intellectual Property

Another reason that the government would supervise the development of the new network is that digitized bits, once they are widely available, could easily be lifted from a television/computer and reproduced for profit. Writers and other creative people who provide the content for the media industries are especially concerned about their ideas being reproduced in other formats, with unauthorized alterations and no compensation for the use of their property. This issue, the protection of what are called *intellectual property rights*, will be another important part of the design of the new communications network.

It would be possible now to capture video from the *X-Files* and join individual bits from that video with bits from an episode of *Friends*, putting the two casts together in a newly digitized program. And once these bits could be captured from a network and stored, they would be available to anyone who wants to manipulate them. This is one of the dilemmas created by digitized images that can be transmitted to anyone's storage system over an international network. The creative people who contribute this content and the people who produce and own these programs are watching carefully so that any new laws and regulations will be structured to protect their intellectual property rights.

Negotiations toward developing a worldwide intellectual property treaty have been underway in Geneva for a number of years under the auspices of the **World Intellectual Property Organization (WIPO)**. However, the enforcement issues appear insurmountable—there are no "copyright cops," and there is little in the way of probable cause to search households for illicit computer files.

Five Challenges for the New Network

"Now comes the interesting part," reports the *Wall Street Journal*. "Builders of the information highway have created a media sensation with their plans for wiring America. But to deliver on their promises they will have to meet challenges of unprecedented complexity and size.... Like early railroad builders who laid their tracks in different widths more than a century ago, the purveyors of the information highway are using largely incompatible technologies."[8]

For the new communications network to work, five technological developments must take place. These are: (1) improved storage, (2) a coordinated delivery system, (3) a "smart" set-top box, (4) usable menus, and (5) secure ordering and billing systems.

Improved Storage

The main technological advance that makes the new communications network possible is that today's electronic systems can now transform all text, audio, and video communication into digital information. However, no system currently exists to store the digitized information that the new network for text, audio, and video would require.

Researchers are trying to eliminate the need for so many bytes. They are turning to a process called **data compression**. "A single copy of *Jurassic Park*, for example, contains about 100 billion bytes of data. Compression will enable the dinosaur epic to be squeezed down to about four billion bytes.... But even then, the movie will be big enough to fill the equivalent of 20 personal computers."[9]

If researchers could perfect data compression, it would mean that a program service, for example, would need much less storage space to keep movies available for use. This could help make the movie affordable for a program service to deliver and usable for the customer, who wouldn't need as much data space on the television/computer to view the movie.

Once the data are compressed, they must be stored by the people who will deliver the service. Then researchers must also invent a machine that will grab a selection from the storage area and deliver it to the customer as requested. This *video transfer* machine is often called a **server** because it must be able to serve hundreds of programs to thousands of subscribers, on demand, all at the same time. No one has yet invented a machine that can handle this much volume.

A Coordinated Delivery System

Today's communication system is a mixture of old and new technologies. For the new communications network, old technology must be replaced with new technology throughout the system.

Broadcasters today, for example, send pictures and sounds over airwaves using the same technology they have used since the 1930s, when broadcasting was first introduced. This technology is called **analog**.

Analog technology encodes video and audio information as continuous signals. Then these signals are broadcast through the air on specific airwave frequencies to your TV set, which translates them into pictures and sounds. Analog technology is a very cumbersome way to move information from one place to another because the signal takes up a lot of space on the airwaves. But because the analog signals travel through the air by transmitter, you can receive them free through an antenna. In Canada, where cable installation began early, most urban communities have the cable-TV infrastructure in place, and many semirural and farming communities now also receive cable.

Cable companies have eliminated the need for antennas by using coaxial cable, buried underground or strung from telephone poles. Coaxial cable also uses analog technology. Cable operators capture programming, such as Bravo!, from satellite systems, put it together with over-the-air analog broadcast signals from your local TV stations, and then deliver all of this programming to you using a combination of coaxial cable, copper telephone wire bundles, and some optical fibre.

Optical fibre is composed of microscopic strands of glass that transmit messages of digitized "bits"—zeroes and ones. Each fibre optic strand can carry 250 000 times as much information as one copper wire. It can transmit the entire contents of the *Encyclopedia Britannica* in one second.[10] A fibre optics communications system is very efficient because digitized information travels easily and quickly from one place to another.

Today's telephone companies have converted almost all of their major communications delivery systems from coaxial cable and copper wire to fibre optics. The incompatibility between analog and digital technology means that all analog signals that are not on fibre optics systems have to first be converted to digital signals to be able to travel on the information network. Conversion can be very expensive. At today's prices, it would cost about $3000 to digitize and store one feature-length movie.

The current communications network is a combination of coaxial cable, copper wire, and fibre optics. It seems as if digital technology would be the most efficient method of delivery, but wiring the whole of North America with optical fibre would be extraordinarily expensive (at least $100 billion by one estimate), and no single company or industry is volunteering to carry out this upgrade to digital technology.

A "Smart" Set-Top Box

Most cable subscribers need a **set-top box**, which translates the various signals so that the TV set can receive the programming and also keep track of which services the subscriber uses. The set-top box sits on top of the TV. For the new national communications network to operate, the set-top box will have to become much "smarter" than it is now.

The set-top box will be like a switching station, connecting the delivery system coming to the television/computer with your directions for service. This will be the gateway. The set-top box also must be affordable. Some researchers have devised a $3000 model, but no one has yet invented a successful, affordable set-top box.

Usable Menus

With all of this programming and all of these services awaiting, the menu will be the tool someone uses to navigate the system. The menus "are the software that viewers will see on their screens. It must be simple so technophobes can use it but powerful enough to navigate a mind-numbing assortment of programs."[11] An easy menu system is important because people who use the system for the first time probably won't be patient enough to figure out something complicated. Researchers say that such a system will require a great deal of consumer testing. "I don't believe we are close to figuring this out," says Arun Netravali, who oversees information highway technology at AT&T Bell Labs.[12]

Secure Ordering and Billing Systems

Of course, once all of these services are available, someone must be billed for the privilege of using them. That's where ordering and billing come in, and developing this process will be challenging. The telephone companies already have a fairly complex system in place that manages to match people with the phone calls they make.

But making sure that your credit card numbers and other personal information are secure from other computer users is more complicated. Software companies must develop systems that will ensure that all the records for interactive transactions are safe. An entirely new industry is being created around this issue of information security.

New communications technology makes on-line access possible just about everywhere. Here, a customer in a cyber café uses one of several available computers while enjoying a cappuccino.

CP Picture Archive (Fred Chartrand)

When Will the New Communications Network Happen?

The new communications network, as envisioned by industry and government leaders today, requires that everyone be able to use digitized technology. Today, broadcasters and cable operators have access to the programming and the services, but they are still using old technology to deliver them. Telephone companies and computer manufacturers are using digital technology, but they don't have access to the programming or the services.

No one has yet created a storage system that can keep the programming and services digitized and ready for you to use on demand. Nor has anyone created a directory system that would help you find your way through the maze of services and programs that could conceivably be offered on such a system. And no one has devised a secure billing system that could charge everyone accurately for all of the services they might choose.

This new communications network, once it is in place, could have a profound impact on individuals, businesses, and the media industries. For individuals, the new network could affect many everyday activities, such as how people shop, get their news, study, pay bills, and socialize with friends. For businesses, national and even global information will be instantly available to more companies at once, making communication much easier, but making competition more intense.

For the media industries, the prospect of a new communications network places every element of each business in transition. Today, owners and managers at the companies that make up the media industries must decide how to invest in equipment, employee training, and research and development to protect current income, while ensuring that the company will be able to adapt to the new demands of the 21st century.

How soon will the new communications network open? No one can predict. One observer called the network a "highway of hype," because so many people are talking about the information highway even though progress in solving the technological problems seems slow. The changes will probably come gradually, as each challenge to the creation of the new network is solved.

"Computers and television are coming together," says *The Economist.* "Computers are continuing their relentless march toward greater power at lower cost: that is how microprocessors work. Some giant industries are betting billions on the new TV business: more deals loom. These facts alone guarantee a revolution.... Whether it arrives in five years or 15 is almost irrelevant. In the history of communications, 2010 is tomorrow."[13]

Understanding the Information Age

When was the last time you spent 24 hours without the media? From the moment you get up in the morning until the time you go to bed at night, the media are waiting to keep you company. Radio news gives you world news headlines in the shower and local traffic reports, as well as national radio programmes such as *This Morning* and *Cross-Country Checkup;* the newspaper offers you national and local news and helps you keep up with the latest hockey scores and Dilbert's wry reflections on workplace irrationality. Magazines describe new computer software for your use in work, study, or play, and during your lunch hour they keep you current with the latest fashions. After work or school, the newest novel competes with your VCR and the latest movie video release, and with pay-for-view movies on cable TV. The World Wide Web tempts you, as well, with e-mail, customized news reports, downloadable magazine articles, and even music.

According to industry estimates, the average adult spends more than half of his or her waking life with the media. This is the breakdown of the way Canadians divide their time watching, listening, and reading:

◎ About 83 percent of all adults had read a daily newspaper in the last week; only 6.7 percent of all adults had not read any newspaper in the last year.

◎ About 62 percent of all adults had read a magazine in the same week.

◎ About 44 percent of all adults had read a book in the same time period; of the books read, approximately 33 percent were fiction and another 33 percent were nonfiction, with the balance probably made of up manuals and reference materials. About 33 percent of adults had borrowed a library book in the last year.

◎ In the same week, 66 percent of adults had listened to records, tapes, or CDs; 38 percent had watched a VCR film; about 80 percent had watched at least one hour of CBC TV; and about 31 percent had listened to CBC radio.[14]

Some form of the mass media touches nearly every adult and child in North America every day—economically, socially, or culturally. The mass media can affect the way you vote, the way you spend your money, and the way you think about your life. They influence the way you eat, talk, work, study, and relax. This is the *impact* of mass media on society.

This wide-reaching presence distinguishes North American media from the media in other areas of the world. In no other countries besides Canada and the United States do the mass media capture so much of people's time and attention. In no other countries do the media affect so many aspects of the way people live. And in no other countries do the media collect so much money for delivering information and entertainment. For instance, the U.S. mass media industries earn about $220 billion a year.[15]

Today's society has inherited the wisdom and the mistakes of the people who work in the mass media and the society that regulates and consumes what the mass media produce. Consider these situations:

◎ You are a newspaper publisher in Toronto in the 1830s. After publishing articles that anger the government, you are harassed with libel suits, threats, and attacks on your printing press. Yet, you want to continue to publish the newspaper. What would you do? (See the discussion of William Lyon Mackenzie in Chapter 2.)

◎ You have just bought a computer and you want to stay current with new developments in software. You subscribe to *PC World* and *Wired*. How does your choice of magazines reflect the changes in the magazine industry? (See "Specialized Magazines Take Over," Chapter 3.)

◎ You are in a bookstore with $20 to spend. You can't decide whether to buy a novel by Margaret Atwood, a book of poems by Michael Ondaatje, a travel guide to Mexico, or a collection of "Calvin and Hobbes" cartoons. What are the economic consequences of these decisions by book buyers for the publishing industry? (See Chapter 4 on consumers' book-buying habits.)

◎ You believe you have been misquoted and misrepresented in a major magazine story written by a freelance journalist, so you sue the author and the magazine in the United States, where the article was published. The case eventually reaches the U.S. Supreme Court. What implications will the court decision have on the media's liability for the stories they print and broadcast? (See "*Masson v. The New Yorker* Magazine," Chapter 14.)

◎ You are a municipal civil servant who loses his job after the *Globe and Mail* runs a series of articles in 1991, which contain allegations that shatter your reputation. You sue the *Globe and Mail* for libel and win a settlement of $880,000. What are the effects on libel law in Canada? (See Chapter 14.)

People who work in the media industries and people who watch, listen to, read, and govern what the media offer make choices and face situations like these every day. The future of the mass media will be determined by these choices.

Understanding the Mass Media Industries: Three Key Themes

This book uses the term **mass media industries** to describe the seven types of mass media businesses: newspapers, magazines, radio, television, movies, recordings, and books. The use of the word *industries* underscores the major goal of mass media in North America—financial success. Publicly financed media, such as the **Canadian Broadcasting Corporation (CBC)** and provincial public broadcasters, have an alternative goal—to provide a public service. However, the weight accorded to commercial mass media seems to be increasing gradually, reflecting governments' fiscal priorities.

But the media are more than just businesses: They are key institutions in our society. They affect our culture, our buying habits, and our politics, and they are affected in turn by changes in our beliefs, tastes, interests, and behaviour. To help organize your thinking about the mass media and their impact, this section introduces three key themes that will recur in the chapters to come: (1) the media are, for the most part, profit-centred businesses; (2) technology changes the media; and (3) the media both reflect and affect the political, social, and cultural institutions in which they operate.

The Media as Businesses

What you see, read, and hear in the mass media may cajole, entertain, inform, persuade, provoke, and even perplex you. But to understand the media, you first need to understand is that the central force driving the media, whether public or private institutions, is the desire to make money. *The media are businesses, vast businesses.* The products of these businesses are information and entertainment.

Other motives shape the media, of course, including the desire to fulfill the public's need for information, to influence the country's governance, to disseminate the country's cultures, to offer entertainment, and to provide an outlet for artistic expression. But the media, above all, are revenue-centred.

Who Owns the Media? In Canada, almost all the print media are privately owned, but radio and television broadcasting is divided between private broadcasters, who are subject to stringent government rules of operation, and public broadcasters, who have a mandate to provide public service, through a mix of direct government funding and advertising revenues. Public broadcasters serve Canadians by providing such services as television for remote northern communities and broadcasts in minority languages, services that could never be justified in strict economic terms. The annual budget for public broadcasting, however, is shrinking. In the United States, almost all of the media are privately owned, with the exception of the Public Broadcasting Service and National Public Radio.

Many family-owned media properties still exist in Canada and the United States, but today the trend in the media industries, as in other industrial sectors, is for media companies to cluster together in groups. A small number of chains in Canada, including Hollinger-Southam, Thomson, and Torstar, own a major share of Canada's daily and weekly newspapers, in addition to other media properties such as local cable TV franchises. These chains are not restricted to operations in one country but, rather, are multinational in scope. For example, the Hollinger group owns and operates *The Jerusalem Post,* several prominent dailies in Great Britain, including the prestigious *London Daily Telegraph*, and hundreds of local newspapers in the United States. This trend is called **concentration of ownership**, and this concentration takes five different forms.

1. Chains. In Canada, the major chains are owned by the Hollinger-Southam and Thomson corporations. To many, these Canadian chains represent a threat to the free expression of opinion. There are also smaller chains, which have a significant presence in limited regional areas, such as the Irving family media companies in New Brunswick.

Benjamin Franklin established North America's first newspaper chain. This tradition was expanded by William Randolph Hearst in the 1930s. At their peak, Hearst newspapers accounted for nearly 14 percent of total daily circulation and nearly 25 percent of Sunday circulation in the United States. Today's U.S. newspaper chain giant is Gannett, with 92 daily newspapers, including *USA Today*.

2. Networks. A network operates similarly to a newspaper chain. It is a collection of radio or television stations that offer programs, usually simultaneously throughout the country, during designated program times. The CRTC regulates broadcast ownership. The major regulated broadcast networks in Canada are Baton, CHUM/CITY, Global, and the CBC. The CRTC also regulates the cable chains owned by Rogers, Shaw, and Cogeco, in addition to the telecommunications companies. In the United States, the public regulator is the Federal Communications Commission (FCC). The four major U.S. networks are ABC (American Broadcasting Company), NBC (National Broadcasting Company), CBS (Columbia Broadcasting System), and Fox Broadcasting. NBC, the oldest network, was founded in the 1920s to deliver radio programming across the United States. The U.S. networks' sphere of influence now extends far beyond the borders of the United States to wherever satellite and/or cable-TV delivery systems exist.

The network concept developed further with the invention of television. Networks can have as many affiliates as they want, but with certain exceptions related to language and other local factors, no network can have two affiliates in the same broadcast area. (Affiliates are stations that use network programming but that may be owned by companies other than the networks.)

3. Cross-Media Ownership. Many media companies own more than one type of media property: newspapers, magazines, and radio and TV stations, for example. In Canada, Rogers Communications, through its acquisition of the Maclean-Hunter assets, gained control of major print publications such *The Financial Post*, in addition to a cable-TV franchise, cellular phone services, video rental stores, Internet service, and The Shopping Channel. Gannett, which owns the largest chain of U.S. newspapers, also owns television and radio stations. The 1996 merger of Capital Cities with ABC joined the programming power of Disney with the distribution system of the ABC television network. Rupert Murdoch's News Corporation owns newspapers, television stations, magazines, 20th Century-Fox Film, and the Fox Broadcasting network.

4. Conglomerates. When you go to the movies to watch a Columbia picture, you might not realize that the Japanese firm Sony owns the film company. Sony is a *conglomerate*—a company that owns media companies as well as companies unrelated to the media business. Media properties can be attractive investments, but some conglomerate owners are unfamiliar with the idiosyncrasies of the media industries.

5. Vertical Integration. The most noticeable trend among today's media companies is **vertical integration**—an attempt by one company to control several related aspects of the media business at once, each part helping the other. Montreal-based Seagrams, for instance, owns MCA, Universal Studios, cable networks in the United States, and now Polygram records, which it recently agreed to buy from the Dutch company Philips. Another such conglomerate is Time Warner. Besides publishing magazines and books, it owns Home Box Office (HBO), Warner movie studios, various cable TV systems throughout the United States, and CNN.

To describe the financial status of today's media is also to talk about acquisitions. The media are buying and selling one another in unprecedented numbers and forming media groups to position themselves in the marketplace to maintain and increase their profits. In the past decade, Conrad Black has dramatically expanded the Hollinger-Southam interests all over the world. (See Impact/Profile, Four Moguls of the Media on page 28.) Such conglomerates can raise the cost of entry for potential competitors into a given media market to prohibitive levels by means of intra-company cross-subsidies and generous use of common company resources such as editorial content and artwork.

Media acquisitions have skyrocketed since 1980 for two reasons. The first is that most conglomerates today are publicly traded companies, which means that their stock is traded on one of the world's major stock exchanges. This makes acquisitions relatively easy.

A media company that wants to buy a publicly owned company can buy that company's stock when the stock becomes available. The open availability of stock in these companies means that anybody with enough money can invest, which is how Rupert Murdoch joined the media business.

The second reason for the increase in media alliances is that since the early 1980s, the public media regulators (the CRTC in Canada and the FCC in the United States) have been gradually deregulating the broadcast media. The

CRTC has allowed the increased presence of privately owned media outlets in major markets in Canada and nonlocal private television signals (such as Toronto's CITY-TV and Hamilton's OnTV) on local cable TV. It has also unleashed a flood of new private cable TV signals, such as Showcase, which have no broadcast signal at all, in addition to new network operations, such as the Global television network. Recently, the CRTC also began allowing companies to own more radio and television stations within one urban market, thereby decreasing the number of distinct voices available to listeners and viewers. In April 1998, the CRTC increased the number of radio stations that a single company could own in a large city market in Canada from two to four.

In the United States, the FCC also raised the number of broadcast holdings allowed for one owner. This trend of media acquisitions is continuing throughout the 1990s, as changing technology expands the market for media products.

The issue of media ownership is important. If only a few corporations direct the media industries in the whole of North America, the outlets for differing political viewpoints and innovative ideas could well be limited.

Who Pays for the Mass Media? In Canada, the situation is complex because the major public broadcaster, the CBC, receives large amounts of public funds as a grant each year, and provincial education networks, such as TVOntario, likewise receive public funds. Coexisting with taxation-supported networks are a variety of privately owned media enterprises. The situation is complicated by government subsidizing of broadcasting and publishing. Subsidies can take many forms, including direct grants, foregone taxes, and accelerated depreciation. Direct subsidies tend to be allowed by **World Trade Organization (WTO)** regulations. Yet globalization will likely reduce both subsidies and national preference practices, as is the announced intention of trade liberalization.

Most of the income that the mass media industries collect comes from advertisers. Advertising directly supports newspapers, radio, and television. (Subscribers pay only a small part of the cost of producing a newspaper.) Magazines receive most of their income from advertising and subscriptions. Income for movies, recordings, and books, of course, comes from direct purchases and ticket sales.

This means that most of the information and entertainment you receive from television, radio, newspapers, and magazines in North America is paid for by people who want to sell you products. You support these media industries *directly* by buying the products that advertisers sell, and *indirectly* through general taxation.

Advertising Pays Most of the Bills. A full-page black-and-white ad in *The Computer Paper*, costs about $11 185. This ad would reach a circulation of 405 000.[16] To place a full-page colour ad in *Rolling Stone* magazine costs about US $50 000. A 30-second television commercial in prime time (8 p.m. to 11 p.m.) costs about $100 000.

You also pay for the media *directly* when you buy a book or a compact disc or go to a movie. This money buys equipment, underwrites company research and expansion, and pays stock dividends. Advertisers and consumers are the financial foundation for the media industries, even when the assets of those industries are publicly owned. (See Figure 1.3.)

Figure 1.3

Yearly Time Each Person Spends Using Media, 1999*

*projected

**includes cable TV

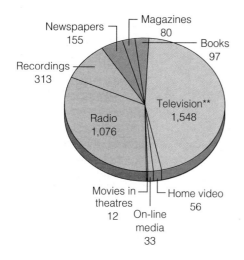

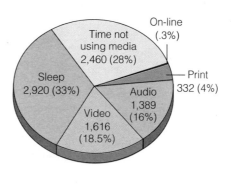

Total hours in a year = 8,760
Total hours using media = 3,370
(58% of total waking hours)

Source: Data from *The Veronis, Suhler & Associates Communications Industry Forecast*, 1997–2001.

How Does Each Media Industry Work? Books, newspapers, and magazines were the only mass media for 250 years after the first book was published. The first half of the 20th century brought four new media—movies, radio, recordings, and television—in less than 50 years.

To understand how this happened and where each medium fits in the mass media industries today, it is important to examine the individual characteristics of each medium.

Newspapers. Evening papers have all but disappeared in Canada, where major newspapers such as the *Toronto Star* have switched to morning distribution. Previously, it had published several editions throughout the afternoon, with a final edition containing end-of-the-day stock market quotations, which appeared on the streets around 6 p.m. The same trend is evident in the United States. Papers that come out in the morning are growing in circulation, and papers that come out in the afternoon are shrinking. The number of weekly newspapers is also declining. Advertising makes up about two-thirds of the printed space in daily newspapers. Newspaper income is expected to grow slightly over the next decade.

Magazines. At least 12 000 magazines are published in North America. To maintain and increase profits, magazines are raising their subscription and single-copy prices and fighting to maintain their advertising income. The number of magazines people buy by subscription is going up, but newsstand sales are going down. Magazine income is expected to decline slightly in the next decade.

Specialty magazines may actually be given away to critical reader segments if advertising revenues justify this strategy. For instance, *Saturday Night* magazine is given to subscribers of Southam newspapers if the average income of subscribers in the area is high enough. This system is designed to deliver a particular audience to the advertisers.

Book Publishing. Thousands of books are published annually in English, although some of these are reprints and new editions of old titles. Retail bookstores account for one-third of all money earned from book sales. The rest of the income comes from books that are sold through book clubs, through on-line book sellers, in university and college book stores, to libraries, and to school districts for use in elementary and high schools. Book publishing income is expected to grow slightly.

Radio. Radio stations broadcast programming all over North America, with the FM stations gaining in importance over AM stations. A minority of these stations are noncommercial, most of them FM. The average Canadian household owns and uses several radios. Radio revenues are expected to grow slightly in the next decade.

Recordings. Most recordings are bought by people who are under 30. Compact discs account for 80 percent of recording industry income. The rest comes from cassettes, vinyls, and music videos. The industry is expected to grow slightly, boosted by sales of CD singles and by the introduction of the new DVD digital recording technology.

Television. Television stations are operated in all major population centres in North America, as well as in many minor centres. Many of the stations are affiliated with one network or another, though there are strong regional television voices, which may be distributed to other regions through satellite rebroadcast packages.

A clear majority of Canadian and U.S. homes are wired for cable, and most of these viewers now receive 30 or more channels and many receive 75 or more. Cable receives about 16 percent of the overall money spent on television advertising. Network income is declining, while income to independents and cable operators is going up. Total industry revenue is projected to grow slightly in the next decade.

Movies. There are thousands of theatre screens in Canada. The major and independent studios combined make about four hundred pictures a year, and offshore producers, particularly those in Asia, make thousands more. The industry is collecting more money because of higher ticket prices, but the number of people who go to the movies is declining.

The major increase in income to the movie industry in the past decade came from video sales. The year 1986 marked the first time that the number of videotape rentals was higher than the number of movie ticket purchases. Industry income is expected to increase slightly.

On-line Media. The newest media industry is also growing the fastest. Economists predict that the number of consumers on-line will double between 1996 and 2001 and that the amount of money spent for on-line advertising will rise 1200 percent—from $200 million in 1996 to $2.5 billion by the year 2001. On-line media is defining itself as a new mass medium, as well as an integral part of traditional print, audio, and video mass media.

Overall, media industries in the North America are prospering. The division of profits is shifting, however, as different media industries expand and contract in the marketplace to respond to the audience. For example, if the population's interest shifts away from the print media to video entertainment, fewer people will buy newspapers, magazines, and books, which means that these industries could suffer. Understanding the implications of these changes is central to understanding the media as businesses.

The Media and Communications Technology

The second theme that you will encounter throughout this book is *the effect of technological change on the mass media*. The development of communications technology directly affects the speed with which a society evolves.

In countries that have encouraged technological advancements, such as Canada, the United States, and Japan, communications changes are moving faster than ever before. For the media industries, this means increasing costs to replace old equipment. For consumers, this means a confusing array of products that seem to be replaced as soon as they are marketed, as audio cassettes, for example, were superseded by CDs, soon to be followed by the new video disk technology, DVD.

By today's standards, the earliest communications obstacles seem unbelievably simple: for instance, how to transmit a single message to several people at the same time, and how to share information inexpensively. Yet, it has taken nearly 5 500 years to achieve the capability for instant communication that we enjoy today.

Three Information Communications Revolutions. The channels of communication have changed dramatically over the centuries, but the idea that a society will pay to stay informed and entertained is not new. In imperial Rome, people who wanted to know the news paid professional speakers a coin (a *gazet*) for the privilege of listening to the speaker announce the day's events. Many early newspapers were called *gazettes* to reflect this heritage.

Written communication began with pictographs. A pictograph is a symbol of an object that is used to convey an idea. If you have ever drawn a heart with an arrow through it, you understand what a pictograph is. The first known pictographs were carved in stone by the Sumerians of Mesopotamia in about 3500 BC.

The stone in which these early pictographic messages were carved served as a medium—a device to transmit messages. Eventually, messages were imprinted in clay and stored in a precursor of today's library. These messages weren't very portable, however. Clay tablets didn't slip easily into someone's pocket.

In about 2500 BC, the Egyptians invented papyrus, a type of paper made from a grasslike plant called sedge. The Greeks perfected parchment, made from goat and sheep skins, in about 200 BC. By about AD 100, before the use of parchment spread throughout Europe, the Chinese had invented paper, which was much cheaper to produce than parchment, but Europeans didn't start to use paper until more than a thousand years later, in about AD 1300. The discovery of parchment and then paper meant that storing information became cheaper and easier.

IMPACT

Profile   *FOUR MOGULS OF THE MEDIA*

Conrad Black, Rupert Murdoch, George Lucas, and Bill Gates offer four distinctly different examples of media moguls. Black's Hollinger Inc. is a large newspaper empire built from a base of small, previously independent newspapers. Murdoch built his News Corporation empire by acquiring many different types of media companies. George Lucas's career began with the modest creation of a set of characters and a story originally called "The Star Wars." Microsoft cofounder and CEO Bill Gates started with software and expanded into developing technologies.

CONRAD BLACK

Standing atop a media empire with the third-largest circulation in the world, Conrad Black is the moving force behind Hollinger Inc. Born in 1944 in Montreal, the son of a successful businessman, Black is a visible and vociferous media presence in Canada and abroad, known for his right-leaning political thought.

Black's interests in the media business began in 1969, when he and a number of like-minded friends, including David Radler and Peter White, acquired the *Sherbrooke Record* and other small English-language newspapers, later consolidated as the Sterling chain. In 1978, Black gained control of the Argus Corporation, which held minority shares in many unrelated Canadian corporations. Black sold off most of these holdings and concentrated on building the Argus Corporation's media interests. He has since acquired major newspaper holdings in Canada and

around the world, including London's *Daily Telegraph, Le Soleil, Le Droit,* and hundreds of small newspapers across the United States. He also now owns *Saturday Night* magazine in Canada, which is distributed to some Canadian households free of charge with their newspapers.

More recently, Conrad Black has acquired the Southam newspaper chain, which publishes the *Ottawa Citizen* and the *Vancouver Sun,* has launched a new Canadian national newspaper, the *National Post,* which will compete directly with the Thomson Corporation's *Globe and Mail.*

Conrad Black, Canadian media giant.
CP Picture Archive (Bill Becker)

RUPERT MURDOCH

In 1952, Rupert Murdoch inherited his father's business, a barely profitable Australian newspaper. Today, Murdoch's media empire spreads across six continents and includes 132 newspapers, 25 magazines, the Fox network, 12 U.S. TV stations,

direct-broadcast satellite TV, home video, and on-line access to the worldwide Internet. Murdoch, 67, who became a U.S. citizen in 1985, continues to pursue media properties that will expand his company's reach.

In 1989, Murdoch created the world's first global satellite media network, and today his two satellite services (Sky TV in Europe and Star TV in Asia) have the potential to reach two-thirds of the world's population. He is negotiating to expand to South America, the Middle East, and Africa.

"Murdoch believes he has built things that will endure," writes media critic Ken Auletta. Still, though the Fox network and Sky and Star TV provide viewers with more choices, they are rarely better choices.... "Murdoch will leave no monument except a successful corporation. He has boldly built a worldwide company, but he has rarely elevated taste or journalism."[17]

Rupert Murdoch, owner of major U.S., Australian, and Asian media properties.
CP Picture Archive (CAP photo/Marty Lederhandler)

GEORGE LUCAS

The *Star Wars* movie trilogy has earned more than $2 billion dollars since the first movie was released in 1977, and this was before the re-release of remastered versions of the movies in 1997. The first of a new trilogy of *Star Wars* movies is planned for release in 1999.

George Lucas, 48, is sole owner of Lucas film, LucasArts, and Industrial Light & Magic, head-quartered at Skywalker Ranch in the hills of Marin County, near San Francisco. The combined value of the Lucas companies has been estimated at $5 billion.

As director of the first *Star Wars* movie, Lucas chose the merchandising and sequel rights to the movie rather than the $500 000 salary he was offered. This key business decision formed the basis of his fortune. The success of *Star Wars* merchandise changed moviemaking forever, as filmmakers today compete for projects that promise as much income from merchandising as from box office receipts.

Lucas's companies produce *Star Wars* toys, novels, CD-ROMs, comic books, and Nintendo and video games. Lucas personally approves all aspects of the development of the *Star Wars* stories. The details about all the characters are kept in a 170-page book called *The Bible*, a chronology of the events portrayed in all of the *Star Wars* adventures.

Why does *Star Wars* continue to succeed? According to Jack Sorensen, president of LucasArts, "*Star Wars* is the mythology of a nonsectarian world. It describes how people want to live. People all view politics as corrupt.... and yet people are not cynical under-neath—they want to believe in something pure, noble. That's *Star Wars*."[18]

George Lukas, creator of *Star Wars*.
© Jeff Slocomb/Outline Press Syndicate, Inc.

BILL GATES

At age 42, he's the richest man in the United States. Microsoft is the world's biggest software company; Gates's personal fortune is estimated to be at least $20 billion. Windows software, produced by Microsoft, operates on tens of millions of computers worldwide. Simply because of its reach and influence in the computer market-place, the company is scrutinized regularly by U.S. government agencies for monopolistic practices, and its overwhelming presence has provoked uneasy scrutiny in other countries, as well.

Gates actively runs the company, which is seeking to expand its media influence as well as bring Microsoft into the home, with computers in use in the kitchen, connected to the phone, running the television, controlling functions in the car, and even regulating the heating system and the lights. All of these systems would be intercon-nected and, of course, all of the systems would be running Windows. "There's one thing I do enjoy," says Gates, "which is going out and talking about personal computers and how they can be used. I think my job is the best in the world."

Because of his widespread influence, says the *Los Angeles Times*, "it must sometimes seem that Microsoft cofounder and CEO Bill Gates is trying to set up branch offices in people's brains." Gates, says the *LA Times*, is "revered or reviled as the most familiar icon of the razzle-dazzle Information Age—the Revenging Nerd incarnate."[19]

Bill Gates, cofounder and CEO of Microsoft.
© William Stevens/Gamma

The Three Information Communications Revolutions: The invention of writing, displayed here on clay tablets, has been called the *first information communications revolution.* Johannes Gutenberg is responsible for the *second information communications revolution,* the invention of movable type. A hand-illuminated page from his Bible is shown here. Computer technology, shown at the top of the next page by a farmer with his notebook computer, represents the *third information communications revolution.*

Top: the Bettmann Archive. Right: the Granger Collection, New York.
Next page: © The Stock Market/Joe Sohm.

The First Information Communications Revolution. In about 3500 BC, pictographs as a method of communication developed into phonetic writing which uses symbols for sounds. Instead of drawing a representation of a dog to convey the idea of a dog, scholars could represent the sounds d-o-g with phonetic writing. The invention of writing has been called the *first information communications revolution.* "After being stored in written form, information could now reach a new kind of audience, remote from the source and uncontrolled by it," writes media scholar Anthony Smith. "Writing transformed knowledge into information."[20]

The Greek philosopher Socrates anticipated the changes that widespread literacy would bring. He argued that knowledge should remain among the privileged classes. Writing threatened the exclusive use of information, he said. "Once a thing is put in writing, the composition, whatever it may be, drifts all over the place, getting into the hands not only of those who understand it, but equally of those who have no business with it."[21]

As Socrates predicted, when more people learned to write, wider communication became possible because people in many different societies could share information among themselves and with people in other parts of the world. But scholars still had to painstakingly copy the information they wanted to keep or pay a scribe to copy it for them. In the 14th century, for example, the library of the Italian poet Petrarch contained more than a hundred manuscripts that he had copied himself.[22]

In Petrarch's day, literate people were either monks or members of the privileged classes. Wealthy people could afford tutoring, and they could also afford to buy the handwritten manuscripts copied by the monks. Knowledge—and the power it brings—belonged to very few people.

The Second Information Communications Revolution. As societies grew more literate, the demand for manuscripts flourished, but a scribe could produce only one copy at a time. What has been called the *second information communications revolution* began in Germany in 1455, when Johannes Gutenberg printed a Bible on a press that used movable type.

More than 200 years before Gutenberg, the Chinese had invented a printing press that used wooden type, and the Chinese also are credited with perfecting a copper press in 1445. But Gutenberg's innovation was to line up individual metal letters that he could ink and then press with paper to produce copies. Unlike the wood or copper presses, the metal letters could be reused to produce new pages of text, which made the process much cheaper. The Gutenberg Bible, a duplicate of the Latin original, is considered the first book printed by movable type (47 copies survive).

As other countries adopted Gutenberg's press, the price for Bibles plummeted. In 1470, the cost of a French mechanically printed Bible was one-fifth the cost of a hand-printed Bible.[23] The second revolution—printing—meant that knowledge, which had belonged to the privileged few, would one day be accessible to everyone. This key development was one of the essential conditions for the rise of modern governments (and their bureaucracies), as well as an important element of scientific and technological progress.

For the first time, knowledge was portable and storable. Before the Gutenberg press, a scholar who wanted special information had to travel to the place where it was kept. But once information could be easily duplicated, it could travel to people beyond the society that created it. The use of paper instead of the scribes' bulky parchment also meant that books could be stacked end to end; thus, libraries now could store vast amounts of information in a small space. And because these smaller, lightweight books could be easily carried, all different kinds of people, in many cities, could read classical works. Another benefit of the development of printing was that societies could more easily keep information for future generations.

This effort to communicate—first through spoken messages, then through pictographs, then through the written word, and finally through printed words—demonstrates people's innate desire to share information with one another. Storability, portability, and accessibility of information are essential to today's concept of mass communication. By definition, mass communication is information that is available quickly to a large audience.

The Third Information Communications Revolution. Today's age of communication has been called the *third information communications revolution* because computers have become the storehouses and transmitters of vast amounts of information that previously were stored through the written word. The University of California, for example, is shifting its storage of scholarship from printed books to digital storage. The university "will create a completely digital library, with the entire collection available online. The California Digital Library will concentrate initially on building a collection of materials related to science, technology and industry. One goal of the digital system will be to encourage professors to publish their research online."[24]

Computer technology, which processes, stores and transmits information much more efficiently than any mechanical device could possibly do, is driving the majority of changes affecting today's media. This means that changes in today's media industries happen much faster than in the past. Satellite broadcasts, digital recordings, and the international computer network called the Internet are just three examples of the third information communications revolution.

IMPACT

Technology *TUNING INTO THE NET*

By Erik Heinrich

The World Wide Web comes to the home TV screen

According to Marshall McLuhan, new media will always cannibalize older ones. Cinema did it to theatre at the turn of the century. And television did it to cinema in the 1950s. (In McLuhan-ese, television made cinema its "content," as cinema had earlier done to theatre.) That theory begs the question: will the Internet now assert its emerging dominance by gobbling up TV? It is too early to say for sure. But efforts to create a TV environment on the Net—for example, U.S.-based America Online Inc.'s use of channels and programs

to lure subscribers to its service—has had limited success. In fact, the process may even be working in reverse: a rash of new products, only now becoming available, offer the Internet as part of the content available on the familiar living-room tube.

The first Canadian foray into television-based Internet access is barely four months old. BeyondTV, from Winnipeg-based ViewCall Canada Inc., made its debut last November, to mixed reviews. BeyondTV gives subscribers access to the Internet and the ability to send and receive e-mail via the same home appliance they use to

watch *Seinfeld* and *Hockey Night in Canada*. All they have to do is connect their TV to a telephone line and a set-top box from Websurfer ($429 including special remote control and wireless keyboard). The Internet connection costs $30 a month, discounted to $10 for subscribers who already have an Internet service provider. "The majority of our subscribers have never used a PC before," says Tim Nickerson, managing director of ViewCall Canada, a division of phone company Manitoba Telecom Services Inc. He adds: "We're trying to position BeyondTV as an entertainment service that cuts

Although each medium has its own history and economic structure, today all of the media industries compete for consumers' attention. As the century ends, satellite and microprocessor technology will transform the media business more than we can foresee—enabling faster transmission of more information to more people than ever before.

The Media and Political, Social, and Cultural Institutions

The media industries, as already discussed, provide information and entertainment. But the media can also affect political, social, and cultural institutions.

This is the third theme of this book—the *impact* of the mass media on the society in which they operate. Although the media can actively influence society, they also mirror it, and scholars constantly strive to delineate the differences.

When the U.S. advertising industry suddenly marched to patriotic themes by using U.S. flags and other patriotic logos in ads following the claimed victory of Coalition forces in the 1991 Gulf War, was the industry pandering, or were advertisers proudly reflecting genuine patriotic sentiment, or both? Did the spread of patriotic themes silence those who felt that the Western powers had overreacted in the Persian Gulf? If you were a scholar, how would you prove your arguments?

This is an example of the difficulty that scholars face when analyzing the media's political, social, and cultural effects. Early media studies analyzed the message in the belief that everyone would perceive it in the same way. Then studies proved that different people perceived messages differently—a phenomenon described as **selective perception**. This occurs because everyone brings their own social learning experience, including family background, interests, and education, to each message.

through the chaos of the Internet." An example of that strategy is BeyondTV's plan to create post-broadcast Internet information sites for such top-rated TV shows as *The X-Files*. Nickerson describes it as "extending the broadcast experience."

ViewCall Canada will not reveal how many subscribers it has signed to date. Its parent, Manitoba Telecom, seems to be taking the long view, launching its Internet TV service as a test platform in preparation for the impending convergence of telecommunications industries that, analysts predict, will pit telephone and cable television

providers against each other in direct competition. In that case, BeyondTV's learning curve is still apparent: a common complaint is that users find it awkward to navigate around the service's on-screen prompts....

Ken Frankum, manager of multimedia products for Thomson (Consumer Electronics Inc.) in Canada, says there are two reasons for people to surf the Internet over the television: it costs less than the PC, and it puts technophobes at ease. There are other reasons for Thomson and its rivals to scent a potential market for Internet TV: while only 36 percent of Canadian homes own a computer and barely

15 percent are on the Internet, virtually all own a television. For Derrick deKerckhove, director of the McLuhan Program in Culture and Technology at the University of Toronto, those facts point the way to a shared future for both media. "WebTV is the Trojan horse of the Internet," says deKerckhove. "Once you allow it into your home, you're caught."

Maclean's, *March 23, 1998, p. 58. Reprinted with permission.*

Complicating the study of the media's political, social, and cultural effects is the recent proliferation of media outlets. These multiplying sources of information and entertainment mean that today very few people share identical mass media environments. This makes it much more difficult for scholars to determine the specific or cumulative effects of mass media on the general population.

Still, studying the media's political, social, and cultural roles in society is important because, once identified, the effects can be observed. The questions should be posed so we do not become complacent about the media in our lives, so we do not become immune to the possibility that our society may be cumulatively affected by the media in ways we cannot yet define.

Once you understand the media separately, you can consider their collective effects. After you understand how each type of media business works, you can examine why people who work in the media make the decisions they do. Then, you can evaluate the impact of these decisions on you and on society.

In Focus

- ◎ The information superhighway is envisioned as an intricate webbed network of many different types of communications systems.

- ◎ The new information network is likely to be an interconnected communications system using broadcast, telephone, cable, and computer technology.

- ◎ Canada is ideally situated to be the first to develop a new information network because many Canadians have the tools that such a system needs to get started—television, telephone, VCRs, cable TV, and computers.

- ◎ Today's delivery system for information and entertainment is primarily a one-way system. The new communications network would be a two-way system.

- ◎ The ability to talk back—to receive as well as transmit messages—makes the telephone interactive. The new communications network must also be interactive.

- ◎ The network of the future needs content, two-way digital communication, and digital storage.

- ◎ A cable company or a telephone company would deliver services on the network.

- ◎ Information and entertainment that have already been produced, stored, and digitized will become the first content on the new network.

- ◎ So far, governments do not regulate content on the Internet, but the issue is still unresolved.

- ◎ The five technological challenges for the new network are: improved storage, a coordinated delivery system, a "smart" set-top box, usable menus, and a secure system for ordering and billing.

◎ Technological changes probably will come gradually, as each challenge to the creation of the new network is solved.

◎ According to industry estimates, the average adult spends more than half of his or her waking life with the media.

◎ Communication is the act of sending ideas and attitudes from one person to another. Intrapersonal communication means communication within one person. Interpersonal communication means communication between two people. Mass communication is communication from one person or group of persons through a transmitting device (a medium) to large audiences or markets.

◎ Many motives shape the media, including the desire to fulfill the public's need for information, to influence government, to disseminate culture, to offer entertainment, and to provide an outlet for creative expression. But, above all, the goal of the media is to make money.

◎ Three key themes can be used to study the media:

1. Most media operate as profit-centred businesses.

2. The media are greatly affected by technological changes.

3. The mass media are political, social, and cultural institutions that both reflect and affect the society in which they operate.

◎ Although many media businesses are still family-owned, the main trend is for media companies to cluster together in groups. This trend is called concentration of ownership and can take five forms: chains, networks, cross-media ownership, conglomerates, and vertical integration.

◎ Media acquisitions have skyrocketed because most conglomerates today are publicly traded companies and because the broadcast industry has been deregulated. These trends are expected to continue into the 21st century as changing technology expands the market for media products.

◎ Media industries continue to prosper, but the share of profits is shifting among the industries; different media expand and contract in the marketplace to respond to the audience.

◎ The information communications revolution occurred in three stages. The invention of written symbols brought about the first communications revolution, the invention of movable type marked the second communications revolution, and the invention of computers ushered in the third communications revolution.

◎ Storability, portability, and accessibility of information are essential to today's concept of mass communication. By definition, mass communication is information that is available to a large audience quickly.

Review Questions

1. Why is the issue of the information superhighway receiving so much attention today?

2. Explain the difference between one-way and two-way communication, and explain why two-way communication is important for the new communications network.

3. Why is the digitization of text, audio, and video necessary to the new communications network?

4. Describe each of the five technological developments that must take place before the new communications network can work. Which development seems the most difficult? The easiest? Explain.

5. Cite three major landmarks in the historical development of mass media from pictographs to today's methods. What did each development contribute to the mass media's evolution?

6. Give an example of your own to demonstrate each of the following types of communication:

    a. interpersonal communication

    b. intrapersonal communication

    c. mass communication

Watching the Web

◎ **All Media E-mail Directory** (e-mail addresses for key editors, columnists, correspondents, and executives in magazines, newspapers, radio, TV, and news syndicates across Canada and the United States)

http://www.owt.com/dircon

◎ **Canadian News and Information**

http://canada-acsus.plattsburgh.edu/cannews/papers.htm

◎ **Communications Topics Web Site**

http://www.syr.edu/~bcfought

◎ **Dilbert (Scott Adams's comic)**

http://www.unitedmedia.com/comics/dilbert

◎ **Media Awareness Network**

http://www.screen.com/mnet/eng/issues/stats/stats.htm

◎ **Media History Project on the Web**

http://www.mediahistory.com

◎ **Newslink to Most Major Newspapers, Magazines, and Broadcasts**

http://www.newslink.org

◎ **Statistics Canada**

http://www.statcan.ca

◎ **TSN Sports Scoreboard**

http://tsn.ca/scoreboard/

◎ **North American Television Listings**

http://www.clicktv.com/

NEWSPAPERS

2

> NEWSPAPERS OF ALL SIZES ...
> ARE BROADENING BEYOND THEIR
> PRINT ROOTS INTO INTERACTIVE
> SERVICES.... THE MOTIVATION
> IS THE SAME: SURVIVAL IN THE
> SWIFTLY CHANGING MEDIA
> LANDSCAPE.

Hanna Liebman, reporter,
Media Week

What's Ahead

This chapter begins with a brief history of the North American newspaper industry. Newspapers played a key role in defining the concept of the independent press—the belief that the press must remain independent from government to fulfill its primary responsibility of keeping the public informed. From the 18th century until the introduction of radio in 1920, newspapers were the only mass medium for the timely delivery of news. Debates about what the public should know, when they should know it, and who should decide what it needs to know happened during a time when newspapers were the main focus of these discussions.

A second theme of this chapter is the role of technology in the 20th century in changing the way newspapers deliver the news. Previously, newspapers provided the only way for large numbers of people to get the same news simultaneously. The invention of broadcasting in the early 20th century changed this exclusive access to news and offered instant access to information. Yet, despite increasing competition for its audience, the newspaper industry continues to prosper.

The third theme of this chapter concerns the huge earnings of newspaper chains and their expanding ownership of smaller newspapers as a significant part of the economic evolution of North American newspapers. Today, newspapers have largely become the instruments of large conglomerates. The Thomson corporation is one example of a contemporary news conglomerate in Canada. Established by Roy Thomson (subsequently Lord Thomson of Fleet), it owns 21 trade and academic book publishers, 27 business information services, a large number of law book publishers, 15 regional newspapers in several countries, the Thomson financial services group, and dozens of Canadian and U.S. daily newspapers. Even more widespread and powerful are the Hollinger-Southam publishing interests, controlled by Conrad Black. The success of corporations such as Thomson and Hollinger-Southam demonstrates the rapid growth of newspapers since their beginnings in Canada more than two centuries ago.

North America's First Newspapers: Toward an Independent Press

The issue of government control of newspapers surfaced early in the history of the North American colonies. At first, newspapers were the mouthpieces of the British colonial regime, and news was subject to British approval. Many colonial newspapers were subsidized by the British government, and publishers actually printed "Published by Authority" on the first page to demonstrate government approval.

The first colonial newspaper angered the local authorities so much that the newspaper issued only one edition. This newspaper, *Publick Occurrences*, which was published in Boston on September 25, 1690, is often identified as North America's first newspaper.

The first and only edition of *Publick Occurrences* was just two pages, each the size of a sheet of today's binder paper (then called a half-sheet), and was printed on three sides. Publisher Benjamin Harris left the fourth side blank so that people could jot down the latest news before they gave the paper to friends. Harris made the mistake of reporting in his first issue that the French king was "in much trouble" for sleeping with his son's wife. Harris's journalism was too candid for the governor, who stopped the publication four days after it appeared.

The first consecutively issued (published more than once) newspaper in North America was *The Boston News-Letter*, which appeared in 1704. It was one half-sheet printed on two sides. In the first issue, editor John Campbell reprinted the Queen's latest speech, some maritime news, and one advertisement, which described how to take out an ad in his paper. Like many subsequent colonial publishers, Campbell reprinted items from the London papers.

The next challenge to British control came when James Franklin started his own newspaper in Boston in 1721. His *New England Courant* was the first American newspaper to appear without the crown's "By Authority" sanction. Thus, Franklin began the tradition of an independent press in the United States.

The first New York paper, the *New York Gazette*, was founded by William Bradford in 1725. Bradford's title was "King's Printer to the Province of New York," for which he received a British salary.

The second New York newspaper was *The New-York Weekly Journal*, begun in 1733 by John Peter Zenger. The *Journal* continually attacked New York governor William Cosby for incompetence, and on November 17, 1734, Zenger was arrested and jailed, charged with printing false and seditious writing. (Seditious language is writing that could incite rebellion against the government.) While Zenger was in jail, his wife, Anna, continued to publish the paper.

Zenger's trial began on August 4, 1735, nine months after his arrest. His attorney argued that truth was a defence against libel, and that if Zenger's words were true, they could not be libellous. (A libellous statement is one that damages a person by questioning that person's character or reputation.) The trial established a landmark precedent for freedom of the press—the concept that if what someone publishes is true, the information cannot be considered libellous. Only in the United States is this defence unequivocally available; in Canada, publishing information about a person with malicious intent limits this defence. (The issue of libel is discussed in Chapter 14.)

Canadian newspapers underwent a similar struggle for independence from governmental influence. In W.H. Kesterson's landmark study, *A History of Journalism in Canada* (1967), the origins of today's newspapers are traced to the 18th century.

It was Kesterson's view that in the early period, Canadian newspapers were essentially copies of the New England newspapers, which themselves were modelled on English newspapers. Canada's first newspaper, the *Halifax Gazette*, was first published in 1752, as an offshoot of a commercial print shop in the service of the colonial government of Nova Scotia. In this respect it was dependent on, and subsidized by, unrelated government printing business and advertising revenues. Early dependence on government printing business made the *Halifax Gazette* and many other early newspapers vulnerable to

John Campbell's *Boston News-Letter,* first published in 1704, was the first consecutively published newspaper in North America.

Courtesy of the Massachusetts Historical Society

threats of withdrawal of government patronage, a situation that thwarted editorial independence.

In Quebec, the situation was further clouded by the opposition of the founding colonial power, France, to the establishment of printing presses in the colony. Printers arrived in what is now Quebec from the American colonies in the 1760s, following the liquidation of French colonial interests in Canada. A bilingual newspaper, the *Quebec Gazette*, was first printed in 1764 by expatriate American printers. In the following year, the *Montreal Gazette*, the oldest continuing newspaper in Canada, commenced publication.

Women's Early Role as Publishers

Although colonial women were discouraged from working outside the home, they too contributed to the emergence of an independent press. The women who published newspapers during the colonial period are especially notable because they are among the few examples of women who managed businesses early in 18th-century North America.

Early colonial women printers, such as Anna Zenger, usually belonged to printing families that trained wives and daughters to work in the printshops. By 1775, at least 14 women had been printers in the colonies.[1] One of these family-trained printers was the first woman publisher.

Elizabeth Timothy became editor of the weekly *South Carolina Gazette* in Charleston when her husband, Lewis, died unexpectedly and her son Peter was only 13. Timothy published her first edition on January 4, 1737, under her son's name. Her first editorial appealed to the community to continue to support the "poor afflicted Widow and six small Children." Mother and son ran the paper together until 1746.[2]

In the 19th century, Robertine Barry became the first woman in Quebec to write newspaper articles for women readers. From 1891 to 1895 she wrote a weekly column in *La Patrie*, under the pseudonym Françoise. She was the first reporter in Quebec to institute a women's page in a newspaper, and in 1902 she began publishing her own bimonthly newspaper, *Le Journal de Françoise*.

An unflagging supporter of women's rights, and of education and literary culture, Françoise raised the ire of Quebec's clerical elite. In 1900 she helped ensure the success of Canada's contribution to the World's Fair in Paris, prepared by the National Council of Women of Canada. Her career prepared the way for women's periodical literature and inspired other women journalists, including "Fadette" (Henriette Dessaules, 1860–1946) and "Madeleine" (Anne-Marie Gleason, 1875–1943), to follow her lead.[3]

Birth of the Partisan Press

As dissatisfaction with British rule grew in the American colonies, both in what is now the United States and Canada, newspapers became political tools that fostered the debate that eventually led to the colonies' independence, in the United States by successful armed insurrection and in Canada by colonial abdication in stages.

The Stamp Act. Opposition to the British Stamp Act signalled the beginning of the revolutionary period. The Stamp Act taxed publishers a halfpenny for each issue that was a half-sheet or less and one penny for a full sheet. Each

Halifax Gazette

Courtesy of the Metropolitan Toronto Reference Library

Quebec Gazette

Courtesy of the Metropolitan Toronto Reference Library

Furious colonists reacting to the Stamp Act in 1765 by threatening to stop publication and by printing editions that mocked the tax. The Stamp Act was repealed a year later.

The Granger Collection, New York

advertisement was taxed two shillings. All of the colonial newspapers, even those loyal to the crown, fought the Act.

Many newspapers threatened to stop publication, but only a few of them did. Most editors published editions that mocked the tax. William Bradford III issued the famous tombstone edition of the *Pennsylvania Journal* on October 31, 1765. The front page, bordered in black, was printed with a skull and crossbones where the official stamp should have been.

The Stamp Act Congress met in New York in October 1765 and adopted the now-familiar slogan "No taxation without representation." The British Parliament, facing united opposition from all of the colonial publishers, repealed the Stamp Act on March 18, 1766.

The Silencing of Critics. During the colonial period, newspapers often were an outlet for journalists opposed to the new government. The Alien and Sedition Laws of 1798 were the U.S. federal government's first attempt to control its critics. Congress said that anyone who "shall write, print, utter, or publish ... false, scandalous and malicious writing or writings against the government of the United States, or either house of the Congress of the United States, or the President of the United States" could be fined up to $2000 and jailed for two years.

Several people went to jail. A Boston publisher spent 30 days in jail for libelling the Massachusetts legislature. A New York editor was fined $100 and jailed for four months. By 1800, the angry rhetoric had dissipated. The Alien and Sedition Laws expired after two years and were not renewed.

In the early 1800s, the Canadian government also attempted to control its critics. One such critic, William Lyon Mackenzie, a strident opponent of Tory governments of Upper Canada, campaigned for paper mill subsidies in order to obtain adequate supplies of paper. In his case, this was akin to asking an adversary to buy him bullets, since the newspaper he edited published incendiary articles on the government. Mackenzie used his newspaper, *The Colonial Advocate* (founded in 1824), to organize resistance in the name of reform by farmers, tradesmen, and ordinary citizens to the Tory elite of the colony which controlled trade and commerce, the institutions of the law, and the established religion.

For his troubles, in 1826 Mackenzie's printing office in York (now Toronto) was trashed by a Tory mob, who threw his type into Lake Ontario. Also a member of the colonial assembly, Mackenzie was expelled five times for "libel" (and was five times re-elected). He was also elected the first mayor of Toronto (1834) and, in his most famous gesture of defiance, organized a military insurrection in 1837 with farmers, many from the United States, playing the role of armed revolutionaries. When this uprising failed, Mackenzie set up a provisional government on Navy Island, in the Niagara River, and was imprisoned for 18 months in the United States for doing so. He ultimately returned to Canada to be elected once again to the legislature in 1849. William Lyon Mackenzie is also remembered as the grandfather of Mackenzie King, prime minister of Canada throughout World War II, and as the spiritual father of the Liberal Party of Canada, the dominant political party of the twentieth century in Canada.

In the *Novascotian* (established in 1824), Joseph Howe waged similar campaigns (though falling well short of revolutionary violence) to undermine the established oligarchy in Nova Scotia and to promote the principles of popular democracy, as they were then understood. The newspaper campaigns were an important ingredient in the eventual establishment of representative government in British North America, leading ultimately to the Confederation of Canada in 1867.

Newspapers multiplied as the number of settlements grew, followed settlers as they moved west across the continent, and finally aggregated into chains, largely for economic reasons. Today, little remains of that early experience of tiny, independent community newspapers. But the legacy of the early period is still with us. For instance, the dominant daily in Canada today, the Thomson newspaper the *Globe and Mail*, is the modern descendant of the *Toronto Mail*, established in 1872 as the voice of the Conservative Party, and the *Toronto Globe*, founded by publisher George Brown as a personal political vehicle. Similarly, the *Toronto Star*, now the newspaper with the largest circulation in Canada, had been founded in 1892 by striking printers and quickly passed into the hands of businesses supporting the Liberal prime minister Sir Wilfrid Laurier.

William Lyon Mackenzie used his newspaper, *The Colonial Advocate,* to organize resistance against the Tory government in 1826.

Taking Advantage of 19th-Century Technology: Newspapers Diversify

The technological advances of the 19th century—such as cheaper newsprint, mechanized printing, and the telegraph—meant that newspapers could reach a wider audience faster than ever before. Confined to a few eastern cities in North America, and to a small educated urban audience during the 18th century, newspaper publishers in the 19th century sought out new readers—on the frontiers of new settlement, from among the growing number of literate immigrants, and from within ethnic groups. This expansion resulted in three additions to newspaper practice: frontier journalism, ethnic and cultural newspapers, and the alternative press.

Frontier Journalism

Precious metals, cheap land, the possibility of shedding one's past, and simple adventure lured many people westward, and when the people arrived they needed newspapers. Newspapers sprang up across Canada to meet the need for information about products, politics, and local events. Victoria's *Daily Colonist* began publication in 1858, the *Winnipeg Free Press* in 1872, the *Saskatchewan Herald* in 1878, and the *Edmonton Bulletin* in 1880. Communication was also aided by the telegraph, which moved news easily from coast to coast.

The wide-open land beckoned many journalists. The most celebrated journalist to chronicle the frontier was Samuel Clemens, who travelled to Nevada in 1861 prospecting for silver. Clemens didn't find any silver, but a year later the Virginia City *Territorial Enterprise*—the area's largest paper—hired him for $25 a week. Clemens first signed his name Mark Twain on a humorous travel letter written for the *Enterprise*.

Ethnic and Aboriginal Newspapers

English-language newspapers did not satisfy everyone's needs. In the first half of the 19th century, many newspapers sought to succeed by catering to ethnic and cultural interests. In the early 1800s, Spanish-speaking people in Georgia could read *El Misisipi*. Herman Ridder's German newspaper, *New Yorker Staats-Zeitung*, founded in 1845, was the most successful foreign-language newspaper in the United States. It formed the financial basis for today's Knight-Ridder chain. People outside of the mainstream of society, such as Spanish and German immigrants, used newspapers to create and maintain a sense of community and ethnic identity.

In Quebec, publication of French-language newspapers was hampered by low literacy rates and a dispersed rural population. One newspaper that attempted to reach this population was *Le Nouveau Monde* (1867), which was closely allied to the conservative Roman Catholicism of the time. In 1910, Henri Bourassa, a

Early Prairie newspapers like the *Regina Leader* had to make do with modest accommodations.

O.B. Buell/National Archives of Canada/PA-118776

political leader and journalist, founded *Le Devoir*, the first quality French-language newspaper in North America, which continues to publish today.

In the 1800s, Aboriginal peoples who had been displaced by the settlers also felt a need to express their culture through a newspaper. As a nonmainstream group, they especially felt the need to voice their complaints. On February 21, 1828, the first Aboriginal peoples' newspaper appeared—*The Cherokee Phoenix*, edited by Elias Boudinot. The Cherokee nation held exclusive control over the four-page paper, which was printed half in English and half in an 86-character alphabet that represented the Cherokee language. Authorities shut down the press in 1832 because they felt that Boudinot was arousing anti-government sentiment, by then a familiar charge for anyone associated with the newspaper business.

Dissident Voices: The Alternative Press

Two strong social movements, emancipation and women's suffrage, brought new voices to the press. This **alternative press** movement signalled the beginning of a significant journalistic tradition. Newspapers became an outlet for the voices of social protest, a tradition that continues today. (The alternative press is also called the **dissident press**.)

Early advocates of domestic change used the press to advance their causes—the abolition of slavery and suffrage for women. Some of those prominent in these movements of social protest were John B. Russwurm, the Reverend Samuel Cornish, Frederick Douglass, Jane Grey Swisshelm, and Mary Ann Shadd.

Russwurm and Cornish, who were African American, started *Freedom's Journal* in 1827 in New York City with very little money. They started their newspaper to respond to racist attacks in several local newspapers. *Freedom's Journal* lasted for two years and reached only a few readers, but it was the beginning of an African American press tradition that eventually created more than 2700 newspapers, magazines, and quarterly journals.[4]

Elias Boudinot published the first Aboriginal newspaper, the Cherokee Phoenix, from 1828 to 1832.

Library of Congress

What has often been called the most important African American pre–Civil War newspaper was Frederick Douglass's weekly *North Star*. "Right is of no Sex—Truth is of no Color—God is the Father of us all, and we are all Brethren" read the masthead. Beginning in 1847, Douglass struggled to support the *North Star* by giving lectures. The newspaper eventually reached 3000 subscribers in the United States and abroad with its emancipation message.

Like Douglass, Jane Grey Swisshelm campaigned for civil rights. Her first byline appeared in 1844 in the *Spirit of Liberty*, published in Pittsburgh. Four years later she began her own abolitionist publication, the *Pittsburgh Saturday Visiter*, which also promoted women's rights.

Mary Ann Shadd, a black woman who was born in Wilmington, Delaware, in 1823, brought the discussion of civil rights to Canadian journalism. Although not a slave herself, she moved to Windsor, Ontario, in 1850 and helped establish a school for black refugees from the United States. In 1853, she established the *Provincial Freeman*, a weekly newspaper concerned with the interests of blacks in Canada. Her editorials dealt with the issue of slavery and its effects. The newspaper ceased publication in 1858 for economic reasons and Shadd returned to the United States in 1860 to work as a recruiter in the American Civil War.

Making Newspapers Profitable

The voices of social protest reached a limited, committed audience, but most people could not afford to subscribe to a daily newspaper. Newspapers were sold by advance yearly subscription for $6 to $10, at a time when most skilled workers earned less than $750 annually. Then, in 1833, Benjamin Day demonstrated that he could profitably appeal to a mass audience by dropping the price of a newspaper to a penny and selling the paper on the street every day.

Toward Mass Readership: The Penny Press

Day's *New York Sun* published sensational news and feature stories to interest the working class. He was able to lower the price to a penny by filling the paper with advertising and by hiring newsboys to sell the paper on street corners. This first successful **penny paper** reported local gossip, sensationalized police news, and carried a page and a half of advertising in a four-page paper. Newsboys bought 100 papers for 67 cents and tried to sell them all each day to make a profit. Even *The New York Times*, founded by Henry J. Raymond in 1851, was a penny paper when it began.

Penny papers eventually emerged in Toronto and Montreal to serve the industrial working class. These newspapers included *La Presse* in Montreal (1884) and the *Toronto Telegram* (1876). The legacy of the penny press continues in today's gossip columns and crime reporting. Newspapers and broadcast stations sometimes report sensationalized stories in an effort to attract an audience.

Cooperative and For-Profit News Gathering

The invention of the telegraph by Samuel F.B. Morse in 1844 meant that news that once took weeks to reach publication could be transmitted in minutes. In 1848, six newspapers in New York City decided to share the costs of gathering foreign news by telegraph from Boston. Henry Raymond drew up the agreement among the papers to pay $100 for 3000 words of telegraphic news.[5]

Soon known as the New York Associated Press, this organization was North America's first **cooperative news gathering** association. This meant that the member newspapers shared the expenses to get the news, returning any profits to the members. Today's Associated Press is the result of this early partnership, as newspapers joined together in a cooperative, with several members sharing the cost of gathering domestic and foreign news.

A different way of sharing information was devised by the United Press, founded in 1882 to compete with the Associated Press. United Press was established not as a cooperative but as a privately owned, for-profit wire service.

Canada's first wire service, Canadian Associated Press, was established in 1903. It was subsidized by the federal government, as was the domestic news cooperative Canadian Press during its formative years, following its founding in 1917.

Canadian newspapers are now filled with stories that come from U.S. news services. This importation of U.S. news stories reflects the high costs of maintaining foreign news desks. Today, the "free flow of information" means an overwhelming presence of U.S. content and interpretation of world events.

Continuing in Brady's tradition are photojournalists Peter Turnley and James Natchway (both with cameras), under fire in South Africa in 1994.

Sygma/Kevin Carter

The Birth of Photojournalism

During the American Civil War, from 1861 to 1865, photographer Mathew Brady was the first to photographically record battle. Previously, photography had been confined primarily to studio portraits because of the cumbersome equipment and slow chemical processing required.

Brady photographed the battles of Antietam and Fredericksburg and sent photographic teams to other battles. Newspapers did not yet have a method to reproduce the photographs, but Brady's pictures were published in magazines, making him the first news photographer. His 3500 photographs demonstrated the practicality and effectiveness of using photographs to help report a news story, although newspaper photographs did not become widely used until the early 1900s. The marriage of photographs and text to tell a better story than either text or photographs could tell alone formed the beginnings of today's concept of **photojournalism.**

Newspapers Dominate Public Discourse

For the first 30 years of the 20th century—before radio and television—newspapers dominated public discussions of events and policies. Newspapers were the single source of daily dialogue about political, cultural, and social issues. This was also the era of the greatest newspaper competition.

Competition Breeds Sensationalism

In large cities such as New York, as many as ten newspapers competed for readers at once, so the publishers looked for new ways to expand their audience. Two New York publishers—Joseph Pulitzer and Randolph Hearst—revived and refined the penny-press sensationalism that had begun in 1833 with Benjamin Day's *New York Sun.* Like Day, Pulitzer and Hearst proved that newspapers could reap enormous fortunes for their owners. They also demonstrated that credible, serious reporting is not all that people want in a newspaper. Pulitzer and Hearst promoted giveaways and fabricated stories.

An ambitious man who knew how to grab his readers' interest, Joseph Pulitzer published the first newspaper comics and sponsored journalist Nellie Bly on an around-the-world trip to try to beat the fictional record in the popular book *Around the World in 80 Days*. Bly finished the trip in 72 days, 6 hours, and 11 minutes, and the stunt brought Pulitzer the circulation he craved.

In San Francisco, young William Randolph Hearst, the new editor of the *San Francisco Examiner*, sent a reporter to cover Bly's arrival.[6] In 1887, he convinced his father, who owned the *Examiner*, to let him run the paper. Hearst tagged the *Examiner* "The Monarch of the Dailies," added a lovelorn column, and attacked several of his father's influential friends in the newspaper. He spent money wildly, buying talent from competing papers and staging showy promotional events. In 1896, Hearst bought the New York *Journal* to compete head-on with Pulitzer.

The Birth of Yellow Journalism: Hearst's Role in the Spanish-American War

In New York, Hearst hired Pulitzer's entire Sunday staff and cut the *Journal*'s price to a penny, so Pulitzer dropped his price to match it. Hearst bought a colour press and printed colour comics. Then he stole Pulitzer's popular comic "Hogan's Alley," which included a character named the Yellow Kid.

Hearst relished the battle, as the *Journal* screamed such attention-grabbing headlines as "Thigh of the Body Found" and offered $1000 for information that would convict the murderer. Critics named this sensationalism **yellow journalism** after the Yellow Kid, an epithet still bestowed on highly emotional, exaggerated, or inaccurate reporting that emphasizes crime, sex, and violence. By 1900, about one-third of the U.S. metropolitan dailies were following the trend toward yellow journalism.[7]

Beginning in 1898, the Spanish-American War provided the battlefield for Pulitzer and Hearst to truly act out their newspaper war. For three years, the two newspapers unrelentingly overplayed events in the Cuban struggle for independence from Spain, each trying to beat the other with irresponsible, exaggerated stories, many of them manufactured.

The events that resulted from the sensational competition between Pulitzer and Hearst showed that newspapers could have a significant effect on political attitudes. The Spanish-American War began a few months after the U.S. battleship Maine sank in Havana harbour, killing 266 men. The cause of the explosion that sank the ship was never determined. But Pulitzer's and Hearst's newspapers blamed the Spanish. Hearst dubbed the event "the *Journal*'s War," but Hearst and Pulitzer shared responsibility, because both had inflamed the public unnecessarily about events in Cuba. The serious consequences of their yellow journalism demonstrated the importance of press responsibility.

Tabloid Journalism: Sex and Violence Sell

The journalistic legacy of yellow journalism surfaced again in the **tabloid journalism** of the 1920s, often called **jazz journalism**. In 1919, the publishers of the *New York Daily News* sponsored a beauty contest to inaugurate the first

U.S. tabloid. A **tabloid** is a small-format newspaper, usually 11 inches by 14 inches, featuring illustrations and sensational stories.

The *Daily News* merged pictures and screaming headlines with reports about crime, sex, and violence, exceeding in sensationalism anything that had appeared before. It ran full-page pictures with short, punchy text. Love affairs soon became big news, as did murders. In the ultimate example of tabloid journalism, a *Daily News* reporter strapped a camera to his ankle and took a picture of Ruth Snyder, who had conspired to kill her husband, as she was electrocuted at Sing Sing in 1928. The photo covered the front page, and the caption stated, "This is perhaps the most remarkable exclusive picture in the history of criminology." Photojournalism had taken a sensational turn, very different from what Mathew Brady had envisioned.

Today, jazz journalism's successors are the supermarket tabloids, such as the *National Enquirer*, which feature large photographs and stories about sex, violence, and celebrities. The French-language tabloids of the late Pierre Peladeau's Quebec publishing empire, Quebecor, have developed this approach to an even higher pitch. Publications such as *Allo Police* typify the highest achievements in this dubious publishing activity.

Unionization Encourages Professionalism

The first half of the 20th century brought about the unionization of newspaper employees, which standardized reporters' wages at many of the largest newspapers. Labour unions were first established at newspapers in 1800, and the International Typographical Union developed in the mid-1850s. The same unions were active on both sides of the Canada–U.S. border. They include unions representing newspaper production workers such as the International Stereotypers and Electrotypers' Union, the International Photo-Engravers' Union, and the International Printing Pressmen and Assistants' Union. But

Unionization of newspaper employees began in the 1800s. Right, workers from the *St. Catherines Standard* walk the picket line outside the annual meeting of Southam Inc.

CP Picture Archive (Frank Gunn)

reporters didn't have a union until 1933, when *New York World-Telegram* reporter Heywood Broun called on his colleagues to organize.

The Newspaper Guild held its first meeting in early 1934 and elected Broun its president. Broun remained president until he died in 1939 at age 51. The Guild continues today to cover employees at many large newspapers. Unions represent roughly one in five newspaper employees.

With the rise of unions, employee contracts, which once had been negotiated in private, became public agreements. In general, salaries for reporters at union newspapers rose, and eventually this led to a sense of professionalism, including codes of ethics.

IMPACT

Point of View

By Anthony Wilson-Smith

GOOSING THE GLOBE

For the estimated 300,000 Canadians who get *The Globe and Mail* every day, one clear sign of a newspaper in transition came in a message from editor-in-chief William Thorsell that appeared on page 2 last September [1997]. He wrote that the next week would see "a set of changes made in the conviction, again, that we are not selling newspapers; we are buying your time." The changes included adding a new daily Politics page in the front section, enhancing the existing Middle Kingdom page, which

emphasized stories on sometimes esoteric topics, gossipy columns called Buzz that would appear in all sections of the paper, and a change in writers and subjects for many columns. Thorsell concluded by asking readers to "please let us know what you think."

... Within two months, many of the changes had disappeared. Six months later, those that remain have been reduced or altered in scope. And other longstanding features have been dropped—including the column of the newspaper's resident

iconoclast, Michael Valpy, whose work Thorsell described in the same September piece as "eloquent." Asked about the changes in a recent *Maclean's* interview, Thorsell said simply: "They were not working."

Instead, say angry anxious staffers, the *Globe*—long considered the "great, grey lady" and newspaper of record in Canadian journalism—is trying a different tack to build readership and discourage Southam. "Thorsell used to tell us to challenge readers to step up

Newspapers in the Television Era

The advent of television dramatically affected the newspaper industry. Newspaper publishers had already learned how to live with the only other 20th-century news industry—radio. In the 1920s, when radio had first become popular, newspapers had refused to carry advertising or time logs for the programs, but eventually newspapers conceded the space to radio.

But in the 1950s, television posed a larger threat; television offered moving images of the news, in addition to entertainment. The spread of television demonstrated how interrelated the media were. The newspaper industry relinquished its supremacy as the major news medium and was forced to share the audience for news with broadcasting. And over time, television's influence changed both the look and the content of many newspapers.

The Revival of the Dissident Press

The social movements of the 1960s briefly revived one portion of the newspaper industry—the alternative press. Like their 1800s predecessors in the abolitionist and emancipation movements, people who supported the alternative press in the 1960s felt that the mainstream press was avoiding important social issues, such as the anti-Vietnam War movement and the civil rights movement.

In 1964, as a way to pass along news about the antiwar movement, the *Los Angeles Free Press* became the first underground paper to publish regularly. *The Barb* in Berkeley, *Kaleidoscope* in Chicago, and *Quicksilver Times* in Washington, D.C., soon followed.

In Quebec, the influential periodical *Cité Libre* was established by Pierre Trudeau, who was soon to be prime minister, and his colleagues to discuss and promote ideas and policies for modernizing Quebec society. Other English-language publications sprang up, as well, including *Canadian Dimension, This*

intellectually," says one veteran *Globe* reporter. "Now, we're told the paper is boring, and we should dumb it down." That is one way to describe the process in the works: the other comes from senior management. "I'm not sure I've called the paper boring, but I've certainly said it lacks élan," says Stuart Garner, president and chief executive officer of Thomson Newspapers. And, adds Garner, who has played a key role in suggesting changes: "Just what does 'dumbing-down' mean? If it suggests fewer academic essays and more stories about real

people, that's what we're doing." A favorite Garner maxim: "Journalists have no right to bore the pants off people."

Whatever the words describing the process, the end result is the same: a *Globe and Mail* in evolution, already different from what it was six months ago. As Thorsell acknowledges, stories are shorter, there is a conscious effort to make headlines "snappier," and less emphasis is given to federal politics and international coverage outside of North America. Changes will continue: on June 1 [1998], the *Globe* [began] using color

photographs, accompanied by a redesign of the newspaper.

Whether all that is for the good depends on who is telling the story. There are two different versions— the one told by management figures such as Thorsell, Garner and publisher Roger Parkinson, and the one told by journalists. The common lament these days among the newspaper's editors and reporters is: "Why fix what's not broken?" To that, Parkinson responds: "The surest guarantee of failure can be past success."

Maclean's, *March 30, 1998, 18–20. Reprinted with permission.*

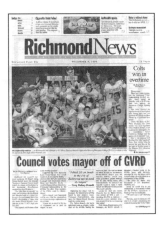

Suburban chain-owned weeklies and bi-weeklies now form part of the Canadian newspaper mix. They deliver highly local news and advertising.

Courtesy of the *Richmond News*

Magazine, and *Our Generation.* Each sought in its own way to promote social change and to hold current policies up to scrutiny and criticism. They tended to mould intellectual debate in such a way that the agenda for change in Canadian society was given a prominent and effective voice.

In Vancouver, the *Georgia Straight* was an important voice for the 1960s counterculture. It still publishes as a free but substantial review of the arts and current issues in the Lower Mainland of British Columbia.

The 1960s underground press showed again what had been proved in the 19th century—that causes need a voice, and if those voices are not represented in the mainstream press, publications emerge to support alternative views.

Declining Readership

Since the 1970s, the number of newspapers has declined. Many afternoon papers died when TV took over the evening news, and others changed to morning papers. Then newspaper publishers realized that although television could provide the news headlines, newspapers could offer the background and in-depth commentary that television news could not.

Newspaper publishers also began to see that they could play on the popularity of television personalities, who became news items. Eventually, realizing that viewers cannot clip coupons out of their television sets or retrieve copies of yesterday's TV ads, advertisers began to use newspapers to complement television advertising campaigns.

Today, the majority of small dailies are part of chains. Many smaller cities have only one newspaper, and major cities have only two or three, which may be published by the same company. In an attempt to match television's visual displays, newspapers have introduced advanced graphics and vivid colour. The newspaper industry still earns more every year than any other media industry.

Working for Newspapers

Many colonial publishers handled all of the tasks of putting out a newspaper, but today's typical newspaper operation is organized into two separate departments: the editorial side and the business side. The *editorial* side handles everything that you read in the paper—the news and feature stories, editorials, cartoons, and photographs. The *business* side handles everything else—production, advertising, distribution, and administration.

On the editorial side at a medium-size daily, different *editors*—a news editor, a sports editor, a features editor, and a business editor, for example—handle different parts of the paper. The managing editor oversees these news departments. A copy editor checks the reporters' stories before they are set in type, and a layout editor positions the stories. Editorial writers and cartoonists usually work for an editorial page editor. All of these people report to the *editor-in-chief,* the *publisher,* or both.

A *business manager* and his or her staff run the business side of the paper: getting the paper out to subscribers, selling advertising, and making sure the paper gets printed every day. These people also ultimately report to the editor-in-chief or the publisher. Sometimes the publisher is also the owner of the paper. If a corporation owns the paper, the publisher reports to its board of directors.

Technology has strongly affected the way newspapers are published. The history of newspapers, like that of all media, is the history of technological advances. In their book *The Press and America*, Edwin and Michael Emery describe the clumsiness of colonial printing:

> The bed of the press is rolled out by means of a wheel and pulley arrangement. The type, all set by hand, is locked tight in the form and is placed on the bed. A young apprentice, or "devil," applies the homemade ink to the type, using a doeskin dauber on a stick for this purpose.
>
> The paper is then moistened in a trough so that it will take a better impression. It is placed carefully over the type. The bed is rolled back under the press.
>
> The "platen," or upper pressure plate, is then pressed against the type by means of a screw or lever device. The platen is released; the bed is wheeled out; the sheet is hung on a wire to dry before it is ready for its second "run" for the reverse side.[8]

In today's newsroom, reporters type their stories at computer terminals. In the composing room, designers lay out the newspaper on a computer screen, joining copy with ads. The final version of the newspaper is transferred to film, from which copies of the paper are made. Nobody touches a piece of metal type. The efficiency of this offset method, compared to the complicated processes of the 18th and 19th centuries, was not possible even 40 years ago.

The Business of Newspapers

As they reach for the 21st century, newspapers taken altogether sell tens of millions of copies daily, and a majority of adults read a newspaper every day. Big-city newspapers are losing readers as people move to the suburbs, and suburban newspapers are growing, as are suburban editions of city papers. Some newspapers, such as the *Toronto Star*, also regularly publish special regional sections. Newspapers depend primarily on advertising for support. Subscriptions and newsstand sales account for only a small percentage of newspaper income.

Newspaper companies in the 1990s, looking for new ways to make money, rediscovered and expanded on some old ideas. The *Globe and Mail* tried to become a national newspaper by printing different editions in most of the large cities across Canada. The news services streamlined their operations, and more newspaper organizations joined the syndication business.

Table 2.1

Canadian Daily Newspaper Circulation, 1985 to 1997					
	Number of Newspapers				
Year	Morning	Evening	All-Day	Total	Total Circulation
1985	27	81	3	111	5 620 811
1986	28	79	3	110	5 681 850
1987	28	78	4	110	5 690 589

Table 2.1 (continued)

Canadian Daily Newspaper Circulation, 1980 to 1997

Number of Newspapers

Year	Morning	Evening	All-Day	Total	Total Circulation
1988	30	77	4	111	5 735 124
1989	28	77	4	109	5 824 736
1990	29	73	6	108	5 814 510
1991	28	74	6	108	5 654 390
1992	33	70	5	108	5 553 409
1993	35	69	4	108	5 536 546
1994	37	67	4	108	5 491 150
1995	42	62	2	106	5 309 600
1996	43	60	2	105	5 087 153
1997	43	60	2	105	5 191 677

Note: The two major chains, Thomson and Southam, have reduced the number of news-papers published by making most Canadian communities one-newspaper towns. Critics have suggested that the two chains colluded in this consolidation; yet, although it was the subject of an anti-combines investigation in the late 1970s, this allegation has never been proven.

Source: Data from the Canadian Newspaper Association. On-line at the Newspaper Association of America Website: http://www.naa.org/info/facts/28.html

On-line Newspapers

Several newspaper publishing companies have launched electronic delivery of news and newspapers to capture new audiences. Newspapers arriving on-screen at computers are just one part of the reader-friendly future, according to many industry analysts.

To expand their readership, many newspapers, including the *Toronto Star*, have created on-line editions.

The *Toronto Star*

Hundreds of newspapers in North America, including the *Globe and Mail*, now offer on-line services. Newspapers may provide either the entire editorial content of the newspaper or selected articles and sections. Newspapers are trying to generate some income from home computer users with modems, and information services also are becoming easier to use. Most on-line editions offer archive services, where readers may search through back issues.

On-line editions sometimes publish highlights of the day's news as updates during the day, as well as special features that don't appear in the daily newspaper. Bulletin boards offer subscribers the chance to discuss the newspaper's movie reviews, for example, or to get more information on subjects that appear in the on-line edition. This new delivery system is just one way that newspapers in the 1990s are trying to retain their audience.

News Services

Using satellites and computer terminals instead of the original telegraph machines, cooperative and for-profit news gathering has grown faster and more efficient. Today, the wire services prefer to be called **news services.** Most newspapers subscribe to at least one news service, such as Canadian Press. Many other news services send stories and broadcasts worldwide; these include Agence France-Presse (France), Reuters (Great Britain), the Russian Information Telegraph Agency (Commonwealth of Independent States), Agenzia Nationale Stampa Associate (Italy), Deutsche Presse Agentur (Germany), and Xinhua (China).

The news services especially help small newspapers (and broadcast stations) that can't afford overseas correspondents. Large dailies with their own correspondents around the world still rely on news services when they can't get to a story quickly.

Some newspaper organizations in the United States—the *New York Times*, the *Washington Post*, the *Los Angeles Times*, and Knight-Ridder—have started their own news services. Newspapers that subscribe can publish each other's news service stories. With the growth of Hollinger/Southam, in essence, an in-house news service has been formed among the many newspapers in the chain. Member papers share editorial content, including news stories. The opinion columns of writers such as Mordecai Richler and Barbara Amiel appear in many of the chain's local papers, as well. For many newspapers, sharing stories fills space at a relatively low cost, since the newspaper doesn't need as many staff reporters.

Syndicates

Newspapers also can add to their content without sending their own reporters to stories by using **syndicates,** which are news agencies that sell articles for publication in a number of newspapers simultaneously. The first syndicated column was a fashion letter distributed in 1857. Today, more newspapers are syndicating their columns and features to try to add income. Syndicates mainly provide columnists and comics—Dave Barry, Molly Ivins, and William Raspberry, as well as "Dilbert" and "Cathy," for example. The price of syndicated copy for each newspaper is calculated on the basis of the newspaper's circulation.

Technology and the Future

Since their colonial beginnings, newspapers have shown their ability to appeal to changing audiences, adapt to growing competition, and continue to attract advertisers. Newspaper analysts project these advances in the future:

◎ Reporters in the field will send more stories from portable computers through cellular telephones in their cars, without needing a telephone line for their computer hookup. Photographers will use video and digital cameras. Their pictures will be sent to the newsroom electronically. Several manufacturers have developed systems that can reproduce still pictures for newspapers from video images.

◎ Newspapers will expand profits by selling more of the information they gather. Once a story is in a computer, the information can be sold to people who want that information, such as lawyers, researchers, and home computer users.

◎ Satellite publishing will bring more customized newspapers in regional editions, and advertisers will be able to choose their audiences more selectively. Cheaper production methods could mean that the cost of starting a newspaper will decrease, which could increase the number of alternative and small community weeklies.

◎ Lower costs for information systems will mean that more newspapers will be able to afford more computer technology.

◎ The offset process may be replaced by a new system called *flexography*, which uses less paper and replaces expensive, toxic oil-based inks with water-based inks.

Three other emerging trends that will affect the future of the newspaper industry are the growing challenges by publishers to newspaper unions, the intensifying concentration of ownership, and the changing newspaper audience.

Computers have replaced metal typesetting machines in most newspaper composing rooms.

CP Picture Archive (Moe Doiron)

IMPACT on You

NEWS AGENCY SWITCHING STYLE ON SPELLING

By Joe Chidley

TORONTO (CP)—Starting today, The Canadian Press will endeavour to write with fervour, humour and candour. Canada's national news agency has spelled these words and about 35 others without the final "u" throughout its 81-year history. But at the urging of many of the newspapers that own CP, editors will switch to "our" for words of more than one syllable in which the "u" is not pronounced. This is the spelling preferred by many readers.

Be forgiving of those of us who edit the daily news. We've been writing with color, ardor and rigor for so long that we may forget—at least until we get the spellchecker adjusted—that those are rumours, not rumors, about Bill and Monica; that the latest government directive is an endeavour, not an endeavor; and that the body of water next to Halifax is a harbour, not a harbor.

At the same time, editors have to remember that although we will now use honour, it is still honorary without a "u." Ditto for labour and laborious; odour and odorous.

Such is the arbitrary nature of spelling, which is governed a lot by history and only a little by consistency.

Canadian spelling, in particular, is schizoid because of our historical ties to Britain and our physical proximity to the United States. We use British spelling for some words (centre, not center, for instance) and American for others (program, not programme).

For those who don't get all worked up about spelling, it may be hard to understand why one little "u" is such a big deal. Trust us: advocates of both spellings feel strongly that theirs is the "proper" Canadian spelling. And they are not hesitant to write or phone editors to complain.

For the "our" advocates, it is a matter of passion. "Or" is an Americanism, as huge a threat to the Canadian cultural identity as zee instead of zed.

The "or" proponents take the logical approach. They feel "or" is the cleaner, more consistent, more modern spelling—there are many more words with "or" endings than "our"—and has been used in Canada long enough to be considered Canadian.

CP has been caught in the middle. On one hand, the news agency is a strong proponent of distinctly Canadian spellings: it publishes spelling and style guides that are followed by most Canadian media and many businesses. At the same time, it stood behind "or."

The roots of the dispute go back to before the last century, when written English—in Britain and elsewhere—began replacing "our" with "or" in such words as governour, terrour and errour. Then Americans began using "or" endings almost exclusively and it became practically a matter of honour outside the United States to retain the remaining "our" spellings.

In Canada, Sir John A. Macdonald decided arbitrarily that Canada would use "our" endings in federal government documents, despite the fact that "or" endings were already in common use and that the Queen's Printer of the day spiritedly resisted the move.

Daily newspapers, which followed CP style, used "or" for most of this century until recently when some made the switch to "our." Most Canadian schools also teach "our" spellings.

Earlier this year, CP surveyed its 95 members and found 77 per cent of respondents wanted the "our" spelling used.

Although one publisher decried the change as "trendy," another argued it would "end the argument and save everyone's time and energy discussing a matter that is not really that important."

Now, you can't really argue with that candour! Patti Tasko, Senior Supervising Editor of The Canadian Press, is responsible for language and style issues at the news agency.

© Canadian Press. Reprinted with permission.

Unions versus Technology

The new technology means that machines are doing work formerly done by people. For newspaper unions, this has meant a consistent effort among newspaper owners to challenge union representation.

Before 1970, newspapers needed typographers to hand-set metal type, and labour unions represented most of these typographers. With the introduction of photocomposition, newspaper management slowly moved to eliminate the typographers' jobs. The unions fought the transition, and many newspaper workers went on strike, with limited success in fighting the loss of their jobs.

With the threat of technology eliminating even more jobs in the future, newspaper unions are worried. Membership in the Newspaper Guild (which covers reporters) has remained steady, but most of the other unions have lost members, especially the International Typographers Union, whose membership is half what it was before photocomposition.[9] Forecasts are that union influence at newspapers with circulations above 50 000 will remain strong, but that the effort to diffuse union influence at smaller newspapers will continue.

Chain Ownership

Chain ownership offers many advantages of scale and cross-use of editorial content. This doesn't mean that every newspaper in a chain speaks with the voice of the chain owner. Chains can supply money to improve a newspaper's printing plant and to add more reporters. But critics say the tendency to form chains can consolidate and limit the sources of information for readers.

Today, three chains control 66 percent of Canadian newspapers: Southam-Hollinger (43 percent), Thomson (12 percent), and the Toronto Sun chain (11 percent). Ownership is also consolidated within some provinces. In New Brunswick, the K.C. Irving family owns all four English-language daily newspapers, and in Quebec, 10 out of 11 dailies are owned by Paul Desmarais, Conrad Black, and the late Pierre Peladeau's company, Quebecor, leaving only *Le Devoir* as an independent daily.[10]

In Vancouver, where both dailies are owned by Pacific Press and share office space and production facilities, there is a real threat of readers having only one source of news and commentary and, thus, being exposed to a single point of view. However, the range of information available from other sources, such as the locally printed edition of the *Globe and Mail* and the Seattle newspapers, offsets this potential liability.

According to media scholar Anthony Smith, "It is obvious that in some of the chains ... there are clear editorial lines to which editors normally adhere."[11] Critics fear that chain ownership may mean less debate on public issues because editorial policy for all newspapers in the same chain will become uniform. (See Chapter 12 for further discussion of this issue.)

Table 2.2

The Ten Largest (by Circulation) Newspapers in Canada, 1996		
Newspaper	**Owner**	**Average Sum of Weekly Circulation**
The Toronto Star	Torstar	3 477 157
The Globe and Mail	Thomson	1 912 372
Le Journal de Montréal	Quebecor	1 903 177
The Toronto Sun	Sun Media	1 734 434
La Presse	Montreal Power	1 318 583
The Vancouver Sun	Southam	1 175 782
The Gazette, Montreal	Southam	1 046 206
Edmonton Journal	Southam	1 026 265
The Ottawa Citizen	Southam	995 769
Winnipeg Free Press	Thomson	986 066

Source: Data from the Canadian Newspaper Association. On-line at the Newspaper Association of America Website: http:www.can-acj.ca/cgi-bin/media?english/circen.hts.

A Scramble for Readers

Although newspapers still hold power for advertisers, recent studies reveal that younger readers are deserting the medium. "It dawned on us that if we don't start luring teenagers into the paper and start them reading us now, they may not subscribe in the future," says Grant Podelco, arts editor of the Syracuse (New York) *Herald-Journal.*[12]

To stop the slide among young readers, many newspapers have added inserts directed to, and sometimes written by, teenagers. In 1998, the *Vancouver Sun* ran a separate section called the "Family School Guide," which contained homework tips for children, guides to current school curricula for parents, comments from students on the coming school year, and an article describing current fads in children's clothing and accessories, in which cellphones were listed as fashion accessories. At the *Chicago Tribune*, five teenage film reviewers appear in the newspaper every Friday with their choices, and a "Preps Plus" section covers high-school sports.

Women readers also are abandoning newspapers in unprecedented numbers. Karen Jurgenson, editorial page editor of *USA Today*, says that readership surveys show that women today are less likely to be daily newspaper readers than men. "Women across the board are more likely than men to feel that the paper doesn't speak to them," she says.[13]

To attract more female readers, Jurgenson says that newsroom employees should more closely reflect society's diversity in gender and ethnic origin and that the newspaper should examine its coverage of issues that primarily concern women. The *Charlotte Observer*, says Jurgenson, has created a daycare beat, and some newspapers are attempting to devote more space to women's sports. Some newspapers are experimenting with a section targeted specifically at women.

Newspaper executives also blame television for the declining audience, but others say that people's reading habits reflect changing uses of family time. "That time has been lost to working moms, aerobic classes, and of course TV," according to Jean Gaddy Wilson, executive director of New Directions for News, an independent research group at the University of Missouri School of Journalism. "Many kids today don't even see a paper at home these days. At best, a paper is in a mix of entertainment and news media."[14]

Newspapers are competing to maintain their audience because audiences attract advertisers—and profits. The average daily newspaper is about two-thirds advertising, and in some newspapers advertising runs as high as 70 percent. National advertisers (such as Procter & Gamble) buy television time as much as they buy newspaper space, but for small businesses, nothing works as well as the local newspaper. Seventy cents of each local advertising dollar goes to newspapers. There may be fewer newspaper owners in the country, but as long as newspapers can maintain their profitability, the survivors will continue comfortably.

In Focus

◎ The tradition of an independent press in North America began when James Franklin published the first newspaper without the heading "By Authority."

◎ Canada's first newspaper, the *Halifax Gazette*, began publication in 1752 as part of a commercial print shop in the service of the colonial government of Nova Scotia.

◎ As dissatisfaction over British rule grew, newspapers became essential political tools in the effort to spread revolutionary ideas.

◎ The technological advances of the 19th century, such as cheaper newsprint, mechanized printing, and the telegraph, meant that newspapers could reach a wider audience faster than ever before. This also lowered production costs, which made newspaper publishing companies attractive investments.

◎ Newspapers spread their reach in the 1800s to include people on the frontier, the growing number of immigrants, the Aboriginal population, and francophones.

◎ The penny press made newspapers affordable for virtually every adult.

◎ The emancipation and suffrage movements found a voice in the dissident press, which marks the beginning of newspapers as a tool for social protest.

◎ Cooperative news gathering began in 1848 with the formation of the New York Associated Press. The United Press followed. AP is a cooperative, as is the Canadian Press.

◎ Mathew Brady's careful documentation of the American Civil War demonstrated that news photography can be practical and effective. This documentary record is the first example of what today is called photojournalism.

◎ Intense competition bred yellow journalism, which nurtured the sensational coverage of the Spanish-American War in 1898. This newspaper war underscored the importance of press responsibility.

◎ Unionization at newspapers standardized wages for reporters and increased professionalism.

◎ Television contributed to a decline in newspaper readership in the 1950s, although the social causes of the 1960s briefly revived the dissident press.

◎ Although individually owned newspapers still exist in some cities, today chains and conglomerates publish 66 percent of Canadian daily newspapers.

◎ Newspapers still hold power for advertisers, but recent studies reveal that younger readers are deserting the medium faster than any other age group. Readership among women also has declined. To stop the slide, many newspapers have introduced features and sections targeted at teenagers and at women.

◎ Several newspaper publishing companies have launched on-line newspapers to capture new audiences for the information they gather.

◎ The future success of newspapers depends on their ability to appeal to a shifting audience, meet growing competition, and continue to attract advertisers.

Review Questions

1. Cite the major landmarks in the development of the newspaper industry from 1690 to today. What did each one contribute to the evolution of the newspaper business?

2. Give three specific examples of yellow journalism and jazz journalism in today's newspapers.

3. Explain how on-line newspapers could change and/or expand the audience for the information that newspapers deliver.

Watching the Web

◎ **Associated Press Wire**

http:www.latimes.com/HOME/NEWS/AUTOAP/ICBTOPAP.html

◎ **Computer-Assisted Reporting**

http:home.att.net/~bdedman/index.html

◎ **Editor & Publisher Interactive**

http://www.mediainfo.com/

◎ **Newspapers on the Web**

http://www.naa.org/hotlinks/index.asp

MAGAZINES

3

THIS IS A REFLECTION OF ADVERTISERS GOING FOR MORE TARGETED MEDIA PLACEMENT. THE PEOPLE WHO REALLY HAVE THE MONEY ARE A VERY SMALL SEGMENT OF THE POPULATION SO YOU HAVE TO LOOK MORE CAREFULLY AT THE AFFLUENT MARKETPLACE.

Valerie Muller, Media Director for DeWitt Media, which places magazine ads for BMW

With certain important exceptions, magazines in Canada have been over-whelmed by the presence of foreign magazines, which are filled with advertising images of other cultures and other places. Though some-what less pronounced today, this problem continues, with the dominant U.S. presence in editorial content and advertising and with a much decreased, though still significant, British influence. In addition, U.S. magazines have been the centre of a controversy concerning trade issues: **split-run editions** (maga-zines that insert local advertising with standard editorial content), differing advertising rates, and preferential mailing rates.

Despite attempts to bolster the domestic industry, it seems clear that imported magazines are more popular with Canadian consumers. About two-thirds of mag-azines sold in Canada are imported (for example, *National Geographic* and *Newsweek*), and about half of the remainder are Canadian editions of foreign magazines, with Canadian editorial content (for example, *TV Guide* and *Reader's Digest*). However, when free, controlled-circulation magazines are added to the mix, the picture changes. About two-thirds of all magazines—both paid and free together—now circulating in Canada are Canadian in origin.

Of magazines published in Canada, *Reader's Digest* is the most widely distributed, followed by *Chatelaine*, *Maclean's*, and *Legion* magazine. Children's magazines have been particularly successful, including *Owl*, which began publication in 1976, and its companion *Chickadee*.

Magazines today are targeted at specific audiences, and reflect national interests and population characteristics.

CP Picture Archive (Peter Bregg)

Colonial Competitors

More than 50 years after the first colonial newspaper, magazines entered the North American media marketplace. Newspapers covered daily crises for local readers, but magazines could reach beyond the concerns of the moment in small communities to carry their cultural, political, and social ideas to a general audience and to foster a less parochial identity in readers. Until the 1920s, magazines were the only medium that could reach a wide readership; there were no national newspapers. For this reason, from 1741 until the 1920s, magazines, much more than newspapers, often provoked and reflected widespread cultural, social, and political changes.

The first North American magazine appeared in 1741 in Philadelphia, when Benjamin Franklin and Andrew Bradford raced each other to become the continent's first magazine publisher. Franklin originated the idea of starting the first American magazine, but Bradford issued his *American Magazine* first, on February 13, 1741. Franklin's first issue of *General Magazine* came out three days later. Neither magazine lasted very long. Bradford published three issues, and Franklin published six. But their efforts initiated a rich tradition.

The first magazine published in Canada was *The Nova Scotia Magazine*, which appeared for three years starting in 1759. Though published by New Englanders, it was concerned predominantly with matters in Great Britain. A second noteworthy magazine was the bilingual *Le Magasin de Québec*, published from 1792 to 1794. Neither these nor any other early magazines in Canada had any long-term success, owing to high production costs, difficulties of distribution, and the small and dispersed number of readers.

Because they didn't carry advertising, early magazines were expensive and their circulations remained small, but like colonial newspapers, early magazines provided a means for political expression.

The First Continental Mass Medium

Newspapers flooded the larger cities by the early 1800s, but they circulated only within each city's boundaries. They were not distributed widely across the settled parts of North America because there was no transportation system capable of carrying them quickly over the long distances between settlements. This being the case, national and international news spread slowly among the scattered communities of Canada and the United States by means of the occasional letter and by the word of mouth of travellers. Attendance at universities and colleges at that time was limited to the children of the wealthy, and books were expensive. In this set of circumstances, magazines became the only medium for the exchange of ideas across the wide expanses of thinly urbanized North America, and subscribers depended on them for news, culture, and entertainment. Magazines became the principal and perhaps only avenue of adult education. The magazine that first reached this large adult public was *The Saturday Evening Post*, started in 1821.

The Post (published every Saturday at a time when there were no Sunday papers) featured news, fiction, poetry, essays, theatre reviews, and a column called "The Lady's Friend." The early *Post*s cost a nickel each and were only four pages, with no illustrations, and one-fourth of the magazine was advertising. For

40 years it was one of the most important weeklies, with a wide circulation in Canada and the United States.

The first long-running Canadian magazine was the *Canadian Illustrated News*, started in 1869, which published engaging photo-engraved images of events and places. Other enduring magazines with sporadic economic success appeared toward the end of the 19th century. *Saturday Night* magazine, for instance, began publication in 1887 as an outlet for urbane commentary and political criticism, as well as for short fiction. *Maclean's* magazine began publishing in 1896 as the *Busy Man's Magazine*. Then, as now, its emphasis was on condensed accounts of current events, though it too carried short fiction for a long while.

A 1913 edition of *Maclean's* magazine.

Courtesy of *Maclean's* magazine

Reaching New Readers

Magazines like *The Saturday Evening Post* reached a wide readership with their general-interest content. But many other audiences were available to 19th-century publishers, and they spent the century locating their readership. Four enduring subjects that expanded the magazine audience in the 1800s were women's issues, social crusades, literature and the arts, and politics.

Women's Issues

Because women were a sizable potential audience, magazines were more open to female contributors than were newspapers. Many early magazines published poetry and stories by women. Although some women wrote under men's names, most used their true names.

In 1830, Louis A. Godey was the first publisher to capitalize on an audience that the *Post* had identified with "The Lady's Friend" column. Women, most of whom had not attended school, sought out *Godey's Lady's Book* and its gifted editor, Sarah Josepha Hale, for advice on morals, manners, literature, fashion, diet, and taste.

As the editor of *Godey's* for 40 years, beginning in 1837, Hale fervently supported higher education and property rights for women. By 1860, *Godey's* had 150 000 subscribers.[1] Hale retired from the magazine when she was 89, a year before she died.

Social Crusades

Magazines also became important instruments for social change. *The Ladies' Home Journal* is credited with leading a crusade against dangerous medicines. Many of the ads in women's magazines in the 1800s were for patent medicines like Faber's Golden Female Pills ("successfully used by prominent ladies for female irregularities") and Ben-Yan, which promised to cure "all nervous debilities."

The Ladies' Home Journal was the first magazine to refuse patent medicine ads. Founded in 1887 by Cyrus Curtis, the *Journal* launched several crusades. It offered columns about women's issues, published popular fiction, and even printed sheet music.

Editor Edward Bok began his crusade against patent medicines in 1892, after he learned that many of them contained more than 40 percent alcohol. Bok revealed that a medicine (laudanum) sold to soothe noisy babies contained opiates. Other magazines joined the fight against ads for potentially dangerous products and, partly because of Bok's crusading investigations, the U.S. Congress passed the Pure Food and Drug Act of 1906.

The most notable Bok crusade began in 1906, when he published an editorial about venereal disease. Bok believed that women should know about the disease's threat, and he continued running articles about the subject even after 75 000 subscriptions were cancelled. Eventually, the readers returned and Bok's crusading made *The Ladies' Home Journal* even more popular.

Fostering a Literary Tradition

In the mid-1800s, U.S. magazines began to seek a literary audience by promoting the work of serious writers. Two of today's most important literary magazines—*Harper's* and *The Atlantic Monthly*—began more than a century ago. *Harper's New Monthly Magazine*, known today as *Harper's*, first appeared in 1850. As a monthly, *Harper's* didn't try to compete for the *Post's* general audience or for Sarah Hale's readers. Rather, the magazine earned an early reputation for its attention to science, biography, travel, and fiction. Today, *Harper's* continues to publish essentially the same mix of articles that made it so popular in the 1800s.

The American literary showcase grew when *The Atlantic Monthly* appeared in 1857 in Boston. In 1909, *Atlantic* editor Ellery Sedgwick said the magazine's purpose was "to inoculate the few who influence the many," a formula that continues today, with *The Atlantic* still provoking literary and political debate. Such unapologetic elitism still prospers today in American literary magazine circles. Within a large population base, even a small elite audience was large enough to support a niche publication. In Canada, however, with a population one-tenth the size of that of the United States, and with an even more geographically dispersed population, this threshold of sustainability has seldom been attained.

Political Commentary

With more time (usually a month between issues) and space than newspapers had to reflect on the nature of political or social problems, political magazines provided a forum for public arguments by scholars and critical observers. Three progressive political magazines that began in the 19th and early 20th centuries have endured: *The Nation*, *The New Republic*, and *The Crisis*.

The Nation, founded in 1865, is the oldest continuously published opinion journal in the United States, offering critical literary essays and arguments for progressive change. This weekly magazine has survived a succession of owners and financial hardship.

Another outspoken publication, which began challenging the establishment in the early 1900s, is *The New Republic*, founded in 1914. The weekly's circulation has rarely reached 40 000, but its readers enjoy its regular criticisms of political leaders. Through a succession of owners and support from sympathetic patrons, the original concept of the magazine has remained, as one of its early editors put it, to start "little insurrections."

The Crisis, founded by W.E.B. Du Bois in 1910 as the monthly magazine of the National Association for the Advancement of Colored People (NAACP), continues to publish today.

The authors wish to thank the Crisis Publishing Co., Inc., the magazine of the National Association for the Advancement of Colored People, for authorizing the use of these covers.

An organization that needed a voice at the beginning of the century was the National Association for the Advancement of Colored People (NAACP). For 24 years, beginning in 1910, that voice was W.E.B. Du Bois, who founded and edited the organization's monthly magazine, *The Crisis*.

Du Bois began *The Crisis* as the official monthly magazine of the NAACP. Du Bois attacked discrimination against black soldiers during World War I, exposed Ku Klux Klan activities, and argued for blacks' voting and housing rights. By 1919, circulation was more than 100 000. *The Crisis* continues today to publish monthly.

American Postal Legislation

As in Canada, the role of postal subsidies was pivotal to the well-being of American magazines. Passage of the Postal Act of 1879 encouraged the growth of magazines. Before passage of the Act, newspapers were carried in the mail system free of charge, whereas magazine publishers had to pay postage.

With the Postal Act of 1879, the U.S. Congress gave magazines second-class mailing privileges. Congress then instituted a rate of a penny a pound for newspapers and magazines. This meant quick, reasonably priced distribution for magazines, and today's magazines still travel on a preferential rate in the United States, a somewhat ironic situation in light of the United States' opposition to Canadian postal subsidies for magazines, which they took before the World Trade Organization (WTO) tribunal.

Aided by cheaper postal rates, the number of American monthly magazines grew from 180 in 1860 to over 1800 by the turn of the century. However, because magazines travel through the mail, they are vulnerable to censorship (see Chapter 14).

The Muckrakers: Magazine Journalists Campaign for Change

The colourful, campaigning journalists just before the turn of the 20th century became known collectively as **muckrakers**. The strongest editor in the first ten years of this century was legendary magazine publisher Samuel S. McClure, who founded *McClure's Magazine* in 1893.

McClure and his magazine were very important to the Progressive era in U.S. politics, which called for an end to the close relationship between government and big business. To reach a large readership, McClure priced his new monthly magazine at 15 cents an issue, whereas most other magazines sold for 25 or 35 cents.

Ida Tarbell joined *McClure's* in 1894 as associate editor. Her series about the 1860 nomination of presidential candidate Abraham Lincoln boosted the magazine's circulation. Subsequently, Tarbell tackled a series about Standard Oil. Tarbell peeled away the veneer of the biggest oil trust in the United States. Her 19-part series began running in *McClure's* in 1904. Eventually the series became a two-volume book, *History of the Standard Oil Company*, which established Tarbell's reputation as a muckraker.

The muckrakers' targets were big business and corrupt government. President Theodore Roosevelt coined the term *muckraker* in 1906 when he compared reformers like Tarbell to the "Man with the Muckrake" who busily dredged up the dirt in John Bunyan's *Pilgrim's Progress*.

An important colleague of Tarbell's at *McClure's* was another muckraker, Lincoln Steffens. His special interest was politics, and for *McClure's* Steffens wrote *Shame of the Cities*, a series about political corruption in major U.S. cities. *McClure's* embodied muckraking at its best. By 1910, many of the reforms sought by the muckrakers had been adopted, and this particular type of magazine journalism declined. The muckrakers often are cited as North America's original investigative journalists.

Targeted versus Broad Readership: The New Yorker and Time Magazines

Magazines in the first half of the 20th century matured and adapted to absorb the invention of radio and then of television. As with magazines today, magazine publishers had two basic choices: (1) publishers could seek a *definable, targeted loyal audience*, or (2) publishers could seek a *broad, general readership*. These two types of publishers in the first half of the 20th century are best exemplified by Harold Ross, founding editor of *The New Yorker*, and Henry Luce, who started Time Inc. (now Time Warner).

Harold Ross and *The New Yorker*

Published since 1925, *The New Yorker* is one of the world's most successful magazines.

Cover drawing by Barry Blitt © 1994 The New Yorker Magazine, Inc.

Harold Ross's *The New Yorker* magazine launched the wittiest group of writers that ever gathered around a table at New York's Algonquin Hotel. The "witcrackers," who met there regularly for lunch throughout the 1920s, included Heywood Broun, Robert Benchley, Dorothy Parker, Alexander Woollcott, James Thurber, and Harpo Marx. Because they sat at a large, round table in the dining room, the group came to be known as the Algonquin Round Table.

Harold Ross persuaded Raoul Fleischmann, whose family money came from the bakers' yeast company of the same name, to invest half a million dollars in *The New Yorker* before the magazine began making money in 1928, three years after its launch. Ross published some of North America's great commentary, fiction, and humour, sprinkled with cartoons that gave *The New Yorker* its charm. Ross edited the magazine until he died in 1951, when he was succeeded by William Shawn.

After one owner—the Fleischmann family—and only two editors in 60 years, *The New Yorker* was sold in 1985 to Advance Publications, owned by the Newhouse family. William Shawn retired in 1987, after the corporation forced his resignation. Despite the corporate takeover of what had been a vibrant independent magazine, *The New Yorker* today continues to be the primary showcase for writers and artists in the United States, as well for Canadian writers, such as Alice Munro, Mavis Gallant, and Mordecai Richler. Its influence extends throughout the literate world.

Henry Luce's Empire: *Time*

Henry Luce is the singular giant of 20th-century magazine publishing. Unlike Harold Ross, who sought a sophisticated, wealthy audience, Luce wanted to reach the largest possible audience.

Luce's first creation was *Time* magazine, which he founded in 1923 with his Yale classmate Briton Hadden. Luce and Hadden paid themselves $30 a week and recruited their friends to write for the magazine.

The first issue of *Time* covered the week's events in 28 pages, minus six pages of advertising—half an hour's reading. "It was of course not for people who really wanted to be informed," wrote Luce's biographer W.A. Swanberg. "It was for people willing to spend a half-hour to avoid being entirely uninformed."[2] The brash news magazine became the foundation of the Luce empire, which now publishes *Time, Fortune, Life, Sports Illustrated, Money,* and *People Weekly,* an entire stable of publications that still caters to readers who want a quick, superficial take on events of the day.

Today, Time Inc. is one of the largest magazine publishers in the United States, but the magazines are only part of the giant company Time Warner, which includes television stations, the CNN family of cable television networks started by Ted Turner, book publishing companies, and Home Box Office.

Many of Luce's magazines fostered lookalikes. *Look* magazine mimicked *Life.* So did *Ebony,* a magazine targeted at black readers, introduced in the 1940s by John H. Johnson, whose chain also launched *Jet* magazine. By the 1990s, *Ebony* and *Jet* had a combined readership of 3 million.

Canadian Law and Imported Magazines

For many years, successive Canadian governments have sought to preserve the economic health and editorial distinctiveness of Canadian magazines. Since 1965, Canada has employed a range of policies intended to protect and promote domestic periodical publications. Devices employed have included special discriminatory postal regulations; postal subsidies; direct subsidies, through funding agencies such as the Canada Council; and import restrictions. For instance, in order to be entitled to sell advertising in Canada, foreign-owned magazines have been required by law to contain at least 80 percent editorial content produced specifically for the Canadian market. But in an age of globalization, such border barriers are becoming more difficult to maintain.

Sports Illustrated attempted to circumvent the import regulations by electronically transmitting its pages to a printer in Canada. In 1995, the Canadian government imposed a new 80 percent excise tax on advertising placed in split-runs. *Sports Illustrated* then withdrew its split-run version from the Canadian market and lodged a trade complaint with the U.S. government. Challenges by such foreign publishers who are eager to import content and advertising, or indeed whole magazines, have raised questions about import restrictions in the new forum for trade dispute settlement and regulation, the World Trade Organization (WTO). A dispute-settlement panel was established in Geneva in June 1996.

In March 1997, the WTO ruled on the trade measures intended to promote the Canadian magazine industry. It upheld three of four complaints made by the United States. Specifically, the WTO ruled that Tariff Code 9958, which prohibited split-run magazines, Canada's Excise Tax Act, which placed an 80 percent excise tax on advertising placed in split-run magazines, and differential postal rates for domestic and foreign publications were all nonconforming and would not be allowed.

The WTO did uphold the right of the Canadian government to maintain a postal subsidy for eligible Canadian publications. Not challenged was a provision of the Income Tax Act, Section 19, which allows Canadian advertisers a tax deduction for the costs of advertising in Canadian periodicals. It remains in effect.

Though the government of Canada subsequently appealed the WTO ruling, the Appellate Body ruled against the appeal in June 1997, as it did against the U.S. government's appeal in the matter of postal subsidies. The conclusion that might be drawn is that henceforth under WTO rules, the only means Canada has to protect its cultural product industries is to directly subsidize domestic industries, rather than bar the entry of foreign products.

Specialized Magazines Take Over

In the 1950s, television began to offer North Americans some of the same type of general-interest features that magazines provided. General-interest magazines collapsed. Gradually, readers began to buy magazines for specialized information that they could not get from other sources. These new specialized magazines segmented the market, which meant that more magazines got fewer readers.

Few general-interest magazines survive today. The trend, since television expanded the media marketplace, is for magazines to find a specific audience interested in the information that magazines can deliver. This is called *targeting an audience*, which magazines can do more effectively today than any other medium.

Today's magazines can be categorized into four types: (1) consumer publications; (2) trade, technical, and professional publications; (3) company publications; and (4) free, controlled-circulation periodicals.

You probably are most familiar with **consumer magazines**, which are popularly marketed: *Maclean's*, *Chatelaine*, and *Saturday Night*, for example. *PC World* and *Muscle & Fitness* also are considered consumer magazines. In the magazine business, consumer magazines are not just those that give buying advice. This term refers to all magazines sold by subscription or at newsstands, supermarkets, and bookstores. As a group, consumer magazines make the most money because they have the most readers and carry the most advertising.

Trade, technical, and professional magazines are read by people in a particular industry to learn more about their business. *Quill & Quire*, for example, is a trade magazine, published "for the Canadian book trade since 1935." The *Ryerson Review of Journalism* (published by Ryerson University) and *American Medical News* (published by the American Medical Association) are two more examples. These magazines are issued by media companies for retail sale or for their subscribers (for example, *Quill & Quire*); universities or university-connected organizations for their subscribers (for example, *Ryerson Review of Journalism*); or professional associations for their members (for example, *American Medical News*). Most trade, technical, and professional magazines carry advertising directed at the professions they serve.

Company magazines are produced by businesses for their employees, customers, and shareholders. These magazines usually don't carry advertising. Their main purpose is to promote the company. The Royal Bank, for instance, publishes the decades-old company magazine *Royal Bank Letter*, and Sympatico publishes *Sympatico NetLife*.

Some companies also publish magazines that promote the products they sell. For instance, Duthie's Books of Vancouver publishes the quarterly magazine *The New Reader* both on paper (available free at their stores) and on the Web (at www.literascope.com/Readers/index.html). The publishing house McClelland and Stewart also distributes a free magazine called *The Book Review* to bookstores.

Free, controlled-circulation magazines do carry advertising. Indeed they rely entirely on ad revenues for their incomes. Contents tend to be extremely focused. Recipients may live in particular areas, or have particular occupational, recreational, or consumer interests. They may subscribe to another publication and receive the magazine as an insert as a result, or their names and addresses may be sold by a third party to a publisher.

Working for Magazines

Magazine employees work in one of five divisions: (1) editorial, (2) circulation sales, (3) advertising sales, (4) manufacturing and distribution, and (5) administration.

The *editorial* department handles everything regarding the content of the magazine, except the advertisements. This is the department for which magazine editors work, and they decide the subjects for each magazine issue, oversee the people who write the articles, and schedule the articles for the magazine. Designers who determine the "look" of the magazine are also considered part of the editorial department. The *circulation* department manages the subscription information. Workers in this department enter new subscriptions and handle address changes and cancellations, for example.

The *advertising* department finds companies that would like to advertise in the magazine. Advertising employees often help the companies design their ads to be consistent with the magazine format. *Manufacturing* and *distribution* departments manage the production of the magazine and getting it to readers. This often includes contracting with an outside company to print the magazine. Many magazine companies also contract with an outside distribution company rather than deliver the magazines themselves. *Administration,* as in any media company, takes care of the organizational details—the paperwork of hiring, paying bills, and managing the office, for example.

Because advertisers provide nearly half of a magazine's income, tension often develops between a magazine's advertising staff and its editorial staff. The advertising staff may lobby the editor for favourable stories about potential advertisers, but the editor is responsible to the audience of the magazine. The advertising department might argue with the editor, for example, that a local restaurant will not want to advertise in a magazine that publishes a critical review of the restaurant. If the restaurant is a big advertiser, the editor must decide how to best maintain the magazine's integrity.

As you can see from Figure 3.1, putting the magazine together and selling it (circulation, advertising, administration, manufacturing, and distribution) cost more than organizing the articles and photographs that appear in the magazine (editorial). Often a managing editor coordinates all five departments.

The magazine editor's job is to keep the content interesting so people will continue to read the magazine. Good magazine editors can create a distinctive, useful product by carefully choosing the best articles for the magazine's audience and ensuring that the articles are well written.

Figure 3.1

Magazine Costs: Where the Revenue Dollar Goes

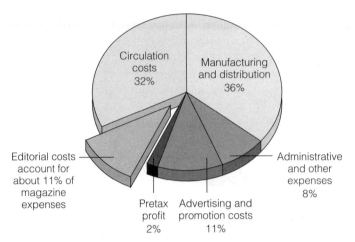

Source: Data from Magazine Publishers of America, 1993.

Many articles are written by full-time magazine staffers, such as a food editor who creates recipes or a columnist who writes commentary. Many magazines, however, use articles by **freelancers**. Freelancers do not receive a salary from the magazine; instead, they are paid for each of their articles published in the magazine. Many freelancers write for several magazines simultaneously. Some freelancers specialize—just writing travel articles, for example. Other free-lancers work just as the tradition of their name implies: They have a pen for hire, and they can write about any subject a magazine editor wants.

The Business of Magazines

Today, trends in magazine publishing continue to reflect social and demographic changes, but magazines no longer play the cutting-edge social, political, and cul-tural role they played in the past. Instead, most magazines are seeking a specific audience, and many more magazines are competing for the same readers. *Maclean's and Newsweek* compete with *Time* to serve the reader who wants a weekly news roundup. *Fortune* is no longer alone; it has been joined by maga-zines like *Business Week* and *Forbes*. Some new magazines, such as *Wallpaper**, have been launched successfully to appeal to a younger audience. However, most magazine audiences have grown older and today read magazines like *PC World*, *Money*, and *Canadian House & Home*.

Women continue to be the most lucrative audience for magazines. *Chatelaine* appeals to a broad readership. *Family Circle* and *Woman's Day*, called point-of-purchase magazines because they are sold only at the checkout stands in super-markets, are only one part of the women's market. *Flare* and *Elle* cater to the fashion-conscious, and women's magazines have matured to include the working women's audience with *Savvy*, *Self*, and *Working Woman*, for example. The market is divided still further by magazines like *Northern Woman's Journal*, aimed at women in Northwestern Ontario, and *Common Ground*, targeted at women in Prince Edward Island.

Segmenting the Audience

The two newest segments of the magazine audience to be targeted by special-interest magazines are owners of personal computers and videocassette recorders. Titles like *PC Magazine*, *PC World*, and *PC Week* already are among the top 500 magazines, as is *Wired*.

This tendency to specialize has not yet reached the level suggested by one magazine publisher, who joked that soon there might be magazines called *Working Grandmother* and *Lefthanded Tennis*. But magazine publishers are seeking readers with a targeted interest and then selling those readers to the advertisers who want to reach that specific audience—skiers, condominium owners, motorcyclists, toy collectors, and even the wealthy (See Impact on You: "Nuvo Aiming for the Rich"). In this category could also be found magazines that bear the name of the city they are published for.

IMPACT on You

By Elizabeth Renzetti

NUVO AIMING FOR THE RICHE: THE FABULOUSLY WEALTHY GET A MAGAZINE OF THEIR OWN

TORONTO — There are Canadian magazines aimed at the tiniest of niche markets, from cat breeds to doll collectors to bikers. Until now, however, one group has been poorly served by the magazine industry: the filthy rich.

The hugely wealthy are the target audience for a new Vancouver-based magazine called *Nuvo*, which carries the subtitle "Reflections on the Good Life" and the slogan "The First Magazine for the Canadian Establishment." (The title is a nonsense word invented to sound like the Italian *nuovo*, or the French *nouveau*, as in *nouveau riche*.)

Nuvo, which will be launched with champagne receptions in various cities on Oct. 28, will be sent free of charge to the country's 42,000 wealthiest households (as determined in a survey by the research firm Compusearch). An additional 8,000 copies will be distributed to assorted private clubs and other loitering spots of the rich.

Is there any indication that the extremely wealthy want or need such a magazine? "No," editor Lyndon Grove admitted in an interview from his Vancouver office,

"but there's an indication advertisers want it."

"The magazine is there partly as an advertising medium, and partly to deliver information and amusement," he added.

Nuvo is the brainchild of Aleder Ozer, a Vancouver resident born in Greece, whose previous publishing experience includes the founding of *Millionaire* magazine in Australia. Ozer "realized on coming to Canada that there wasn't a magazine designed for what one might crudely call the high end of the market," Grove said.

"Just as *The New Yorker* defines sophistication in Manhattan and *Harper's & Queen* chronicles the fashions and foibles of the English aristocracy, *Nuvo* will reflect the good life as it is lived by Canadians," reads the magazine's glossy promotional brochure. It also features photographs of attractive people engaging in rich-person activities such as sailing, lounging seaside, and nuzzling their horses....

The magazine will have a controlled-circulation distribution (that is, free) until its third issue. That's when its creators hope the circulation will jump to 220,000

copies—the number of people in Canada with investable assets of $1-million or more, according to a 1996 survey. At that point, if *Nuvo* still exists, it will be distributed to paid subscribers and on newsstands.

Grove, currently the creative director of a Vancouver public-relations firm, is prepared for the scorn of those who might find this new enterprise a tad vulgar. "I anticipate some resistance to that," Grove said. "But it's not going to be a magazine that says to people, 'If you don't have a lot of money you can't read this.' It won't be any more elitist in its approach than *The New Yorker* or *Vanity Fair* or *GQ*."

He added, "There are mags produced specifically for very poor people, and I buy them all the time. ... I don't think there should be a prejudice against people because they have money."

The Globe and Mail, *August 20, 1998. Reprinted with permission from* The Globe and Mail.

The trend toward specialized audience targeting will continue. As the audience becomes more segmented, magazine publishers will seek more specific readership, such as the Italian-Canadian audience sought by the magazine *Eyetalian.*

Courtesy of *Eyetalian* magazine

Besides targeting a special audience, such as gourmets or computer hackers, magazines today also target readers in different regions with regional and special editions, which provide articles for specific areas, along with regional advertising, a variation on the split-run magazine. The news weeklies, for example, might insert advertising for a local bank or TV station next to national ads. This gives the local advertiser the prestige of a national magazine, at a lower cost.

One specialization success is *CARP News*, published by the Canadian Association of Retired Persons (CARP) and filled with helpful articles and focused advertising. This magazine addresses the problems and concerns of older people (liberally defined by CARP as anyone over 50 years of age). It also offers senior subscribers special discounts on travel packages, insurance for snowbirds, and brokerage packages for RRSPs and RRIFs.

The success of this publication is a comment on the current state of the magazine industry. The audience for magazines, as for newspapers, is growing older, and younger readers are less likely to read magazines than their parents are.

Magazine Start-Ups

Deirdre Carmody, writing in the *New York Times*, explains that most new magazines "started each year are modest publications, probably designed on someone's kitchen table, produced on a laptop computer and financed by loyal relatives or friends. But the choices of subject often mirror those coming out of the boardrooms of the giant media companies." Sex is the favourite category for new magazines, followed by lifestyle, sports, media personalities, and home subjects.[3]

But very few new magazines succeed. Today, only one in three new magazines will survive more than five years.[4] The reason most magazines fail is that many new companies do not have the money to keep publishing long enough so that they can refine the editorial content, sell advertisers on the idea, and gather subscribers: in other words, until the magazine can make a profit. And all magazines are vulnerable to trends in the economy.

The number of magazines people buy each year remains static, but revenues are increasing. Although magazines once were inexpensive to run and advertising paid most of the cost of production, publishers gradually have been charging more, and subscribers are willing to pay more for the magazines they want.

A Valuable Audience

The average magazine reader is a high-school graduate, married, owns a home, and works full time.[5] This is a very attractive audience for advertisers. Advertisers also like magazines because people often refer to an ad weeks after they first see it. Magazines tend to be retained in the household longer than newspapers, which are often on their way to the dump or the recycling bin within 24 hours of delivery.

Many readers say they read the magazine as much for the ads as they do for the articles. This, of course, is also very appealing to advertisers. The Magazine Publishers Association reports that people keep a magazine an average of 17 weeks and that each magazine has at least four adult readers. This magazine sharing is called **pass-along readership**. Some magazines have almost nothing but ads, such as *Applied Arts*, a full-colour publication designed to inform workers in the graphic arts industry .

Technology and the Future

In 1984, for the first time, the price paid for individual magazine companies and groups of magazines bought and sold in one year reached $1 billion. *U.S. News & World Report* sold for $100 million. *Billboard* sold for $40 million. The Newhouse chain paid $25.5 million for 17 percent of *The New Yorker*, which the company eventually bought for more than $150 million.[6] Like other media industries, magazines are being gathered together under large umbrella organizations, and this trend is continuing. *Maclean's* magazine, probably the most prominent of all Canadian magazines, was acquired by Rogers Communication as part of the deal to buy the previous owner Maclean-Hunter. Maclean-Hunter has for many years published a large number of magazines, including *Maclean's*, *Chatelaine*, and dozens of specialized trade serials.

The trend toward more refined audience targeting by magazines will also continue. As the audience becomes more segmented, magazine publishers envision a time when they will deliver to each reader exactly what he or she wants to read. This means an infinitely defined readership, so that advertisers will be able to reach only the people they want.

Changes in the way that magazines do business in the future will be affected by technology as well as by the shifting economics of the industry. Magazine editors predict these developments:

◎ On-line magazines will expand magazine readership. In 1996, for example, Chatelaine launched an on-line edition of its magazine, which makes its content available to everyone on the World Wide Web. It offers discussion groups, recommends Web sites, and provides selections from the current issue.

◎ More editors will review the final copy on a screen and transmit the full-colour product by satellite directly to remote printing plants located for the quickest distribution to subscribers, newsstands, supermarkets, bookstores, and other outlets.

◎ Advertisers will be able to target their audience better because magazines can divide their audiences not only by geography, income, and interest, but also by postal code.

◎ Subscribers may be asked to pay as much as half the cost of producing each magazine. If subscription prices rise substantially, fewer people will be able to afford to buy magazines, thus decreasing the potential audience.

◎ Desktop publishing will expand the number of small publishers. Using a personal computer, a scanner, desktop publishing software, and image-setting equipment, desktop operations can do everything to get a magazine ready for production. The same is true of book page preparation, something we will discuss in the next chapter.

IMPACT
Technology

By Daniel Kucharsky

TELEMEDIA TAKES THE INTERNET ONLINE WITH NEW NATIONAL MAGAZINE

The popularity of the Internet has pushed many Canadian magazines online. But the opposite is happening, too, with a wave of new print magazines about the Net itself.

First off the blocks in September was *Sympatico Netlife*, billed as Canada's first national consumer Internet magazine. The magazine is named after Ma Bell's Internet service provider, Sympatico. But the magazine's backers are quick to emphasize that the magazine will be more than just a purely promotional advertorial vehicle for the ISP. "It's really about the Internet itself," says Sharon Salson, Telemedia's director of communications. "It goes beyond Sympatico."

Telemedia is producing and publishing the glossy bimonthly for MediaLinx Interactive Inc., a subsidiary of BCE Inc. and the telephone companies that make up the Stentor Alliance, which will handle the distribution. Telemedia says the venture fits its new corporate aim of concentrating on service journalism.

Salson says the magazine is designed not for the typical *Wired* magazine reader, but for Internet users who aren't accustomed to the technology in a major way—the so-called second wave of Internet users. Like Compuserve's users' guide, the magazine aims to give Internet users a jargon-free explanation of what the Internet can do for them. It will also delve into some of the issues currently enmeshing the Net. The launch issue, for example, carries a comment piece called "Surfing

Silicone Valley," which says there is far too much of *Bay Watch*'s Pamela Anderson on the Internet and not enough useful information.

Sympatico NetLife's release beats to the market *Internet Quarterly*, another general-interest Internet publication for newbies, which is slated for controlled-circulation distribution starting in November. But the release of *Sympatico NetLife* doesn't concern *Internet Quarterly* publisher Jonathon Starr. "The only people they're appealing to really are their subscribers," he says. "My magazine is not just targeting people who are on the Internet." He adds, however, that everyone will eventually be online. Starr's publication will look at the online explosion—where it came from, where it's going—and censorship.

Sympatico editor Paul Sullivan, formerly a vice-president at Telemedia, will oversee the magazine out of Vancouver. The 52-page first issue includes articles on how the Internet can be useful as a research tool for homework or term papers, reviews of World Wide Web sites, new products, surfing tips and a guide to health-related sites.

The magazine has a total circulation of 90,000 with 80,000 copies distributed free to *Sympatico* subscribers and the remaining 10,000 sold on newsstands for $2.99 each in major cities. There are no plans to make the publication available for subscription to non-Sympatico users.

The magazine has regional editions for Atlantic Canada, Ontario and Quebec, the Prairies and B.C.,

with a regional editor for each. Each region will have four pages in each issue, with articles ranging from travelling in B.C. to science-centred web sites in Ontario.

First-issue advertisers include such computer-related firms as Hewlett Packard and U.S. Robotics, as well as Kodak and Absolut Vodka. A one-time full-page ad costs $4,500.

Masthead, Nov./Dec. 1996, p.16. Reprinted with permission from the author.

Magazines survive because they complement the other media and have their own special benefits. Wayne Warner, president of Judd's Inc., which prints more than 77 magazines as diverse as *The New Republic*, *Modern Plastics*, and *Newsweek*, best describes the advantages of magazines as a medium: "With magazines, we can read what we want, when we want, and where we want. And we can read them again and again at our pace, fold them, spindle them, mutilate them, tear out coupons, ads, or articles that interest us and, in short, do what we damn well please to them because they are 'our' magazines."[7]

In Focus

◎ North American magazines began in 1741 when Andrew Bradford published *American Magazine* and Benjamin Franklin published *General Magazine*. Like colonial newspapers, early magazines provided a means for political expression. U.S. magazines have always formed the core of magazines purchased and read in Canada.

◎ *The Saturday Evening Post*, first published in 1821, was the first general-interest magazine. In Canada, the *Canadian Illustrated News* occupied this niche.

◎ Magazines widened their audience in the 1800s by catering to women, taking on social crusades, becoming a literary showcase for writers, and encouraging political debate.

◎ The U.S. Postal Act of 1879 encouraged the growth of magazines because it ensured quick, reasonably priced distribution for magazines; today, magazines still travel on a preferential rate.

◎ Investigative reporting was pioneered by *McClure's Magazine* at the turn of the century. *McClure's* published the stories of Lincoln Steffens and Ida Tarbell, who were critical of public officials and industrialists.

◎ Magazines in the first half of the 20th century adapted to absorb the invention of radio and television. To adapt, some publishers sought a defined, targeted audience; others tried to attract the widest audience possible. *The New Yorker* and *Time* magazines began publishing during this period.

◎ Magazines in the second half of the 20th century have survived by targeting readers' special interests. Specialization segments an audience for advertisers, making magazines the most specific buy an advertiser can make.

◎ Magazines can be grouped into four types: (1) consumer publications; (2) trade, technical, and professional publications; (3) company publications; and (4) free, controlled-circulation magazines.

◎ Women continue to be the most lucrative audience for magazines.

◎ Few general-interest magazines survive today. Most magazines target a specific readership.

◎ The audience for magazines, as for newspapers, is growing older. In 1990, for the first time, the number of magazines published stopped growing.

◎ Magazine prices will probably rise as each subscriber is asked to pay as much as half the cost of producing each magazine. This rise in prices may mean that the audience for magazines will become smaller than it is today.

◎ On-line magazines will expand magazine readership.

Review Questions

1. Cite the major landmarks in the development of the magazine industry from 1741 to today. What did each development contribute to the evolution of the magazine industry?

2. What important tradition in magazine journalism was established by Ida Tarbell and Lincoln Steffens?

3. Why have subsidies played an important role in Canadian periodical publication?

4. Why have today's magazines targeted specialized audiences for readership? Provide three examples of specialized magazines in Canada.

5. If you were to start a magazine today, what kind of magazine would you launch? How would you fund it? Who would read it? Who would advertise in it? What could you do, using examples from the chapter, to assure its success?

Watching the Web

◎ **Chatelaine Magazine**

http://www.chatelaine.com

◎ **Editing for Magazines**

http://www.well.com/user/mmcadams/copy.editing.html

◎ **Maclean's Magazine**

http://www.macleans.ca

◎ **Ryerson Review of Journalism On-line**

http://www.ryerson.ca/rrj/

◎ **Salon Magazine**

http://www.salonmagazine.com

BOOKS

4

> YOU DON'T SELL BOOKS, YOU
> SELL AUTHORS.

Jack McClelland,
Publisher

"I'm not sure I can explain how to write a book," said essayist and author E.B. White, who wrote 19 of them, including *Charlotte's Web.* "First you have to *want* to write one very much. Then, you have to know of something that you want to write about. Then, you have to begin. And, once you have started, you have to keep going. That's really all I know about how to write a book."[1]

The process of writing a book is a little more complex than White suggests, but every year, publishers produce millions of titles in many languages worldwide. This avalanche includes revised editions of already published books, but most of the titles are new.

The publishing industry always has been tugged by what sociologists Lewis A. Coser, Charles Kadushin, and Walter W. Powell call "the culture and commerce of publishing"—the desire to preserve intellectual ideas versus the desire to make money. But a publisher who doesn't make a profit cannot continue to publish books, unless government subsidies are available, as they sometimes are for publishers in Canada.

Coser and his colleagues describe the four characteristics of book publishing today:

1. The industry sells its products—like any commodity—in a market that, in contrast to that for many other products, is fickle and often uncertain.

2. The industry is decentralized among a number of sectors whose operations bear little resemblance to each other.

3. These operations are characterized by a mixture of modern mass-production methods and craftlike procedures.

4. The industry remains perilously poised between the requirements and restraints of commerce and the responsibilities and obligations that it must bear as a prime guardian of the symbolic culture.[2]

Many new owners of publishing houses try to bring some predictability to the market. Says Coser, "Publishers attempt to reduce ... uncertainty ... through concentrating on 'sure-fire' blockbusters, through large-scale promotion campaigns, or through control over distribution, as in the marketing of paperbacks. In the end, however, publishers rely on sales estimates that may be as unreliable as weather forecasts."[3]

How North American Book Publishing Grew

The first books in North America were imports, brought by the new settlers or ordered from Europe after the settlers arrived. Prominent in the sparse collections of the time were collections of maps, commentaries of previous travellers, and Bibles. In 1638, American colonists set up a press at Cambridge, Massachusetts, and in 1640 they printed North America's first book: *The Bay Psalm Book*. As the only book, it became an instant bestseller. Although there were only about 3500 families in the colonies at the time, the book's first printing of 1750 sold out.[4]

By 1680, Boston had 17 booksellers, but most of the books still came from England. Between 1682 and 1685, Boston's leading bookseller, John Usher, bought 3421 books. Among the books he ordered were 162 romance novels.

In 1731, Benjamin Franklin decided that Philadelphia needed a library. So he asked 50 subscribers to pay 40 shillings each to the Library Company. The company imported 84 books, which circulated among the subscribers. This circulating library was North America's first.

The year after he established the circulating library, Franklin published *Poor Richard's Almanack*. Unlike most printers, who waited for someone to come to them with a manuscript, Franklin wrote his own books. Most authors sought a patron to pay for the book's printing and then sold the book at the printshop where it was published.

The first books published in Canada appeared in Quebec in the 1760s and included a primer and pieces of legal scholarship. In 1789, Thomas Cary published in Quebec a long poem on the battle of the Plains of Abraham of 1759, called *Abram's Plains: A Poem*.

Reaching a Wider Audience

To expand readership, early publishers sold political pamphlets, novels, poetry, and humorous works. In addition, three events of the 19th century ensured that the book publishing industry would prosper in the 20th century: the passage of the U.S. International Copyright Law, the formation of North American publishing houses, and the establishment of compulsory education.

Political Pamphlets

The big seller of the 1700s was Thomas Paine's revolutionary pamphlet *Common Sense*, which argued for the independence of the American colonies from Great Britain. From January to March 1776, colonial presses published 100 000 copies of Paine's persuasive political argument—one copy for every 25 people in the colonies—a true bestseller. Throughout the Revolutionary War, Paine was America's most popular author.

Novels and Poetry

Political pamphlets became much less important as newspapers and magazines of political opinion appeared in increasing number and size. Therefore, printers turned their attention to other popular reading, especially fiction. Benjamin Franklin is credited with selling *Pamela* by Samuel Richardson in 1744, the first novel published in North America, although it was a British import that had first appeared in England in 1740. Because there was no international copyright law, colonial printers freely reprinted British novels such as *Pamela* and *Clarissa* and sold them. It was cheaper than publishing local authors, who could demand royalties.

Like other media industries, book publishing has always faced moral criticism. Novels, for example, started out with a bad reputation. One critic said that the novel "pollutes the imaginations." Women wrote one-third of all of the early novels, and women also bought most of them.[5] The main characters of these novels were women who triumphed over one tragedy after another.

In Canada, Rosanna Leprohorn's *The Manour House of De Villerai* (1859) and *Antoinette de Mirecourt* (1864) were part of this genre. Especially popular in the mid-1800s were dime novels, the earliest paperbacks. Eventually, most of them cost only a nickel, but some early paperbacks were as expensive as 20 cents.

Poetry generally has been difficult to sell, and it is correspondingly difficult for poets to get published. Literary scholar James D. Hart says that, although poetry was never as popular as prose, the mid-1800s were "the great era of poetry.... It was more widely read in those years than it has been since."[6]

Humorous Works

Humorous writing has been a durable category in book publishing since the days of humorist Mark Twain. Made famous by his *Celebrated Jumping Frog of Calaveras County*, Twain became a one-man publishing enterprise. One reason his books sold well was that he was the first North American author to recognize the importance of advance publicity.

Like most books, Twain's novels were sold door to door. Sales agents took advance orders before the books were published so that the publisher could estimate how many to print. More than three-fourths of the popular books sold in the United States before 1900 were sold door to door.[7]

In Canada, the works of humour by Stephen Leacock (though not his economics text) achieved wide acceptance, such as his *Arcadian Adventures with the Idle Rich* (1914). Leacock set the stage for a Canadian humour industry, which has developed to include stage and television performers who are instantly recognizable all over the Western world.

International Copyright Law

Before 1891, U.S. publishers were legally required to pay royalties only to U.S. authors, and not to foreign authors. This hurt both U.S. authors (because their books were more costly to publish in the United States) and Canadian authors (since cheap reproductions of foreign texts could be dumped copyright-free on the Canadian market). Because British copyright laws did not bind U.S. publishers, cheap imported editions swamped the Canadian market, and Canadian authors often found that publishing with a foreign publishing house was the only avenue available to them. By the late 1800s, most prominent British and U.S. publishers had local offices in Canada.

CLARISSA.
OR, THE
HISTORY
OF A
YOUNG LADY:
Comprehending
The most Important Concerns of Private LIFE.
And particularly shewing,
The DISTRESSES that may attend the Misconduct
Both of PARENTS and CHILDREN,
In Relation to MARRIAGE.

Published by the EDITOR of PAMELA.

VOL. I.

LONDON:
Printed for S. Richardson:
And Sold by A. MILLAR, over-against Catharine-street in the Strand;
J. and JA. RIVINGTON, in St. Paul's Church-yard;
JOHN OSBORN, in Pater-noster Row;
And by J. LEAKE, at Bath.
M.DCC.XLVIII.

Most of the early novels sold in North America were British imports directed toward women, such as *Clarissa*, which, on its title page, described itself as "particularly shewing [showing] the distresses that may attend the misconduct both of parents and children, in relation to marriage."

The Granger Collection, New York

In 1891, a new U.S. copyright law, the International Copyright Law, and the companion treaty, the Anglo-American Copyright Agreement, put an end to the blatant book piracy. All authors, foreign and domestic alike, now had to give permission to publish their works. The Anglo-American Copyright Agreement gave a certain protection to Canadian authors on this newly levelled playing field, as well. For the first time, U.S. authors cost U.S. publishing houses the same amount as foreign authors. One effect was that U.S. publishers were motivated to look for more domestic writers. After 1894, of the novels published in the United States, more were written by U.S. writers than by foreign writers.[8]

The present copyright legislation in Canada is the Copyright Act of 1921, amended in 1988. It is intended to prevent the unauthorized copying or use by others. Protected works may take many forms, but they must be "original" in order to secure protection. The 1988 amendments extended copyright to a much wider range of works, including computer programs, tables, compilations, and translations. Owners of copyright may, and often do, assign their rights to others. Copyright persists for the life of the author plus 50 years. Since January 1, 1996, performers have also had the sole right to reproduce their performance, such as on videotape. Under s. 27 (2)(a) of the Copyright Act, "fair dealing with any work for the purposes of private study, research, criticism, review or newspaper summary" is allowed. This provision would generally cover the use by students and scholars of extracts of copyright text for inclusion in their own writings.

Canada is also a signatory to the 1928 Rome revision of the Berne Convention and to the 1952 Universal Copyright Convention. These agreements provide reciprocal protection for copyright in other countries that have joined the treaties. The United States is also a member of these protective arrangements.

" 'How I Spent My Summer Vacation,' by Lilia Anya, all rights reserved, which includes the right to reproduce this essay or portions thereof in any form whatsoever, including, but not limited to, novel, screenplay, musical, television miniseries, home video, and interactive CD-ROM."

Publishing Houses

By the mid-1800s, several book publishers were established in Toronto, Montreal, and Quebec City. Many publishing houses that began in the late 18th century or at some time during the 19th century continued into the 20th century. Yet book publishing houses in the 19th century were nothing like today's multimedia corporations. These pioneering companies housed all aspects of publishing under one roof: They sought out authors, reviewed and edited copy, printed, and then sold the books.

Compulsory Education

By 1900, most jurisdictions in North America had either passed compulsory education laws or were actively planning to do so. This development was important to book publishing because schools buy textbooks, and also because education creates more readers. Widespread public education meant that schools broadened their choices and that textbook publishing flourished.

Expanded public support for education also meant more money for libraries— more good news for the publishing industry.

Schoolbook publishing gave rise to many Canadian publishing houses, which served the domestic educational market for decades. Their names are familiar to Canadian adults today as part of their early childhood school experience: Ryerson, Gage, Dent, Copp Clark, and Nelson. Other publishing houses that arose in this period were Musson, McLeod and Allen, the University of Toronto Press, Macmillan of Canada, and the predecessor of McClelland and Stewart, McClelland and Goodchild. Of publications from the early 20th century, John McCrae's poem *In Flanders Fields* (published in book form in 1919) is perhaps the best known today.

Creating a Mass Market

Book Clubs

Book clubs replaced the door-to-door sales agent as a way to reach people who otherwise wouldn't buy books. The Book-of-the-Month Club was founded in 1926, and the Literary Guild book club in 1927. By 1946, there were 50 book clubs in North America, and the Book-of-the-Month Club was selling nearly 12 million copies a year.[9]

Paperbacks

In 1939, Robert de Graff introduced the first series of paperback bestsellers, called Pocket Books. Unlike the paperbacks published after the American Civil War, which appeared only in paperback, Pocket Books issued titles that had already succeeded as hardbound books. They were inexpensive, and they fit in a pocket or a purse. "Suddenly, a book could reach not hundreds or thousands of readers but millions, many of whom had never owned a book before. Universally priced at 25 cents in its early years, the paperback democratized reading in America."[10]

Other publishers joined Pocket Books in publishing paperbacks: New American Library (NAL), Avon, Popular Library, Signet, and Dell. British publisher Penguin Books, which had successfully introduced paperbacks in England before de Graff's Pocket Books hit America, joined the North American market with British titles. NAL distinguished itself by being the first mass-market reprinter willing to publish serious books by black writers—Richard Wright's *Native Son*, Lillian Smith's *Strange Fruit*, and Ralph Ellison's *Invisible Man*, for example. Signet's unexpected hit was J.D. Salinger's novel *Catcher in the Rye*.

Testing Censorship

Book publishers have always resisted any attempts by governments to limit freedom of expression. One of the first publishers to test those limits was Grove Press. In 1959, Grove published the sexually explicit *Lady Chatterley's Lover* by D.H. Lawrence (originally published in 1928); in 1961, the company published *Tropic of Cancer* by Henry Miller (originally published in Paris in 1934). Both books were banned for being obscene. The legal fees to defend Miller's book against charges of pornography cost Grove more than $250 000, but eventually the U.S. Supreme Court cleared the book in 1964.[11]

Harvest House Publishers in Montreal also tested society's tolerance by publishing *The Impertinences of Brother Anonymous*, an attack on the Roman Catholic church in Quebec by an anonymous ex-priest (now known to be Jean-Paul Desbiens) in 1963. The book was seen as a catalyst of the Quiet Revolution of secularization in Quebec society.

Books imported from the United States were often blocked at the border by Canada Customs, whose officers had the authority to seize books based on their own judgment of whether they contained offensive material. They regularly confiscated single copies from returning travellers' luggage, a practice that continued well into the 1970s. Commercial shipments of books are still occasionally confiscated today, particularly erotic gay/lesbian and pedophile literature. For example, Canada Customs often seizes shipments of books addressed to Little Sisters, a bookstore in Vancouver that sells lesbian and erotic literature. Although Canadian courts continue to uphold the right of Canada Customs officials to make such seizures, the Little Sisters case is wending its way to the Supreme Court of Canada for what may be a landmark ruling. For the most part now though, international borders have become mere speedbumps in the intellectual life of the Western world.

Book Publishing Consolidates

Forecasts for growing profits in book publishing in the 1960s made the industry attractive to corporations looking for new places to invest. Before the 1960s, the book publishing industry was composed mainly of independent companies whose only business was books. Then rising school and college attendance from the post-World War II baby boom made some areas of publishing, especially textbooks, lucrative investments. Beginning in the 1960s, publishing companies began to consolidate. Publishing expert John P. Dessauer said, "Publishing stocks, particularly those of educational companies, became glamour holdings. And conglomerates began to woo every independent publisher whose future promised to throw off even a modest share of the forecast earnings."[12]

Dessauer acknowledges that the new owners often brought a businesslike approach to an industry that was known for its lack of attention to the bottom line. But, according to Dessauer, another consequence of these large-scale acquisitions was that "in many cases they also placed the power of ultimate decision- and policymaking in the hands of people unfamiliar with books, their peculiarities and the markets."[13] The same pace of acquisitions continues today.

Working in Book Publishing

When authors get together, they often tell stories about mistakes publishers have made—about manuscripts that 20 or 30 publishers turned down but that some bright-eyed editor eventually discovered and published. The books, of course, then become bestsellers. Some of the stories are true.

But the best publishing decisions are made deliberately, to deliver an awaited book to an eager market. Successful publishing companies must consistently anticipate both their competitors and the market.

Books must not only be written, they must be printed and they must be sold. This whole process usually takes at least 18 months from the time a book is signed by an editor until the book is published, so publishers are always working ahead. The classic publisher's question is, "Will someone pay $25 (or $5 or $10—whatever the projected price of the book is) for this book 18 months after I sign the author?"

Authors and Agents

Publishers acquire books in many ways. Some authors submit manuscripts "over the transom," which means they send an unsolicited manuscript to a publishing house, hoping the publisher will be interested. However, many of the larger publishers refuse to read unsolicited manuscripts and accept only books that are submitted by agents.

Agents who represent authors collect fees from the authors they represent. Typically, an agent's fee is 10 to 15 percent of the author's royalty, and a typical author's royalty contract can run anywhere from 10 to 15 percent of the *cover price* of the book. If a publisher priced a book at $20, for example, the author would receive from $2 to $3 per book, depending on the author's agreement with the publisher; the agent would then receive 20 to 45 cents of the author's $2 to $3, depending on the agent's agreement with the author.

Today the author is only one part of publishing a book. Departments at the publishing house called acquisitions, production, design, manufacturing, marketing, and fulfillment all participate in the process. At a small publishing house, these jobs are divided among editors who are responsible for all of the steps.

BIZZARO © by Dan Piraro. Reprinted with permission of Universal Press Syndicate. All rights reserved.

Authors often use the media to sell their books. W.O. Mitchell discusses his writing with Peter Gzowski on the CBC radio program *Morningside.* The program went off the air in 1997, but during its 15 years with CBC it was influential in popularizing Canadian writing.

Courtesy of the Canadian Broadcasting Corporation.

The Publishing Process

The *author* proposes a book to the acquisitions editor, usually with an outline and some sample chapters. Sometimes an agent negotiates the contract for the book, but most authors negotiate their own contracts.

The *acquisitions editor* looks for potential authors and projects and works out an agreement with the author. The acquisitions editor's most important role is to be a liaison among the author, the publishing company, and the book's audience. Acquisitions editors also may represent the company at book auctions and negotiate sales of **subsidiary rights,** which are the rights to market a book for other uses—to make a movie, for example, or to print a picture of a character from the book on T-shirts.

The *production editor* manages all of the steps that turn a word processed manuscript into a book. After the manuscript comes in, the production editor sets up a schedule and sees the manuscript through all of the editorial and type-setting stages.

The *designer* decides what a book will look like, inside and out. The designer chooses the typefaces for the book and determines how the pictures, boxes, heads, and subheads will look and where to use colour. The designer also creates a concept—sometimes more than one—for the book's cover.

The *manufacturing supervisor* buys the typesetting, paper, and printing for the book. The book usually is sent outside the company to be manufactured.

Marketing, often the most expensive part of creating a book, is handled by several different departments. *Advertising* designs ads for the book. *Promotion* sends the book to reviewers. *Sales representatives* visit bookstores and university and college campuses to tell book buyers and potential adopters about the book.

Fulfillment makes sure that the books get to the bookstores on time. This department watches inventory so that if the publisher's stock gets low, more books are printed.

Large book retailing chains can give new books prominent display space and help them achieve commercial success.

CP Picture Archive (John Lehmann)

The Business of Book Publishing

In the postwar period, Canadian book publishing rapidly expanded. Canadian authors began to achieve international recognition for their works, which were reprinted abroad in other languages. Authors such as Margaret Atwood, Mordecai Richler, Mavis Gallant, Alice Munro, Michael Ondaatje, and Leonard Cohen are known worldwide for their writing. Despite this recognition, the publishing industry in Canada is always in precarious health. This is particularly true of the many small publishing houses, such as Western Prairie Producer Books, Peter Martin, James Lorimer, and Fiddlehead Books. Many depend on the revenues they earn through distributing books for foreign publishers in Canada. Together, Canadian publishing houses release about 5000 new titles a year.

Canadian books make up about one-quarter to one-third of the books sold in Canada. Though this may not seem like a large proportion, it is much greater than it once was. The bulk of the estimated $2 billion dollar market in Canada for books and associated products, such as CD-ROMs, is still made up of imports. One conspicuous exception to the one-third rule of Canadian sales is mass-market paperbacks, very few of which are written by Canadian authors.

In terms of Canadian ownership of publishing enterprises, the picture is somewhat different according to the 1996/97 Book Publisher survey carried out by Statistics Canada. The approximately five hundred Canadian-owned publishers and agents accounted for almost two-thirds of total publishing revenues in 1996/97. Canadian-owned publishers reported revenues of just under $1.3 billion. Profit margins were lower for these firms, at 3 percent of revenues, compared to 5.4 percent for foreign-controlled firms.[14]

In the United States, twenty thousand American companies call themselves book publishers today, but only about two thousand publishing houses produce more than four titles a year. Most North American publishing houses are small: 80 percent of all book publishing companies have fewer than 20 employees.[15]

Books fall into six major categories, listed below. These classifications once described the publishing houses that produced different types of books. A company that was called a textbook publisher produced only textbooks, for example. Today, many houses publish several different kinds of books, although they may have separate divisions for different types of books and markets.

Table 4.1

Total Number of Establishments* in the Canadian Book Publishing Industry	
Year	Number
1982	165
1984	171
1986	177
1988	166
1990	180
1992	159
1994	162
1996	165
1998	205

*The term *establishments* is used by Statistics Canada to refer to companies; each company may have several publishers.

Source: Adapted from the CANSIM Database, Series No. D665344. Reprinted with permission from Statistics Canada.

RIDING OUT THE STORM: INDIES TAKE THE LONG VIEW AS CHAPTERS' EXPANSION REDRAWS THE RETAIL MAP

By John Lorinc

This spring, the Canadian Publishers' Council released to its members the results of a market survey that seems to confirm an essential fact about the superstore trend in Canada. "Chain superstore customers," the report's authors observed, "are different from the chain mall store customers, and are very close to general independent customers, who match the overall profile of book buyers in almost all ways." While the survey—1,003 customers were interviewed across the country during the spring and fall of 1997—revealed that superstore shoppers tend to be somewhat younger than independent patrons, the findings prove the original premise behind the Chapters venture: that superstores do tap into a suburban demographic long overlooked by traditional, downtown-oriented, independent book retailers.

The study, in fact, indicates that superstores are competing head-to-head with the independents, both for new customers and existing ones. Publishers, moreover, say that the superstores seem to be gaining ground in some areas. One industry executive notes that, factoring out the mini-chains like Lichtman's, Book City, and Duthie's, the independent sector's share of his company's trade book sales slipped from 36% in 1995 to 19% in 1997....

Gerry Ruby, who runs the nine-store Lichtman's mini-chain in Toronto, uses a simple principle for gauging the impact of superstores on his outlet. "It all depends on proximity," he says. Though sales remain strong at most of his loca-tions, three within close range of a superstore have suffered a dip in sales.

Ruby has noticed what other independents are reporting about changes in sales patterns when the superstore comes to town: there's a dip, followed by a gradual recovery back to previous levels, as old customers return or new ones come through the door. Michael Legris, manager of Books for Business, says this is the pattern the Toronto specialty stores experienced after Chapters opened. In the last four or five months, he says, "people we thought we'd lost are coming back because of the greater depth of titles and the expertise of the staff."

Most surviving independents are now trying to meet the price competition from Chapters, either by discounting frontlist titles (culled either from the *Globe and Mail* bestseller list, or directly from the shelves of the local Chapters), offering consumers a variety of loyalty programs, or trying to provide more expedient special order business....

One publishing executive offers independents this clue about competing with the chain superstores: in the suburban outlets, title breadth tends to narrow "soon after" the store opens. "It's more of a box mall store," says this source. "That's a cue for independents to pull out the stops and pick up the slack."...

Different Drummer's Richard Bachmann offers up a somewhat contrarian view about how to ride out the superstore storm. He has the dubious distinction of having the most experience with super-store competitors, as his down-town Burlington store became the first Canadian independent to go up against Chapters. He doesn't offer loyalty cards—"I don't believe they create loyalty; I believe they create a heavy wallet"—and he won't discount his frontlist titles. "Why should you give away your good margins?" he asks, noting that he'd be selling the new Atwood or the new Richler with or without the lower price. It is interesting to note, too, that deep discounts did not save Ottawa's Food for Thought, which aggres-sively cut its prices in anticipation of Chapters' arrival last year.

Bachmann's approach is simply to sell books the way he's always sold books: choose well, order cautiously, and provide good ser-vice to a community that places a premium on the presence of a quality independent bookstore. Which doesn't mean that keeping the business afloat has come easily or even automatically. "It's like the mantra for the 1990s," he says. "You work really hard and then ... things get harder. But in a way, I am more optimistic than I was two years ago because we've managed to keep it working."

Excerpted from John Lorinc, "Riding out the storm: Indies take the long view as Chapters' expansion redraws the retail map." Quill & Quire, *June 1998. Reprinted with permission from the author.*

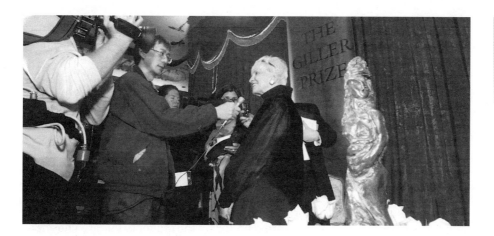

Trade Books

These are books designed for the general public. Usually, they are sold through
bookstores and to libraries. Trade books include hardbound books and trade (or
"quality") paperbound books for adults and children.

Typical trade books include hardcover fiction, current nonfiction, biography,
literary classics, cookbooks, travel books, art books, books on sports and
music, and books containing poetry and drama. Many university classes use
trade books as well as textbooks. Juvenile trade books can be anything from
picture books for children to novels for young adults.

One of the strengths of the Canadian book publishing business has been
children's literature. Several small Canadian companies successfully publish
children's books. Among these publishing houses are Annick Press, Kids Can
Press, Orca Books, and Red Deer College Press. In this genre, there have been
many successes, including Farley Mowat's *The Dog Who Wouldn't Be*, Sheila
Burnford's *The Incredible Journey*, Leslie McFarlane's Hardy Boys series,
Mordecai Richler's *Jacob Two-Two Meets the Hooded Fang*, and, of course, Lucy
Maude Montgomery's *Anne of Green Gables*.

Religious Books

Hymnals, Bibles, and prayer books fall into this category. Recently, religious
publishers have begun to issue books about social issues from a religious point
of view, but these are considered trade books, not religious books.

Professional Books

These are directed to professional people and are specifically related to their
work. Professional books fall into three subcategories. *Technical and science
books* include the subjects of biological and earth sciences, as well as
technology. They may be designed for engineers or scientists, for example.
Medical books are designed for doctors and nurses and other medical professionals. *Business and other professional books* are addressed to business
people, librarians, lawyers, and other professionals not covered in the first two
categories.

Mass-Market Paperbacks

Here, definitions get tricky. These books are defined not by their subjects but by where they are sold. Although they can also be found in bookstores, mass-market paperbacks are mainly distributed through "mass" channels—newsstands, chain stores, drugstores, and supermarkets—and usually are "rack-sized." Many are reprints of hardcover trade books; others are originally published as mass-market paperbacks. Generally they're made from cheaper paper and cost less than trade paperbacks.

Textbooks

These books are published for elementary, secondary, and postsecondary students. Most postsecondary texts are paid for by the students but are chosen by their professors.

Very little difference exists between some postsecondary texts and trade books. Often the only real difference is that textbooks include what publishers call *apparatus*—for example, test questions and summaries. The difference may be difficult to discern, so these two types of books (that is, trade books and textbooks) are classified according to where they are sold the most. A book that is sold mainly through university bookstores, for example, is called a textbook.

University Press Books

A small proportion of books is published every year by university presses. These books are defined solely by who publishes them: A university press book is one that is published by a university press. Most university presses are nonprofit and are connected to a university, museum, or research institution. These presses produce mainly scholarly materials in hardcover and softcover. Most university press books are sold through the mail and in university bookstores.

Figure 4.1

Book Purchases in Canada

Source: Data from the Canadian Publishers' Council's 1997 survey of book buyers.

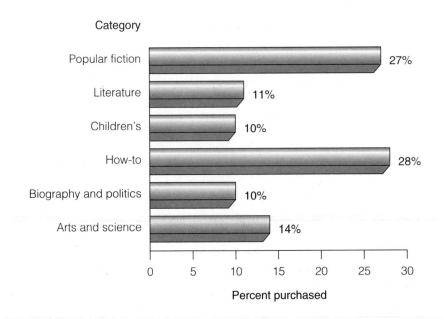

Corporations Demand Higher Profits

The result of consolidation is that the giants in today's publishing industry are demanding increasingly higher profits. The companies look for extra income in three ways: subsidiary rights, blockbuster books, and chain bookstore marketing.

Subsidiary Rights

Trade and mass-market publishers are especially interested in books with the potential for subsidiary-rights sales. The rights to make a CD-ROM version of a book, for example, are subsidiary rights. "In the nineteenth century, a hardcover trade book's profit was determined by the number of copies sold to individual readers. Today, it is usually determined by the sale of subsidiary rights to movie companies, book clubs, foreign publishers, or paperback reprint houses."[16] The same rights govern whether a book character becomes a star on the front of a T-shirt. For some houses, subsidiary-rights sales are the difference between making a profit and going out of business.

Blockbusters

Selling many copies of one book is easier and cheaper than selling a few copies of several books. This is the concept behind publishers' eager search for block-buster books. Publishers are attracted to bestselling authors because they are usually easy to market. There is a "brand loyalty" among many readers that draws them to buy every book by a favourite author, and so publishers try to capitalize on an author's readership in the same way movie producers seek out stars who have made successful films.

Judith Krantz, who received $3.2 million for her sex-filled *Princess Daisy*, explained the benefits of being a blockbuster author: "I'm no Joan Didion—there are no intelligent, unhappy people in my books. I want to be known as a writer of good, entertaining narrative. I'm not trying to be taken seriously by the East Coast literary establishment. But I'm taken very seriously by the bankers."[17]

Some recent amounts that publishers and moviemakers paid for block-busters:

◎ Mystery writer Mary Higgins Clark received $35 million in advance from Simon & Schuster for her next six books. Simon & Schuster says that 22 million copies of Clark's books are in print in the United States.

◎ Random House paid $6.5 million in advance for General Colin Powell's auto-biography, about $1.5 million more than his military colleague, General Norman Schwarzkopf, received for his. Both men figured prominently in the Gulf War.

◎ Michael Crichton, author of *Jurassic Park*, received $2.5 million from Time Warner for film rights to his next book. This amount tied the record paid for movie rights to John Grisham's *The Client*.

◎ Tom Clancy, who wrote *The Hunt for Red October* and *Patriot Games*, also received a $2.5 million advance for film rights to his new novel *Without Remorse*.

Only the big publishing houses can afford a high bidding game. Some publishers have even developed computer models to suggest how high to bid for a book, but these high-priced properties are a small part of book publishing, perhaps 1 percent. The majority of editors and writers rarely get involved in an argument over seven-figure advances. Many authors would be pleased to see five-figure advances in a contract.

Some critics feel that what has been called a blockbuster complex among publishing houses hurts authors who aren't included in the bidding. One Harper & Row editor told *The Wall Street Journal* that seven-figure advances "divert money away from authors who really need it and center attention on commercial books instead of less-commercial books that may nonetheless be better. God help poetry or criticism."[18]

Chain Bookstores

The most significant change in book marketing in the past 30 years has been the growth of book chains. The two largest chains in Canada—Chapters and Indigo—account for a large portion of the bookstore sales of trade books. These chains have brought mass-marketing techniques to the retail book industry, offering book buyers an environment that is less like the traditional cozy atmosphere of a one-owner bookstore and more like a department store, often with a coffee shop or restaurant on the premises.

Discount chains such as Coles are another factor in book marketing. The discount chains buy in huge volume, and they buy books only from publishers that grant them big discounts. Books that are published by smaller publishing houses, which usually cannot afford these large discounts, never reach the discount chain buyer. But for the blockbusters, issued by bigger houses, the discount chain is just one more outlet.

Like the resistance to book clubs when they were first introduced, the skepticism among book publishers about chain bookstores has changed into an understanding that chain stores in shopping malls have expanded the book market to people who didn't buy very many books before. But a major unknown factor is what happens when the distribution of an industry's products is controlled by so few companies.

Chain bookstores (left) account for at least half the sales of trade books in North America. Smaller, independent bookstores (right) compete by appealing to a local and loyal customer base.

IMPACT

Technology

JEFF BEZOS PUTS THE BOOK BUSINESS ON-LINE AT AMAZON.COM

The most successful on-line company so far is Amazon.com, founded by Jeff Bezos. Started in Seattle in 1994, the company offers Internet consumers a choice of more than one million book titles. Eric Scigliano, writing in The New Yorker, *charts the company's success.*

The nerve center of Amazon.com Books, the world's biggest electronic bookseller, is on the fourth floor of an old building in Seattle. Reached by what local messenger services agree may well be the slowest elevator in town, it is a warren of offices, furnished with desks assembled from door panels and two-by-fours, that reflects a business whose accelerated rate of growth is remarkable even by the heady standards of Seattle's software startups. [In 1994], Jeff Bezos, the company's founder and C.E.O., left Wall Street, moved to the nimbus of Microsoft, in suburban Seattle, and, naming his new company after the world's largest river, began building Amazon.com's software systems in his garage, with five employees. They went on-line in July of 1995, and have since moved four times—most recently to their present offices, which are supplemented by a forty-six-thousand-square-foot warehouse. Bezos, who grins a lot, now commands 160 employees—including editors, marketers, programmers and packers. At thirty-two, he is trying to cope with an annual sales revenue that *Business Week* has pegged at seventeen million dollars.

Bezos argues that the convenience of shopping on the Internet will encourage people to buy more books....

But Amazon.com's biggest boon may be to publishers—an end to returns, which can consume half the volume of a front list. The company's warehouse stocks only its own list of best-sellers— approximately two hundred titles at any given time—and orders everything else. And, by preselling upcoming titles through E-mail recommendations, Bezos promises to provide publishers with "advance information about public demand." For the first time, he says, publishers will be able to accurately calculate initial print runs. That, he expects, will drive the price of books down dramatically.

Expanding on the truism that the Internet has made everyone an author, Bezos aims to turn everyone into a reviewer and a salesperson as well. Amazon.com welcomes people who run Web pages, from mainstream magazines to cyberjunkies, to pitch in as "associates." They receive a referral fee of eight percent for every sale they generate. In this fashion, as Bezos foresees things, the river may soon become an ocean. "We may not know what the best book on model rocketry or Labrador retrievers is," he says. "But there's already a Website out there run by a passionate person who does."

Small Presses Challenge Corporate Publishing

The large publishing houses (those with one hundred or more employees) publish 80 percent of the books sold each year. But many publishers are small operations with fewer than ten employees. These publishers are called small presses, and they counterbalance the corporate world of large advances and multimedia subsidiary rights.

Small presses do not have the budgets of the large houses, but their size means that they can specialize in specific topics, such as the environment or bicycling, for example, or specific types of writing that are unattractive to large publishers, such as poetry.

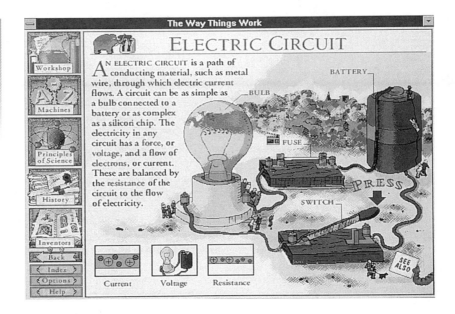

Small presses are, by definition, alternative. Many are located in areas outside of the large urban centres and specialize in subjects related to their locale. Some small press books are quite successful.

Technology and the Future

Technology will be a factor in most of the future changes in book publishing. Because books cost so much to publish, any advances in technology that lower production costs benefit the industry. Several changes are coming:

1. Computers already can more closely monitor inventories and retail sales so that publishers can order a new printing of a book that is running low in stock.

2. Book publishing is becoming an on-screen industry. Publishers can now receive manuscripts from authors by modem over phone lines or as attachments to ordinary e-mail. These manuscripts are edited on a computer screen and then sent into page design and production by computer, the same process now used at many newspapers. One more step in the integration process would be to have the authors themselves create the finished pages on their home computers. This is starting to happen in some areas of book publishing, such as self-publishing.

3. Electronic graphics will make books more interesting to look at, and some book publishers are using CD-ROMs to produce expanded versions of traditional books. In addition, parts of books can be posted on the World Wide Web as samples or promotional vehicles.

4. Desktop publishing will lower the cost of book production. The result might be more new small presses to publish specialized books for targeted audiences, or it could just enhance the commercial position of the big publishers.

5. Writers' organizations have lobbied for years for an authors' lending royalty—a computer-assisted system of payment to authors every time someone borrows a book from a library. Lending royalties are now paid to writers in ten countries, including Canada and Great Britain. In Canada, this principle is embodied in the CANCOPY arrangement, which is meant to compensate authors for library traffic. Every time someone checks out a book from a library, the author's account is, at least in theory, credited. The money, which ultimately comes from tax revenues, is paid to the author periodically. However, in practice, the growing availability of cheap scanners and copiers will likely undermine any such arrangement.

6. Although the larger publishers are buying one another, the number of small publishers that issue less than 20 books a year is increasing. New York and London are still the centres of English-language book publishing, but a large volume is now published in other countries, such as India.

Because book publishing has been part of Western culture for so long, the contrast between book publishing's simple beginnings and its complicated corporate life today is especially stark. In part, this may be based on an unrealistic romanticized idea about book publishing's early days:

> The myth is widespread that book publishing in the nineteenth and twentieth centuries was a gentlemanly trade in which an editor catered to an author's every whim, whereas commercialism and hucksterism have taken over in our day. It is a useful myth, to be sure, for it permits authors to point to a golden past and allows publishers to fashion for themselves a fine pedigree going back to a time when their profession was not sullied by the crass requirements of the marketplace. There once may have been more gentlemen in publishing than there are now, but there were surely sharp operators, hucksters, and pirates galore. In publishing, as in many other spheres of social life, there is very little that is new.[19]

In Focus

◎ The book publishing industry has always been divided by what publishing scholars call the culture versus the commerce of publishing—the desire to preserve intellectual ideas versus the desire to make money.

◎ North America's first book was *The Bay Psalm Book*, printed in 1640.

◎ Early publishers widened their audience by publishing political pamphlets, novels, poetry, and humorous works.

◎ Many of the major publishing houses were founded in the 19th century; these pioneering companies housed all aspects of publishing under one roof.

◎ The U.S. International Copyright Law of 1891 expanded royalty protection to foreign writers, which also benefited U.S. authors. The formation of publishing houses centralized the process of producing books.

◎ Compulsory education was good for book publishing because schools buy textbooks and education creates more readers. Expanded support for education also meant more money for libraries.

◎ Book clubs and the introduction of paperbacks made books available to more people at a lower cost. The Book-of-the-Month Club, founded in 1926, was the first book club.

◎ One of the first publishers in North America to resist government limits on freedom of expression was Grove Press. Government censorship still takes place in Canada, as Canadian Customs officials have the right, based on their own judgment, to seize books with pornographic or violent content at the border.

◎ The process of publishing a book usually takes at least 18 months from the time an author is signed until the book is published.

◎ The six departments at a publishing house are called acquisitions, production, design, manufacturing, marketing, and fulfillment.

◎ Canadian book publishers produce about 5000 titles a year, while U.S. book publishers produce about 40 000.

◎ Books can be grouped into six categories: trade books, religious books, professional books, mass-market paperbacks, textbooks, and university press books.

◎ Before the 1960s, the book publishing industry was composed mainly of independent companies whose only business was books. Publishing company consolidation began in the 1960s and continues today.

◎ To reduce their risks, many publishers look for blockbuster books (and bestselling authors) that they can sell through large-scale promotion campaigns. Publishers are especially interested in books with subsidiary-rights potential.

◎ One significant change in book marketing in the past 30 years has been the growth of bookseller chains.

◎ Most books are published by the large publishing houses, but many specialized books are issued by small presses.

◎ Computer technology and desktop publishing are changing the way books are published, lowering the cost, streamlining the process, and creating new products, such as CD-ROMs, for book publishers.

Review Questions

1. Cite the major landmarks in the development of the book publishing industry from 1620 to today. What did each development contribute to book publishing's evolution?

2. Name one Canadian book that has been successful, and describe why it may have succeeded.

3. Discuss the ways in which computer technology has transformed the book publishing industry.

4. Explain the process that a book goes through to become published. About how long does it take, and why does it take this long?

5. How do book chains affect the economics of book publishing? What relationship, if any, do you see between book chains and the trend toward blockbuster books?

Watching the Web

◎ **Amazon Books Online**

http://www.amazon.com

◎ **Duthie Books**

http://www.literascape.com

◎ **ITP Nelson**

http://www.nelson.com

◎ **McClelland & Stewart**

http://www.mcclelland.com

◎ **Society for the History of Authorship, Reading and Publishing**

http://www.indiana.edu/~sharp

RADIO

5

> IN A COUNTRY OF THE VAST GEOGRAPHICAL DIMENSIONS OF CANADA, BROADCASTING WILL UNDOUBTEDLY BECOME A GREAT FORCE IN FOSTERING NATIONAL SPIRIT AND INTERPRETING NATIONAL CITIZENSHIP.

Sir John Aird, Chairman of the Royal Commission on Broadcasting, The Aird Report *(1929)*

What's Ahead

R adios have brought peoples of the world closer together and have allowed many to participate in the information society in ways that would otherwise be impossible. Shortwave broadcasting, for instance, has brought world events to millions of people in all parts of the world in unexpected and influential ways. In times of crisis, shortwave broadcasts by the state broadcasting agencies of the world (such as the BBC World Service, Deutsche Welle, and Radio Canada International) have brought critical information and news to millions. Indeed, these services still have more listeners outside of their national borders than inside. Because they are relatively inexpensive and can be run on little power by batteries, solar power, or windup mechanisms, radios are the most common source of information for people around the world. Radio is a truly global medium.

The immediacy of radio is what gives it its distinctive flavour. This is nowhere more evident than in the reporting of warfare, as in the excerpt that follows .

Imagine that you and your family are gathered around a radio in September 1940, listening intently in your living room as news broadcaster Edward R. Murrow describes the effects of the first German bombing of London:

> men with white scarves around their necks instead of collars … dull-eyed, empty-faced women…. Most of them carried little cheap cardboard suitcases and sometimes bulging paper shopping bags. That was all they had left…. A row of automobiles with stretchers racked on the roofs like skis, standing outside of bombed buildings. A man pinned under wreckage where a broken gas main sears his arms and face … the courage of the people; the flash and roar of the guns rolling down streets … the stench of air-raid shelters in the poor districts.[1]

From 1921 until the advent of television news in 1947, broadcast reporters like Murrow painted pictures with words. Radio reporters described funerals of kings and queens, military assaults, political conventions, the stock market crash, the Great Depression, and the signing of the armistice that ended World War II.

Today, our collective memory of events that happened in the quarter-century, beginning in 1921, is keenly tied to radio. Newspapers offered next-day reports and occasional extras, movie theatres offered weekly newsreels, magazines offered long-term perspectives. But radio gave its listeners an immediate record at a time when world events demanded attention.

Radio also gave people entertainment: big bands, Jack Benny, George Burns and Gracie Allen, Abbott and Costello, Peter Sellers and the Goon Show on the BBC, Ma Perkins and other daytime soap opera serials, and the original Shadow

"What evil lurks in the hearts of men? The Shadow knows!"). As well, it provided special children's programming, such as the CBC's *Maggie Muggins*, and popular quiz shows, such as *20 Questions*.

In the 1920s and 1930s, radio became a national medium for Canada's sparse, dispersed population, eager for news of the world and for a sense of national community. Radio transformed national politics by transmitting the voices of public debate, providing political analysis, as well as paid-time broadcasts by religious demagogues and political agitators (who were often one and the same). Radio expanded access to both popular and classical culture; opera played on the same dial as slapstick comedy.

The legacy of news, music, and drama remains on radio today, but the medium that was once the centre of attention in everyone's living room has moved into the bedroom, the car, and even the shower. Radio wakes you up and puts you to sleep. Radio goes with you when you run on the trail or sit on the beach. Today, virtually every Canadian household, and even the average jail cell, has a radio, and most have many.

IMPACT

Profile   *CANADIAN WARTIME RADIO REPORTING*

Two voices brought to Canadians the experience of World War II: Lorne Greene and Matthew Halton. Lorne Greene (who later played Ben Cartwright on the successful TV series *Bonanza*) was the main newsreader at the CBC in Toronto during the early war years. Born in Ottawa, Greene, following amateur dramatics, moved into radio, where he eventually became the chief news broadcaster for the CBC from 1939 to 1942. Greene's deeply sonorous voice announced some of the worst early war disasters

and reversals. For this reason he became widely known as "The Voice of Doom." After the war, Greene ran a training school for radio announcers in Toronto, and in 1953 he headed south for Broadway acting jobs.

Along with other CBC announcers, such as Joel Aldred, Greene established a well-worn track southward to U.S. broadcasting and acting after the war.

Matthew Halton (whose son David is today the chief political correspondent for CBC television) was the voice from the battlefront for CBC radio. He was a war correspondent during the Spanish Civil War (of 1936), where Canadians fought in the Mackenzie-Papineau Brigade as "premature anti-fascists," during the Russo-Finnish War, from 1939 to 1940, and in Italy and Western Europe following the Normandy invasion of 1944, where he was the senior war correspondent for the CBC. He sent many recorded broadcasts back from the front. Actuality broadcasting

brought the sounds of the sharp end of modern warfare into the living rooms of Canadian families by means of primitive wire and wax disk recordings.

Photos courtesy of the Canadian Broadcasting Corporation

Although radio is more accessible today than ever, what you hear is not the same as what your parents or grandparents heard. Advertisers, who once sought radio as the only broadcast access to an audience, have many more choices today. For audiences, radio has become an everyday accessory rather than a necessity. No one envisioned radio's place in today's media mix when radio's pioneers began tinkering just before the turn of the century. All they wanted to do was send information along a wire, not through the air.

Radio: A Technological Leap

Today, we are so accustomed to sending and receiving messages instantaneously that it is hard to imagine a time when information took more than a week to travel from place to place. In the early 1800s, if you wanted to send a message across the country or even into the next town, you hired a messenger. Postal messages had to travel torturously slowly by boat, rider, and cart to their destinations, often taking weeks if not months, to arrive.

Radio technology can be traced back to Michael Faraday, who in 1831 discovered the principle of electromagnetic induction. This and a long series of further discoveries led to the discovery that electrical currents could be induced purposefully at a distance by means of man-made electrical waves, which made radio possible.

Technological advances brought rapid changes in how quickly information could move throughout the country. First came the invention of the telegraph and the telephone, which depend on electrical lines to deliver their messages, and then wireless telegraphy, which delivers radio signals through the air.

In 1835, Samuel F.B. Morse first demonstrated his electromagnetic telegraph. In 1843, he asked the U.S. Congress to give him $30 000 to string four telegraph lines along the Baltimore & Ohio Railroad, from Baltimore to Washington. The first official message—"What hath God wrought?"—was sent from Baltimore to Washington, D.C., on May 24, 1844.

Telegraph lines followed the railroads, and for decades ordinary citizens depended on Morse's coded messages printed on tape, sent from one railway station to another to conclude important business arrangements and to pass on curtly phrased announcements of personal triumphs and tragedies. Then on March 10, 1876, Alexander Graham Bell sent a message on his new invention, the telephone, to his associate Thomas A. Watson in an adjoining room of their Boston laboratory: "Mr. Watson, come here. I want you." Bell was at the time commuting to a school for the deaf in Boston for the academic term while his family remained in their home in Brantford, Ontario. From his Ontario home, Bell made the first building-to-building phone call, to his uncle in Brantford on August 3, 1876. The often-absent Mr. Watson also received the first transcontinental phone call in San Francisco from Bell in New York on January 25, 1915.

Both Morse's telegraph and Bell's telephone used wires to carry messages. Then in Germany in 1887, the physicist Heinrich Hertz began experimenting with radio waves, which became known as Hertzian waves—the first discovery in a series of theoretical and practical refinements that led to the development of radio broadcasting.

Using perhaps the first version of today's Walkman, a couple on Guglielmo Marconi's yacht *Electra* do the foxtrot in 1922.

Library of Congress

Radio's Revolution

Broadcasting was truly a revolutionary media development. Imagine a society in which the only way you can hear music or enjoy a comedy is at a live performance or by listening to tinny noises on a windup record machine. The only way you can hear a speech is to be in the audience. Movies show action but no sound. Without the inventions of broadcasting's early pioneers such as Heinrich Hertz, you could still be living without the sounds of media that you have come to take for granted. Five pioneers besides Hertz are credited with advancing early radio broadcasting: Guglielmo Marconi, Reginald Fessenden, Lee de Forest, David Sarnoff, and Edward Rogers.

Wireless Breakthrough: Marconi. Twenty-year-old Guglielmo Marconi, the son of wealthy Italians, used the results of the three discoveries by Morse, Bell, and Hertz to expand his idea that messages should be able to travel across space without a wire. Marconi became obsessed with the idea, refusing food and working in his locked upstairs room.

Soon Marconi could ring a bell across the room or downstairs without using a wire. His father sponsored Guglielmo and his mother on a trip to England, where Marconi showed the invention to the chief telegraph engineer in the British Post Office. Their first messages, sent in Morse Code, travelled 100 yards (84m). Eventually, Marconi was able to broadcast over a distance of nine miles (23 km). "The calm of my life ended then," Marconi said later.[2]

Marconi set up temporary stations in Poldhu, on the Cornish coast of England, and in St. John's, Newfoundland. In 1901 he received the first trans-Atlantic radio transmission, in St. John's.

Amateur radio operators created clubs to experiment with the new technology. Two experimenters, Reginald Fessenden and Lee de Forest, advanced the Marconi discovery to create today's radio.

Experimental Broadcasts: Fessenden. Reginald Fessenden, a Canadian, set up his National Signaling Company to attempt to send voices by radio waves. On Christmas Eve, 1906, "ship wireless operators over a wide area of the Atlantic … were startled to hear a woman singing, then a violin playing, then a man reading passages from Luke. It was considered uncanny; wireless rooms were soon crowded with the curious."[3] The noises were coming from Fessenden's experimental station at Brant Rock, Massachusetts. Fessenden's experiment in 1906 is considered the world's first voice and music broadcast.

Detecting Radio Waves: De Forest. In 1907, Lee de Forest perfected a glass bulb called the Audion, which could detect and amplify radio waves. "Unwittingly then," wrote de Forest, "had I discovered an invisible Empire of the Air."[4]

Besides being an inventor, de Forest was a good publicist. He began what he called "broadcasts" from New York and then from the Eiffel Tower. In 1910 he broadcast Enrico Caruso singing at the Metropolitan Opera House. Later, his mother broadcast an appeal to give women the vote. Gradually, the Audion became the foundation of modern broadcasting.

Radio for the People: Sarnoff. In 1912, 21-year-old David Sarnoff relayed news from Nantucket Island, Massachusetts, that he had received a distress call from the *Titanic* on his Marconi Wireless. Four years later, Sarnoff was working for the Marconi Company in New York. He wrote a visionary memo that predicted radio's future, although in 1916 his ideas were widely ignored:

> I have in mind a plan of development which would make radio a household utility. The idea is to bring music into the home by wireless. The receiver can be designed in the form of a simple radio music box, and arranged for several different wave lengths which should be changeable with the throwing of a single switch or the

Broadcasting from station XWA, in Montreal, 1919— scene of first commercial radio transmission of Canadian Marconi Company. They produced the first regular broadcast programs in the world.

Courtesy of Canadian Marconi Company

pressing of a single button. The same principle can be extended to numerous other fields, as for example, receiving lectures at home which would be perfectly audible. Also, events of national importance can be simultaneously announced and received. Baseball scores can be transmitted in the air. This proposition would be especially interesting to farmers and others living in outlying districts.[5]

Eventually, as commercial manager and then president of RCA, Sarnoff would watch his early vision for radio come true.

No More Batteries: Rogers. Another early figure of note was Edward Samuel Rogers of Toronto. His rectifier vacuum tube, patented in 1925, allowed radios to be run off household current, rather than batteries. Rogers's radios plugged into a wall outlet. His "batteryless" radio, manufactured by a firm he set up in Toronto called Rogers Majestic, did away with bulky and dangerous acid batteries that had previously powered household radios. Without the rectifier tube, television would not have been possible, as the early models required so much power that a conventional battery could power them for only a few minutes.

Rogers and his father also established one of the first radio stations in Toronto. The family business continues today as Rogers Communications, the largest cable TV operator in Canada, currently managed by Edward's son Ted.

Governments Police the Airwaves

Governments in both Canada and the United States became involved in regulating broadcasting almost as soon as it was invented. This decision to regulate separated the broadcast media, which were regulated early, from the print media, which are not directly regulated by any government agency. In part, this difference stems from the view that the airwaves are a public resource that cannot be owned as property; thus, governments must issue licences for broadcasting frequencies.

International agreements between governments allocated parts of the radio spectrum for different purposes. Although some of these purposes have changed over the years, and some radio frequencies have been reallocated (such as for cellphones), the concept of public ownership of the airwaves survives. Friction between governments arises when countries seek to allocate frequencies in different ways. For instance, the most powerful AM transmitters in North America reach all parts of the continent, especially at night. For this reason, some of the most powerful transmitters (50 000 watts and above) are designated "clear channels" over all of North America; however, less powerful transmitters can share the same frequencies, provided they are far enough away from each other. Nevertheless, interference between different stations' transmissions is a continuing problem with AM radio.

Experimental Stations Multiply

Station XWA, the first Canadian radio station, was established and operated in Montreal by Canadian Marconi Company in 1915. Subsequently renamed CFCF in 1920, it continues to this day. It is reputed to be the oldest continuously

IMPACT

Profile

STATION XWA BRINGS CANADIANS A "BRASH NEW TOY"

The origin of XWA has been traced to the Sessional Papers of the House of Commons for 1915, which lists licensed experimental stations. The only one on the list is XWA. Experiments were carried out from the Marconi Wireless Telegraph Company of Canada factory building at 173 William Street [Montreal]. It was often difficult for these pioneers to know if they were even being received, as their audience consisted of a few "hams" and a handful of ships in the St. Lawrence River, which were equipped with crystal receiving apparatus. Speaking to the Parliamentary Committee of 11 March 1932, Commander C.P. Edwards, Director of Radio, Department of Marine, said:

> Broadcasting in Canada started with some test programs in 1919 by the

Canadian Marconi Company of Montreal. Regular organized programs commenced in December 1919 by the same company, and by 1922 broadcasting had been definitely established throughout the country.

The Marconi station was, of course, XWA, which became CFCF on 4 November 1920. These early programs from XWA/CFCF consisted mainly of weather reports and the playing of gramophone records on a wind-up Victrola. The first operator was J.V. Argyle, who later worked for the Department of National Defence in Ottawa. One of the first musical sounds aired by XWA, which was merely a box of wireless telegraph equipment in the corner of the factory building, was that of a small Swiss music box, owned by D.P. Coates of Calgary.

On 20 May 1920 a special program, with an orchestra and soloist Dorothy Lutton, was broadcast by XWA in conjunction with the annual meeting of the Royal Society of Canada at the Chateau Laurier in Ottawa. Reception was good in Montreal more than 160 kilometres away, and both the *Ottawa Citizen* and the *Montreal Star* carried feature stories the next day. It was one of the first times the newspapers even acknowledged this brash new "toy." Among those who heard the broadcast at the Chateau were Sir Robert Borden, the Duke of Devonshire, William Lyon Mackenzie King, and Sir Henry Drayton.

From XWA to CIQC: A History of Canada's First Radio Station. *Reprinted with permission. On-line: http://www.ciqc.com/ history/xpref.html*

licensed radio station in the world. (See Impact Profile: "Station XWA Brings Canadians a 'Brash New Toy,'" above.)

With the exception of XWA in Montreal, early radio operators broadcast messages to each other and their friends, but not to the general public. These amateur radio operators were early examples of broadcast entrepreneurs. They were tinkerers, fascinated with an invention that could carry sounds through the air. One of these tinkerers, Frank Conrad, is credited with sending the first on-air election reports.

Conrad often broadcast concerts from his garage on his station 8XK. But his boss at Westinghouse, Harry P. Davis, had an idea: Why not improve the broadcasts so more people would want to buy radios? Davis talked Conrad into setting up a more powerful transmitter at the Westinghouse plant by November 2, so that Conrad could broadcast election returns.

Conrad directed construction of a 100-watt transmitter, and the *Pittsburgh Post* agreed to telephone election returns to the station. On October 27, 1920, using the powers of the 1912 Radio Act, the U.S. Department of Commerce licensed station KDKA as the first U.S. *commercial* station. The broadcast began at 8 p.m. on November 2, 1920, and continued past midnight, reporting that Warren G. Harding was the next president of the United States. KDKA immediately began a daily one-hour evening schedule, from 8:30 to 9:30 p.m.

The Radio Audience Expands Quickly

The crude early broadcasts directed at anyone with a receiver proved that regular programming could attract a loyal audience. KDKA was just the beginning of what eventually became the U.S. private radio networks. Most Canadian stations were run by the government-owned Canadian National Railways. (CNR).

The radio craze led almost immediately to a period of rapid expansion, as entrepreneurs and advertisers began to grasp the potential of the new medium. Almost as quickly, governments were compelled to step in to expand the regulation of radio broadcasting.

More than 500 stations began broadcasting in 1922 in the United States alone.[6] Radio's potential as a moneymaker for its owners incited competition for the airwaves. Two important developments for radio's future were the blanket licensing agreement and the decision that radio would accept commercial sponsors.

Blanket Licensing

At first, stations played phonograph records; then they invited artists to perform live in their studios. The novelty of radio attracted some of the best talent, who sought the publicity that radio could give them. But eventually the performers asked to be paid.

In 1923, the American Society of Composers, Authors, and Publishers (ASCAP) sued several stations for payment, claiming that broadcasting ASCAP-licensed music on the radio meant that people would buy less sheet music. Station owners argued that playing the songs on their stations would make more people want to buy the sheet music.

Eventually the stations agreed to pay ASCAP royalties through a **blanket licensing agreement,** which meant that the stations paid ASCAP a fee ($250 a year at first). In exchange, the stations could use all ASCAP-licensed music on the air. (ASCAP licenses its music to stations the same way today.) Eventually another licensing organization, Broadcast Music Inc., would also collect broadcast royalties.

Performance rights for broadcast music have gone through many organizational frameworks in Canada, based on the original ASCAP agreement. The Canadian counterpart of ASCAP was established in 1925 by the Performing Right Society (U.K.) and the American Society of Composers, Authors and Publishers (U.S.). It became an independent Canadian organization and changed its name to the Composers, Authors, and Publishers Association of Canada (CAPAC) in 1963.

Similarly, PROCan (the Performing Rights Organization of Canada) began as BMI Canada Limited in 1940, when it was formed by Broadcast Music Inc. of the United States to license its music in Canada. In 1947, BMI Canada began to license music for Canadian composers, lyricists, songwriters, and publishers. In 1976, BMI Canada became an independent Canadian not-for-profit society, changing its name to PROCan the next year to reflect the corporate change.

It was subsequently integrated as part of the Society of Composers, Authors and Music Publishers of Canada (SOCAN) in 1990. Performance royalties are now collected and disbursed by CAPAC and PROCan.

Commercial Sponsorship

Once station owners agreed to pay for their programs, they had to figure out where they would get the money. AT&T had the answer in an idea they pioneered at their station WEAF in New York. WEAF inaugurated the policy of selling time. Its first sponsored program cost $100 for ten minutes.

The success of commercial sponsorship as a way to support radio settled the issue of who would pay the cost of airing programs in the United States. In Canada, however, the public broadcaster came to dominate. Advertisers in both countries would pay for programming through their advertising; the public would pay for the programs indirectly by supporting the advertisers who supported radio.

The commercialization of broadcasting gave advertisers access to the audience at home. Radio's massive audience sat enraptured with sponsored programming of many types: comedy, music, serials, drama, and news. Eventually, all of these types of programming migrated to television.

The CNR Brings Drama to the Public

By 1924, the whole of North America was covered by competing broadcasters, though often only in the evening hours, when reception improved. The early household radios, called *crystal sets*, received transmissions on long wire antennas, often hung outside houses like clotheslines.

Canadian public radio broadcasting began in 1925 in the studios of the CNR. Early CNR stations tended to be located in CNR railway hotels. The CBC studios in Ottawa are still located in the Chateau Laurier Hotel, on the top two floors under the eaves of the ornate copper roof.

In Canada, core content, such as news, and other noncommercial broadcasts, such as those intended for children in schools, were government-subsidized. In the 1930s, the government began to standardize network content across the country with the goal of fostering national unity.

CNR passengers listen to the radio in 1922—the uniquely Canadian marriage of publicly owned railway transport and radio production.

Vancouver Public Library/Photograph Number 8371

In this early period, CNR radio drama had a central importance in the lives of isolated rural families, and it formed the focus of evening entertainments. The first regular drama series produced in Canada was *The CNRV Players* (1927–1932), later joined by series produced in Montreal, Toronto, and Edmonton.

"War of the Worlds" Challenges Radio's Credibility

On Halloween Eve, October 30, 1938, the *Mercury Theater on the Air* broadcast a dramatization of the H.G. Wells story "War of the Worlds." The live 8 p.m. broadcast played opposite the very popular Edgar Bergen program on NBC and rarely had even 4 percent of the audience. Very few people heard the announcement at the beginning of the program that said the Mercury Theater was performing a version of the Wells story.

The program began with the announcer introducing some band music. A second voice then said, "Ladies and gentlemen, we interrupt our program of dance music to bring you a special bulletin. At 20 minutes before 8 o'clock Central Time, Professor Farrell of Mount Jennings Observatory, Chicago, reports observing several explosions of incandescent gas occurring at regular intervals on the planet Mars."

More dance music followed, and then more bulletins about the Martians. Next came the startling news that 1500 people near Princeton, New Jersey, had died when they were hit by a meteor. Then the announcer said it was not a meteor but a spaceship carrying Martians armed with death rays.

Two professors from the Princeton geology department actually set out to locate the "meteors." In Newark, families rushed out of their homes, covering their faces with wet handkerchiefs to protect themselves from the "gas." After a burst of horrified calls, CBS began repeating the announcement that the program was just a play.

The episode demonstrated how easily alarming information could be innocently misinterpreted, especially because the listeners had no other source to check the reliability of what they were hearing. Radio listeners truly were a captive audience.

Radio Networks Expand

The formation of the networks as a source of programming and revenue is a crucial development in the history of radio. A **network** is a collection of stations (radio or television) that offers programs, usually simultaneously, throughout the country, during designated times. As networks were stretched across the continent, they provided a dependable source of programming. Many stations found it easier to affiliate with a network and receive its programming than to develop local programs.

In Canada, privately owned stations grew into strong local voices in the major cities. They could not, however, match the national coverage provided by the Canadian Broadcasting Corporation (CBC), especially at times of national crisis or celebration.

The CBC Links Canadians

The CBC was established as a crown corporation on November 2, 1936, taking over the radio assets and operations of the CNR and succeeding the Canadian Radio Broadcasting Commission, the first public broadcaster. After hearing about the successes of the British Broadcasting Corporation (BBC), the Canadian Radio League, set up by Graham Spry in 1930, championed the case for public broadcasting in Canada. The league achieved its goal in 1932, when the government passed the Canadian Radio Broadcasting Act. The Act established the Canadian Radio Broadcasting Commission, with a broad national mandate to cover all settled areas of the country. The mandate was continued and expanded under the CBC charter. Like the BBC, the CBC was to be financed by licensing fees paid by the owners of radios and would regulate the privately owned stations. This regulatory role is now performed by another government body, the CRTC.

The CBC initially had eight of its own stations and sixteen privately owned affiliates. Under the North American agreement signed in Havana in 1937, the CBC was allocated six clear channel frequencies for 50 000 watts or more and eight further clear channels for transmitters up to 50 000 watts. The CBC began installing low power repeaters in local communities across Canada (a process not completed until the late 1960s), providing much of the population access to a usable CBC AM signal. Most also had access to usable signals from U.S. network stations.

The CBC produced numerous weekly drama series from the 1930s to the 1950s. Of these programs, perhaps the most influential was W.O. Mitchell's Sunday night series, called *Jake and the Kid*, set in the fictional town of Crocus, Saskatchewan. Immensely evocative of life on the prairies in the 1940s, the program had a devoted audience.

Radio in the 1930s and 1940s became a powerful cultural and political force, providing many Canadians with a new, inexpensive source of information and entertainment. Behind the CBC drama programs of the 1940s and 1950s stood a talented producer, Andrew Allan, the national drama supervisor. His productions became the training ground for a whole generation of actors, whose faces became familiar in the television drama that succeeded radio drama in the late 1950s, including Austin Willis and Lloyd Bochner (who played stereotyped suave villains in dozens of U.S. television crime shows and movies in the early 1960s), James Doohan, William Shatner ("Beam me up, Scotty"), Kate Reid, and Christopher Plummer.

Farcical comedy programs were also part of the mix. A prime example was *Rawhide*, with Max Ferguson and Alan McFee. Its daily at dinner time half-hour was filled by a continuing cast of eccentric characters, strange recorded music, and sarcastic humour at the expense of CBC management.

Childrens' programming was also memorable, with the *Small Types Club* with Byng Whittaker. The show was an elaborate continuing fantasy that aired every weekday lunch hour, following the rebroadcast of the BBC world service news at noon; this scheduling drew young listeners to the news very early on.

For a time, the CBC operated two English-language AM networks. There was a separate French-language network, and programming in Aboriginal languages and Gaelic was attempted in some areas. Today, the northern service carries a great deal of Aboriginal-language programming to dispersed settlements. The last Gaelic programming ended in Cape Breton in the late 1960s.

Canadians in border towns also received U.S. NBC, CBS, and ABC stations. The U.S. radio networks prospered until the 1980s, when NBC sold its radio network and CBS and ABC gave more attention to their television holdings.

Radio in the TV Era

Initially, it seemed that television would cause the death of radio. As soon as television proved itself, advertisers abandoned radio, said comedian Fred Allen, "like the bones at a barbecue."[7] The talent fled, too—Bob Hope, Milton Berle, Jackie Gleason, even Burns and Allen.

The U.S. radio networks, which at first tried to compete with television, eventually lost most of the big-name shows. Some radio programming made the transition to television gracefully, notably *Hockey Night in Canada*, which had overlapping radio and television versions. Some comedians, such as Jack Benny, worked in both radio and television. Other radio comedians never succeeded in recreating themselves as television performers.

Four developments in the 1940s and 1950s changed the medium of radio and guaranteed its survival alongside television: the introduction of stereo FM radio, a new source of recorded music for broadcast, radio formats, and portable radios.

FM Radio Takes Over

After working for more than a decade to eliminate static from radio broadcasts, engineer Edwin H. Armstrong applied to the Federal Communications Commission (FCC) in the United States in 1936 to broadcast using his new technique, frequency modulation (FM). Because of the way FM signals travel through the air, FM offered truer transmission with much less static. Also, because FM transmissions do not follow the curvature of the earth, there was much less chance of interference from other stations operating on the same frequency. FM eventually became the spectrum of choice for music lovers, far surpassing the broadcast quality of AM.

Licensed Recordings Launch Disc Jockeys

Early radio station owners avoided playing records because they would have had to pay royalties. Stations that played records were also obliged to remind their audiences every half-hour that they were listening to recorded music, not a live orchestra. This discouraged record-spinning.

In 1935, newscaster Martin Block at New York's independent station WNEW began playing records in between his newscasts, and then he started a program called *Make Believe Ballroom*. He is generally considered the first disc jockey. In 1940, the FCC ruled that once stations bought a record, they could play it on the air whenever they liked, without the half-hour announcements.

To counteract ASCAP's insistence on royalties, broadcasters formed a cooperative music licensing organization called Broadcast Music Inc. which expanded into Canada and later became PROCan. Most rhythm and blues, country, and rock 'n' roll artists eventually signed with BMI, which charged stations less for recording artists than ASCAP. With an inexpensive source of music available, a new media personality was created—the DJ.

Gordon McLendon Introduces Format Radio

How would the stations know which mix of records to use? The answer came from Gordon McLendon, the father of format radio. McLendon first became known as a play-by-play baseball announcer on KLIF in Dallas in 1948. He also outfitted KLIF news cars to search for local news. McLendon targeted local people for interviews on national subjects. He beat television, which was burdened with heavy camera equipment. KLIF's innovative news coverage gave rise to McLendon's first idea for a successful format: all-news radio.

Then McLendon combined music and news in a predictable rotation of 20-minute segments, and eventually KLIF grew very popular. Next he refined the music by creating the Top 40 format. Top 40 played the top-selling hits continually, interrupted only by a disc jockey or a newscast.

In 1959, McLendon launched the beautiful-music format at KABL in San Francisco. In 1964, he used a 24-hour news format for Chicago's WNUS, using three news vans with a "telesign" that showed news on the roof in lights as the van drove around town. Formats meant that stations could now share standardized programs that stations previously had to produce individually. Eventually, the idea of formatted programming spread, making network programming and the networks themselves less important to individual stations.

Clock and Car Radios Make Radio Portable

Two technological innovations helped ensure radio's survival by making it an everyday accessory. Transistor radios, first sold in 1948 for $40, were far more reliable and cheaper than tube radios, you didn't have to wait for them to warm up, as you did with conventional tube sets, and they were portable. Clock radios woke people up and caused them to rely on radio for the first news of the day.

The car radio was invented in 1928 by William Lear, who designed the Lear jet. Early car radios were enormous, with spotty reception, but technology developed during World War II helped refine them. In 1946, 9 million U.S. cars had car radios. By 1963, the number was 50 million.[8] **Drive-time audiences** (who listened between 6 and 9 a.m. and 4 and 7 p.m.) were growing at the time that radio station owner Gerald Bartell coined the term in 1957.

A Columbia University report, commissioned by NBC in 1954, defined radio's new role. "Radio was the one medium that could accompany almost every type of activity.... Where radio once had been a leisure-time 'reward' after a day's work, television was now occupying that role. Radio had come to be viewed less as a treat than as a kind of 'companion' to some other activity."[9] Like magazines, radio survived in part because the medium adapted to fill a different need for its audience.

Alan Freed and the Payola Scandals

The rise of rock 'n' roll coincided with the development of transistor and portable radios, which meant that radio played a central role in the rock revolution. "Rock and radio were made for each other. The relationship between record companies and radio stations became mutually beneficial. By providing the latest hits, record companies kept stations' operating costs low. The stations, in turn, provided the record companies with the equivalent of free advertising."[10]

Figure 5.1

Where Radio Listeners Tune In

Source: *1997 Radio Marketing Guide and Fact Book for Advertisers.*

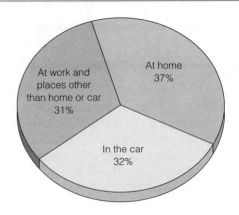

Eventually, this relationship would prove too close. On February 8, 1960, the U.S. Congress began hearings into charges that disc jockeys and program directors had accepted cash to play specific records on the air. The term **payola** was coined to describe this practice, combining pay and Victrola (the brand name of the RCA windup record player).

In May 1960, a Manhattan grand jury charged eight men with commercial bribery for accepting more than $100 000 in payoffs for playing records. The most prominent among them was Alan Freed, who had worked in Cleveland (where he was credited with coining the term *rock 'n' roll*) and at New York's WABC. He was charged with 26 counts of accepting payoffs when he went on trial in February 1962. He pleaded guilty to two counts, paid a $300 fine, and received six months' probation. Then Freed was found guilty of income tax evasion. He died in 1965 while awaiting trial, at age 43. In September 1960, Congress amended the Federal Communications Act to prohibit the payment of cash or gifts in exchange for air play.[11]

Working in Radio

There are now over 12 000 stations on the air in North America. They are about evenly divided between FM and AM.

The CBC's dominance has declined in recent years because the CRTC licensed has many new outlets. Many commercial stations today use *program services,* which provide satellite as well as formatted programming. This is the contemporary equivalent of network programming, though it is not branded as such; packaged program services are supposed to sound as if they could be local in origin.

Many stations are part of a *group,* which means they are owned by a company that owns more than one station in more than one broadcast market. Other stations are part of a *combination AM/FM* (a *combo*), which means that one company owns both an AM and an FM station in the same market. And many stations remain family-owned, single operations that run just like any other small business.

Today's radio stations are highly automated. Often, the on-air talent simultaneously runs the equipment.

The *Toronto Star*/S. Russell

The *general manager* runs the radio station. The *program manager* oversees what goes on the air, including the news programs, the station's format, and any on-air people. Salespeople, who are called *account executives*, sell the advertising for the programs.

Traffic people schedule the commercials, make sure they run correctly, and bill the clients. *Production people* help with local programming and produce commercials for the station. *Engineers* keep the station on the air. And *administrative people* pay the bills, answer the phones, and order the paper clips. At a small station, as few as five people will handle all of these jobs. At certain times of day in small stations, there may be only one person physically present to handle all of the work in keeping the station on the air.

The Business of Radio

Instead of dying after the spread of television, radio managed to thrive by adapting to an audience that seeks the portability and immediacy that radio offers. Nothing can beat radio for quick news bulletins or the latest hits. Radio also delivers a targeted audience much better than television because the radio station you prefer defines you to an advertiser more than does the television station you watch.

The advertising potential of an intimate medium like radio is attracting entrepreneurs who have never owned a station and group owners who want to expand their holdings, given the move to deregulation. When you listen to your radio in your car or through earphones while you jog, for instance, radio is not competing with any other medium for your attention. Advertisers like this exclusive access to an audience. Four important issues for radio people today are the rise of FM over AM, ratings, Canadian content rules, and formats.

FM Beats AM

The way that FM signals travel makes them better carriers for stereo sound than AM. So in most markets, FM is more attractive to advertisers than AM.

"Although radio is prospering, AM stations are losing listeners at an alarming rate," reports the *Wall Street Journal*. In 1970, two out of three listeners regularly tuned in to AM. By 1991, FM had captured three-fourths of the audience.[12]

AM typically fares best with news, sports, local information, and call-in shows. This type of programming attracts a more loyal audience than the audience for music, which tends to be fickle, switching the dial to hear favourite songs.

Today, radio as a mass medium has receded into the background. However, radio still generates enough money to make it an attractive investment. Part of the reason is that although most AM radio is full of chatter and nondescript music, some is still arresting in its brashness.

Are Radio Ratings Accurate?

Radio station owners depend on ratings to set advertising rates, and the stations with the most listeners command the highest ad rates. Ratings are also used to gauge the degree of acceptance of various types of programming. In Canada, listener data are collected by the Bureau of Broadcast Measurement (BBM), a not-for-profit broadcast research company, and in the United States by a company called Arbitron. Both companies request that selected listeners complete and return listening diaries.

The jargon of radio ratings relates to the number of people who are listening in any number of 15-minute periods throughout the week.

1. *Average quarter-hour audience (AQH)* means the average number of people in a target group listening to a station, or to the radio, during an average quarter-hour, in a given time period.
2. *Cume* or *reach* stands for the cumulative audience. It describes (a) the number of people who listen to a station, or to the radio, for at least one quarter-hour during a given period of time; and (b) the number of people who are exposed to a radio commercial schedule, during a given period of time (usually one week).
3. **Ratings** are the percentage of the total population that a station is reaching.
4. **Share** (or *Share of Hours* or *AQH Share*) is the percentage of the total radio audience listening to a particular station during a given period of time.[13]

The diary method is often criticized because minorities, non-English-speaking and non-French-speaking listeners, and people age 18 to 24 don't return the diaries in the same proportion as other people who are surveyed. The methodology is sometimes varied to include telephone interviews to overcome this problem.

Though it may be flawed, the information generated from these surveys is pivotal in setting advertising rates and assessing the success of programming.

The CRTC Prescribes Canadian Content

In Canada, freedom in programming is circumscibed by Canadian content regulations: stations must adhere to the CRTC's current formula for content. But this control does not extend to format, unless a station requests a specific licence.

The CRTC has maintained Canadian music quotas for Canadian AM and FM radio stations since 1971. Today, regulations require that stations' play lists be made up of at least 30 percent Canadian music content **(CANCON).** Stations can play 25 percent on weekdays from 6 a.m. to 6 p.m. and then load up on Canadian content to make their weekly 30 percent quota late at night and on weekends. There are detailed rules as to what constitutes Canadian content (see Chapter 6).

According to new regulations announced April 30, 1998, this quota will rise to 35 percent, effective January 3, 1999. Balancing over the 24-hour cycle and weekends to meet the quota will no longer be allowed—the new 35 percent quota will apply at all times.

At the same time, the CRTC announced that companies are now allowed to own up to four radio stations, two on each band, in cities with eight or more radio stations.

Radio Depends on Ready-Made Formats

Today's private radio station owner looking for an audience can use one of several ready-made formats. By adjusting their formats, radio station managers can test the market until they find a formula that works to deliver their audience to advertisers. If you were a radio station manager today and you wanted to program your station, you could choose from several popular formats, listed here in order of the number of stations currently using them, from most to least.

Country. This is the most popular radio format. It is aimed at 25- to 45-year-olds in urban as well as rural areas.

Adult Contemporary. This program format includes adult rock and light rock music by artists such as Celine Dion and Bryan Adams. It aims to reach 25- to 40-year-olds in all types of markets.

News/Talk. A station with this format devotes most of its air time to different types of talk shows, which can include call-in features that allow listeners to question on-the-air guests. Its typical audience is 35 and older. Some programs are syndicated features or national phone-ins, which are purchased by the local station. The CBC runs successful phone-in shows, such as *Cross-Canada Checkup.*

Religious. "Here's the news of today and the promise of tomorrow," begins one station with religious programming. Although some denominations own stations and broadcast their points of view, many stations have adopted religious programming purely as a way to make a profit. These stations offer inspirational music, news, weather, sports, and drama. About 970 stations broadcast a religious format.

News. It is difficult for a radio station to survive on news alone, so most news stations are located in big cities where there is a continuing source of news stories. A more recent variant is the all-sports station.

Album-Oriented Rock (AOR). Directed toward 18- to 24-year-olds, this format delivers contemporary hits, like Top 40, but with songs from a longer span of time—from within the past two years, for example, instead of the past month.

Contemporary Hits/Top 40. Playing songs on *Billboard*'s current hits list, a Top 40 station closely follows trends among listeners, especially teenagers.

Foreign Language. Stations broadcasting in languages other than English are growing in the large population centres. Johnny Lombardy's multi-ethnic CHIN-AM station in Toronto and CHMB in Vancouver are two such stations in Canada. Both official languages in Canada are represented by CBC outlets.

Middle of the Road (MOR). "Not too hard, not too soft" is the phrase most often used to describe this format. You could also add "not too loud, not too fast, not too slow, not too lush, not too new." The audience is 25 to 35 years old, and the music may include the Beatles, Blood Sweat and Tears, James Taylor, and Stevie Wonder.

Stations can divide these traditional formats into even more subcategories: AOR is splitting into modern rock and oldies; some adult contemporary stations play only love songs. The use of taped program formats means that a station can specialize its programming simply by changing the tapes or discs.

This makes disc jockeys as personalities much less important than they once were. Many stations operate without disc jockeys altogether or limit personality programming to morning and evening drive-times. The rest of the day and evening, these stations can rely on an engineer and an announcer to carry the programming.

Today, networks, which once dominated radio programming, mainly provide national news to their affiliates. Station managers can program their own stations, mixing local news, music, and announcements. Stations also can get programming from syndicated and satellite program services. Syndicates provide

Figure 5.2

Average Share of Radio Listening by Canadians 12 Years and Over, Fall 1996

Source: Adapted from *The Daily*, "Television and Radio Audiences," Catalogue No. 11-001, February 5, 1998. Reprinted with permission from Statistics Canada.

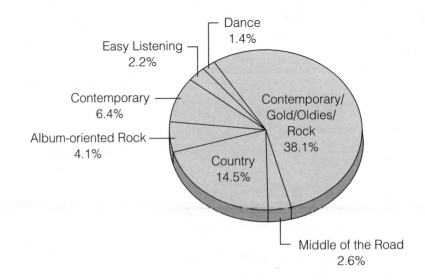

prepackaged program formats. Satellites make program distribution easier; satellite networks, such as Satellite Music Network, promise the broadcaster original, up-to-date programming without a large local staff.

Technology and the Future

The most significant trend in radio is the move toward greater segmentation of the audience, similar to the division of audiences in the magazine industry. Identifying a specific audience segment and programming for it is called **narrowcasting.** "With narrowcasting, advertising efficiency goes way up as overall costs go down.... We are approaching the unstated goal of all radio programmers: to create a station aimed so perfectly that the listener will no longer have to wait, ever, for the song that he wants to hear."[14]

Media businesses are viewing the Internet as their next great broadcast medium, with companies such as Walt Disney and NBC making plans to offer video and multicasting entertainment services in the next few months. Radio stations have already staked their claims, with more than 1100 stations broadcasting 24 hours a day over the Internet.

Demand programming is a new term that describes radio's future possibilities. In the ultimate form of narrowcasting, a listener would be able to order up any particular selection at any time.

In an *Esquire* magazine article, entitled "Radio Lives!" Eric Zorn predicted:

> Listeners of the future, instead of having access to just 30 or 40 stations (many playing the same music and aimed at the same mainstream audiences), will be able to hook into hundreds of channels: blues stations, business-news stations, Czech-language stations, even full-time stations for the blind, anything you can't hear now because the audience for it is too small and scattered for even the biggest cities to support.[15]

Zorn's prediction may be borne out before the next century begins through a new technology known as **digital audio broadcast (DAB).** Digital audio can send music and information in the form of zeroes and ones, as in a computer code. This eliminates all of the static and hiss of current broadcast signals and could mean infinite program choices for consumers.

Discussions have even begun about global radio, using DAB as the standard, combining transmission from satellites and land-based towers on a single radio digital dial that would no longer distinguish among AM, FM, satellite, or other programming. You would simply dial up a number for the signal and the receiver would translate the programming using digital codes. (See "Impact/Technology, Radio Waves to the Future" on page 120.)

As radio technology grows more complex, and new formats and different program delivery systems are tested, the competition for your ear will expand the choices that advertisers can make to reach you. The more stations there are competing for customers, the harder every station must compete for each advertising dollar. This means less revenue for each station because each station's potential audience becomes smaller. In the 1950s, radio learned how to compete with television. Now it must learn how to compete with itself.

IMPACT

Technology   *RADIO WAVES TO THE FUTURE*

By Josh Hyatt

Radio broadcast technology, like TV broadcast technology, is changing. This article explains how radio is adapting to the new marketplace.

Isn't radio dead ... yet? You remember. The turn-of-the-century technology that enjoyed its heyday in the 1930s and 1940s, the era of Jack Benny and *The Green Hornet.* The technology that TV threatened in the 1950s, and that was almost finished off by automobile cassette decks and cellular telephones in the 1970s and 1980s.

Now that enduring medium, which today is best-known for its celebrated talk show hosts ... is finally scheduled for demolition. It will be crushed as the data superhighway, with its promise of 500 TV stations, and movies on demand, is laid across the nation.

Right?

Wrong....

While cable operators, phone companies and computer makers have been jockeying very publicly to build the data superhighway, the high-capacity network that promises to deliver new interactive video services, radio, is making its own grand plans, quietly and much further from public view.

Its future is brightened both by finances and technology.

Thanks to a 1992 ruling by the Federal Communications Commission, the medium's strongest operators are acquiring more stations and increasing their financial clout. And they are exploring new technologies that will turn the most universal of all media—99 percent of households own a radio, compared with 98 percent for TV and 93 percent for phones—into a wireless freeway of its own, capable of delivering audio programming more flexibly, as well as sending out other forms of visual information: song titles, station format, traffic bulletins, even ads.

"We're a little disappointed that we've been left out of all the discussion about the information superhighway," says John Abel, executive vice president of the National Association of Broadcasters in Washington. "But the fact is that you won't be able to participate in that information highway without being connected by phones or cable wire. We're the most mobile of all. And we'll be able to carry all kinds of human communication."

Like television's, radio's transformation hinges on its starting to deliver its programming in digital bits, allowing computers to store and manipulate it. Once that happens, listeners will be freed from the top-of-the-hour tyranny of newscasts, and will be able to assemble their own personalized audio programs.

A receiver outfitted with a so-called Radio Data System, known as RDS, could be instructed to interrupt a cassette for traffic reports, or to hunt for an "alternative rock" station as the listener whizzes along from town to town. By pressing a special button, listeners might receive additional audio reports and even some visuals about big stories....

In Focus

◎ Radio has been a national medium in linking the distant, sometimes isolated, communities of Canada. Radio transformed national politics and expanded access to popular, as well as classical, culture.

◎ Radio technology began with Samuel F.B. Morse's invention of the telegraph, first demonstrated in 1835; Alexander Graham Bell's invention of the telephone, demonstrated in 1876; and Heinrich Hertz's description of radio waves in 1887.

◎ Guglielmo Marconi's promotion of wireless radio wave transmission began in 1897. Reginald Fessenden advanced wireless technology, and Lee de Forest invented the Audion tube to detect radio waves. David Sarnoff made radio

Change will come. And every night, Christopher Schmandt (Principal Research Scientist at the Massachusetts Institute of Technology Media Lab) eavesdrops on radio's possibilities.

As he takes his evening constitutional, the 41-year-old listens to his favorite shows. But he carries only a cellular phone. With it, he dials up a high-powered computer in which he has stored audio selections ranging from National Public Radio's *All Things Considered* to a weekly interview show called *Geek of the Week*.

By pressing buttons on the phone, he can instruct the computer to skip boring stories or long-winded introductions, and he can even speed things up, taking in a recorded 15-minute newscast in nine perfectly audible minutes.

Schmandt's primitive experiment has its flaws—"I have to shift my hands constantly, and it's a pain with gloves in this cold"—but he predicts that soon all radio listeners will enjoy similar advantages: the ability to interact with programming so that they can change its time, alter its speed, and rearrange its contents.

"As the whole communications world shifts to being interactive and multimedia, radio is going to be right there with it," declares Schmandt.... Radio's success in positioning itself as a wireless lane on the superhighway hinges less on the content of its programming than on its ability to change the way listeners experience it....

[Once radio] turns digital, he predicts, radios will be able to pluck out the headlines from a newscast and store them for later playback— over the phone if necessary. Equipped with hard disks, car radios will be able to store an entire Rush Limbaugh broadcast for his aficionados. Schmandt even foresees a new form of audio browsing in which listeners take in a handful of audio headlines at once, processed through different channels on a headphone.

"So far, the focus of the interactive technology has been on all the video possibilities," says Schmandt, whose computer feeds a digitized version of a BBC newscast into his answering machine every morning. "But the superhighway is coming to ears as well. Radio will bring it there."

Boston Globe, *January 23, 1994, Dow/Quest ID#0000302397DC. Reprinted courtesy of the* Boston Globe.

broadcasting a viable business, and Edward Samuel Rogers created the "batteryless" radio, which eventually made television possible.

◎ Governments intervened to regulate broadcasting almost as soon as it was invented. This early regulation separated the broadcast media from the print media, which are not regulated directly by governments.

◎ Two important developments in the 1920s were blanket licensing and commercial sponsorship. Blanket licensing meant that radio owners could use recorded music inexpensively. Commercial sponsorship established the practice of advertisers underwriting the cost of broadcasting.

◎ Canadian public radio broadcasting began in 1925 in the studios of the CNR, owned by the government of Canada. Early stations tended to be located in CNR railway hotels.

◎ The CBC was established as a crown corporation on November 2, 1936, taking over the radio assets and operations of the CNR and succeeding the CRBC, the initial public broadcaster.

◎ The CBC produced numerous weekly drama series from the 1930s to the 1950s. Of these programs, perhaps the most influential was W.O. Mitchell's Sunday night series, called *Jake and The Kid*.

◎ Radio in the 1930s and 1940s became a powerful cultural and political force. Radio programming expanded to include comedy, music, serials, drama, and news. Radio also indirectly created a collective national experience that had not existed before, particularly in wartime.

◎ A broadcast of "War of the Worlds" by the *Mercury Theater on the Air* demonstrated the vulnerability of a captive audience.

◎ Originally, networks provided most radio programming. Today, most stations program themselves using a variety of sources.

◎ Clock and car radios made radio more accessible, but the role of radio changed with the advent of TV, which could offer visual entertainment and news.

◎ Edwin H. Armstrong is responsible for the invention of FM radio. Today, FM stations are three times as popular as AM stations.

◎ BBM is the primary ratings service for radio in Canada. Stations use ratings to set their rates for advertising.

◎ The most significant trend in radio today is the move toward more and more segmentation of the audience, similar to the division of audiences in the magazine industry.

◎ Demand programming and digital audio broadcast may soon offer even more program choices for listeners, another challenge to the radio industry's growing competition within itself.

Review Questions

1. Cite the major events and key people in the development of the radio industry from 1835 to today. What did each development contribute to the evolution of the radio industry?

2. Discuss whether the CBC has been successful in fostering national unity.

3. Compare Gordon McLendon's formats of the 1950s to three of the most popular formats today. How are they similar? How are they different?

4. Describe the effects that narrowcasting may have on the radio industry. Give specific examples.

Watching the Web

◎ **Bureau of Broadcast Measurement**

http://www.bbm.ca/

◎ **Canadian Association of Broadcasters Hall of Fame**

http://www.rcc.ryerson.ca/schools/rta/ccf/personal/hof/hof.html

◎ **Canadian Broadcasting Corporation Radio (audio and text)**

http://www.radio.cbc.ca/radio/programs/news/headline-news/

◎ **National Public Radio**

http://www.realaudio.com/content/nrp.html

◎ **Radio History**

http://www.home.luna.nl/~arjan-muil/radio/history.html

◎ **Surfing the Aether: Radio and Broadcasting Technology History**

http://www.the-bridge.net/~bchris/index.htm

RECORDINGS

6

> THE INFORMATION HIGHWAY COULD BE BAD NEWS IF WE [RECORDING COMPANIES] DON'T CONTROL THE RIGHT OF DISTRIBUTION AND RECEIVE FAIR REMUNERATION... I WANT MY HANDS ON THE WHEEL.

James Fifield, President, EMI Music

"**P**opular music is like a unicorn," writes R. Serge Denisoff in his book *Solid Gold.* "Everyone knows what it is supposed to look like, but no one has ever seen it."[1] More than half the recordings sold every year are categorized as popular music.

If the average person buys four recordings a year, as the Recording Industry Association suggests, popular music is recorded on two of them. Other types of music—country, gospel, classical, show tunes, jazz, and children's recordings—make up the other half, but most of the big profits and losses in the recording business result from the mercurial fury of popular music.

Like the radio and television industries, the recording industry is challenged by rapidly changing technology. And, like the movie industry during the first half of this century, the recording industry is at the centre of recent debates over the protection of free artistic expression versus the industry's perceived effect on moral values.

From Edison's Amazing Talking Machine to 33⅓ RPM Records

Today's recording industry would not exist without Thomas Edison's invention, more than a century ago, of what he called a phonograph (which means "sound writer"). In 1877, *Scientific American* reported Thomas Edison's first demonstration of his phonograph. Edison's chief mechanic had constructed the machine from an Edison sketch that came with a note reading "Build this."

In 1887, Emile Berliner developed the gramophone, which replaced Edison's cylinder with flat discs. Berliner and Eldrige Johnson formed the Victor Talking Machine Company (later to become RCA Victor) and sold recordings of opera star Enrico Caruso. Edison and Victor proposed competing technologies as the standard for the industry, and eventually the Victor disc won. Early players required large horns to amplify the sound. Later, the horn was housed in a cabinet below the actual player, which made the machine a large piece of furniture.

In 1925, Joseph Maxfield perfected the equipment to eliminate the tinny sound of early recordings. The first jukeboxes were manufactured in 1927 and brought music into restaurants and nightclubs.

An early ad shows a phonograph, complete with a case that contained cylinders to be played on the phonograph and a picture of Thomas Edison.

Library of Congress

By the end of World War II, 78 rpm (revolutions per minute) records were standard. Each song was on a separate recording, and "albums" in today's sense did not exist. An album in the 1940s consisted of a bound set of ten envelopes about the size of a photo album. Each record, with one song recorded on each side, fit in one envelope. (This is how today's collected recordings got the title "album.") They featured the era's popular musicians, opera stars, and orchestras. Each shellac hard disc recording ran three minutes. Peter Goldmark, working for Columbia Records (which was owned by CBS), changed that.

Peter Goldmark Perfects Long-Playing Records

In 1947, Goldmark was listening with friends to Brahms's Second Piano Concerto played by pianist Vladimir Horowitz and an orchestra led by the world-famous conductor Arturo Toscanini. The lengthy concerto had been recorded on six records, or twelve sides. Goldmark hated the interruptions in the music every time a record had to be turned over. He also winced at the sound defects he detected.

"He asked his friends to play the records again," reports Robert Metz in his book *CBS: Reflections in a Bloodshot Eye*, "and while they did so, he sat gritting his teeth and racking his brain. Finally he produced a ruler and started calculating, counting 80 grooves to the inch, and he began pondering the principle of the phonograph.... He concluded that he could get more mileage by slowing the turntable speed while crowding significantly more grooves onto a disk."[2] The result, after several refinements and the approval of CBS's William Paley, was the long-playing (LP) record, which could play for 23 minutes.

Paley Battles Sarnoff for Record Format

Paley realized, however, that he was taking a big risk by introducing this product when most people didn't own a record player that could play the bigger 33⅓ rpm LP records at the slower speed. While the LP record was being developed, Paley decided to call RCA executive David Sarnoff, since RCA made record players, to convince Sarnoff to form a partnership with CBS to manufacture LPs. Sarnoff refused.

Stubbornly, Sarnoff introduced his new 7 inch, 45 rpm records in 1948. Forty-fives had a quarter-size hole in the middle and required a different record player, which RCA started to manufacture.

Forty-fives were a perfect size for jukeboxes, but record sales slowed as the public tried to figure out what was happening. "General Sarnoff was foolish to refuse Paley's offer of a license [to manufacture LPs]," says Robert Metz. "When Sarnoff decided to fight against Columbia's superior system he was guilty and not for the first time of allowing pride to triumph over good sense."[3]

Eventually, Toscanini convinced Sarnoff to manufacture LPs and to include the 33⅓ speed on RCA record players to accommodate classical-length recordings. CBS, in turn, agreed to use 45s for its popular songs. Later, players were developed that could play all three speeds (33⅓, 45, and 78 rpm).

Hi-Fi and Stereo Rock In

The introduction of rock 'n' roll redefined the concept of popular music in the 1950s. Contributing to the success of popular entertainers such as Elvis Presley were the improvements in recorded sound quality that originated with the recording industry.

First came *high fidelity*, developed by London Records, a subsidiary of Decca. The hi-fi collector preferred good recordings of boat whistles, passing trains, or even geese in flight to the muddy music of the old 78s.[4]

Tape recorders grew out of German experiments during World War II. European radio stations were playing recorded tapes as early as 1941. Ampex Corporation built a high-quality tape recorder, and Minnesota Mining and Manufacturing (3M) perfected the plastic tape. Tape meant that recordings could be edited and refined, something that couldn't be done on record discs.

The smooth sound of today's recording artists, such as Celine Dion, is a direct result of the development of sophisticated technology that began with CBS Records' introduction of long-playing records (LPs) in the 1940s.

E. Scorcelletti and A. Benaimous/Gamma Liaison

Stereo arrived in 1956, and soon afterward came the Motown sound, which featured the music of black blues and rock 'n' roll artists, such as the Supremes. At the same time, the FCC approved "multiplex" radio broadcasts so that monaural and stereo could be heard on the same stations. The development of condenser microphones helped bring truer sound.

In the 1960s, miniaturization resulted from the transistor. Eventually, the market was overwhelmed with tape players smaller than a deck of playing cards. Quadraphonic (four-track) and eight-track tapes seemed ready to become the standard in the 1970s, but cassette tapes proved more adaptable and less expensive. In 1979, the Japanese company Sony introduced the Walkman as a personal stereo. (The name Sony comes from the Latin *sonus* for sound and *sunny* for optimism.) In one way, Walkmans were a throwback to the early radio crystal sets, which also required earphones.

Today's compact discs promise crystal clear sound, transforming music into digital code on a 4.7-inch plastic-and-aluminum disc both manufactured and read by lasers. Discs last longer than records and cassettes, and they can play for as long as 74 minutes. Compact discs quickly became the technology of choice. "It took VCRs seven years to get to the point where we got in just two years," said Leslie Rosen, executive director of the Compact Disc Group.[5] Music videos and the cable TV music channels MTV and MuchMusic expanded the audience and the potential income for featured artists. Another form of non-digital recording still in use is the optical process used in depositing the soundtrack of movies onto the projection copy of the finished film. The intensity of the recording beam leaves a path of variable light and darkness on the film itself in any area set aside for the soundtrack.

Figure 6.1

Recorded Music Sales

The industry's youthful market is reflected in the music that consumers buy. In dollar volume, rock far outstrips all other kinds of music.

Source: Data from Veronis, Suhler & Associates, Recording Industry Association of America, and Wilkofsky Gruen Associates.

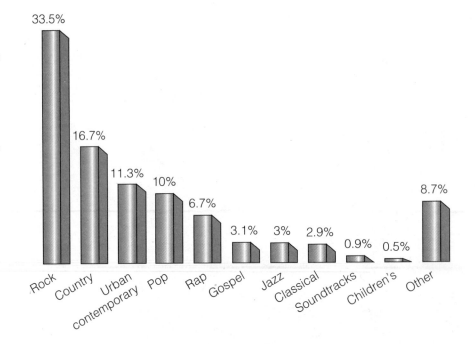

CANCON Promotes Canadian Music

The first records in Canada were made in 1900 by Emile Berliner's Berliner Gramophone Company in Montreal, using master copies from the United States and Europe. The habit of importing content in the Canadian record industry continued for decades, with few exceptions. But, as we said in Chapter 5, the pattern was finally broken by the CANCON or Canadian content, requirement, imposed by the CRTC in 1970, for 30 percent of all AM music to be Canadian in origin. In order to be Canadian in origin, a piece of music must contain two of four of the so-called MAPL elements (music, artist, production, and lyrics). This provision encouraged the production of indigenous recordings and the development of Canadian talent.

By any standard, CANCON regulations have been a success. Initial exposure on Canadian AM and FM radio has led to international success for a long string of Canadian musicians, arrangers, and producers. Performers such as Anne Murray, David Foster, Alanis Morissette, Holly Cole, Daniel Lanois, Sarah McLachlan, Celine Dion, Bryan Adams, and Oscar Peterson may well have been successful in any case, but their careers were boosted by CANCON in exactly the way intended.

Prior to the CANCON regulations, the CBC played a direct role in the Canadian recording industry by producing and selling its own records of performances for radio and television programs. The CBC was instrumental in fostering the recording career of Glenn Gould, a classical pianist of extraordinary talent. It was at one time the largest manufacturer of classical music records in Canada, and it continues to record Canadian performers and composers and to promote their work internationally.

Oscar Peterson, a consummately talented Toronto jazz pianist.

Photo courtesy of Al Gilbert, F.R.P.S., Toronto, Canada

Table 6.1

Sound Recording Sales in Canada, by Format			
	1993	**1994**	**1995**	**1996**
	($ million)			
Music videos	7.1	9.1	10.6	12.3
Singles	2.4	1.8	2.2	3.0
Albums*	515.8	615.0	661.8	623.4
Totals	**525.3**	**625.9**	**674.6**	**638.6**

*The term *album*, derived from the bound sleeves used to store 78 rpm records, is still used to refer to collections of music issued as a unit, such as one or more CDs packaged in a single container.

Source: Adapted from "Canada's Culture, Heritage, and Identity: A Statistical Perspective," 1997, Catalogue No. 87-211-XPB, Table 4.5d, p. 114. Reprinted with permission from Statistics Canada.

IMPACT on You

By Nicholas Jennings

SONGS OF THE SIRENS

They read tarot cards on the grass in the afternoon sun and danced under the moon to the sounds of Tracy Chapman. And before they left the Shoreline Amphitheatre in Mountain View, Calif., a number of women—faced with lengthy lineups at the ladies' rooms—took matters into their own hands and simply went into the men's. Welcome to Lilith Fair, an event organized and headlined by Canada's Sarah McLachlan, that is changing the nature of summer rock festivals. Dubbed everything from "Chickapalooza" to "Estrofest," Lilith Fair offers a kinder, gentler alternative to the aggressive mosh-pit scenes of male-dominated events like H.O.R.D.E. and Lollapalooza.

Lilith Fair continues a tradition that began in the 1970s with women's music festivals featuring the likes of folksingers Holly Near and Ronnie Gilbert. But those events were small, even quaint, by comparison—socially conscious, Birkenstocked gatherings that had little commercial impact within the music industry. By contrast, Lilith Fair—named after Adam's rebellious first wife—is an economic force to be reckoned with. The first four dates of its 35-city North American tour are sold out, in 10,000- to 22,000-seat venues, making Lilith already this summer's biggest ticket....

Ironically, it was the raging, emotional blasts of Alanis Morissette that paved the way for Lilith's more hopeful brand of fem-pop. Ever since Morissette's *Jagged Little Pill* album hit sales of 15 million copies, the music industry has begun waking up to the commercial potential of singers like Jewel, Cole and McLachlan. Still, Terry McBride, McLachlan's Vancouver-based manager and a partner in Lilith, remembers encountering resistance to the idea of an all-woman tour when he began booking venues last September. "Most concert promoters are guys in their 40s and 50s," says McBride, "and some didn't think an all-woman tour offered enough diversity." According to Suzanne Vega, who was around during pop music's earlier flirtation with female musicians in the 1980s, the same attitude prevails at many radio stations. "A lot of programmers are older men who think of women as a 'type' of music," she says. "They don't see that women play many different styles."

That diversity comes through loud and clear in Lilith's lineup, especially on the smaller, secondary stages that feature up-and-coming talent. McLachlan and McBride also show a commitment to Canadian artists. Montreal's Lhasa, an expatriate American of Mexican extraction, may well be Lilith's most exotic addition, blending Hispanic, gypsy and Parisian café music like a globe-hopping Edith Piaf. Meanwhile, Dayna Manning of Stratford, Ont., only 18 and still in braces, has a spirited, confident debut album of modern folk, *Volume 1*, out on EMI. Mudgirl, led by Vancouver singer Kim Bingham, leavens crunching guitars and slamming drums with a sunny, buoyant chorus on songs like the rocking *This Day*. And Tara MacLean, also of Vancouver, sings rich, moody ballads for the same record label, Nettwerk, that has fostered McLachlan.

But Lilith's most singular new Canadian talent is Vancouver's Kinnie Starr. Combining hip-hop beats, choppy rhythm guitar and provocative rap, Starr wowed the crowd at the Shoreline with a solo set. Relaxing backstage after her performance, Starr was enthusiastic about Lilith's feminine focus. "It's nice to be around other female players to see what they're doing, what equipment they use and just to talk," she said. "When I go into a recording studio and it's only men, I feel intimidated. Here, I feel totally safe and confident."

That sense of community is exactly what McLachlan had in mind when she conceived Lilith Fair last summer, with a successful trial tour of four cities. At the same time, with corporate sponsors who donated money to charities ranging from an AIDS organization to a rape and incest hotline, Lilith is making a highly visible statement about its organizers' social concerns. But McLachlan does not see her baby remaining a girls-only club for long, and says she wants to broaden it in future to include male singer-songwriters. "There are a lot of great men out there like [Toronto musician] Ron Sexsmith, who maybe aren't getting all the recognition they deserve," she says. "I'd like to bring them into the fold and spread it around."

Maclean's, *July 28, 1997.*
On-line. Reprinted with
permission. Available:
http://www.maclean's.ca/newsroom
072897/music1072897.html

Working in the Recording Industry

Recordings, like books, are supported primarily by direct purchases. But a recording company involves five separate levels of responsibility before the public hears a sound: artists and repertoire, operations, marketing and promotion, distribution, and administration.

Artists and repertoire, or A&R, functions like an editorial department in book publishing to develop and coordinate talent. Employees of this division are the true talent scouts.

Operations manages the technical aspects of the recording, overseeing the sound technicians, musicians, even the people who copy the discs. This work centres on creating the master recording, from which all other recordings are made. Before stereophonic recording was developed in 1956, a recording session meant gathering all the musicians in one room, setting up a group of microphones, and recording a song in one take. Today, artists on the same song—vocals, drums, bass, horns, guitars—are recorded individually, and then the separate performances are *mixed* for the best sound.

The producer, who works within the operations group, can be on the staff of a recording company or may be an independent freelancer. Producers coordinate the artist with the music, the arrangement, and the engineers.

Marketing and promotion decides the best way to sell the record. These employees oversee the cover design and the copy on the cover (jacket or sleeve). They also organize giveaways to retailers and to reviewers to find an audience for their product. Marketing and promotion might decide that the artist should tour or that the record needs a music video to succeed. Recording companies often use promoters to help guarantee radio play for their artists.

Distribution gets the record into the stores. There are two kinds of distributors: independents and branches. Independents contract separately with different companies to deliver their recordings. But independents, usually responsible for discovering a record that is outside of the mainstream, are disappearing as the big studios handle distribution through their own companies, called *branches*. Because branches are connected with the major companies, they typically can offer the retailer better discounts.

Administration, as in all industries, handles the bills. Accounting tracks sales and royalties. Legal departments handle wrangles over contracts.

All of these steps are important in the creation of a recording, but if no one hears the recording, no one will buy it. This makes record promotion particularly important.

A new type of promotional partnership between a recording company and a television show was introduced in 1992. Giant Records, which produced the soundtrack for the television program *Beverly Hills, 90210*, ran videoclips from the album during the closing credits of the 1992–1993 season of the television show. After the first video—"Saving Forever for You," featuring *90210* star Brian Austin Green—played during the closing credits of a November episode, the song reached number 8 on the *Billboard* Hot 100 Singles Chart in two weeks.[6]

Figure 6.2

Average Age of Record Consumers

The recording industry's average consumer is younger than consumers in any other media industry. People under 34 account for more than half of the industry's revenues.

Source: Data from Veronis, Suhler & Associates, Recording Industry Association of America, and Wilkofsky Gruen Associates.

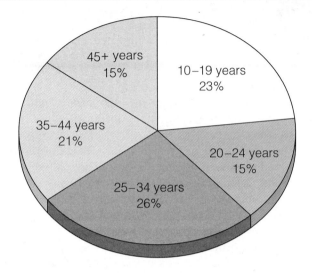

The Recording Business

About 200 companies in Canada and about 5000 companies in the United States produce tapes and CDs. These companies sell over one billion records, cassettes, and compact discs each year. The biggest recording-industry profits are divided among the six major companies: Sony (formerly CBS Records), Time Warner, Philips (Polygram sold to MCA in 1998), Thorn/EMI, Bertelsmann (RCA), and Seagram (MCA)(see Table 6.2). The main recording centres are Los Angeles, New York, and Nashville, but most cities have at least one recording studio to handle local productions.

The recording industry, primarily concentrated in large corporations, generally chooses to record what has succeeded before. "Increasingly, the big record companies are concentrating their resources behind fewer acts," reports the *Wall Street Journal*, "believing that it is easier to succeed with a handful of blockbuster hits than with a slew of moderate sellers. One result is that fewer records are produced."[7]

Most radio formats today depend on popular music, and these recordings depend on radio to succeed. The main measurement of what is popular is *Billboard*, the music industry's leading trade magazine. *Billboard* began printing a list of the most popular vaudeville songs and the best-selling sheet music in 1913. In 1940, the magazine began publishing a list of the top-selling records.

Today, *Billboard* offers more than two dozen charts that measure, for example, air play and album sales, as well as the sale of singles. Elvis Presley has had 149 recordings on the charts, and 20 Beatles hits reached Number 1. Radio, governed by ratings and what the public demands, tends to play proven artists.

Where the Money Is: Sales and Licensing

The industry collects income from direct sales and from music licensing.

Table 6.2

The Music Industry's Big Six	
COMPANY	**COUNTRY**
Bertelsmann (RCA)	Germany
Seagram (MCA)*	Canada
Philips (Polygram)*	Netherlands
Sony	Japan
Thorn/EMI	United Kingdom
Time Warner	United States

* In the spring of 1998, Seagram made a successful $10.4 billion bid for Polygram. At the time of writing, the transaction had not yet been completed.

Source: Data from Standard and Poor's *Industry Surveys*, March 11, 1993.

Direct Sales. The promotional tour once was the major way a company sold records. But in the 1980s, music videos became very visible promotion for an artist. This shift changed the industry's economics. Celine Dion and the Fugees are attractive to record companies because they are recording artists who also can perform well in videos.

> It is now virtually impossible for an LP to succeed without the exposure that a video can generate. So promoting a record these days requires not only the extra expense of producing a video but also the complications of battling others for air time on the cable channel Music Television (MTV) and on other video-oriented programs over network and cable TV.[8]

Music Licensing. For the first 30 years of commercial radio, one of the reasons broadcasters used live entertainment was to avoid paying royalties to the recording companies. Today in Canada, there are several interlocking payment arrangements. Recording artists receive royalties on units sold. Publishers and composers receive a fixed fee for each unit manufactured. Fees are collected on their behalf by the Canadian Mechanical Reproduction Rights Agency. Performance royalties are paid to publishers and composers for radio and television broadcast use. Two other organizations, CAPAC and PROCan, manage these performance payments.

In the United States, two licensing agencies handle the rights to play music for broadcast: ASCAP and BMI.

Today's popular recording artists must make music videos to survive in an industry driven by technology. Here Bryan Adams performs during the MuchMusic Video Awards Ceremony.

CP Picture Archive (Moe Doiron)

Challenges to Income and Content

Three issues face today's recording industry: piracy, attempts to control the content of recordings, and the authenticity of artists' performances.

Pirates Steal Industry Revenue

The recording industry loses substantial income when people make their own tapes. The Japan Phonograph Record Association estimates that cassette-recorder owners make 8 billion illegal copies of tapes and CDs every year.[9] The Recording Industry Association of America (RIAA) has even proposed royalties for music that is digitally transmitted on cable.

A more threatening type of piracy for the industry is overseas copying of prerecorded cassettes that are then sold in North America. Pirates control 18 percent of tape and album sales; the recording industry estimates this represents $300 million a year in lost income.[10]

Content of Recordings

In the mid-1980s, a protest movement emerged in the United States that objected to the lyrics of some popular recorded music. One group, calling itself the Parents Music Resource Center (PMRC), lodged complaints in 1985 with various regulatory bodies and industry associations. The result was that beginning in January, 1986, the Recording Industry Association of America urged its members to provide warning labels or to print lyrics on the packaging of music products with potentially offensive content. However, the RIAA Web site (www.riaa.com) in 1998 contains no reference to such a recommendation or, indeed, any mention of the issue at all.

The Canadian recording industry does not have such a policy. Even so, there have been isolated examples of music products being removed from Canadian retail shelves because of consumer complaints about lyrics. Locations of both K-mart and Wal-Mart in Canada have removed music that offended some consumers from their shelves.

Authenticity of Performances

In 1990, a new controversy arose in the recording industry when the Grammy-winning duo Milli Vanilli admitted that they did not sing a note on the album that won them the award. (The album had sold more than 10 million copies worldwide.) The National Academy of Recording Arts and Sciences, which awards the Grammys, asked the group to return the prize. No artist in the Grammys' history had been charged with similar allegations.

The two Milli Vanilli singers (Robert Pilatus and Fab Morvan) were hired as front men for the actual singers, to appear on the album cover and in promotional materials and to lip-synchronize for music videos.

"Technology is helping a growing number of performers expand truth as it never has been expanded before," wrote *Los Angeles Times* columnist Robert Epstein. Epstein described recent technological changes in the industry that

RECORDING INDUSTRY: BETWEEN ROCK AND HARD PLACE

By David Lieberman

Since 1995, slow music sales have been significantly threatening the recording industry. Music sales increased only 2 percent in 1995 and just 1 percent in 1996. This is a big shift from the late 1980s and early 1990s when recording industry income often grew 10 to 20 percent from year to year. The reasons are complex, but many observers say that the industry desperately needs a new musical trend to invigorate the business.

NEW YORK—Record industry executives are starting to face the music. The boom years—which began around 1987 as consumers flocked to buy clear-sounding compact discs—are over. Sales growth is anemic for the second year in a row. And [1997] "will definitely be tougher, with more companies jockeying for position," Sony Music President Thomas Mottola says.

"Every major label is loaded with too many artists," says industry veteran Al Teller, CEO of music producer and wholesaler Alliance Entertainment. And the records coming out now "are not driving people into the stores."

Music is still a lucrative business, although a company's performance can vary dramatically from year to year.

"Show me an executive who's complaining about market conditions and I'll show you an executive who doesn't have any hits," says BMG Entertainment North America CEO Strauss Zelnick.

Yet until [1995], record companies had grown accustomed to watching revenue roar ahead. They were at double-digit growth levels for six of the nine years from 1987 to 1995. Revenue soared 20% in 1994. When that sputtered to 2% in 1995, some insisted it was a blip.

It wasn't....

Slowdown for CDs

Music executives cite several reasons for the sour notes they're hearing in the business. One popular explanation is that few consumers are still switching over from records to CDs. New buyers of CD players typically pick up about 30 recordings over the course of the first year. Purchases quickly dwindle after that.

"There was an artificial growth rate," says Mercury Records' chief Danny Goldberg. "It's close to maturing."

After 14 years on the market, CD albums and singles represent about 72% of the 1.1 million units of recorded music that U.S. consumers probably will buy this year [1996].

Although CD unit sales are expected to rise 8% in 1996, that will be largely offset by a nearly 16% drop in sales of recorded music audiocassettes. In 1990 album-length cassettes accounted for half of the record industry's unit sales. By year's end, they might only be 20%.

Record companies can't blame all their woes on aging technology. Some executives acknowledge that pop music has lost its beat. "If you look at this year [1996], we haven't seen much that's exciting," says Charles Koppelman, CEO of EMI-Capitol Music Group North America. "Music is the driver."

Hitmakers Hard to Find

Without a hot musical trend in sight, companies have to make tough choices. Their big profits come from the gambles they make on new performers who might create a sensation and zoom to the top of the charts. Everyone wants the next come-from-nowhere hitmakers like the Fugees or Hootie & the Blowfish or a novelty phenomenon like the Macarena, which originated in Spain and spent 14 weeks as the USA's No. 1 song.

Too many bad bets can be costly. Only about one out of every five new music acts sell enough records to merely break even.

To cut through the clutter in the market, record companies often pay more than $500,000 and sometimes as much as $1 million to promote a release by a new performer. It takes about $100,000 just to produce a music video, which is now standard for anyone who must attract a broad following. Companies also pay for the free concerts, give-away records and ads.

At that rate, it's often not good enough for an album to sell 1 million copies which could send it to the top of the charts in the USA.

"We're moving away from a marketplace that's stampeded by the tastemakers.... Right now the public is saying, 'We're open to something new.'"

Sony Music President Thomas Mottola and other industry executives are crafting bold new strategies, including mega-promotions with the film industry and global marketing to counter slowing growth in revenue and album sales. Independent labels, meanwhile, are taking off.

And the Beat Goes On

Music distributors, faced with too many new artists who don't zoom to the top of the record charts, increasingly rely on proven hitmakers to keep the industry pumping.

contributed to the problem: (1) singers use body microphones, which amplify their voices; (2) pop and classical recordings are dubbed and enhanced to a degree "only dreamed of by mere human performers"; and (3) most of the video industry seems based on lip-synchronized and computer-engineered performances.[11]

Recording industry executives claimed that the Milli Vanilli incident was an isolated event. Ironically, though, the technology that contributed to the quality of today's recordings also made the Milli Vanilli hoax possible.

Technology and the Future

From the beginning, profits in the recording industry have been tied to technology. Ever since William Paley and David Sarnoff decided to produce LPs and 45s, the consumer has tracked the equipment manufacturers, looking for better, more convenient sound.

Today, recording companies worry that music pirates will copy digitized music, which can be sent over the Internet. On-line subscribers can now browse through on-line music catalogues, downloading samples of music they like. But once digitized, the music is available to anyone and can be sent over the Internet around the world. The challenge for music company executives is to develop a way to protect this new technology with an even newer technology that will make copying impossible. "The information highway could be bad news if we don't control the right of distribution and receive fair remuneration," says James Fifield, president of EMI Music. "I want my hands on the wheel."[12]

CDs have become the leading format for recordings, boosting industry income because CDs cost consumers more than tapes.

David R. Frazier/Tony Stone Images

Table 6.3

World CD Sales 1996			
Country	CD Sales* in Millions	Population in Millions	Yearly Sales of CDs per Inhabitant
USA	780	260	3
Japan	283	125	2.3
Germany	166	82	2
United Kingdom	160	56	2.6
France	98	56	1.8
Brazil	89	160	0.5
Canada	42	29	1.7
Benelux	52	25	2
Australia	35	18	2
Spain	35	38	0.9
Mexico	31	90	0.3
Italy	28	57	0.5
South Korea	22	44	0.5

*These figures are estimates; the data do not include self-produced albums by musicians, small labels, or illegal CDs.

Source: By permission of Alex Merck. Online: http://www.move.de/amm/CDMarket.htm.

When Thomas Edison demonstrated his phonograph for the editors of *Scientific American* in 1877, the magazine reported that

> Mr. Thomas Edison recently came into this office, placed a little machine on our desk, turned a crank, and the machine inquired as to our health, asked how we liked the phonograph, informed us that it was very well, and bid us a cordial good night. These remarks were not only perfectly audible to ourselves, but to a dozen or more persons gathered around.[13]

None of the discoveries by Edison's successors has been a new invention, only a refinement. Berliner flattened the cylinder; Goldmark and Sarnoff slowed down the speed; hi-fi, stereo, and quadraphonic sound increased the fidelity; and cassettes, compact discs, and digital recorders refined the sound further. But the basic invention remains Edison's.

Reflecting on the movie version of Edison's life, Robert Metz discusses the importance of Edison's development of the phonograph:

> [A] tinkerer employed in the Edison labs ... was shown playing with a makeshift device consisting of a rotating piece of metal with a pointed piece of metal scratching its surface. The device was full of sound and fury and signified a great deal. Edison seized upon the idea and labored to construct a better device. Eventually he was seen speaking into a metal diaphragm whose vibrations in turn wiggled a needle pressed against a rotating cylinder of wax. And thus, supposedly through idle play, came the first permanent "record" of ephemeral sound. By any measure, it was an invention of genius.[14]

In Focus

◎ Rapidly changing technology affects the recording industry more quickly than some media industries.

◎ Thomas Edison first demonstrated his phonograph in 1877. Emile Berliner developed the gramophone in 1887. Berliner and Eldrige Johnson formed the Victor Talking Machine Company (later RCA Victor) to sell recordings. Joseph Maxfield perfected recording equipment to eliminate the tinny sound.

◎ The first standard records were 78 rpm. The long-playing record (33⅓ rpm) was developed by Peter Goldmark, working for William Paley. The 45 rpm record was developed by David Sarnoff's staff at RCA. Eventually, record players were sold that could play all three record speeds.

◎ High fidelity became popular in the early 1950s, and eventually stereo and quadraphonic sound followed.

◎ The recording industry's efforts to improve recorded sound quality contributed to the success of rock 'n' roll entertainers like Elvis Presley.

◎ The CRTC imposed the CANCON requirement in 1970, which stated that 30 percent of all AM music must be Canadian in origin. In order to be Canadian in origin, a piece of music must contain two of four of the so-called MAPL elements (music, artist, production, and lyrics). This provision encouraged both the production of Canadian recordings and the development of Canadian talent.

◎ A recording company is divided into artists and repertoire, operations, marketing and promotion, distribution, and administration.

◎ About 200 companies in Canada and 5000 companies in the United States produce recordings. These companies sell about 900 million records, cassettes, and compact discs a year. The industry collects income from direct sales, music licensing, and music videos, but recording industry income today is flat.

◎ Three issues facing today's recording industry are piracy, attempts to control the content of recordings, and the authenticity of artists' performances.

◎ The recording industry, like the movie industry, responded to threats of government regulation of music lyrics by adopting its own standards for record labelling.

◎ Technology is changing the industry very quickly. Advances in recording technology contributed to the possibility of inauthentic performances being sold as authentic. Digital audiotape (DAT) recorders could replace today's current technologies. Other promising projects include: recordable compact discs; compact discs that provide audio, video, and computer information; digital audio on television; and a credit card-sized audio disc.

Review Questions

1. Describe the battle waged between David Sarnoff and William Paley. Whose technology ended up as the industry standard? Why?

2. Why are the recording industry and the radio industry so interdependent?

3. Describe how each of the following issues has affected the recording industry:
   a. piracy
   b. CANCON
   c. record labelling for explicit content

4. Name the six big companies of the recording industry. How do they control most of the music heard in North America?

Watching the Web

◎ **CD Now (CD Sales)**

   http://www.cdnow.com

◎ **Grateful Dead Concerts Online**

   http://www.deadradio.com

◎ **Lilith Fair**

   http://lilithfair.excite.com/

◎ **Real Networks**

   http://www.real.com

◎ **Recording Industry Association of America**

   http://www.riaa.com/

◎ **Sony**

   http://www.sony.com

TELEVISION

7

> FROM THE BEGINNING, OUR TELEVISION POLICY HAS EITHER BEEN CULTURE-BUILDING OR INDUSTRY-BUILDING ... IT'S TIME TO SHIFT THE EMPHASIS MORE TOWARD THE CULTURAL PRONG.[1]

Pat Ferns, organizer of the Banff Television Festival

What's Ahead

Canadians watched television an average of 22.8 hours a week in the fall of 1996, a substantial number, though lower than the 23.2 hours they logged in 1995.[2] Americans spent even more time in front of the TV— on average, 49 hours a week, according to the A.C. Nielsen Company, which monitors television usage for advertisers.

It's not surprising that the effects of such a pervasive medium have attracted so much attention from parents, educators, social scientists, religious leaders, public officials, and anyone else who is concerned with society's habits and values. TV has been blamed for everything from declines in literacy to rises in violent crime to the trivialization of politics. And every once in a while it is praised, too, for giving viewers instant access to world events and uniting audiences in times of national crisis.

An industry with this much presence in the household is bound to affect the way we live. Someone who is watching television is not doing other things: playing a sport, visiting a museum, or looking through a telescope at the stars, for instance. Television, however, can bring you a museum you might never visit, take you to a basketball game you cannot attend, or show you more of the solar system than you could ever see through a telescope.

The technology of television, adding the reach of pictures to the sounds of radio, has truly transformed North American living and learning patterns. And the word *television*, which once meant programs delivered by antennas through over-the-air signals, now means a *television screen*, where a variety of delivery systems brings viewers a diversity of programs.

The programs we watch today are delivered by antennas, cables, and satellites, but they all appear on the same television screen; as a viewer, you can't tell how the program arrived at your television set and probably don't care. What you do know is that television gives you access to all types of programs—drama, comedy, sports, news, game shows, and talk shows. You can see all kinds of people—public officials, foreign leaders, reporters, soldiers, entertainers, athletes, detectives, criminals, doctors. The television screen is truly, as scholar Erik Barnouw observed, a "tube of plenty."

Commentator Jeff Greenfield writes:

> The most common misconception most people have about television concerns its product. To the viewer, the product is the programming. To the television executive, the product is the audience.
>
> Strictly speaking, television networks and stations do not make any money by producing a program that audiences want to watch. The money comes from selling advertisers the right to broadcast a message to that audience. The programs exist to capture the biggest possible audiences.[3]

To understand why we get the programming we do, it is important to remember that *television exists primarily as an advertising medium.* Programming surrounds the advertising, but it is the advertising that is being delivered to the audience. Commercial television, from its inception was created and nurtured to deliver audiences to advertisers.

Because television can deliver a larger audience faster than any other medium, television can charge the highest rates of any medium for its advertising—which makes TV stations rich investments. A 30-second ad during a U.S. network television program, for example, costs an average of US$134 000, but during a widely watched program like the Super Bowl (with an estimated audience of half the U.S. population), a 30-second ad costs nearly US$1.3 million. A prime-time, 30-second spot sold by Global TV costs C$60 000.

Today, even the smallest television station is a multimillion-dollar operation. The television era began much more humbly, and with very little excitement, near the turn of the century.

Table 7.1

Television Advertising Volume

Network	Time Period	Minutes of Commercial Time Allowed per Hour
TVO	Children's programming, all hours	0*
CBC, YTV	Children's programming, all hours	12* (max.)
	pre-school programming	0*
Other Canadian networks	Children's programming, all hours	8
	All shows, after 6 p.m.	12.5
U.S. networks	Children's programming, 4–6 p.m.	12
U.S. networks	Children's prime time programming	9.5
	All other shows	16

Source: Prime Time Parent Kit, 1996 (*updated 1998). The Alliance for Children and Television. Reprinted with permission.

Television Technology: Beginnings

The word *television* first appeared in the June 1907 issue of *Scientific American*.[4] Before then, experiments in image transmission had been called "visual wireless," "visual radio," and "electric vision."

Alexander Graham Bell's telephone and Samuel F.B. Morse's telegraph contributed to the idea of sending electrical impulses over long distances. The first major technological discovery to suggest that pictures also could travel was the *Nipkow disk*. Twenty-four-year-old Paul Nipkow patented his "electrical telescope" in Germany in 1884. This disk, which formed the basis for television's development through the 1920s, was about the size of a phonograph record, perforated with a spiral of tiny holes.

Also crucial in television's (and radio's) development were Guglielmo Marconi, Lee de Forest, and Edward Samuel Rogers (see Chapter 5). Marconi eliminated sound's dependence on wires and put sound on airwaves. De Forest contributed the Audion tube, which amplified radio waves so that people could hear the sound clearly, and Samuel Rogers's tube allowed the device to be plugged into a wall socket.

IMPACT

Point of View

By John Allemang

CHANNEL SURFING THROUGH THE DIFFERENT APPROACHES TO PUBLIC MOURNING

Grief, it used to be said, is a very private thing. No longer. The displays of emotion that accompanied the death and funeral of Diana, Princess of Wales, have brought mourning into the public domain. Of all the ways that members of the House of Windsor have come to seem out of date, their innate ability to repress feelings has come to bother people the most.

This is one of Diana's lasting achievements, that she took a virtue of the Royal Family—a stiff-upper-lip fortitude that was disturbed by nothing—and turned it into an object of scorn. When we watched the Royal Family emerge from Buckingham Palace on Saturday morning to meet the funeral cortege, it was an acknowledgement that Diana had won, but also a belated acceptance that television tells the real story.

It doesn't, of course. It tells many different stories. If you wanted Diana's funeral to be a thing of quiet and dignified reverence – the kind of WASPish qualities the Windsors are scorned for, but never mind – then there was the CBC and the respectful Peter Mansbridge. If you like your anchor to be more of a showman, then CTV's grandiose Lloyd Robertson was the better choice.

Both C-PAC and A&E picked up the hushed-voice but urbane BBC coverage that makes a solemn ceremonial occasion sound exactly like the final hole at the British Open. The BBC was exceptionally skilled at spotting celebrities, which was an important part of the TV coverage. Certainly when Elton John's male companion could be seen blowing kisses across Westminster Abbey, it was clear that, as analysts never tired of

saying, a new Britain was being ushered in.

But it was the three major U.S. networks that were the most interesting to watch, if only because they don't seem to share the Canadian networks' deference to death and royalty. While CTV squeezed few insights out of the bland, amiable Robertson and flighty Valerie Pringle, Global was essentially limited to the over-correct Peter Kent and CBC was low-key to the point of silence (not a bad decision, especially when the alternative was Mansbridge obsessing about the speed of the motorcade), the U.S. networks were abuzz with gush, wordy solemnity and unstoppable analysis.

Americans, while more infatuated with the glamour of royalty, are also more willing to question its assumptions. CBS was least able to rise to the challenge, combining fuddy-duddy commentary of British experts with the empty babbling of a portentous Dan Rather. Not only did he make British historian David Starkey recite *God Save the Queen*, but he then asked him whether Diana's burial on an island was a reminder of the legend of King Arthur.

NBC and ABC were much more clued in to the real world, to the point of offence for those who prefer their funerals straight. NBC was the most intrusive of all the networks, providing voice-over commentary during the service in the abbey, with even the hymns being analysed by a Church of England cleric. Anchor Tom Brokaw could not get New Yorker editor (and British expatriate) Tina Brown to open up. She was oddly maudlin, worrying about Diana's children in a way that suggested

she was too close to the subject, showing the kind of feelings journalists are normally expected to leave at the door. Her reticence had its opposite in the uncontrolled outbursts of NBC's Katie Couric—"O look, there's Tom Hanks."

The U.S. networks' reverence for celebrities was given a new legitimacy with the death of Diana. Elton John's elegy during the funeral service was treated as a solemn rock video by NBC and CBS. But ABC carried itself with more sophistication. Like other networks, it caught the telling scenes of the day—the Queen giving a slight nod as Diana's cortege went by, Prince Harry's handwritten card reading "Mummy" propped up on the flowers on the coffin—but the network attempted to tell as well as show.

ABC anchor Peter Jennings was masterly in presiding over an argumentative and energetic group of experts that included the doyenne of celebrity chasers, Barbara Walters, Prince Charles's hypercritical biographer, Anthony Holden, and Diana's former journalistic confidant, Andrew Morton. Here, and here alone, the British contingent seemed to be modern in its outlook and clued in to North American needs, refusing to dwell on the ceremonial archaisms that entranced the other networks. And perhaps because Jennings is a Canadian, he could talk about both Diana and the Royal Family with a brisk confidence and no-nonsense directness

The Globe and Mail, *September 8, 1997, p. A4. Reprinted with permission from the Globe and Mail.*

In 1927, U.S. Secretary of Commerce Herbert Hoover appeared on a 2-inch screen by wire in an experimental AT&T broadcast. On September 11, 1928, General Electric broadcast the first dramatic production, *The Queen's Messenger*—the sound came over station WGY, Schenectady, and the picture came from experimental television station W2XAD. All of the pictures were close-ups, and their quality could best be described as primitive.

Two researchers, one working for a company and one working alone, brought television into the electronic age. Then the same man who was responsible for radio's original popularity, RCA's David Sarnoff, became television's biggest promoter.

Vladimir Zworykin was working for Westinghouse when he developed an all-electronic system to transform a visual image into an electronic signal. Zworykin's electronic signal travelled through the air. When the signal reached the television receiver, the signal was transformed again into a visual image for the viewer.

Philo T. Farnsworth, working alone in California, developed the cathode ray tube (which he called a dissector tube). He later received financial and lab support from the Philco Company in Philadelphia. Farnsworth's cathode ray tube used an electronic scanner to reproduce the electronic image much more clearly than Nipkow's earlier mechanical scanning device. In 1930, 24-year-old Farnsworth patented his electronic scanner.

NBC television's commercial debut was at the 1939 World's Fair in New York City at the Hall of Television. On April 30, 1939, U.S. president Franklin D. Roosevelt formally opened the fair and became the first president to appear on television. Sarnoff also spoke, and RCA displayed its 5-inch and 9-inch sets, priced from $199.50 to $600.[5]

NBC and CBS were the original TV networks. As explained in Chapter 5, a network is a collection of radio or television stations that offers programs, usually simultaneously, during designated program times. ABC, developed from the old Blue network of NBC in 1943, laboured from its earliest days to equal the other two networks but didn't have as many affiliates as NBC and CBS. The two leading networks already had secured the more powerful, well-established broadcast outlets for themselves. David Sarnoff, head of NBC, and William Paley, head of CBS, controlled the network game.

Canadian television broadcasting can be traced back to the early 1930s and a rudimentary system established by Alphonse Ouimet in Montreal. Though this system foundered, Ouimet himself became a senior engineering officer at the CBC (and later was president). Once given the permission by the federal government to proceed, Ouimet established the first television stations in Canada for the CBC in Montreal (CBFT—initially handling both English and

French broadcasts) and Toronto (CBLT) in September of 1952. At that time, U.S. television signals were already present in those two cities, but only with the use of expensive and cumbersome mast antennas on houses. These antennas eventually adorned the roofs of houses in urban Canada until the advent of cable TV signal delivery in the mid-1950s. In many locations, the antenna mast itself included a motor, controlled from inside the house, to rotate and reorient the antenna to pick up distant and faint U.S. channels.

By 1954, CBC stations had been constructed in Halifax, Ottawa, Vancouver, and Winnipeg, and privately owned affiliates were beginning to appear in smaller cities. By 1957, 85 percent of the Canadian population could receive CBC programming.

Today, the CBC television networks deliver programming to all parts of the country by direct transmission, repeater transmitters in rural locations, cable-TV systems, community antennas, and direct satellite transmissions. The CBC enjoys a wide measure of public acceptance. It even has its own independent nongovernmental cheering section, the Friends of Public Broadcasting. Its spokesperson, Ian Morrison, can be counted on for a supportive public statement in times of budgetary stress and cutbacks.

Television Takes Over Radio

In 1945, ten U.S. television stations were on the air. Black-and-white television replaced radio so quickly as the major advertising medium that it would be easy to believe that television erupted suddenly in a surprise move to kill radio. But remember that the two major U.S. network executives who developed television—Sarnoff and Paley—also held the largest financial interest in radio. They used their profits from radio to develop television, foreseeing that television would eventually expand their audience and their income.

A New Kind of News

Long before there was significant television broadcasting in Canada, the standard means and methods of television programming emerged south of the border. Border stations were viewable in southern Ontario, and the programming was influential in establishing the principles of how television programs were to be produced. Nowhere were these conventions more evident than in the news.

Broadcast news, pioneered by radio, adapted awkwardly at first to the new broadcast medium—television. According to David Brinkley, a broadcast news pioneer who began at NBC,

> When television came along in about 1947–48, the bigtime newsmen of that day—H.V. Kaltenborn, Lowell Thomas—did not want to do television. It was a lot of work, they weren't used to it, they were doing very well in radio, making lots of money. They didn't want to fool with it. So I was told to do it by the news manager. I was a young kid and, as I say, the older, more established people didn't want to do it. Somebody had to.[6]

In 1947, CBS initiated *Television News* with Douglas Edwards, and NBC broadcast *Camel News Caravan* (sponsored by Camel cigarettes) with John

Cameron Swayze. Eventually, David Brinkley joined Swayze for NBC's 15-minute national newscast. He recalls:

> The first broadcasts were extremely primitive by today's standards. It was mainly just sitting at a desk and talking. We didn't have any pictures at first. Later we began to get a little simple news film, but it wasn't much.
>
> In the beginning, people would call after a program and say in tones of amazement that they had seen you. "I'm out here in Bethesda, and the picture's wonderful." They weren't interested in anything you said. They were just interested in the fact that you had been on their screen in their house.[7]

At first, network TV news reached only the East Coast of the United States because the necessary civilian web of microwave transmission networks was not yet in place to deliver television across the continent. By 1948, AT&T's coaxial cable linked Philadelphia with New York and Washington. In 1952, AT&T's national coaxial hookups joined 108 stations across the United States.

In Canada, regular news programs began in 1954 on both French and English networks. There were also distinctive public affairs telecasts, such as *Close-Up* and *Point de Mire* with René Lévesque, and a dinnertime chat show from Toronto called *Tabloid*, which captured a dedicated audience.

News and public affairs programming proved to be much cheaper to produce than entertainment programming, so there was a powerful impetus for its development at the CBC. From the news tradition eventually emerged *This Hour Has Seven Days* in 1963, an innovative public affairs show that involved pointed political criticism, editorializing, audience participation, and novel camera work. Its style was widely copied. A counterpart on CTV was the program *W5*, which is still on the air. All in all, the strength of early Canadian television was in news and public affairs, a situation which remains true today, though the professional sports telecasting in Canada is without peer anywhere.

Despite the critical success of some Canadian television shows, such as CTV's *Due South*, Canadian programs make up less than 9 percent of the dramas we watch.[8]

CP Picture Archive (Chris Wood)

Entertainment Programming

By the time the CBC began television broadcasts in 1952, the stream of programming from the U.S. networks had already become familiar fare in many Canadian households. The task of the CBC and the private affiliates was to create distinctive programming, which would enhance the imported content. The CBC's nationalistic mandate to create programs that reflected the Canadian reality led to tension with the affiliates whose motives were more profit-oriented. Much of the evening schedule belonged to imported U.S. programs.

Canadian content (CANCON) regulations for television appeared in 1959. According to rules announced by the Board of Broadcast Governors, television stations would have to program at least 45 percent Canadian content by April 1, 1961, and 55 per cent by April 1, 1962.

Additional private networks were also licensed to provide alternatives, including CTV in 1961, TVA in Quebec in 1971, and Global in 1974. Provincial educational networks were added to the mix around this time as well (for instance, TVOntario, ACCESS, and B.C.'s Knowledge Network). Cable television service was also promoted in order to multiply the range of viewing choices.

Giving up direct competition with Hollywood productions, Canadian networks sought to create their own niches in news and public affairs and minor entertainment programming, including musical shows, such as *The Irish Rovers*, and children's programs).

Early television was like late radio with pictures: It offered quiz shows, variety shows, situation comedies, drama, Westerns, detective stories, Hollywood movies, soap operas, talk shows, and children's programs. The only type of show that television offered that radio did not (besides movies, of course) was the talk show. (Ironically, today's radio has created call-in programs, its own version of the talk show.)

Quiz Shows. CBS's *$64,000 Question* premiered June 7, 1955, and was sponsored by Revlon. Contestants answered questions from a glass "isolation booth." Successful contestants returned in succeeding weeks to increase their winnings, and Revlon advertised its Living Lipstick. By September, the program was drawing 85 percent of the audience, and Revlon had substituted an ad for another product; its factory supply of Living Lipstick had completely sold out.

Many network quiz shows like *The $64,000 Question* were produced by sponsors for the networks, and these programs often carried the sponsor's name. In the 1958–59 quiz show scandals, Revlon was implicated when a U.S. congressional subcommittee investigated charges that the quiz shows were rigged to enhance the ratings.

Charles Van Doren admitted before the congressional subcommittee that he had been fed the answers by the quiz show *Twenty-One*'s producer. Staff members from other quiz shows added to Van Doren's testimony. The scandals caused the networks to reexamine the relationship between advertisers and programs. Before the scandals, one-quarter to one-third of network programming was produced by advertisers and their agencies. The networks began to look to other sources, and by the late 1960s, advertisers provided less than 3 percent of network programming. Soon, advertisers provided no network shows, and the networks programmed themselves.

The Canadian quiz show *Front Page Challenge* went on the air in 1957 and featured a panel of prominent media figures in Canada, who tried to guess the identity of a mystery guest. Quiz shows have resurfaced today with *Wheel of Fortune*, *Family Feud*, and *Jeopardy*.

Variety Shows. The biggest radio stars jumped to the new medium. Three big variety-show successes were Milton Berle's *Texaco Star Theater*, *The Admiral Broadway Revue* (later *Your Show of Shows*) with Imogene Coca and Sid Caesar, and Ed Sullivan's *Toast of the Town* (later *The Ed Sullivan Show*). These weekly shows featured comedy sketches and appearances by popular entertainers. *The Ed Sullivan Show*, for example, is where most North Americans got their first glimpse of Elvis Presley and the Beatles. The Wayne and Shuster comedy programs were popular in Canada, and were later transplanted to the *Ed Sullivan Show* in New York. All of the shows were broadcast live.

The time slot in which these programs were broadcast, 7–11 p.m., is known as **prime time**. Prime time simply means that more people watch television during this period than any other, so advertising during this period costs more. Berle's 8 p.m. program during prime time on Tuesday nights often gathered 85 percent of the audience. *Texaco Star Theater* became so popular that one laundromat installed a TV set and advertised "Watch Berle while your clothes twirl."

Situation Comedies. Along with drama, the **situation comedy** (sitcom) proved to be one of TV's most durable types of programs. The situation comedy, a decidedly American invention, established a fixed set of characters in either a home or work situation. *I Love Lucy*, starring Lucille Ball and Desi Arnaz, originated from Los Angeles because the actors wanted to live on the West Coast. In 1951, Ball began a career as a weekly performer on CBS that lasted for 23 years. *Friends* and *Frasier* are examples of more contemporary situation comedy successes.

Drama. *The Loretta Young Show* offered noontime drama—broadcast live—every day in the 1950s. *The Hallmark Hall of Fame* established a tradition of high-quality dramatic, live presentations. For many years, TV dramas were limited to 1- or 2-hour programs. But in the 1970s, encouraged by the success of Alex Haley's *Roots*, which dramatized Haley's search for the story of his African ancestry, television began to broadcast as many as 14 hours of a single drama over several nights.

Canadian attempts to duplicate the success of American dramatic television series have not been very successful, though the 1960s productions of *Wojack* (starring John Vernon as a crusading coroner modelled on Morton Shulman) and *Quentin Durgens MP* (starring Gordon Pinsent) were successes in their time, as has been *Due South*, which went on the air in 1994. Other past successes include *The Beachcombers*, with Bruno Gerussi, which depicted life in a rustic town on the coast of British Columbia. It is still shown around the world in reruns. *The Beachcombers* was essentially a situation comedy filmed on location.

Often, the Canadian series that are domestically successful are those that step outside of the U.S. model. Programs such as *The Beachcombers*, *North of 60*, and *E.N.G.* are popular because they are innovative formats and, perhaps, because they reflect to Canadians our unique culture. Shows such as these would be unlikely to receive a warm welcome south of the boarder. Some Canadian programs, however, have been successful when broadcast to the PBS audience in the United States, including low-budget comedy shows such as *The Red Green Show*, *Kids in the Hall*, and *SCTV*.

French-language television drama, in particular, has been voluminous, with hundreds of plays, miniseries, and children's programs broadcast in Canada over the years. The tradition of dramatic television programming began on the first evening of television broadcasting in Montreal, in September 1952, when Cocteau's *Oedipe-Roi* was shown. In the early days, CBFT broadcast at least one play a week, and by 1958 it was producing 100 hours of televised theatre annually.

On the French network of the CBC, *La Famille Plouffe* went on the air in 1953 and lasted for many years, for some time with a parallel English-language variant. Written by Roger Lemelin, the show was broadcast in weekly 30-minute segments from September to May. The show dealt with the everyday lives of members of a large, traditional Quebec family. It may have been loosely modelled on a popular U.S. television show called *Momma*, which predated it, though the U.S. show contained more sentimentality and stereotypical relationships.

Much of the dramatic production for television has been of the works of Quebec playwrights, such as Michel Tremblay. In this way, television drama has played a central role in the development of serious culture in Canada's francophone communities. Running parallel with the dramatic productions have been a succession of popular variety and music shows, as well as a number of successful comedy productions.

Westerns. TV went Western in 1954, when Jack "I'm just another millionaire" Warner of Warner Bros. (another Canadian in the U.S. entertainment business) signed an agreement with ABC to provide the network with a program called *Cheyenne*. The outspoken Warner had openly criticized TV's effect on the movie business, but when ABC asked Warner to produce programs for them, Warner Bros. became the first movie company to realize that the studios could profit from television.

Detective Stories. *Dragnet*, with Sergeant Friday, was an early TV experiment with detectives. The genre became a TV staple: *Dragnet*'s successors in the 1990s are programs like *NYPD Blue* and *Law and Order*.

Movies. The movie industry at first resisted the competition from TV but then realized there was money to be made in selling old movies to TV. In 1957, RKO sold 740 pre-1948 movies to television for US$25 million. The other studios followed. Through various distribution agreements, movie reruns and movies produced specifically for television were added to television's program lineup.

Soap Operas. Borrowed from radio serials, soap operas filled in morning television programming. Today, game shows and reruns are more popular choices, but programs like *The Young and the Restless* survive. Soap operas have their own magazines, and some newspapers carry weekly summaries of plot development.

Talk Shows. Sylvester "Pat" Weaver (actress Sigourney Weaver's father) created and produced television's single original contribution to programming: the talk show. Weaver's *Tonight Show* (originally *Jerry Lester's Broadway Open House*) first appeared in 1954. Through a succession of hosts from Lester to Steve Allen to Jack Paar to Johnny Carson and Jay Leno, *The Tonight Show* has lasted longer than any other talk show on television. Modern-day imitators include David Letterman and Conan O'Brien, and the format has been copied on networks around the world, with mixed results. One of the weirdest talk shows was a 1990 British program in which the guest joined the host in bed for their televised conversation.

Children's Programs. One of the strengths of Canadian Television has been its programming for children. Beginning with radio segments broadcast in mid-morning to children in schools, often on school intercoms, the CBC has produced a large volume of programming directed at children. Most notable in this long tradition are *Chez Hélène*, which attempted to bring elementary French instruction to anglophone primary-school students, and, of course, *The Friendly Giant*, with Bob Homme, a gentle mid-afternoon program of fantasy and stories aimed at the very young. *Mr. Dressup* also deserves a mention. It was produced for many years by CTV as a mid-morning story-telling show, with Ernie Coombs and his cast of puppets.

Table 7.2

Milestones in Canadian Television
1957 *Front Page Challenge* (CBC)
1963 *This Hour Has Seven Days* (CBC)
1965 *W5* (CTV)
1971 *The Beachcombers* (CBC)
1973 *Definition* (CTV)
1974 *King of Kensington* (CBC)
1977 *SCTV* (City-TV/Global)
1979 *The Littlest Hobo* (CTV)
1984 *Night Heat* (CTV)
1985 *Street Legal* (CBC)
1989 *E.N.G.* (CTV)
Road to Avonlea (CBC)
1993 *This Hour Has 22 Minutes* (CBC)
1994 *Due South* (CTV)
1996 *Traders* (CTV)

Source: Doug Saunders, "Why Canadian TV Will Soon Be More Canadian," the *Globe and Mail*, July 25, 1998. Reprinted with permission from the *Globe and Mail*.

Canadian Government Subsidizes TV

In addition to providing operating grants for the CBC, the government of Canada is currently spending $100 million per year through the Canada Television and Cable Production Fund. Federal funding is matched by money from the cable companies and Telefilm Canada, resulting in a fund of $200 million annually. Leveraged with private money, this funding resulted in $625 million worth of Canadian television production in 1997 (or about 2200 hours of content at about $300 000 per finished hour to produce). Much of this programming is seen on networks both inside and outside of Canada. The main purpose of these programs is to support the production of Canadian content. A secondary purpose is to expand sales of Canadian programs to other countries.

IMPACT

on You   *TV FOR C.B.*

By Lila MacLellan

In this humorous article, a Vancouver writer describes watching BCTV on a cable channel in C.B.—Cape Breton, that is.

It's Saturday night, and two men are sitting in front of a colour TV in Shindigs, a Granville Street bar, watching indifferently as the Canucks struggle through a home game. During the break, a news update reports yet another home invasion on the east side. "Geez, b'y," says one to the other, "You're hardly safe in your own living room out there. It's right wild."

The lilting accent is your first clue that all is not what it appears. There's also the lack of traffic outside. And even if Squire Barnes is on the screen, you can't see Grouse Mountain from here. Finally, a sure sign that this isn't lotus land: not a single creamy, pale or auburn microbrew on tap. Shindigs sits on Granville Street, true—but it's Granville Street in Port Hawkesbury, Nova Scotia.

Illogical as it sounds, the Strait of Canso cable company in Port Hawkesbury—a mill town of 4,800 people, some 6,000 kilometres from Vancouver—has included BCTV in its package for the past seven months. People there appreciate the opportunity to watch soaps in the evening and sitcoms until the wee hours. Thanks to BCTV newscasts, they also enjoy keeping up on what's happening at this end of the country. Every day they get a close look at our city, a peek at our collective diary. Vancouverites couldn't point to Port Hawkesbury on a map, people there know us well—and they offer mixed reviews.

Thumbs up, they say to the highrises, golf courses, bridges, mountains and warm weather. Tired of their own dismal news of plant closures and layoffs, they turn to Channel 28 for a rosier example of Canadian coastal living. "It seems like a clean, nice, decent city," says Chuck Moar, a Port Hawkesvury resident. His teenage son, Joey, agrees. "It's like they can't help but have a beautiful scene in the background." A skyline of condo towers and the heavy Asian influence give Vancouver a cosmopolitan, city-of-the future air (unlike charming, antiquated Halifax). Not surprisingly, Vancouver is most often compared to Hong Kong or Los Angeles, not Montreal or Toronto.

However, press on and these objective observers will tell you other things about Vancouver. "Nice," one says, "but isn't it awful, all the drugs out there." The people of Port Hawkesbury sometimes catch nightmarish glimpses of the downtown eastside (which they confuse with the downtown area in general). They can list our main concerns: crime, teenage delinquency, homelessness, the rapid spread of HIV. Archie MacInnis takes issue with the B.C. logging industry. "I mean, god almighty, everyone has to make a living, but once you cut down all those trees you'll never get them back," he notes. "I'm fascinated by the cost of living," says Mayor Billy Joe MacLean. "You wonder how an average Joe could afford a house."

Back at Shindigs, your average Joe takes a swig of Moosehead as weatherman Wayne Cox sips a latte before his live forecast. Cox tries to make five more days of rain sound enjoyable. The viewer knows better: "She's beautiful, but she's a wet one," Looks like we can keep our greener grass (and smoke it, too).

Vancouver, 31, no. 3, April 1998, p. 12. Reprinted with permission.

Canadians Have Diverse Viewing Habits

Basic viewing and listening data for Canada are collected by the BBM and are analyzed by Statistics Canada. The target population includes all persons two years of age and older in the case of television, and data are collected annually over a four-week period in November. Another organization, Nielsen Media Research, collects weekly data through providing paper diaries and electronic devices. Nielsen numbers tend to be a bit lower because they do not include the viewing of videotapes, which are not really broadcasts at all.

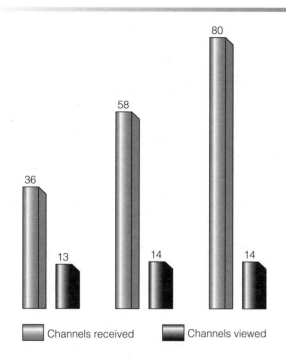

Figure 7.1 Number of Channels Received and Viewed in the Average Household

People don't watch more channels when more are available. The average household receives 36 TV channels but watches fewer than half. Even when people can receive as many as 80 channels, they watch only 14.

Source: Data from Nielsen Media Research for the Network Television Association.

■ Channels received   ■ Channels viewed

Of the various broad population groups, older Canadian women watch the most television and young men the least. Canadian viewers have a wide set of choices (possibly the largest TV menu in the world) among Canadian- and U.S.-produced content and a limited amount of programming produced elsewhere (for example, TV5 from France is provided on many cable systems and the BBC World Service news is periodically available).

Francophone and anglophone communities in Canada have markedly different viewing habits, as do households where neither official language is spoken. Francophones tend to watch more Canadian than U.S. programs as a result of the thriving Quebec star system and the fact that television in Quebec enjoys an uncommon acceptance among intellectuals. The francophone audience for news and public affairs programming is substantially larger than for comedy shows. (See Table 7.2 on the following page.)

Canadians tend to watch more dramatic programming of foreign origin, probably because of the greater selection of high-budget U.S. programs. However, many dramatic series of "foreign" origin are, in fact, produced for U.S. networks in either Vancouver or Toronto (for instance, *Millennium*, *The Sentinel*, *Highlander*, and *Nikita*). The same is true for much comedy programming. Though produced in the United States, many comedy programs feature Canadian actors, writers, producers, and directors. This presence goes right back to the beginnings of film comedy, with Ben Blue and Mack Sennett, who was born in Richmond, Ontario, in 1880, and became the founder of Keystone Studios, patron of the Keystone Kops series of slapstick silent movies, and the man who brought Charlie Chaplin from England to Hollywood via a vaudeville stage in Vancouver.

Table 7.2

Type of Program	Canadian Programs		Foreign Programs		Total	
	Anglo	Franco	Anglo	Franco	Anglo	Franco
Distribution of Television Viewing by Persons Two Years and Older of Each Official Language Community in Canada, Fall 1996						
News & public affairs	15	28	6.6	1.4	22	29.4
Documentary	0.8	1.1	2.3	0.7	3.2	1.9
Instruction						
Academic	0.6	1.4	0.7	0.1	1.3	1.5
Social/recreational	0.3	0.3	0.9	0.2	1.2	0.5
Religion	0.2	0.3	0.1	–	0.3	0.3
Sports	6.8	4.6	3.2	0.8	10.0	5.4
Variety and games	1.5	15.8	6.8	1.7	8.3	17.5
Music and dance	0.5	0.8	0.6	0.2	1.1	1.0
Comedy	0.2	1.5	15.2	7.6	15.4	9.2
Drama	2.4	12.5	25.3	15.3	27.7	27.8
Other/unknown						
VCR	–	–	6.4	4.2	6.4	4.2
Other	–	–	3.1	1.4	3.1	1.4
Total	**28.3%**	**66.3%**	**71.2%**	**33.6%**	**100.0%**	**100.0%**

Note: A dash indicates a proportion too small to be expressed.

Source: Adapted from unnumbered tables in "Television and Radio Audiences," *The Daily*, Catalogue No. 11-001, February 5, 1998. Reprinted with permission from Statistics Canada.

TV Dominates the Airwaves

The 1950s were a trial period for television, as the networks and advertisers tested audience interest in various types of programming. Captured by the miracle that television offered, audiences at first seemed insatiable; they would watch almost anything that TV delivered. But in the 1960s, audiences became more discriminating and began to question how well the medium of television was serving the public.

Newton Minow Targets TV as a "Vast Wasteland"

With television established even in the smaller cities, the medium needed a public conscience. That public conscience was Newton Minow.

An unassuming soothsayer, Minow was named chairman of the U.S. Federal Communications Commission in 1961 by newly elected President John F. Kennedy.

On May 9, 1961, speaking to the National Association of Broadcasters in his first public address since his appointment, Minow articulated what he felt were the broadcasters' responsibilities to the public.

> The public is your beneficiary. If you want to stay on as trustees, you must deliver a decent return to the public—not only to your stockholders....

Ours has been called the jet age, the atomic age, the space age. It is also, I submit, the television age. And just as history will decide whether the leaders of today's world employed the atom to destroy the world or rebuild it for mankind's benefit, so will history decide whether today's broadcasters employed their powerful voice to enrich the people or debase them.[9]

Minow then asked his audience of broadcast station owners and managers to watch their own programs. He said they would find a "vast wasteland," a phrase that resurfaces today during any critical discussion of television.

Satellites Bring Technological Breakthrough

By 1965, all three U.S. networks were broadcasting in colour. Television demonstrated its technological sophistication in December 1968 with its live broadcast from the Apollo spacecraft while the spacecraft circled the moon, and seven months later television showed Neil Armstrong stepping onto the moon.

On July 10, 1962, Telstar I sent the first trans-Atlantic satellite broadcast. Before Telstar, copper cable linked the continents, film footage from overseas travelled only by plane, and in most homes a long-distance telephone call was a special event.

Canadian signal traffic was carried on the U.S. satellites until 1972, when the first of a series of Anik satellites was launched. These satellites now carry most of Canadian domestic communications traffic, including television transmissions. TV cable systems now pick up their signals from these satellites. Direct-to-home satellites, another family of satellites, use different signal frequencies and transmission intensities. Soon, yet another family of satellites will provide telephone and pager communications for any person, anywhere in the world, who has the appropriate handset.

TV News Documents Conflict and Tragedy

Just as radio matured first as an entertainment medium and then expanded to cover important news events, television first established itself with entertainment and then developed a serious news presence. Politicians appeared who instinctively knew how to use television. Television, in turn, learned to use politics as entertainment.

Observers credited John F. Kennedy's 1960 presidential victory partly to his success in his televised debates with Richard Nixon. Kennedy was the first U.S. president to hold live televised news conferences. In July 1962, he oversaw the launch of the first communications satellite, Telstar I. So it was fitting that he be the first president to play Cold War brinksmanship on television, when TV grew to become a part of politics, not just a chronicler of political events.

TV and the Cold War

President Kennedy asked all three networks to clear him time on Monday, October 22, 1962, at 7 p.m. Eastern time. The president had learned that missile sites were being built in Cuba with Russian help.

Kennedy used television to deliver his ultimatum to dismantle the missile bases. "Using the word 'nuclear' eleven times, Kennedy drew a panorama of devastation enveloping the whole hemisphere. The moves that had made such things possible, said Kennedy, could not be accepted by the United States 'if our courage and our commitments are ever to be trusted again by either friend or foe.'"[10]

Kennedy admonished Russian Premier Nikita Khrushchev to stop the ships that the Soviet Union was sending to Cuba to help build the missile sites. Faced with such a visible challenge, the Soviet Union turned its ships around in the Atlantic and sent conciliatory messages to reach a settlement. The Cuban missile "crisis" had, in fact, been a carefully constructed live television drama in which Kennedy performed well.

The Vietnam War

Soon after Kennedy's assassination, the longest-running domestic protest program in Western experience began appearing on U.S. television news, as anti-Vietnam War marchers showed up on camera daily. During live coverage of the Chicago Democratic Convention in 1968, demonstrators faced police in a march toward the convention hall, chanting "The whole world is watching [on television]." Television covered the resulting violence, which caused injuries to hundreds of protesters and to 21 reporters and photographers. Police violence galvanized resistance to this war, to governments, and to the police themselves.

> When the war in Vietnam began to escalate in 1965, it was the television networks, covering the war with few official restrictions, that brought to American homes pictures of the face of war that had never been shown before: not friendly troops welcomed by the populace, but troops setting fire to villages with cigarette lighters; troops cutting off the ears of dead combat foes; allies spending American tax money for personal gain.[11]

Candid reporting from the war itself shook viewers as previous war reporting never had. It contributed very heavily to a crisis of confidence in governmental institutions across the Western world and, arguably, to a similar crisis in Eastern Europe, as well. Morley Safer, a Newfoundlander reporting for CBS television news, covered some of the uglier abuses of U.S. military power in Vietnam in the late 1960s. In one particularly memorable item, shown nationally in the United States on the *CBS Evening News* with Walter Cronkite, he showed U.S. marines setting fire to peasant huts with cigarette lighters. This item had a great effect on the level of domestic support for the war in the United States.

Television Changes Politics

Ironically, television's next live marathon broadcast would chronicle an investigation of the lawlessness of the Nixon presidency—Watergate. The Watergate scandal began when burglars broke into the offices of the Democratic party's national headquarters in the Watergate complex in Washington, D.C., on June 17, 1972. Some of the burglars had ties to President Nixon's reelection committee, as well as to other questionable activities originating in the White House. In the following months, the president and his assistants sought to squelch the resulting investigation. Although Nixon denied knowledge of the break-in and its cover-up, the Senate hearings on the scandal, televised live across the world, created a political sensation. In short, politics became entertainment.

> Running from May through August 1973, and chaired by North Carolina's crusty Sam Ervin, these hearings were a fascinating live exposition of the political process in America, and were "must" television watching as a parade of witnesses told—or evaded telling— what they knew of the broad conspiracy to assure the reelection of Nixon and then to cover up the conspiracy itself.[12]

In 1987, television repeated its marathon coverage of an important national investigation with the Iran–Contra hearings, a congressional investigation of the Reagan administration's role in providing weapons illegally to Nicaraguan Contra rebels. Unlike the Watergate hearings, however, which were covered live by all of the networks daily, the Iran–Contra hearings were covered piecemeal by the networks, which cited commercial considerations. Only Cable News Network (CNN) offered gavel-to-gavel coverage.

The Iran–Contra hearings gave CNN its first opportunity to show that it could offer more comprehensive news programming than the news operations of the three major networks. The all-news network has grown rapidly in recent years, and in 1991 presented precedent-setting news coverage of another kind with its around-the-clock coverage of the Gulf War. Live news reports from the El Rashid Hotel in Baghdad showed errant cruise missiles flying by the hotel room of the two stranded CNN reporters who were giving a play-by-play commentary on the bombardment to viewers worldwide. Politics as entertainment had been succeeded by war as entertainment.

Another pivotal televised event occurred during the days preceding the second secession referendum in Quebec held on October 30, 1995. Voters in Quebec, presented with a somewhat vague and ambiguous question, seemed likely to vote yes to secession on the day before the referendum.

As the defeat of federalism seemed imminent, Prime Minister Jean Chrétien made a televised live address to the entire country. Visibly nervous about the possible outcome of the referendum, he made a sombre plea to Quebec voters to vote no to separation and promised action to recognize Quebec as a distinct society and to guarantee Quebec a de facto veto over constitutional changes.

On the eve of the 1995 Quebec referendum, Jean Chrétien broadcast a message to Canadians on television, promoting federalism.

CP Picture Archive (Jacques Boissinot)

In 1997, television became an international window on grief when the networks broadcast live coverage of the funeral of Diana, Princess of Wales.

Agence France Presse/Corbis-Bettman

Together with a hastily arranged rally in Montreal, the speech helped to change just enough votes to narrowly defeat the yes side.

In 1997, TV became an international window on grief when the networks carried nonstop coverage of the events surrounding the death and funeral of Diana, Princess of Wales.

Television news has matured from its early low-budget beginnings as a 15-minute talking head newscast to today's access to 24-hour coverage of significant news events, and possibly to being an active ingredient in political and military calculations. Today, network television news plays an important role in setting the agenda for discussion of public issues.

Television Captures Courtroom Drama

No account of contemporary television would be complete without mention of the coverage of criminal and civil trials in California. Blessed with access to the courtrooms of California, the worldwide television industry latched on to the Simpson trials and carried hundreds of hours of live coverage and commentary. This coverage made due process into entertainment and elevated live coverage of court proceedings to high drama. If there is a lesson to be learned from this episode, it might be that there is a substantial audience interest in viewing other human beings under stress in an adversarial setting. The winners and losers in the courtroom can be at times as absorbing and fascinating as those in televised professional sports.

MOSES ZNAIMER AND IN-YOUR-FACE TELEVISION

In the former headquarters of the Methodist Church of Canada, on Queen Street West in downtown Toronto, lives CITY-TV, since September of 1972 the oldest Canadian UHF television station and Moses Znaimer's personal experiment in television novelty. First known for broadcasting soft-core pornography (*The Baby Blue Movies* series), it has blossomed into something unique in television. Studios can be viewed through large picture windows at street level; a video booth on the corner is a place where the public can find an audience; dances regularly spill out onto the street; and concerts occur in the parking lot.

All events are covered with handheld mobile cameras. On newscasts, one often sees the face of a victim of crime, lying prone on the street, shot from above by a jiggling camera with continuous commentary from the camera-person-reporter, transmitted live to air from the street. Also ongoing in the same garishly lit building (or on the street in front of it) is *MuchMusic* (*MuchaMusic* in Buenos Aires), Canada's English-language contemporary music channel; *Space the Imagination Channel; Bravo!*, the national arts cable network; and *Fashion Television*, a program that is syndicated around the world. The

building and its activities are what founder Moses Znaimer calls his "Living Movie." Before television, he had dreamed up *Cross-Canada Checkup*, the national phone-in show that CBC radio has been running on Sunday afternoons for decades.

Long gone are the men in suits sitting behind desks and reading scripts. When all is said and done, it is Znaimer's local newscast with its mobile cameras, the editorializing on the street, the standup moving casts of anchors wandering in the red newsroom, and the entertainment acts embedded in the news that have become models for local newscasts everywhere.

Working in Television

A typical television station has eight departments: sales, programming (which includes news as well as entertainment), production, engineering, traffic, promotion, public affairs, and administration.

People in the *sales* department sell the commercial slots for the programs. Advertising is divided into *national* and *local* sales. Advertising agencies usually buy national ads for the products they handle.

The Ford Motor Company, for instance, may buy time on a network for a TV ad that will run simultaneously all over the country. But the local Ford dealers who want you to shop at their showrooms buy their ads directly from the local station. These ads are called local (or spot) ads. For these sales, salespeople (called account executives) at each station negotiate packages of ads, based on their station's rates. These rates are a direct reflection of that station's position in the ratings.

The *programming* department selects the shows that you will see and develops the station's schedule. Network-owned stations, located in big cities, are called **O & O's**, which stands for owned-and-operated. Stations that carry network programming but that are not owned by the networks are called affiliates. Although in the beginning of television in Canada, CBC and, to a lesser extent, CTV, had many affiliates, their numbers have declined as cable delivers network signals from network-owned stations. Previous affiliates are now predominantly independents in local communities.

Independent stations must buy and program all of their own shows, but independents also can keep all of the money they make on advertising. They run some individually produced programs and old movies, but most of their programming consists of reruns of shows that once ran on the networks. Independents buy these reruns from program services called **syndicators**.

Syndicators also sell independently produced programs such as *The Oprah Winfrey Show* and *Wheel of Fortune*. These programs are created and sold either by non-network stations or by independent producers. Stations pay for these first-run syndication programs individually; the price is based on the size of the station's market.

Local news usually makes up the largest percentage of a station's locally produced programming. In some large markets, local news programming runs as long as three hours.

The *production* department manages the programs that the station creates inhouse. This department also produces local commercials for the station.

The *engineering* department makes sure that all of the technical aspects of a broadcast operation are working: antennas, transmitters, cameras, and any other broadcast equipment.

The *traffic* department integrates the advertising with the programming, making sure that all of the ads that are sold are aired when they're supposed to be. Traffic also handles billing for the ads.

The *promotion* department advertises the station—on the station itself, on billboards, on radio, and in the local newspaper. These people also create contests to keep the station visible in the community.

The *public affairs* department often helps organize public events, such as mass jogging events to raise money for a local charity.

Administration handles the paperwork for the station—paycheques and expense accounts, for example.

The Business of Television

Today's most-watched television programs are situation comedies, sports, and feature movies.

Four developments promise to affect the television industry over the next decade: station ownership changes, the shrinking role of the networks, the growth of cable, and changing technology.

Station Ownership Changes

The relaxation of station ownership rules in both Canada and the United States in the last decade means that the major characteristic of the television business today is changing ownership. Television is *concentrating* ownership, but it is also *shifting* ownership, as stations are bought and sold at an unprecedented rate. This has introduced instability and change to an industry that, as recently as 1980, witnessed very few ownership turnovers.

The Networks' Shrinking Role

Advertisers have always provided the economic support for television, so in 1986 the networks were disturbed to see the first decline in revenues in 15 years.

New and continuing developments—such as cable, satellite broadcast, and VCRs—have turned the television dial into a smorgasbord of choices. The audience—and advertisers—are deserting the networks, and network ratings are declining as a result. Because there are so many new sources of information and entertainment for the audience, advertisers are looking for new ways to capture viewers.

The network share of the *prime-time audience* in the United States has gone from 90 percent in 1978 to about 58 percent today, reflecting the continued growth of independent TV stations, syndicated programming, and satellite and cable systems. The networks' share of the audience for the evening news also is shrinking. The proliferation of new independent stations, regional networks, cable channels, and U.S. superstations on cable TV has had a similar effect on the major networks in Canada.

The story is a familiar one, paralleling radio in the late 1940s as it first was supplanted by television and then began competing with itself. More stations and more sources of programming mean that the networks will have to redefine their audience and give the audience what it cannot get elsewhere.

Cable Challenges Broadcast

Canada has relied on coaxial cable distribution systems for television transmission from an early date. Because of the huge distances between populated areas in the country, cable proved an ideal alternative to high transmission and reception towers. First with local community antenna systems, and then with commercial franchise operators and satellite "head ends," cable TV has become standard in Canadian households (of which approximately 80 percent now have cable). One of the first places where commercial cable TV appeared was in London, Ontario, in the mid-1950s. It was installed to deliver off-air signals from stations in Cleveland, Erie, and Detroit. In a sense, London was the proving ground for the use of community antennas, and its easy acceptance led to the advanced systems we have today. London Cable also experimented with two-way cable in the early 1970s.

Tiered services appeared later as the conventional dial filled up. At first, converters were required and later, descramblers. The technical arrangements in many areas allow cable operators to offer premium tiers of services, and in some places, pay-TV programming on demand. In most of urban Canada today, 75 different signals or more are offered to each household, with more in the works. The threat of direct-to-home satellite transmission of hundreds of signals has driven cable operators to expand their offering dramatically in recent years. All told, the revenues of the Canadian cable industry 1996 were about $2.7 billion, with about $775 million a year derived from the upper-tier services.[13]

TV Changes Professional Sports

Within the past 30 years, the most profitable type of television programming has been sports. Sports broadcasts on Canadian television have always had large and devoted audiences.

Beginning with the Saturday night tradition of *Hockey Night in Canada*, transplanted from radio, along with the familiar voice of Foster Hewitt and, later, his son Bill, sports continues to be a large part of network programming. CBC-TV and The Sports Network also broadcast over 100 Toronto Blue Jay baseball games each year across the country, along with a lesser but still substantial number of Montreal Expos games. In addition, The Sports Network televises many games from the Canadian Football League and other kinds of sporting events from Canada and around the world, in addition to commentary and phone-in shows as a basic cable TV component. To be added to Canadian cable TV in the fall of 1998 is a CTV sports channel, which will feature still more sporting events, most notably European football games, which previously have not been generally available to Canadians.

Added to this mix are more baseball and NFL football games from the U.S. networks, superstations on cable, and the Fox network. Rupert Murdoch has pursued his plans for the Fox network by buying professional sports franchises, including the Los Angeles Dodgers baseball club and, in the fall of 1998, the premier European football team, Manchester United, for US $1 billion.

Television fees fund most of the cost of organized sports. ESPN, the largest cable sports network in the United States, was launched in 1979. From 1990 to 1993, it contributed $450 million cumulatively to the fees collected by the NFL. Owned primarily by Capital Cities/ABC, ESPN annually offers more than 8000 hours of televised sports.

The most profitable type of TV programming is sports. *Hockey Night in Canada* is one of the most popular Canadian shows.

CP Picture Archive (Hans Deryk)

Televised sports has become spectacularly complex entertainment packaging, turning athletes as well as sports commentators into media stars. The expansion of sports programming beyond the networks to cable channels such as ESPN means even more sports programming choices for viewers, and more money for major league sports teams. The rules and practices of major sports have been changed to accommodate the needs of television, for example, by adding time-outs to allow a break for commercials. Many commentators feel that this is one reason that soccer, the world's most popular sport, has never become established as a major sport in North America—it is a continuous game with few breaks in the action.

Technology and the Future

When technological developments move like a rocket, as they have in the past decade, program delivery becomes easier and less expensive. New technologies have brought more competition.

Significant Technological Developments

Several new delivery systems have been developed to bring increasingly more choices to consumers. Some of the most important recent technological developments are described here.

High-Definition Television (HDTV). A normal television picture scans 525 lines across the screen. **High-definition television (HDTV)** scans 1125 lines. CBS first demonstrated HDTV in the United States in 1982. HDTV, which would mean a wider, sharper picture and better sound, is waiting for a practical method to transmit the higher-resolution picture, since it requires more spectrum space than conventional television signals. HDTV is already in use in Japan but has not been very successful, mainly because HDTV sets are priced at the equivalent of $3000.

Direct Broadcast Satellites (DBS). In 1994, two companies called DirecTV and DSS (Digital Satellite System) began offering services directly to the home by satellite. Subscribers pay $500 or less for a miniaturized 18-inch dish, and, for a monthly fee, DirecTV provides access to 70 different *worldwide* channels, with a promise of 150 channels in the future. The monthly fee is about the same cost as, or cheaper than, a monthly cable bill. The main advantages are access to worldwide programming at a reasonable cost and the elimination of the cable converter box. The main disadvantage is that this satellite service offers only national and global programming; local stations are not on the satellite service yet. So subscribers who want to receive local channels must use a separate antenna.

VCRs. Both the movie and the television industries are monitoring the growth of videocassette recorders (VCRs), which celebrate their 25th birthday in 2001. Most Canadian households have at least one VCR.

The movie industry collects substantial income from videocassette sales. For the television business, the VCR is a threat because someone who tapes a program can fast-forward through ("zap") the commercials, and commercials pay for television programs. The next generation of VCRs may offer built-in editing equipment to make zapping effortless.

VCR owners also can watch what they want when they want, a practice known as **time-shifting**. Cable operators and commercial broadcasters are afraid that, as time-shifting spreads, it will create havoc in the ratings system.

Web Television. The first adaptation of traditional TV sets as a consumer appliance for using the Internet was announced in 1997 as Web TV. This service allows a consumer to use an existing TV set like a computer by connecting the two through telephone lines. Then, using an expanded keypad similar to a remote control, the user can direct the Internet activity from across the room. The remote control works through a set-top box, which translates the computer signal so it can be viewed on the TV screen.

Enhanced Television. The latest development using traditional broadcast television technology to give consumers on-line access is enhanced television, announced late in 1997. Enhanced television merges information from the World Wide Web and television programs on one screen. This technology allows someone to watch a football game as it's happening and, at the same time, follow a discussion about the game taking place in a Web-based chat session on a separate portion of the screen. To use the new technology, consumers will have to buy a decoder device that attaches to the TV set.

Forecasting the Future: A *Telepresence*?

Forecasts for the future of television parallel the forecasts for radio—a menu board of hundreds of programs and services available to viewers at the touch of a remote control button. Telephone companies (called **telcos**) are considering duplicating the services currently offered by cable TV companies and vice versa. "Cable TV companies and telephone companies are joining forces because each has something valuable that the other wants," reports the *Los Angeles Times*.

"Telephone companies have wired virtually every household in their service area and want to deliver the wide variety of program and information services controlled by the cable companies," says the *Times*. "The cable operators, on the other hand, want to use their cable TV wires to go into the phone business, delivering voice, data and video over ... fiber-optic lines."[14]

The result of these mergers will be that some new media powerhouses will be able to invest large sums of money in research and expansion for developing technologies with vast potential, such as fibre optics. Fibre optics, which allows the transmission of huge amounts of data using clear glass strands as thin as a human hair, forms the basis for many of today's cable systems and could change television dramatically.

Imagine your television as an artificial reality machine. This machine, says the *Wall Street Journal*, would use "remarkably crisp pictures and sound to 'deliver' a viewer to a pristine tropical beach, to a big football game or to a quiet mountaintop retreat. Japanese researchers envision golfers practicing their swings in front of three-dimensional simulations of courses."[15]

The definition of television today is expanding faster than our ability to chronicle the changes. Lanny Smoot, an executive at Bell Communications Research, calls the future of television a *telepresence*. "This," he says, "is a wave that is not possible to stop."[16]

In Focus

◉ The word *television*, which once meant programs delivered by antennas through over-the-air signals, today means a television screen, where a variety of delivery systems brings viewers a diversity of programs.

◉ More than any other media industry today, commercial television exists primarily as an advertising medium.

◉ Guglielmo Marconi put sound on airwaves. Lee de Forest invented the Audion tube. Edward Samuel Rogers created a tube that allowed TVs to be plugged into a wall socket. Vladimir Zworykin turned an electronic signal into a visual image. Philo T. Farnsworth added the electronic scanner.

◉ Alphonse Ouimet established the first Canadian television system in Montreal in the 1930s and set up the first stations in Canada for the CBC in Montreal and Toronto in 1952.

◉ By 1957, 85 percent of Canadians received the CBC.

◉ The first television news broadcasts were primitive compared to today's broadcasts. At that time, television news, like radio news, developed its own standard of excellence.

◉ Most early television entertainment programming was derived from radio. The only type of program that didn't come from radio was the talk show. The situation comedy proved to be one of television's most durable types of programming.

◉ Canadian content (CANCON) regulations appeared in 1959 to ensure that a certain percentage of television programs were indigenous.

◉ The 1950s quiz show scandals caused the networks to eliminate advertiser-produced programming.

◉ In the 1960s, audiences grew more discriminating and began to question how well the medium of television was serving the public. An influential spokesperson for these views was FCC Chairman Newton Minow, who coined the phrase "vast wasteland" to describe television.

◉ French-language television in Canada has always been distinctive and more popular with francophones than English-language programming has been with anglophones.

◉ Deregulation, with relaxed ownership rules, means that instability and change have become a major characteristic of the television industry today.

◉ Today, traditional network audiences are shrinking, as more stations are licensed to broadcast and as rapidly changing technology competes for TV audiences.

◎ Televised sports are television's second biggest moneymaker after prime-time programming, and television fees fund most of the cost of organized sports. The pace and the rules of professional sports have been altered to accommodate broadcasting requirements.

◎ The result of technical innovation and corporate consolidation will be some new media powerhouses with the ability to invest large sums of money in research and expansion for fibre optics and interactive video. One executive has defined the new world of television as a *telepresence*.

◎ Digital television offers better pictures, clearer sound, and a flatter screen than traditional TV. Digital TV will make it easier for manufacturers to combine the functions of TV and the functions of a computer in the same TV set.

Review Questions

1. Cite the major landmarks in the development of the television industry from 1907 to today. What did each development contribute to television's evolution?

2. How have CANCON regulations affected Canadian programming and audiences?

3. How has the role of the TV networks changed from the 1930s to today?

4. Which of the technological developments described in this chapter are most likely to affect the economics of TV? Why?

Watching the Web

◎ **CNN Audioselect (audio tracks of all CNN channels)**

http://www.cnn.com/audioselect

◎ **BBC News (text, audio and video)**

http://news.bbc.co.uk/default.htm

◎ **CBC Television**

http://www.tv.cbc.ca/

◎ **David Letterman**

http://www.cbs.com/lateshow

◎ **Pauly Report on Broadcast Journalism**

http://www.spj.org/pauleyreport/index.htm

◎ **PBS**

http://www.pbs.org/Welcome.html

MOVIES

8

> EXCESSIVE AND LUSTFUL KISSING, LUSTFUL EMBRACES, SUGGESTIVE POSTURES AND GESTURES ARE NOT TO BE SHOWN.

*Motion Picture
Production Code, 1930*

What's Ahead

"In no other business is a single example of product fully created at an investment of millions of dollars with no real assurance that the public will buy it. In no other business does the public 'use' the product and then take away with them ... merely the memory of it. In the truest sense, it's an industry based on dreams."[1]

It would be easy to assume that the movie industry is one of the biggest media industries because the publicity surrounding movie celebrities captures a great deal of attention. So it is often surprising to learn that the movie industry accounts for the smallest amount of media industries income—about 4 percent.

Movies and movie stars need the public's attention because the audience determines whether or not movies succeed. Movies are very costly investments, and most movies lose money. Private investors, therefore, often favour "bankable" talent that will bring a following to a movie, rather than new, untested talent. Yet, even movies featuring established talent can fail; no one in the movie industry can accurately predict which movies will be hits.

Writes film scholar Jason E. Squire:

> At its simplest, the feature film is the shuffling of light images to win hearts in dark rooms. At its most complex, it is a massive venture of commerce, a vast creative enterprise requiring the logistical discipline of the military, the financial foreshadowing of the Federal Reserve, and the psychological tolerance of the clergy, all harnessed in private hands on behalf of the telling of a story. In the commercial movie industry, the idea is to make movies that attract vast audiences who cumulatively pay enough money for the privilege so that all the costs involved in making that movie are recouped, with enough left over to make more movies. The profit motive is at work here, but the formula that attracts audiences is as elusive as can be.[2]

Movies mirror the society that creates them, though often in unintentional ways. Some movies offer an underlying political message. Other movies reflect changing social values or lifestyles. And still other movies are just good entertainment. But all commercial movies need an audience to succeed.

Like other media industries, the movie industry has had to adapt to changing technology. Before the invention of television, movies were the nation's primary form of visual entertainment. Today, the extensive use of special effects—something that until very recently you seldom got from television—is one way the movie industry competes with television for your attention and your dollars. But special effects don't fit every movie, and they are very expensive. Today, the economics of moviemaking is very important.

Capturing Motion on Film: How Movies Began

Movies were invented at a time when industry welcomed any new gadget, and inventors wildly sought patents on appliances and electrical devices. The motion picture camera and projector were two of the Industrial Revolution's new gadgets.

Early Inventors in the Movie Industry

Movies were not the invention of one person. First, a device to photograph moving objects had to be invented and then a device to project those pictures was needed. This process involved six people: Étienne Jules Marey, Eadweard Muybridge, Thomas Edison, William K.L. Dickson, and Auguste and Louis Lumière.

Marey and Muybridge. Étienne Jules Marey, a scientist working in Paris, sought to record an animal's movement by individual actions—one at a time—to compare one animal to another. He charted a horse's movements on graphs and published the information in a book, *Animal Mechanism.*

Unknown to Marey, photographer Eadweard Muybridge was hired by railroad millionaire and horse breeder Leland Stanford to settle a $25 000 bet. Stanford had bet that during a trot, all four of a horse's feet simultaneously leave the ground. In 1877, Muybridge and Stanford built a special track in Palo Alto, California, with 12 cameras precisely placed to take pictures of a horse as it moved around the track. The horse tripped a series of equidistant wires as it ran, which in turn tripped the cameras' shutters. Stanford won his $25 000—one photograph showed that all four of the horse's feet did leave the ground—and the photographic series provided an excellent study of motion.

Muybridge expanded to 24 cameras, photographed other animals, and then took pictures of people moving. He travelled throughout Europe showing his photographs. Eventually, Muybridge and Marey met. In 1882, Marey perfected a photographic gun camera that could take 12 photographs on one plate—the first motion picture camera.[3]

Thomas Edison. Thomas Edison bought some of Muybridge's pictures in 1888 and showed them to his assistant, William K.L. Dickson. Edison then met with Marey in Europe, where Marey had invented a projector that showed pictures on a continuous strip of film. But the strip film moved unevenly across the projector lens, so the pictures jumped.

This woman in motion is one of the early images photographed by Eadweard Muybridge.

The Bettmann Archive

William K.L. Dickson. Dickson perforated the edges of the film so that, as the film moved through the camera, sprockets inside the camera grabbed the perforations and locked the film in place, minimizing the jumps. Dickson looped the strip over a lamp and a magnifying lens in a box 2 feet wide and 4 feet tall. The box stood on the floor with a peephole in the top so people could look inside. Edison named this device the kinetoscope.

On April 11, 1894, North America's first kinetoscope parlour opened in New York City. For 25 cents, people could see ten different 90-second black-and-white films, including "Trapeze," "Horse Shoeing," "Wrestlers," and "Roosters."

Auguste and Louis Lumière. In France, the Lumière brothers, Auguste and Louis, who were manufacturers of photographic materials, developed an improved camera and a projector that could show film on a large screen. The first public Lumière showing was on December 28, 1895: ten short subjects with such riveting titles as "Lunch Hour at the Lumière Factory," which showed workers leaving the building, and "Arrival of a Train at a Station." Admission was 1 franc and the Lumières collected 35 francs.[4]

Edison Launches North American Movies

Four months after the Lumière premiere in France, Edison organized the first North American motion picture premiere with an improved camera developed by independent inventor Thomas Armat. Edison dubbed the new machine the Vitascope, and its first public showing was on April 23, 1896, at Koster and Bial's Theater in New York. Edison sat in a box seat, and Armat ran the projector from the balcony.

At first, movies were a sideshow. Penny arcade owners showed movies behind a black screen at the rear of the arcade for an extra nickel. But soon the movies were more popular than the rest of the attractions, and the arcades were renamed *nickelodeons*.

In 1900, there were more than 600 nickelodeons in New York City, with more than 300 000 daily admissions.[5] Each show lasted about 20 minutes. The programs ran from noon until late evening, and many theatres blared music outside to bring in business.

By 1907, Edison had contracted with most U.S. movie producers, as well as the Lumière brothers and the innovative French filmmaker Georges Méliès, to provide movies for the theatres. Licensed Edison theatres used licensed Edison projectors and rented Edison's licensed movies, many of which Edison produced at his own studio.

The important exception to Edison's licensing plan was his rival, the American Biograph and Mutoscope Company, commonly called Biograph. Biograph manufactured a better motion picture camera than Edison's, and Edison was losing business. In 1908, Biograph signed an agreement with Edison, forming the Motion Picture Patents Company (MPPC).

Licensed exhibitors paid $2 a week to MPPC, and any distributor or exhibitor who violated the agreement by handling independent films was banned from the MPPC. The MPPC collected more than $1 million the first year, with Edison receiving most of the royalties.[6] Thomas Edison thus established the first motion picture trust, which gave him a virtual monopoly on the movie business.

Georges Méliès created these fanciful creatures for his 1902 movie, *A Trip to the Moon*, introducing fantasy to motion pictures.

Courtesy of the Academy of Motion Picture Arts and Sciences

Novelty Becomes Art

All of the early films were black-and-white silents. Sound was not introduced to the movies until the 1920s, and colour experiments did not begin until the 1930s. Two innovative filmmakers are credited with turning the novelty of movies into art: Georges Méliès and Edwin S. Porter.

Georges Méliès. French filmmaker Georges Méliès added fantasy to the movies. Before Méliès, moviemakers photographed theatrical scenes or events from everyday life. But Méliès, who was a magician and a caricaturist before he became a filmmaker, used camera tricks to make people disappear and reappear and to make characters grow and then shrink. Méliès' 1902 film *A Trip to the Moon* was the first outer-space movie adventure, complete with fantasy creatures. When his films, which became known as trick films, were shown in the United States, U.S. moviemakers stole his ideas.

Edwin S. Porter. Edison hired projectionist/electrician Edwin S. Porter in 1899, and in the next decade Porter became the United States' most important filmmaker. Until Porter, most U.S. films were trick films or short documentary-style movies that showed newsworthy events (although some filmmakers used titillating subjects in movies such as *Pajama Girl* and *Corset Girl* to cater to men, who were the movies' biggest fans). In 1903, Porter produced *The Great Train Robbery*, an action movie with bandits attacking a speeding train.

Instead of using a single location like most other moviemakers, Porter shot 12 different scenes. He also introduced the use of dissolves between shots, instead of abrupt splices. Porter's film techniques—action and changing locations—foreshadowed the classic storytelling tradition of movies in the United States.

The Studio System Is Born

None of the players in the early movies received screen credit, but then fans began to write letters to Biograph star Florence Lawrence addressed "The Biograph Girl." In 1909, Carl Laemmle formed an independent production company, stole Florence Lawrence from Biograph, and gave her screen credit. She became North America's first movie star.

Biograph was the first company to make movies using the **studio system**. The studio system meant that a studio hired a stable of stars and production people who were paid a regular salary. These people were then under contract to that studio and could not work for any other studio without their employer's permission.

In 1910, Laemmle lured Mary Pickford away from Biograph by doubling her salary. He discovered, says film scholar Robert Sklar, "that stars sold pictures as nothing else could. As long as theatres changed their programs daily—and the practice persisted in neighbourhood theatres and small towns until the early 1920s—building up audience recognition of star names was almost the only effective form of audience publicity."[7]

The star system, which promoted popular movie personalities to lure audiences, was nurtured by the independents. This helped broaden movies' appeal beyond the working class. Movie houses began to show up in the suburbs. From 1908 to 1914, movie attendance doubled.[8]

D.W. Griffith Introduces the Spectacular

In 1915, the first real titan of the silent movies, director D.W. Griffith, introduced the concept of spectacular entertainment. His movies were so ambitious, so immense, that no one could ignore them.

Most early movies were two reels long, lasting 25 minutes. At first Griffith made two-reelers, but then he began making his movies four reels and longer, pioneering the feature-length film.

Griffith's best-known epic was as controversial as it was spectacular. In *The Birth of a Nation* (1915), the Southern-born Griffith presented a dramatic view of the American Civil War and Reconstruction, which portrayed racist stereotypes of black characters. It was an ambitious film on a bitter, controversial topic, shown to an audience that had not reconciled the war's divisions. The movie's cost—about $110 000—was five times more than that of any American film until that time.[9]

With this and his subsequent epics, Griffith showed the potential that movies had as a mass medium for gathering large audiences. He also proved that people would pay more than a nickel or a dime to see a motion picture. Films had moved from the crowded nickelodeon to respectability.

New production companies quickly formed to feed what seemed to be the public's unquenchable desire for movies. The biggest companies were First National, Famous Players-Lasky, Metro, Loew's, Fox, and Paramount. In 1918, Paramount distributed 220 features, more in one year than any single company before or since.[10]

The Movies Become Big Business

In the 1920s, the movie business was changing quickly. Five important events in the 1920s transformed it: the industry's move to California, the adoption of block booking, the formation of United Artists, the efforts at self-regulation, and the introduction of sound.

The Movies Go to Hollywood

During the first decade of the 20th century, the major movie companies were based in New York, the theatre capital. Film companies sometimes travelled to Florida or Cuba to chase the sunshine because it was easier to film in natural light. But this soon changed.

In 1903, Harry Chandler owned the *Los Angeles Times*, but he also invested in Los Angeles real estate. Chandler and his friends courted the movie business, offering cheap land, moderate weather, and inexpensive labour. The moviemakers moved to Hollywood.

Block Booking

People who owned theatre chains soon decided to make movies, and moviemakers discovered that they could make more money if they owned theatres, so production companies began to build theatres to exhibit their own pictures. The connection between production, distribution, and exhibition grew, led by Paramount's Adolph Zukor, who devised a system called **block booking**.

Block booking meant that a company such as Paramount would sign up one of its licensed theatres for as many as 104 pictures at a time. The movie package contained a few "name" pictures with stars, but the majority of the movies in the block were lightweight features with no stars. Because movie bills changed twice a week, the exhibitors were desperate for something to put on the screen. Often without knowing which movies they were getting in the block, exhibitors accepted the packages and paid the distributors' prices.

United Artists Champions the Independents

In 1919, the five biggest movie names—cowboy star William S. Hart, Mary Pickford, Charlie Chaplin, Douglas Fairbanks, and D.W. Griffith—decided it was time to rebel against the strict studio system of distribution.

On January 15, 1919, the stars announced:

> A new combination of motion picture stars and producers was formed yesterday, and we, the undersigned, in furtherance of the artistic welfare of the moving picture industry, believing we can better serve the great and growing industry of picture productions, have decided to unite our work into one association, and at the finish of existing contracts, which are now rapidly drawing to a close, to release our combined productions through our own organization.[11]

Eventually, Hart withdrew from the agreement, but the remaining partners formed a company called United Artists. They eliminated block booking and became a distributor for independently produced pictures, including their own.

In its first six years, UA delivered many movies that today are still considered classics: *The Mark of Zorro*, *The Three Musketeers*, *Robin Hood*, and *The Gold Rush*. These movies succeeded despite the fact that UA worked outside of the traditional studio system, proving that it was possible to distribute films to audiences without using a major studio.

Left to right: Douglas Fairbanks, Mary Pickford, Charlie Chaplin, and D.W. Griffith founded United Artists in 1919.

The Bettmann Archive

Moviemakers Use Self-Regulation to Respond to Scandals

In the 1920s, the movie industry faced two new crises: scandals involving movie stars and criticism that movie content was growing too provocative. As a result, the moviemakers decided to regulate themselves.

The star scandals began when comedian Roscoe "Fatty" Arbuckle hosted a marathon party in San Francisco over Labour Day weekend in 1921. As the party was ending, model Virginia Rappe was rushed to the hospital with stomach pains. She died at the hospital, and Arbuckle was charged with murder. Eventually the cause of death was listed as peritonitis from a ruptured bladder, and the murder charge was reduced to manslaughter. After three trials, two of which resulted in a hung jury, Arbuckle was acquitted.

Then director William Desmond Taylor was found murdered in his home. Mabel Normand, a friend of Arbuckle's, was identified as the last person who had seen Taylor alive. Normand eventually was cleared, but then it was revealed that "Taylor" was not the director's real name, and there were suggestions that he was involved in the illegal drug business.

Hollywood's moguls and business people were aghast. The Catholic Legion of Decency announced a movie boycott. Quick to protect themselves, Los Angeles business leaders met and decided that Hollywood should police itself.

The *Los Angeles Times*' Harry Chandler worked with movie leaders to bring in ex-Postmaster General and former Republican Party Chairman Will Hays to respond to these and other scandals in the movie business. Hays's job was to lead a moral refurbishing of the industry.

In March 1922, Hays became the first president of the Motion Picture Producers and Distributors Association (MPPDA), at a salary of $100 000 a year. A month later, even though Arbuckle had been acquitted, Hays suspended all of Fatty Arbuckle's films.

Besides overseeing the stars' personal behaviour, Hays decided that his office also should oversee movie content. The MPPDA, referred to as the Hays Office, wrote a code of conduct to govern the industry.

On February 17, 1930, the MPPDA adopted a production code, which began by stating three general principles:

1. No picture shall be produced which will lower the moral standards of those who see it. Hence the sympathy of the audience shall never be thrown to the side of crime, wrongdoing, evil or sin.
2. Correct standards of life, subject only to the requirements of drama and entertainment, shall be presented.
3. Laws, natural or human, shall not be ridiculed, nor shall sympathy be created for its violation.[12]

The code then divided its rules into 12 categories of wrongdoing, including:

◎ Murder: "The technique of murder must be presented in a way that will not inspire imitation."

◎ Sex: "Excessive and lustful kissing, lustful embraces, suggestive postures and gestures are not to be shown."

◎ Obscenity: "Obscenity in word, gesture, reference, song, joke, or by suggestion (even when likely to be understood only by part of the audience) is forbidden."

◎ Costumes: "Dancing costumes intended to permit undue exposure or indecent movements in the dance are forbidden."[13]

An acceptable movie displayed a seal of approval from the Production Code Administration (PCA), the movies' self-regulating agency, in the titles at the beginning of the picture. Producers balked at the interference, but most of them, afraid of censorship from outside the industry, complied with the monitoring. Although standards have relaxed, self-regulation of content still operates in the motion picture industry today.

New Technology Brings the Talkies

By the mid-1920s, silent movies were an established part of movie entertainment, but technology soon pushed the industry into an even more vibrant era—the era of the talkies. MPPDA President Will Hays was the first person to appear on screen in the public premiere of talking pictures on August 6, 1926, in New York City. Warner Bros. and Western Electric had developed the sound experiment, which consisted of seven short subjects, including a concert by the New York Philharmonic and a vaudeville comedy skit. Together, the short subjects were called *The Vitaphone Preludes*.

The Warner brothers—Sam, Harry, Jack, and Albert—were ambitious, upstart businessmen who beat their competitors to sound movies. On October 6, 1927, *The Jazz Singer*, starring Al Jolson, opened at the Warners' Theater in New York, the first feature-length motion picture with sound. The movie was not an all-talkie, but instead contained two sections with synchronized sound.

The success of *The Jazz Singer* convinced Warners' competitors not to wait any longer to adopt sound. By July 1, 1930, 22 percent of theatres still showed silent films; by 1933, only 0.5 percent of the movies shown in theatres were silents.[14]

The Rise of the Moguls: The Studio System Flourishes

In the 1930s, the movie business was dominated by the Big Five: Warner Bros., Metro-Goldwyn-Mayer, Paramount, RKO, and 20th Century-Fox. The Big Five collected more than two-thirds of the box office receipts in the United States.[15] United Artists remained solely a distribution company for independent producers.

The Big Five all were vertically integrated: They produced movies, distributed them worldwide, and owned theatre chains, which guaranteed their pictures a showing. The studios maintained stables of stars, directors, producers, writers, and technical staff. Film scholar Tino Balio calls the studios at this point in their history a "mature oligopoly"—a group of companies with so much control over an industry that any change in one of the companies directly affected the future of the industry.

In the 1930s, Walt Disney became the only major successful Hollywood newcomer. He had released *Steamboat Willie* as "the first animated sound cartoon" in 1928. Disney was 26 years old, and he sold his car to finance the cartoon's soundtrack.

After some more short-animated-feature successes, Disney announced in 1934 that his studio would produce its first feature-length animated film, *Snow White and the Seven Dwarfs*. The film eventually cost Disney $2.25 million, more than MGM usually spent on a good musical. *Snow White* premiered December 21, 1937, at the Cathay Circle Theater in Hollywood.

Box office receipts sagged in the 1930s as the Depression settled into every aspect of the Western economy. Facing bankruptcy, several theatres tried to buoy up their profits by adding Bingo games and cut-rate admissions. The one lasting innovation of the 1930s was the double feature: two movies for the price of one.

The Depression introduced one more factor into motion picture budgets: labour unions. Before the 1930s, most aspects of the movie business were not governed by union agreements. But in 1937, the U.S. National Labor Relations Board held an election that designated the Screen Actors Guild to bargain for wages, working conditions, and overtime. The Screen Writers Guild was certified in 1938 and the Screen Directors Guild soon afterward.

Unionization limited the moguls' power over the people who worked for them but the studio heads approved the union agreements in the late 1930s. The Depression ended, and the studios once again prospered.

A Canadian Studio Grows: The National Film Board

In 1939, the Canadian government established the **National Film Board (NFB).** Originally a wartime information agency, under John Grierson, it grew to one of the world's largest film studios by the end of World War II in 1945. Subsequently much reduced in size, it began producing documentary films for television and experimented with animation techniques. Pioneer animators, such as Norman McLaren, developed special animation techniques. Since 1946, the NFB has won 9 Academy Awards and received 50 nominations for its short animated films.

Today, the NFB continues to produce a small number of feature films, such as *The Boys of St. Vincent,* and many shorter films for television, such as *The Avro Arrow,* together with its innovative animation shorts. One of the world's most widely respected national film agencies, the NFB has produced many films that would likely have never been made without government subsidization.

Movies Glitter During the Golden Age

With glamorous stars and exciting screenplays, supported by an eager pool of gifted directors, producers, and technical talent, plus an insatiable audience, the movie industry reached its apex in the late 1930s and early 1940s. The most successful studio in Hollywood was MGM, which attracted the best writers, directors, and actors. MGM concentrated on blockbusters, such as *The Great Ziegfeld, The Wizard of Oz,* and *Gone with the Wind.* Not only did *Gone with the Wind*'s phenomenal success demonstrate the epic character that movies could provide, but also the movie was a technological breakthrough, with its magnificent use of colour.

The movie business was so rich that even MGM's dominance didn't scare away the competition.

In the late 1930s and early 1940s, spectaculars such as *The Wizard of Oz* helped to make MGM the most successful studio in Hollywood.

The Kobal Collection

IMPACT

Point of View

FROM SARAJEVO WITH LOVE: BOSNIAN WRITER IS A TIRELESS PROMOTER OF CANADIAN CINEMA

By Jay Stone

Bojan Bosiljcic, author of the best book on Canadian cinema ever written in Serbo-Croatian, just loves Canadian movies.

Everyone in the former Yugoslavia does, he says. David Cronenberg is a familiar name. Atom Egoyan's *Exotica* is a cult hit. *The Decline of the American Empire* is huge.

Bosiljic, who has lived in Ottawa since 1995, was back in his native Yugoslavia last year and on Belgrade TV, in prime time on Sunday night, without commercial interruption, he saw *When Night is Falling* by Patricia Rozema and *I Love a Man in Uniform* by David Wellington. In Canada, he says, you'd be lucky to see either on *Cinema Canada* after midnight.

"Maybe it sounds unbelievable, but people in the former Yugoslavia are very familiar with the Canadian film industry," he says with a wide-eyed intensity. "Much more, I realize, than Canadians.

"It's some kind of shame that Canadian movies are still searching for a place in the hearts of domestic viewers."

Bosiljcic, 40, is the author of *Severno Od Holivuda* (North of Hollywood), which is doing well in the former Yugoslavia and which he is trying to get translated into English. It contains interviews with Rozema and Cronenberg and many others. Bosiljcic is a tireless promoter of Canadian movies.

"Last year, when I was in Belgrade, everybody was talking about (the David Cronenberg movie) *Crash*. And here, I go to this movie in one theatre in Ottawa, and it was around 50 people in the cinema, and during the projection around 15 people just left.

"It's a very controversial movie, very provocative, it's very difficult to understand, but I think what is the purpose of movies? Not just to entertain, but to give you some new prospects."

To Bosiljcic, *Crash* is "a very exciting exploration of sexuality at the end of the 20th Century."

The Canadian movie industry is similar to that of Europe, he says, where the audience is used to seeing more artistic films. It's also similar to the cinema of his old homeland.

"Yugoslavian film-makers are making small movies, they are dealing with serious problems, with the political bedrock, but the whole story is always told in a funny way

Challenges from the U.S. Congress and the Courts

Before television arrived for good in 1948, two other events of the late 1940s helped reverse the prosperous movie bonanza that began in mid-1930: the hearings of the House Committee on Un-American Activities in Washington and the 1948 U.S. Supreme Court decision in *United States v. Paramount Pictures, Inc., et al.*

The Hollywood Ten. In October 1947, the world was entering the Cold War. In the United States, many public officials, government employees, and private citizens were preoccupied with the threat of communism and people identified as "subversives." The House of Representatives' Committee on Un-American Activities, chaired by J. Parnell Thomas, summoned ten "unfriendly" witnesses from Hollywood to testify about their communist connections. (Unfriendly witnesses were people whom the committee classified as having participated in the past in "un-American activities." This usually meant that the witness was believed to have been had been an associate member of some left-wing organization in the decade before World War II.) These eight screenwriters and two directors came to be known as the Hollywood Ten.

so the audience could easily accept the movie. The directors are using pure film language, using mostly pictures and metaphors to say what they want to say.

"They don't have big stars. They are not making status quo movies like Hollywood.

"It's the same story with the Canadian film industry, and I must admit that I have fallen in love with Canadian films ... it is an extraordinary cinema."

Bosiljcic, who sees himself as a cinematic bridge between the former Yugoslavia and Canada, is also a tireless promoter of Balkan cinema in this country. He organized the Balkan film series for the Canadian Film Institute in Ottawa and Montreal, and he has written several freelance articles on the subject for Ottawa newspapers....

Before the war, he was a film critic and writer on movies in Sarajevo, filing stories to seven newspapers and a broadcast outlet and publishing a book of essays on Hollywood called *Oscar Is to Blame for Everything*.

"I spent two war years in Sarajevo and of course it's a sad story," he says. "It's not only my sad story it's a sad story for all Bosnians. It was war and things change and it was not a place for me to live, like for thousands of Bosnians, people who lived there, they are now spread out around the world, from New Zealand to Canada."

His mother and teenage sister still live in Sarajevo.

Bosiljcic arrived in Ottawa knowing no one. He looked up Film in the telephone directory and got the number of the Canadian Film Institute. The executive director, Tom McSorley, helped him arrange the Balkan film program and Bosiljcic began writing his book on Canadian movies. He's now working on a new one, about Hollywood.

He and McSorley are now involved in a new project, a retrospective of [Emir] Kusturica's movies next fall at CFI. [Kusturica is a Yugoslavian director.] Featured will be a showing of his new movie, *Cat Black, Cat White.*

Ottawa Citizen, *February 6, 1998. Reprinted with permission.*

The Hollywood Ten, targeted by the House Committee on Un-American Activities, eventually went to jail for refusing to answer questions before the committee about their political beliefs.

The Kobal Collection

The Ten's strategy was to appear before the committee as a group and to avoid answering the direct question "Are you now or have you ever been a member of the Communist party?" Instead, the Ten tried to make statements that questioned the committee's authority to challenge their political beliefs.

In a rancorous series of hearings, the committee rejected the Ten's testimony; the witnesses found themselves facing trial for contempt. All of them were sentenced to jail, and some were fined. By the end of November 1947, all of the Hollywood Ten had lost their jobs. Many more movie people would follow.

In an article for the *Hollywood Review*, Hollywood Ten member Adrian Scott reported that 214 movie employees eventually were blacklisted, which meant that many studio owners refused to hire people who were suspected of taking part in subversive activities. The movie people who were not hired because of their political beliefs included 106 writers, 36 actors, and 11 directors.[16] This effectively gutted Hollywood of some of its best talent.

United States v. Paramount Pictures. The U.S. Justice Department began an antitrust suit against the studios in 1938. In 1940, the studios came to an agreement with the government, while admitting no guilt. They agreed to:

1. Limit block booking to five films.

2. Stop **blind booking** (the practice of renting out films without showing them to the exhibitors first).

3. Stop requiring theatres to rent short films as a condition of acquiring features.

4. Stop buying theatres.

After this agreement, the Justice Department dropped its suit with the stipulation that the department could reinstitute the suit again at any time.

By 1944, the government was still unhappy with studio control over the theatres, so it reactivated the suit. In 1948, *United States v. Paramount Pictures* reached the Supreme Court. Associate Justice William O. Douglas argued that, although the five major studios—Paramount, Warner Bros., MGM-Loew's, RKO, and 20th Century-Fox—owned only 17 percent of all theatres in the United States, these studios *did* hold a monopoly over first-run exhibition in the large cities.

As a result of the Supreme Court decision against Paramount Pictures, by 1954 the five major production firms had divested themselves of ownership or control of all of their theatres. Production and exhibition were now split. Vertical integration was crumbling.

When the movie companies abandoned the exhibition business, banks grew reluctant to finance film projects because the companies could not guarantee an audience—on paper. Soon the studios decided to leave the production business to the independents and became primarily distributors of other people's pictures. The result was the end of the studio system.

TV Transforms the Movie Industry

In the 1950 Paramount movie *Sunset Boulevard*, aging silent screen star Norma Desmond (played by Gloria Swanson) romances an ambitious young screenwriter (played by William Holden) by promising him Hollywood connections.

"You're Norma Desmond. You used to be in silent pictures. You used to be big," says the screenwriter.

"I *am* big," says Desmond. "It's the pictures that got small."

Desmond could have been talking about the picture business itself, which got much smaller after 1948, when television began to offer home-delivered entertainment.

The House hearings and the consent decrees in the Paramount case foretold change in the movie business, but television truly transformed Hollywood forever. In the 1950s, the number of television sets grew by 400 percent, while the number of people who went to the movies fell by 45 percent.[17]

Theatres tried to make up for the loss by raising their admission prices, but more than 4000 theatres closed in the United States alone from 1946 to 1956.[18] Attendance has levelled off or risen briefly a few times since the 1950s, but the trend of declining movie attendance continues today. The movie industry has tried several methods to counteract this downward trend.

Wide-Screen and 3-D Movies. Stunned by television's popularity, the movie business tried technological gimmicks in the 1950s to lure its audience back. First came 3-D movies, using special effects to create the illusion of three-dimensional action. Rocks, for example, seemed to fly off the screen and into the audience. To see the 3-D movies, people wore special plastic glasses. The novelty was fun, but the 3-D movie plots were weak, and most people didn't come back to see a second 3-D movie.

Next came Cinerama, Cinemascope, VistaVision, and Panavision—wide-screen colour movies with stereophonic sound. All of these techniques tried to give the audience a "you are there" feeling—something they couldn't get from television.

Changes in Movie Censorship. On May 26, 1952, the U.S. Supreme Court announced in *Burstyn v. Wilson* that motion pictures were "a significant medium for the communication of ideas," which were designed "to entertain as well as to inform." The effect of this decision was to protect movies under the First Amendment. The result was fewer legal restrictions on what a movie could show.

In 1953, the director Otto Preminger challenged the movies' self-regulating agency, the Production Code Administration. United Artists agreed to release Preminger's movie *The Moon Is Blue*, an adaptation of a successful Broadway play, even though the PCA denied the movie a certificate of approval because it contained such risqué words as *virgin* and *mistress*. Then in 1956, United Artists released Preminger's *Man with the Golden Arm*, a film about drug addiction, and the PCA restrictions were forever broken.

Buoyed by the Burstyn decision and the United Artists test, and following the lead of the French and Italian movie industries, U.S. moviemakers tried sex and violence to attract audiences away from television. In the 1950s, Marilyn Monroe and Jane Russell were generously proportioned examples of the new trend. Foreign films also became popular because some of them offered explicit dialogue and love scenes.

Movie Spectaculars. One by one the studio moguls retired, and they were replaced by a new generation of moviemakers. "They [the second generation] inherited a situation where fewer and fewer pictures were being made, and fewer still made money," says Robert Sklar, "but those that captured the box office earned enormous sums. It was as if the rules of baseball had been changed so that the only hit that mattered was a home run."[19]

Calvin and Hobbes   by Bill Watterson

Spectaculars like *The Sound of Music* (1965) and *The Godfather* (1971) and its sequels rewarded the rush for big money. But then a few majestic flops taught the studios that nothing can demolish a studio's profits like one big bomb.

The Business of Movies

In today's system of moviemaking, each of the six major studios (Columbia, Paramount, 20th-Century Fox, MCA/Universal, Time Warner, and Walt Disney) usually makes fewer than 20 movies a year. The rest come from independent producers, with production, investment, distribution, and exhibition each handled by different companies. Most of these independently produced movies are distributed by one of the six large studios.

Today, the dream merchants aim at youthful buyers. Nearly half of the people who go to the movies today are under 30. So the biggest box office successes are movies that appeal to this younger audience. Adult films such as *The English Patient* sometimes succeed, but films that chase the under-30 audience usually top the box office list.

Movies are created by one group (the writers and producers), funded by another group (the investors or government), sold by a third group (the distributors), and shown by a fourth group (the exhibitors). No other mass media industry is so fragmented.

Independent films can become commercially successful when they are widely distributed. Actor Adam Beach's movie *Smoke Signals* was distributed by Miramax.

CP Picture Archive (Craig Robertson)

Table 8.1

Who's Who in Hollywood: The Big Six Movie Studios		
Studio	**Parent Company**	**Country**
MCA / Universal	Seagram	Canada
Sony Pictures Entertainment	Sony	Japan
20th-Century Fox	News Corp.	Australia
Walt Disney	Disney	U.S.
Warner Bros.	Time Warner	U.S.
Viacom / Paramount	Viacom	U.S.

Source: Data from *Standard & Poor's Industry Surveys*, March 11, 1993; Value Line, Inc., Value Line Publishing, 1993.

Losing Money: Ticket Sales Drop

Weakened by declining box office proceeds and fewer movies, the studios became attractive targets for conglomerates: Viacom bought Paramount; Sony bought Columbia Pictures. Movies, like many other media, are part of corporate media ownership, which means that stockholder loyalty comes first. These studios tend to choose safer projects and seek proven audience-pleasing ideas rather than take many risks.

One way the movie industry collects predictable income is to make movies for television. Half of the movies produced every year are made for television and are underwritten by the networks. Videocassette sales and rentals also bring reliable revenues.

Two important factors for the future funding of the movie industry are the sale of ancillary rights and the advances of new technology.

Making Money: Selling Ancillary Rights

In 1950, a ticket to a movie cost about 50 cents. Today you can still see a movie for 50 cents if you rent a video for $2.50 and invite four friends to join you at home to watch it. The explosion of video rentals and sales since the VCR was first marketed in 1976 is having a powerful effect on how the movie business operates today (see Figure 8.1). The sale of movies for video is part of the **ancillary-rights market**.

The median cost to make a theatrical movie (as opposed to a made-for-television movie) is $36 million,[20] and only two out of ten theatrical movies make money.[21] "Some pictures make a lot of money," says David V. Picker, ""and a lot of pictures make no money."[22] Before a theatrical movie starts shooting, the investors want to be sure they'll make their money back. They may look to ancillary rights to secure a return on their investment. Ancillary rights can include:

◎ Pay television rights

◎ Network television rights

◎ Syndication rights (sales to independent TV stations)

◎ Airline rights for in-flight movies

◎ Military rights (to show films on military bases)

◎ College rights (to show films on campuses)

◎ Song rights for soundtrack albums

◎ Book publishing rights (for original screenplays that can be rewritten and sold as books).[23]

Movies also have been getting more commercialized in the sense that they are tied to products. And products can become another way of advertising a movie. A movie that can be exploited as a package of ancillary rights with commercial appeal is much more attractive to an investor than a movie with limited potential.

Often the only choice for a filmmaker who wants to make a film that doesn't have substantial ancillary-rights potential is to settle for a low budget. Once the film is made, the difficulties are not over. The filmmaker must then find a way to distribute the movie. This severely limits the number of independent films that make it to the box office.

Figure 8.1

Shares of Worldwide Movie Revenues, 1999*

Movie industry revenue comes from three major sources: home video, box office tickets, and movies made for television.

*projected

Source: Data from *The Veronis, Suhler & Associates Communications Industry Forecast,* 1997–2001.

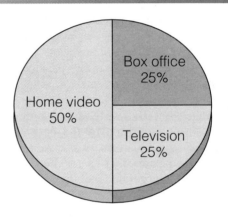

Canadian Films: Supporting a Small but Vibrant Industry

Motion pictures are at once entertainment vehicles, investments, and influential cultural products. Governments in Canada have subsidized the production of movies for decades, either directly through the NFB, for instance, through tax breaks, or through joint financing vehicles such as Telefilm Canada. One of the benefits of this mix of support arrangements is that it allows films of merit, which are unlikely to recover their costs to be made.

Through Telefilm Canada, the NFB, and the Canadian Television and Cable Production Fund, large amounts of public money support film and television production. For example, federal and provincial governments gave about $317 million in grants and subsidies to film and video producers in 1994–1995.[24] In return, Canadians produced 38 feature films as well as numerous video and television movies in 1994–1995, down from a total of 56 in 1991–1992, but a substantial total nevertheless.[25] Canadian coproduction agreements with foreign producers totalled 32 in 1996 and were valued at $241 million.[26]

Approximately 16 000 people worked in the film and video industry in Canada in 1994–1995.[27] Most of this activity was in Ontario, followed by Quebec and British Columbia. Postproduction facilities (special effects companies and film production labs) in Canada had revenues of about $400 million in 1994–95.[28]

Government involvement in film production, and in cultural production overall, is justified on the grounds that it is important to preserve and foster Canada's unique culture, which is threatened by the overwhelming presence of U.S. entertainment industries. Although Canada's regulation of cultural industries has been under continuous attack by the U.S. industries, Canada's practices are exempted from the free trade provisions of NAFTA. Canada's position in these matters is closely matched by that taken by the European community. The United States stands virtually alone in the world in its position that cultural policies should be abandoned.

The Canadian dramatic feature film industry has had many successes and notable people. The late Philip Borsos, who died of leukemia in 1995 at age 41, had directed several successful features, including *The Grey Fox*, (perhaps the first large-scale Canadian feature film to be successful) and *Bethune*. Recent Canadian international successes include *Margaret's Museum*, *Léolo*, *Jesus of Montreal*, *Le Confessionel*, *The Sweet Hereafter*, and *Crash*.

Distribution is the key to financial success for motion pictures, and it has always been a problem for Canadian films. Until recently, simply getting a movie shown on Canadian screens has been difficult because of the absence of a large-scale Canadian motion picture company.

Much of the success of recent Canadian films can be traced to the emergence of Alliance Communications and other smaller Canadian film production companies that arrange financing and local production support for filming. Alliance is now considered a studio in the Hollywood sense because it makes money. Its 1995 production *Johnny Mnemonic*, a science fiction film starring Keanu Reeves, was judged a critical flop, but it grossed $60 million—double its budget.

Alliance was started by Robert Lantos, an emigrant from Austria. The studio produces and distributes films and television programs made in Canada. It also coproduces movies and television programs with foreign companies, such as Turner Pictures, part of the Time-Warner communications empire in the United States and operator of the Home Box Office cable channel.

Alliance works with financial backing from Telefilm Canada (about 10 percent of its budget) to produce movies and television programs in Canada. Filmmaking in Canada offers the advantages of low production costs and a trained and skilled workforce of production personnel, located mainly in Toronto and Vancouver. The Canadian Film Institute in Toronto, run by the director Norman Jewison, is also producing a new generation of Canadian directors and technical production workers.

On July 20, 1998, Alliance announced that it would merge with Atlantis Communications (a similar company founded by Michael MacMillan) to form a larger production company, Alliance Atlantis Communications Inc. The new company is now approaching the scale necessary to become a major player in the global motion picture industry. Robert Lantos will continue to produce films for the new company.

HOLLYWOOD GOES AFTER INTERNET PIRATES

By Constance Sommer

Hollywood is starting to learn the hard way that current copyright law cannot protect the movie industry from rampant piracy. All over the Web, unauthorized users are snatching copyrighted digital images of movie icons, from Star Wars to Beavis and Butthead. This article explains the potential consequences for the movie industry when their most valuable properties become available on-line.

Los Angeles—Two and a half years ago, Jason Ruspini, a self-pro-claimed "member of the *Star Wars* generation," paid his beloved saga the ultimate high-technology tribute: He designed and posted a *Star Wars* site on the World Wide Web.

Fans loved the page; Lucasfilm, which owns the rights to *Star Wars*, did not. With devotees dropping in at a rate of up to 40,000 per day, Lucasfilm made a discreet phone call to the University of Pennsylvania student.

"They nicely asked me to shut it down, with the implication that if I didn't they would bring in a lawyer or something," says Mr. Ruspini, now 21. "It was a total surprise."

What happened next, though, apparently came as a total surprise to Lucasfilm, the San Rafael, California-based company owned by *Star Wars* creator George Lucas.

Lucasfilm was about to learn the hard way what the rest of Hollywood is just beginning to understand: that ownership on the Web may be one of the prickliest problems facing copyright law since the codes were written years ago.

Mr. Ruspini posted excerpts on the Web site of his conversation with a Lucasfilm executive. Outraged *Star Wars* devotees vented their furor on Lucasfilm. Mr. Ruspini says they flooded the company with angry e-mails, demanding to know how it could presume to assert such totalitarian control over a product some fans had woven into the very fabric of their lives.

Four months after the January 1996 phone call to Mr. Ruspini, Lucasfilm backed down. In a letter posted on Mr. Ruspini's Web site, the company apologized for apparent "miscommunication" and vowed to develop a Web policy soon.

"Technology is advancing fast enough to worry about copyrights of film now," says John Raffetto, a spokesman for the Creative Incentive Coalition, a Washington, D.C., lobbying group representing the movie industry.

Hollywood Dither

Hollywood is in a dither over the possibility that its greatest asset—motion pictures—is easily available, for free, to anyone with a sufficiently powerful computer and an Internet account.

Industry executives say current copyright law cannot protect them from rampant piracy—they need precision-sharp technologies and enhanced legislation to block limitless video reproduction in cyberspace.

This call to action has incited its share of controversy; as the industry pushes for legislative changes on Capitol Hill, it has run up against law professors, librar-

ians and movie fans who call the new copyright proposals a covert grab for control of now-public information....

The industry is fighting back on two fronts, the high-tech and the legislative.

In the technology field, moviemakers—concerned that computer users soon will be able to easily download and view entire videos—are actively encouraging the development of protection devices.

In one scenario, distributors would make movies available via the Internet for a fee, but rig the system so that each downloaded film could not be copied and used by someone else's computer.

In Washington, entertainment lobbyists are joining forces with their counterparts in the music, publishing and software industries to push for updated copyright laws, specifically prohibiting piracy in cyberspace and slapping offenders with up to $250,000 in fines and five years in jail.

"I think a lot of people right now believe anything on the Internet is free and up for grabs," Mr. Raffetto says. People seem to think "if you can get it on the Internet, you're free of copyright law."

Mr. Ruspini, the *Star Wars* Web site creator, was not one of those people. He knew that even current copyright law gives intellectual property owners like Lucasfilm rights on the Internet. But he went ahead with his site anyway, he says, figuring the worst they could do was order him to shut down.

Associated Press; The Dallas Morning News, *January 1, 1997. Reprinted by permission.*

Working in the Movies

Today, the centre of the movie industry is movie production. Most of the movies that are distributed by the major studios and exhibited at your local theatre result from independent companies that produce movies under agreements with individual studios.

Although these production companies work independently, and each company is organized differently, jobs in movie production fall mainly into the following categories: screenwriters, producers, directors, actors, production, marketing, and administration.

The beginning for each movie is a story idea, and these ideas come from *screenwriters*. Screenwriters work independently, marketing their story ideas through agents, who promote their clients' scripts to the studios and to independent producers.

Typically, *producers* are the people who help gather the funding to create a movie project. Financing can come from banks or from individuals who want to invest in a specific movie. Once the funding for the story is in place, a director is assigned to organize all of the tasks to turn the script into a movie. The director oversees the movie's budget.

Obviously, *actors* are important to any movie project. Sometimes the producer and director approach particular stars for a project even before they seek funding, to attract interest from the investors and also to help assure the investors that the movie will have some box office appeal.

Production includes all of the people who actually create the movie—camera operators, set designers, film editors, script supervisors, and costumers, for example. Once the movie is made, the *marketing* people seek publicity for the project. They also design a plan to advertise and promote the movie to the public. As in any media industry, people who work in *administration* help keep all of the records necessary to pay salaries and track the employees' expenses, as well as keeping track of the paperwork involved in organizing any business.

Technology and the Future

Technology affects three aspects of the movie business: production, distribution, and exhibition.

Production. Smaller portable cameras mean that a camera operator can move more easily through a crowd. New types of film mean that filmmakers can shoot more scenes at night and in dark places with less artificial lighting.

Most directors videotape scenes as they film them and immediately play back the videotape to make sure they have the shot they want. Computer technology offers exciting special-effects possibilities. Filmmakers also are experimenting with the holograph, which uses lasers to make a computer-generated three-dimensional image from a flat picture.

The ability to digitize colour using computers also means that the images in movies can be intensified, adjusted, and even totally transformed after the movie is shot, in a way that was impossible even ten years ago.

Producers depend on established stars to help sell new films to fickle moviegoers. Events such as the Toronto International Film Festival showcase new productions and their stars.

CP Picture Archive (Rene Johnston)

Distribution. Reproducing copies of films to send to theatres and guaranteeing their arrival is one of the costliest aspects of moviemaking. In the future, companies will probably send their movies by satellite to satellite dishes on top of each theatre. Live performances, such as a symphony concert or a major sports event, might be available by satellite at your local theatre or, as they are now, in your home on pay-per-view television.

Exhibition. The number of admissions to motion picture theatres and drive-ins in Canada hit its maximum in 1952–53 at 256 million.[29] By 1991–92 most Canadian households had at least one colour television and one VCR, and attendance fell to 71.6 million. Since then the total has been rising again, reaching 81 million in 1994–95. Canadians attend movies about 2.6 times a year (about 60 percent of the U.S. rate).[30] In part, the revival of movie audiences may be related to the improved, grander theatres that have been recently constructed. These improved theatres, most of which are owned by chains, are recreating the picture-palace environment that enchanted moviegoers in the 1930s. "The movie theatre will have to become an arena; a palace to experience the full grandeur and potential of the theatrical motion picture," says futurist and electronic technology consultant Martin Polon.[31]

In the mid-1990s, the Cineplex chain began remodelling its theatres and building new ones to make a night out at the movies seem more of a treat. Some of its theatres offer stadium-style seats and VIP screening rooms. The Famous Players chain also has built big-screen multiplexes, with fast-food outlets inside the theatres. In 1994, one of the United States' largest theatre chains, United Artists, announced that it would begin to offer "motion simulation" in some of its theatres. Specially controlled seats will move in conjunction with a "ridefilm" to give the feeling of space travel or other adventures.

"We're looking to marry the moviegoing experience to different kinds of technological experiences, thereby enhancing the attractiveness of the whole complex," said United Artists chairman Stewart Blair.[32]

IMAX. The IMAX Corporation of Toronto makes the world's most widely used large-screen cinema system. Special theatres and projectors are necessary for showing **IMAX films**. When projected, the 70 mm image is ten times the size of conventional 35 mm film images. Of recent IMAX films, *The Fires of Kuwait* is likely the best known; most IMAX films are documentaries, though some are concert films and dramatic features. In 1994, the IMAX Corporation was merged with Trumball Company Inc. and its Ridefilm division.

International Markets and Concentrated Power

Today's movie industry is undergoing two major changes. One recent trend in the movie business is global ownership and global marketing. The second trend is the merging of the movie industry with the television industry.

Global Influence. Non-U.S. companies own half of the major studios in the United States. (For example, Sony owns Columbia Pictures; the Bronfman family's Seagram Corp. bought MCA—which made *Jurassic Park*, *Schindler's List*, and *ET*—from Matsushita Electric; and Rupert Murdoch's News Corporation owns 20th-Century Fox.) These foreign acquisitions all happened throughout the late 1980s and the first half of the 1990s. The degree of foreign ownership in the movie industry is higher than in any other U.S. media business.

Multinational ownership means easier access to foreign markets. Motion pictures are one of the strongest U.S. exports, and income from foreign sales accounts for more than one-third of the movie industry's profits. "If Hollywood has learned anything the past few years," says *Business Week*, "it's that the whole world is hungry for the latest it has to offer."[33]

Concentrating Media Power. Today, people in the television business are buying pieces of the movie business, and people in the movie business want to align themselves with television companies. The U.S. Federal Communications Commission in 1993 voted to allow the TV networks to make and syndicate their own programs. This opens the door for TV networks to enter the movie business.

The result could be consolidated companies that would finance movies, make movies, and show those movies in their own theatres, on their own television stations, and on video. By controlling all aspects of the business, a company would have a better chance to collect a profit on the movies it makes. Sound familiar? The studios held this type of controlling interest in their movies before the 1948 consent decrees.

The studios' latest hope is that the 1948 consent decrees will be rescinded so they can once again control production, distribution, and exhibition.[34] Reports the *Wall Street Journal*: "The more aggressive players, some industry experts believe, could build concentrations of market power surpassing that enjoyed by the movie studios in the late 1930s and the 1940s—with severe consequences for weaker competitors."[35] Today's major studios are trying to become again what they once were: a mature oligopoly in the business of dreams.

In Focus

◎ Étienne Jules Marey, a French scientist, created a photographic gun camera that took 12 photographs on one plate—the first motion picture camera.

◎ Eadweard Muybridge demonstrated how to photograph motion, and Thomas Edison developed a projector, the kinetoscope. Edison also organized the Motion Picture Patents Company (MPPC) to control movie distribution.

◎ French filmmaker Georges Méliès created the first fantasy movies. Edwin S. Porter assembled scenes to tell a story. D.W. Griffith mastered the full-length movie.

◎ Biograph became the first studio to make movies using what was called the studio system. This system put the studio's stars under exclusive contract, and the contract could not be broken without an employer's permission.

◎ The practice of block booking, devised by Adolph Zukor, obligated movie houses to accept several movies at once, usually without previewing them first.

◎ The formation of United Artists by Mary Pickford, Charlie Chaplin, Douglas Fairbanks, and D.W. Griffith was a rebellion against the big studios; UA distributed films for independent filmmakers.

◎ In the 1920s, the movie industry faced two new crises: scandals involving movie stars and criticism that movie content was growing too explicit. The movie industry responded by forming the Motion Picture Producers and Distributors Association (MPPDA), under the direction of Will Hays.

◎ As the studio system developed, the five largest Hollywood studios were able to control production, distribution, and exhibition. In the 1930s, labour unions challenged studio control and won some concessions.

◎ The National Film Board of Canada was established in 1939 as a wartime government information agency. It later produced mainly documentaries and animated films.

◎ The movies' golden age, supported by the studio system and an eager audience, was the 1930s and the 1940s.

◎ Three factors caused Hollywood's crash in the 1950s: the House Committee on Un-American Activities hearings, the U.S. Justice Department's antitrust action against the studios, and television.

◎ Hollywood tried to lure audiences back with technological gimmicks and sultry starlets, but these efforts did not succeed. Today, the number of moviegoers continues to decline, although video sales and rentals have added to movie industry income; nearly half of the moviegoers are under 30.

◎ The median cost to make a movie today is $36 million, and two out of ten theatrical movies make money. Most movies are funded in part by ancillary-rights sales. Thus, most movies are sold as packages, with all of their potential media outlets underwriting a movie before it goes into production. This makes independent filmmaking difficult.

◎ The Canadian government subsidiizes the film industry through tax breaks and grants. Filmmaking in Canada offers the advantage of skilled production personnel and low production costs.

◎ Foreign corporations own half of the major U.S. movie studios. This is a higher degree of foreign ownership than in any other media industry in the United States.

◎ Movies are a major U.S. export; foreign sales account for more than one-third of movie industry income.

◎ In 1993, the U.S. Federal Communications Commission voted to allow the TV networks to make and syndicate their own programs. This means that, in the future, the movie industry and the television industry may align themselves more closely, which eventually would mean that one company could control all aspects of moviemaking.

Review Questions

1. Cite the major developments in the movie industry from 1882 to today. What did each development contribute to the movie industry's evolution?

2. Hollywood's response to the movie scandals of the 1920s was self-regulation. Which events affected the evolution of self-regulation from 1922 to 1956?

3. Although often critically acclaimed, Canadian films are rarely as successful at the box office as U.S. films. Describe three difficulties Canadian films face in achieving financial success.

4. What effect do ancillary rights have on moviemaking today? Why?

Watching the Web

◎ **Market Guide to the Motion Picture Industry**

http://www.marketguide.com/MGI/INDUSTRY/movies.htm

◎ **Internet Movie Database**

http://us.imdb.org/Movies/credits.html

◎ **Motion Picture Industry: Behind the Scenes**

http://library.advanced.org/10015

◎ **Motion Picture Industry Book**

http://www.studentcenter.com/where/industry/IN7822.htm

◎ **Women in Film**

http://www.cinema.ucla,edu/women/

9

NEW MEDIA, ON-LINE MEDIA, AND THE WEB

What's Ahead

What Is New Media?

What's Happening Here? Mediamorphosis

Are the Old Media Dying?

New Media Convergence

On-line Media and the Web

Predicting the Pace of Change

WWW.com: Understanding the World Wide Web

What's on the Web?

Commercializing the Web

Buying Products on the Web

The Future of New Media, On-line Media, and the Web

NOBODY EVER DESIGNED THE WEB. THERE ARE NO RULES, NO LAWS.

Anon.

The Internet, as well as its technological offspring the World Wide Web, is a new frontier for people and communities in all parts of the world. But what is there today may not be there tomorrow. Sites arise and disappear just as quickly. Over the long run, sites backed by large commercial interests seem to have the most staying power.

The Internet is actually a combination of thousands of computer networks sending and receiving data from all over the world — competing interests joined together by a common purpose, but no common owner. "No government or commercial entity owns the Net or directly profits from its operation," notes information designer Roger Fidler. "It has no president, chief executive officer, or central headquarters."[1]

In its global size and absence of central control, the Internet is completely different from traditional media. Originally developed to aid communication among researchers and educators, the Internet has "evolved in a way no one planned or expected," says Fidler. "Important scientific data and scholarly thoughts have continued to account for much of the traffic [on the Internet], but it is the relationships among people that have shaped the medium. What has mattered most to Internet users is the free exchange of ideas and discussion of values."[2]

As of late August 1998, according to one estimate there were approximately 133 million people in the world with e-mail access to the Internet. Of these, about 62 percent were native English speakers, about 31 percent were native speakers of another European language, and the balance was split among the other languages of the world. Thus, English has established a formidable dominance on the Internet, one that is unlikely to diminish soon.[3]

On-line media are simultaneously frustrating and invigorating. The on-line world is based both on old and new technology, with a terminology all its own. On-line media also are the fastest growing type of media and, because of their rapid growth, promise to become the biggest factor in the future development of the mass-media industries.

Figure 9.1

Computer Technology Varies Coast to Coast, 1997

Source: Adapted from "Household Facilities and Equipment, 1997." Catalogue No. 64-202 XPB, Text Table II, pp. 20–21. Reprinted with permission from Statistics Canada.

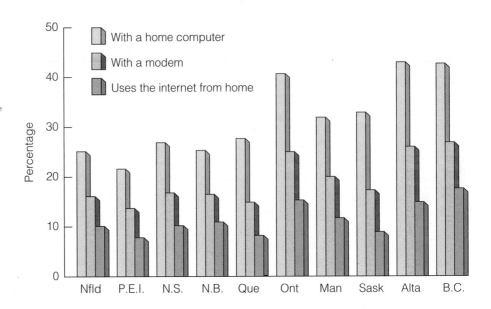

What Is New Media?

New media could be described simply as what is clearly not old media. Old media would be defined as the seven traditional media—print (newspapers, magazines, and books); audio (radio and recordings); and video (television and movies) that are discussed in Chapters 2 through 8.

The term **new media** is used to describe all forms of emerging communications media. New media combines text, graphics, sound, and video, using computer technology to create a product that is similar to, but clearly different from, traditional media.

The term **multimedia** is used to describe any media that combines text, graphics, sound, and video. Video games, the most familiar early form of multimedia, combined text, graphics, sound, and video to create games that could be played on a TV set. The latest video games, which can be played on a computer and also on-line, are a form of multimedia that have developed into new media.

Emerging Forms of New Media Technologies

Since the definition of new media is so broad, the term is thrown around easily by people hoping to get attention and financial support for new products. Emerging forms of new media are being developed every day by people who are experimenting with the process.

As you know from learning about the history of traditional media, some new media inventions will succeed, some will be transition products that will help to develop new products, and many will fail. Until the new media landscape is clearer, however, it is important to follow emerging developments because no one can predict exactly where new media, now in their infancy, are headed.

Some examples of currently emerging new media technologies are the following.

Immersive Virtual Reality Systems. In the 1960s, computer flight simulators began to be used to train military pilots. These simulators were predecessors of today's virtual reality systems. By the 1980s, this technology was called *artificial reality*.

Today, virtual reality systems have been refined to present a remote experience that is even closer to the real thing. The 1995 movie *Disclosure* showed an example of an immersive virtual reality system, when the lead characters in the film "walked" through a database that made them look like they were inside the New York Public Library.

Virtual reality (VR) systems can give people the experience of being somewhere by creating the reality of that place around them, but may require special equipment (a helmet and/or special eyeglasses, for example). These systems, which have been popularized for their entertainment value, actually could have important future applications, allowing a doctor to examine a patient from a distance, for example, and give advice to the attending physician.

Holographic Theatres. A hologram is a three-dimensional image, created on a flat surface, but viewed without special equipment. A holographic theatre would allow you to attend a live music concert at your local theatre, performed by your favourite rock group at another location. What you would see at your local theatre would be a holographic image of the group, projected into the theatre, transmitted from the original location. The holographic image could be projected simultaneously to locations throughout the world.

Personal Channels. This technology would allow you to create your own set of programs and services to be delivered either on your television set, your computer, or both. "By using an on-screen guide ... viewers could select the programs they regularly watch and the movies they may want to see, then have their VCR, or digital successor, automatically record the programs as they are broadcast and sequence them to match their schedule," says Roger Fidler.[4]

Public videoconferencing payphones may become commonplace in the future.

CP Picture Archive (Shizuo Kambayashi)

Personal channels are similar to today's practice of recording a favourite program for viewing later, but with a personal channel, you would be able to record a collection of programs whenever they were available and then view them whenever you wanted.

Intelligent Video Agents. Once you decided which programs you wanted to watch on your personal channel, an intelligent video agent would be able to track the history of the choices you've made, and would then be able to "learn" your interests, hunt for programs for you, and keep them waiting for you to watch at your leisure.

Digital Paper. Researchers at MIT are working on an entirely new type of paper. This paper would look and feel like high-quality paper, but it would be totally erasable. Digital paper pages would be bound like a book, and could be turned to be read like a book, but the pages would be blank.

Digital images could be "printed" on the digital paper and viewed, then the pages could be "erased," to be replaced by new material. MIT researchers suggest that this technology could be used to create the world's first one-volume library. A book that was *Moby Dick* one day could become *The Iliad* the next."[5]

Portable Tablets. These palm-size devices, being developed by several companies, would provide digital readouts of information, delivered by cellular or other technologies.

Some of today's mobile digital pagers already provide a version of this technology, providing running news bulletins and sports scores on the pager's small screen. The information is transmitted either through the cellphone/pager transmitter network or from a communications satellite. Portable tablets would receive, but also could send information that would be written with an electronic pen or typed on the tablet, using a small keypad about the size of today's TV remote control.

Larger, Clearer TV Screens. A common TV screen size is 32 to 36 inches, but some of today's new home theatre systems include 125-inch TV screens. Current TV screens cannot deliver the picture quality that high-definition television (HDTV) and Web TV (devices that show Web pages on a television screen) demand.

Current broadcast TV images are created from 550 horizontal lines that run across the screen. Pictures and text that appear on screens larger than 36 inches are hard to read, but new technology called **line doublers** and **line quadruplers** can actually double and quadruple the number of lines scanning the screen to make the picture sharper.

Doubler technology receives the 550-line broadcast image, changes it into a digital signal, and doubles or quadruples the number of lines to as high as 2200. The result is a much clearer picture. (The clarity of the picture is called **resolution**.)

Doubler technology could be especially important for the development of Web TV because people who are sitting far across the room won't be able to see the image on the screen without better picture resolution. However, the cost of such a home theatre system today is prohibitive for most people.

Personal "digital assistants" can take the place of paper agendas. They can also communicate with other computers and share scheduling information.

CP Picture Archive (Suzanne Tobias)

A 125-inch projection TV, with video player, laserdisc player, quadrupler, digital satellite dish and cable access can run into the hundreds of thousands of dollars for custom high-quality electronics.[6] The high cost will discourage widespread adoption of this technology quickly, but as the price drops, larger screens could become the standard.

Flat Panel Video Display Screens. About the same size as today's TV screens or larger, but only about 4 inches deep, flat panel video display screens hang on the wall like a picture, instead of requiring the large cabinet that houses today's TV and computer screens. Sony introduced its first flat panel video screen in 1998 with a price tag starting at $6000. Screens like this, once they are affordable, will make all video technologies much more convenient to use.[7]

What's Happening Here? Mediamorphosis

This constantly changing media landscape has been called **mediamorphosis**, a word coined by information designer Roger Fidler to describe the way today's media are evolving. Fidler combined the words *media* and *morphosis* (a scientific term used to describe the way an organism or any of its parts undergoes change) to create a new word to describe the simultaneous changes taking place in the media world today.

New media forms "do not arise spontaneously and independently from old media," says Fidler. New media are related and connected to old media. Mediamorphosis "encourages us to examine all forms [of communication media] as members of an interdependent system, and to note the similarities and relationships that exist among past, present and emerging forms."[8]

The new media that are emerging will be similar to the old media, yet different in ways that will make them distinct from their predecessors, says Fidler. Because of the interdependence of all media, this change will be more intense, as changes will happen simultaneously.

IMPACT

on You

By Nathaniel Wice

NO ONE WILL BE FAMOUS UNLESS THEY'RE FAMOUS ONLINE

"I'm sorry if I've upset your concept of celebrity by actually participating in this," declared an unapologetic Courtney Love in one of her first posts two years ago to alt.fan.courtney-love. The grunge widow remains one of the few well-known pop culture figures to invest in an online counterpart to her public persona—maintaining a brawling, semi-regular presence ever since in the America Online bulletin board set aside for discussion of her band, Hole—but her example offers a glimpse of the future when no one will be famous unless they're famous online.

The Internet is already beginning to transfigure popular culture in its own protean image, creating new more direct connections—not just between artists and audiences, but also among fans themselves. The result is a feedback system of flickering, hair-trigger sensitivity in which fame is becoming easier to get and more difficult to maintain.

… The fan communities create a breeding ground for super-fans who soon eclipse the celebrated one, at least in the local discussions. Which was more interesting, the Grateful Dead on stage or their fans in the parking lot? The center of gravity on alt.fan.letterman, one of the biggest fan newsgroups, is not the Ed Sullivan Theater, but a one-bedroom apartment farther up Broadway where the group's resident expert donz5@aol.com lives, works, and maintains a massive database of "Letterman" trivia. His mastery of "Letterman" minutiae— i.e., which guest has most often been on the show and what song the band plays for that guest— transforms him from marginal obsessive to authority figure.

It's a small step from the self-published mailing lists of a Matt Drudge (www.lainet.com/-drudge/) or a Robert Seidman (www.clark.net/pub/robert/), to Web sites where super-fans enshrine their priestly powers, displaying their bootlegged and autographed relics for the extended contemplation of other admirers. … Here's the biggest crack in the system, the best chance for revolution against passive consumption as fame is retrofit for the next millennium: It's the possibility that fans may someday discover they're more interested in each other than they are in their idols.

Yahoo! Internet Life, *October 1996, pp. 31–32. Copyright © 1996 Ziff Davis. Reprinted with permission.*

Are the Old Media Dying?

Will the development of new media mean the death of old media? Some observers have predicted, for example, that the medium of print is dead. "The end of the book is near!" is a headline that has appeared frequently. Yet, book sales continue to be healthy, and are currently at an all-time high.

The history of the evolution of media shows that the introduction of a new medium does not mean the end of the old medium. The continuing overall growth and expansion of the media industries during the last century support this conclusion.

When television was introduced, for example, radio did not disappear. Instead, radio adapted to its new place in the media mix, delivering music, news, and talk. Today, radio exists very comfortably alongside television.

Movies, which also were threatened by the introduction of television, responded by delivering more spectacular and more explicit entertainment than people could see on television, and today movies still play an important role in the business of media.

"When newer forms of communication media emerge, the older forms usually do not die—they continue to evolve and adapt," says Fidler.[9] In this way, the different media compete for the public's attention and jockey for positions of dominance, but no medium has yet disappeared. Instead, each medium contributes to the development of its successors. Together, all media that now exist will contribute to the media that are yet to be invented.

New Media Convergence

In 1978, Nicholas Negroponte at the Massachusetts Institute of Technology began popularizing a theory called **convergence**. This theory gave a name to the process by which the work of the various media industries was beginning to intersect, and MIT was among the first places to foresee and identify this trend.

The media industries not only were combining economically, as media companies began to buy and sell each other, but the technology of the industries also was merging, according to MIT, which meant that eventually the products the media companies produced would begin to resemble each other.

Negroponte also said that the combination of the media industries with the computer industry would create a new type of communication. To identify what was happening, Negroponte created two diagrams to show the position of the media industries in 1978 and his projected vision for those industries in the year 2000. He listed three segments of the media business: (a) print and publishing; (b) broadcast and motion pictures, and (c) the computer industry.

Manufacturers are testing new ways for people to use computers in their lives.

CP Picture Archive (Reed Saxton)

Figure 9.2

How the MIT Media Lab described convergence.

Source: MIT Media Lab

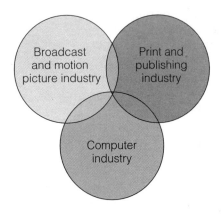

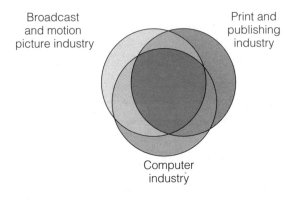

The first diagram displays the alignment of the media industries in 1978, which shows them with a small amount of integrated territory. In the second diagram, which shows Negroponte's predictions for the year 2000, the three segments of the media industries are completely overlapping.[10]

Negroponte's forecast was an accurate prediction of exactly what is happening today, and it helped to establish the framework for today's thinking about future media.

Today's economic and technological convergence in the media industries is the most important reason for the development of new media. Each of the media industries is equally well positioned to take advantage of new developments, and all media industries will benefit from convergence.

Today, many media companies, because of their size, also have the money available to invest in new technologies. These companies also have a shared interest in seeing their investments succeed. So, convergence is likely to continue at a rapid pace, which means that many new media products will become available quickly.

Which New Media Products Will Succeed?

As all of these new media products flood the marketplace, some will succeed, and many will not. However, the potential reward if consumers adopt a new media product is so big that all types of media companies are willing to take the risks associated with developing new products. For consumers, this means a confusing array of product choices bombarding the marketplace as each

company tries to develop the one product that a large group of consumers will embrace.

There are parallels between the early history of traditional media and the emerging technologies that are being used to create a new popular product, which will eventually result in the development of a new medium.

New Media Lessons from History

In the early 1900s, when movies first were introduced as flickering images on a small screen, the moving images were something consumers hadn't seen before, but many people saw the silent movies as just a passing fad (see Chapter 8). The inventions that had been introduced by Thomas Edison and his colleagues at the time made the movies technologically possible, but the movies also needed creative minds like that of director D.W. Griffith and stars like Mary Pickford to create the epic stories that people wanted to see.

When new inventions brought sound to the movies, the success of the new medium was unstoppable. This combination of technological development, creative expression, and consumer demand was crucial for the movies' enduring prosperity.

A mix of economics, technology and creativity is also behind today's race to develop new media. Today, media and computer entrepreneurs are hoping to capitalize on fast-moving developments in technology to be the first to deliver a new creative product that large numbers of people want.

On-line Media and the Web

The first sign of the expansion of the Internet to consumer and educational users in the late 1980s was the adoption by businesses and private users of electronic mail, or **e-mail**, technology. With a computer, a modem, and a telephone line, just about anyone could learn how to communicate electronically on-line.

"The driving force for achieving large subscriber gains is the incorporation of the Internet by consumers as part of their routine," says Veronis, Suhler & Associates, a media research company. "The Internet has become a tool that allows users to economize on what has become their scarcest resource—time. Virtually all of the leading Internet applications allow users to accomplish tasks more quickly than they can through alternative means."[11]

Just as telephone answering machines changed voice communication by allowing people to send and receive messages on their own time schedule, e-mail allows people to communicate and receive information at their convenience. People who are on-line at home today are most likely to use the technology to gather news and information or to send and receive e-mail.[12] (See Figure 9.2.)

E-mail at school, work, or home is the way most people first experience communicating in an electronic environment. E-mail is easy to use and convenient, and it is a text-based system, which means that people type in messages on a keyboard, which is a familiar tool.

Familiarity and convenience are important in the adoption of new technologies because people fear what they don't understand, and misunderstandings about how new technologies work can keep them from changing their current habits.

Predicting the Pace of Change

Just how quickly consumers will adopt new technology is predictable, according to Paul Saffo, a Director of the Institute for the Future in Menlo Park, California. Saffo theorizes that for the past five centuries the pace of change has always been 30 years, or about three decades, from the introduction of a new idea to its complete adoption by the culture.

Saffo called his theory the **30-year rule**, which he has divided into three stages. In the first decade, he says, there is "lots of excitement, lots of puzzlement, not a lot of penetration." In the second decade, "lots of flux, penetration of the product into society is beginning." And in the third decade, the reaction to the technology is "'Oh, so what? Just a standard technology and everybody has it.'"[13]

Figure 9.3

On-line Activities

Sources: Veronis, Suhler & Associates, Wilkofsky Gruen Associates, Advertising Age/Market Facts.

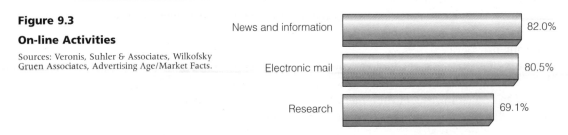

News and information — 82.0%

Electronic mail — 80.5%

Research — 69.1%

How people on-line use their computers

Figure 9.4

Only a few Web businesses have been commercially successful, but the Web medium is still in its infancy, with a potential for remarkable revenue growth, unmatched by any of the traditional media.

Sources: Veronis, Suhler & Associates, Wilkofsky Gruen Associates, SIMBA Information, Find/SVP, Jupiter Communications.

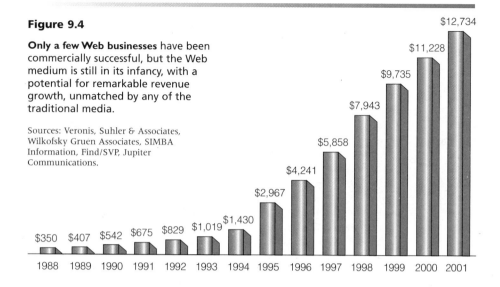

1988	1989	1990	1991	1992	1993	1994	1995	1996	1997	1998	1999	2000	2001
$350	$407	$542	$675	$829	$1,019	$1,430	$2,967	$4,241	$5,858	$7,943	$9,735	$11,228	$12,734

By Saffo's standard, North America is probably entering its second stage of acceptance of on-line technology because use of the Internet by consumers started growing quickly beginning in 1988. In June of 1998, Neilson Media Research estimated there were 8.5 million adult Internet users in Canada aged 16 years and over and 70.5 million in the United States, compared to a combined total of 58 million in September 1997.[14]

Saffo's description of the second decade of change coincides with the fluctuation now taking place in the media marketplace. People are faced with choices that seem to emerge daily: different combinations of new and existing media technology are "guaranteed" to create the best on-line world. While this technological transformation is underway, the on-line world seems very confusing.

The most confusing, yet promising, place of all is the newest on-line media development, the World Wide Web.

Cyber-cafés are becoming more and more popular. This high-tech café in Paris is just one more venue where people can ride the information superhighway.

CP Picture Archive (Michel Enlor)

IMPACT

Profile

TIM BERNERS-LEE: THE MAN WHO INVENTED THE WEB

By Robert Wright

You might think that someone who invented a giant electronic brain for Planet Earth would have a pretty impressive brain of his own. And Tim Berners-Lee, 41, the creator of the World Wide Web, no doubt does. But his brain also has one shortcoming, and, by his own account, this neural glitch may have been the key to the Web's inception.

Berners-Lee isn't good at "random connections," he says. "I'm certainly terrible at names and faces." (No kidding. He asked me my name twice during our first two hours of conversation.) Back in 1980 he wrote some software to

CP Picture Archive (Greg Gibson)

help keep track of such links—a "memory substitute." The rest is history. This prosthetic extension of his mind took a vast evolutionary leap a decade later, and then grew to encompass the world. It is the reason that today you can be online looking at a photo, then mouse-click on the photographer's name to learn about her, then click on "Nikon" to see the camera she uses—traveling from computers in one end of the world to those in another with no sense of motion.

Berners-Lee is the unsung—or at least undersung—hero of the information age. Even by some of the less breathless accounts, the World Wide Web could prove as important as the printing press. That would make Berners-Lee comparable to well, Gutenberg, more or less. Yet so far, most of the wealth and fame emanating from the Web have gone to people other than him. Marc Andreessen, co-founder of Netscape, drives a Mercedes-Benz and has graced the cover of several major magazines. Berners-Lee has graced the cover of none, and he drives a 13-year-old Volkswagen Rabbit. He has a smallish, barren office at M.I.T., where his nonprofit group,

the World Wide Web Consortium, helps set technical standards for the Web, guarding its coherence against the potentially deranging forces of the market.

Is Berners-Lee's Volkswagen poisoning his brain with carbon monoxide? He wonders about this by way of apologizing for the diffuseness of his answers. "I'm not good at sound bites," he observes. True, alas. But what he lacks in snappiness he makes up in peppiness. Spouting acronyms while standing at a blackboard, he approaches the energy level of Robin Williams. He is British (an Oxford physics major), but to watch only his hands as he talks, you'd guess Italian. Five, six years ago, during his "evangelizing" phase, this relentless enthusiasm was what pushed the Web beyond critical mass.

The breathtaking growth of the Web has been "an incredibly good feeling," he says, and is "a lesson for all dreamers ... that you can have a dream and it can come true."

Time *magazine, May 19, 1997.* *© 1997 Time Inc. Reprinted by permission.*

WWW.com: Understanding the World Wide Web

Exchanging text through e-mail is now a simple electronic operation, but several more developments were necessary for people to be able to share text, graphics, audio, and video on-line. These developments made the creation of the World Wide Web possible.

The person most responsible for creating the World Wide Web is Tim Berners-Lee, a British native with an Oxford degree in physics. Working in 1989 in Geneva, Switzerland, at the CERN physics laboratory, Berners-Lee created several new programming languages.

These new programming languages included **HTML** (**hypertext markup language**) and **HTTP** (**hypertext transfer protocol**), which allowed people to create and send text, graphics, and video information electronically and also to set up connections (called "**links**") from one source of information to another. (These developments were very important in the Web's early days, but today, just a few years later, people can create their own Web pages without knowing HTML and HTTP.)

After he had invented the language and mechanisms that would allow people to share all kinds of information electronically, Berners-Lee gave this invention its name—the World Wide Web. "The original goal was working together with others," says Berners-Lee. "The Web was supposed to be a creative tool, an expressive tool."[15]

Berners-Lee also created the first **browser**, which allowed people to search electronically among many documents to find what they wanted. The idea of the browser was further refined by Marc Andreessen and his colleagues at the University of Illinois, and in 1994 they introduced software called Mosaic, which allowed people to put text and pictures in the same on-line document. The principals of the Mosaic project subsequently moved on to create Netscape Navigator, currently one of the two most widely used commercial browsers.

Another level of help for Web access is the **search engine**. This is a tool used to locate information in a computer database. Some familiar search engines are Lycos, Infoseek, Excite, Yahoo!, and Canada.com. These sites turn your typed request for information into digital bits that then go and search for what you want and return the information to you.

Sample tracks from new music CDs and even live performances can be downloaded from websites and saved, altered, and shared over the Internet or combined on made-at-home CDs.

CP Picture Archive (Thomas Aoyagi)

Technology

CANADIANS ON CUTTING EDGE WITH FIRST INTERNET FILM

By Lydia Zajc

TORONTO (Reuters)—Move over *Titanic*, make room *Ally McBeal*, there is a new show in town and its producers see you, the viewers, playing a leading role. Welcome to the new world of "Netertainment," where movies and television meet the interactive world of the Internet.

Canadian movie and Web site makers have unleashed a groundbreaking film on the Net that invites viewers to choose the order in which they watch its scenes. The creators claim their baby, made exclusively for the Web and called *Monster Home*, is the first of its kind.

The people who produce Internet content believe these projects are the next wave in the entertainment business and will change the way films and shows are made forever. Potential viewers are the growing numbers of people— about 102 million in July—who are turning to the Internet to surf for information, chat with others, see pornographic pictures and, increasingly, watch some type of video clip.

U.S. entrepreneur Josh Harris, who founded a creative Web content business called Pseudo Programs Inc., thinks eventually everyone will emigrate to watching entertainment on the Net.

The eight hours a day that people have the TV on is reducing and people are crossing over to the Net because it's a more compelling experience," he said.

Canadian Geoffrey Shea, president of Image Business, hopes Harris is right. The six-member firm in Dundas, Ontario, unveiled the hour-long *Monster Home* on June 18. The Web site is www.monster-home.com.

Goal Is to Entertain, Bemuse, Engage
"Our goal for this particular work is ... to have it entertain, or bemuse [sic], or otherwise engage as many people who are interested in using the Internet for entertainment," Shea said. "Our goal beyond that is to develop more sophisticated, more ambitious, more advanced Net-specific entertainment content. And as the Net evolves, the nature of that content will evolve as well ... more like a game, more like a puzzle, more like information." Harris takes it a step further. "We're the next generation of television, we make television. It just happens instead of being on cable it's on the computer. Simple as that."

Monster Home follows the fate of a family invited to a high-tech mansion to earn the love—and money— of a shadowy millionaire grandfather. The film, cut up into snippets that a Net viewer must click, follows the quarrelsome siblings and their children deeper into a murky world of dubious doings.

As the observer, the viewer hacks into someone else's electronic mail, reads a fictitious

---

To encourage people to use their systems, both Berners-Lee and Andreessen placed their software innovations in the public domain, which meant that anyone with a computer and a modem could download them from the Internet and use them for free. This culture of free information access, coupled with a creative, chaotic lack of direction, still permeates the Web today.

The process of putting documents on the Web drew its terminology from print, the original mass medium. Placing something on the Web is called **publishing** and begins with a **home page**, which is like the front door to the site, the place that welcomes the user and explains how the site works.

However, even though Web sites are similar to published documents in the way they are described, what is created on the Web has few of the legal limitations or protections placed on other published documents. A Web page can be copied onto a user's computer, but subsequent use of this material by the user may be subject to copyright limitations.

Web site and views cartoons and scenes from the perspective of the indoor video cameras.

Canada's national newspaper, *The Globe and Mail,* said *Monster Home* was "like a B-grade suspense flick crossed with *The X-Files.*" Shot in nine days with local actors for C$120,000, it is not likely to eclipse the epic *Titanic* which starred heart-throb Leonardo DiCaprio, won 11 Oscars and cost more than US$200 million.

Film "Pushing the Boundaries"
But in a small way the film is "very ambitious," said Paul Hoffert, a York University professor who is on the selection committee of telephone company Bell Canada, which paid half the costs. Broken down into scenes and including animation and video, "it is an example of a project that is pushing the boundaries a little bit," Hoffert said. "Maybe a year from now it'll be commonplace and lots of people will be doing it."

Millions have seen *Titanic* and thousands watch *Ally McBeal* each week, but *Monster Home* snags about 350 viewers a day. That is respectable, considering viewers need lots of high-tech gadgetry to watch, including a high-speed modem, sound cards for audio and other bits of hardware and software.

The actual picture, the size of a business card on the computer screen, features jerky motion and poor sound quality reminiscent of the early talkies. And the problem of "net congestion"—when too many people are surfing the Web at the same time—sometimes pops up to interrupt the flow.

Despite technological draw-backs, however, Internet creations like *Monster Home* could help revolutionize the movie industry, somewhat like the video machine did. Once VCRs become common, movies could be created and distributed with the knowledge that

they did not have to cater solely to a mainstream audience to make money.

"I think that lower-budget movies with more specific appeal are going to become more possible because you're not going to have a-million-people-have-to-see-this-to-break-even kind of economics," Shea said.

"Imagine when it gets even cheaper and even more convenient, when you don't even have to bother going all the way down to the corner video store but can just click on something on your computer and get that movie directly across the Internet."

He says massive spectacles such as *Titanic* will always exist but quirky Netertainment vehicles, where you can watch characters real-time or have a virtual confer-ence with other viewers, could be coming soon to a computer near you.

Copyright Reuters Limited, 1998.

What's on the Web?

Anything that can be given digital form. Once Berners-Lee had created the tools for access so that all types of text and video images could become available on the Web, it was left to anyone who could use the tools to create whatever they wanted and make it available to anyone who wanted it.

Nobody designed the Web in its present form: There are no rules, no laws. The Web also exists without national boundaries. Any type of information—pictures, voice, graphics, and text—can travel virtually instantly to and from anyone with a computer and access to the Internet anywhere in the world.

There are Web sites devoted to every imaginable aspect of human communi-cation. One woman, who learned that a friend had cancer, researched informa-tion about cancer treatment on the Web and then established a cancer informa-tion site to help others.

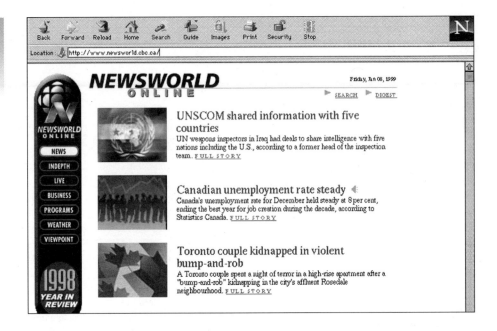

Banking is moving on-line as well, allowing electronic transactions that can occur anytime, not just when someone can get to a bank machine or branch. One company, the Citizens Bank of Canada, an offshoot of the credit union movement in British Columbia, is a virtual bank. The bank is totally on-line, without any physical storefront offices, just an on-line "branch," and a telephone call centre.

Early in 1998, the Web exploded with images of a dancing baby created by a software developer and popularized by the television program *Ally McBeal*. The baby drew even more attention when *Ally McBeal* won the Golden Globe Award for Best Television Series and the sequence, showing the main character dancing with the baby on the program, appeared as part of the Golden Globe broadcast.

Universal access, limited only by the available technology, is what gives the Web the feeling and look of what has been called "anarchy"—a world without rules. The Web is a new medium, but its progress towards becoming a true mass medium for a majority of people seeking information and entertainment is still limited by technology and the economics of being on-line.

JEFF STAHLER reprinted by permission of Newspaper Enterprise Association, Inc.

INTERNET SEX IS TOP CASH MAKER ON THE WEB

WINNIPEG (CP) —Sex sells, and that's the naked truth on the Internet.

But has the World Wide Web gone from geek show to peep show in the last decade, or is the extent of the Internet's X-rated content exaggerated?

Just about everything that can turn bits and bytes into a buck is there, from the merely titillating to the hardest of hard-core, on subtly named Web sites like smutcity and throbnet.

There are chat rooms where the liberal-minded engage in virtual cybersex, phone-sex services, steaming video and on-line shopping malls for adult products.

You can hunt for an E-mail-order bride (or groom) or just rent for the night. A long list of escort agencies is neatly classified by city.

Sex and the computer are fodder for academic study and pop literature: Try The Joy of Cybersex by Australian Carol Parker, a self-confessed cybersex junkie who spent 16 hours a day on her computer until it wrecked her marriage.

"But is it as massive as everyone says, pervasive, dominant?" asks Canadian Internet watcher Jim Carroll. "I don't think so."

Yet Carroll says sex is unquestionably the No. 1 money maker on the Internet, followed by finance and gambling.

The unregulated nature of the Net and the sex trade make it impossible to estimate just how much money is changing hands this way. Some estimates suggest sex sites comprise perhaps 2 per cent of the sites on the Web, but it's a 2 per cent that has a lot of people concerned. And there's no

question sex is hot on the Net. Some sites have had millions of visitors.

"It will never be controlled. You will never control the flow of information on the Net," says Carroll.

© Canadian Press. Reprinted with permission.

Commercializing the Web

When television was introduced to the public in the late 1940s, the assumption from the beginning was that it would be a commercial medium—that is, the programming would be paid for by the advertisers who bought the commercials surrounding the programming. This concept of advertisers underwriting the programs was a natural evolution from radio, where commercials also paid for the programming.

The Web, however, began as a free medium. Many people pay an on-line service such as America Online to organize and deliver information and entertainment from many sources, including the Web, but the actual information—what's on the Web—is available for free. Attempts to charge users for content have not been very successful. Public sharing of account access information is one reason why charging seldom works.

Paying for Media on the Web

"Even as Internet use continues its dramatic surge, many if not most Internet ventures are losing money.... The standing joke on the Web is that the letters 'ISP' don't really stand for 'Internet Service Provider' but for 'I'm still profit-less.'"[16] People are still unwilling to pay for most of the information that's available on the Web.

Slate, the on-line literary magazine published by Microsoft, planned to start charging subscribers in 1997, but then decided against it. Editor Michael Kinsley said, "It would be better to establish a brand name with wide readership first."[17]

Nathan Myhrvold, who directs technology operations at Microsoft, says that Internet users will not pay for access to one site when "a million free sites are just a click away.... There's no incentive until people are too addicted to the Net to turn off their computers, yet are bored with what's available."[18]

Myrhvold says that once people exhaust what's available for free on the Web, they may be willing to pay. The situation is similar, he says, to people who were previously satisfied with network and local television, but who now pay for cable or satellite TV to get access to expanded programming.

Some sexually explicit Web sites do charge for access, and some information sites, such as the *Wall Street Journal*, charge a nominal subscription fee (the *Journal* claims to have 160 000 on-line subscribers).

Other sites, such as the sports network ESPN and CBS Interactive Baseball, give away some information and then charge for "premium" services. On-line, interactive gamemakers, who offer videogames on the Web, charge by the hour or use a tiered pricing structure—free, basic, and premium. "Everybody's fishing right now," says Chris Sherman, director of games for Concentric Networks, "and nobody knows what they're going to catch."[19]

Buying Products on the Web

What makes the Web different from traditional media is its capacity to combine information, entertainment, and commerce. People not only retrieve information and entertainment from the Web, they can also buy things. The Web is inter-active, which means that people can send information back and forth. Retailers can use the Web to sell products directly, without setting up a store or spending a lot of money on expensive advertising.

Two of the most successful commercial operations on the Web offer tradi-tional media for sale—Amazon.com sells books and CD Now (ww.cdnow.com) sells CDs. Amazon.com sells many books at a discount and features book reviews and author profiles, and it advertises that it can search more than one million titles. At CD Now, you can listen to 30 seconds of a song before buying it.

"The Internet has the potential to be the best sales tool—the best advertising and direct marketing vehicle—ever devised," says *Los Angeles Times* media critic David Shaw. "The Internet can turn any advertiser—any product manufac-turer or service provider—into the equivalent of a direct marketer. On the Internet, consumers looking for a particular product or service can shop over the entire country—the entire world—looking at photographs and comparing prices, features and terms, and then buy what they want with a credit card and arrange to have the purchase delivered to their home."[20]

Most Web sites now carry some form of advertising. These appear as banners across the top of the site, or run as borders alongside the site's pages (see the Canada.com screen on page 205). But just like traditional media, advertising can crowd out the original message and turn consumers away. Although few commercial on-line operations have been successful (and many have gone out of business) new Web site entrepreneurs continue to test the market to develop a pricing structure that will pay the bills.

Tracking On-line Buyers

Because the Web is such a targeted medium—the seller can know exactly who the buyer is—the Web holds better potential for monitoring consumers' buying habits than traditional methods of advertising. Ultimately, Web advertisers "can achieve the merchandiser's dream—targeting an audience far more precisely than it can with either newspapers or television by advertising a product only on sites that draw people likely to be interested in that product," says David Shaw.

"Moreover, they will be able to get nearly instantaneous electronic feedback on whether their ads are effective: How many people saw the ad? How many 'clicked' on it and went on to a more detailed presentation? How many bought the product right then, on-line?"[21]

Software is already available that offers "tracking" information for advertisers. Many sites give advertisers information about how many "hits" the sites receive—how many times people looked at the site—but this is not very reliable information because advertisers have no way to track how much of the ad people read, how much time they spent at the site, or, most importantly, if they eventually bought a product that was advertised.

By Sarah Scott

It is riskier to give a credit card to a waiter in a restaurant than send it through the Internet to a virtual store, says Rick Broadhead, a consultant and co-author of the *1998 Canadian Internet Handbook.* You have a greater risk of getting held up at the corner store, Broadhead says.

Yet perception, in this case, is more important than reality. The widespread belief that the Internet is not secure for credit-card purchases is the biggest barrier to an explosion of Internet shopping, according to Broadhead and other industry experts. Although one-quarter of Canadians use the Internet right now, only 2.5 per cent have ever bought anything on the Net, according to a survey by TWA Consulting Services Inc., a firm that advises financial institutions on payment systems for electronic

commerce. Internet purchases, mostly computer-related products, have jumped from nearly zero two years ago, but break-through growth will only occur when card-carrying Canadian shoppers know that large, trusted financial institutions guarantee the security of their credit-card purchases, says TWA president Thomas Atkin. "When that happens, it will take Internet shopping through the roof."

That day could be sooner than many people think. The worlds two largest credit card associations, Visa and MasterCard, are testing new, super-secure procedures to make credit-card purchases on the Internet as safe as purchases in a regular store. The new security protocol—called SET, or secure electronic transaction—has been developed by the credit-card

giants with the backing of major players in the computer business, including Microsoft, IBM and Netscape.

Others are more skeptical, "Let's face it," says Randy Scotland, vice-president of communications for the Retail Council of Canada, "the Internet cannot replace the store-shopping experience." People still like to wander through malls on a Saturday afternoon and touch the things they are going to buy. While they might like buying books and computer software on the Net, the medium has its limitations, no matter how tight the security. It is, notes Scotland, "difficult to try on a new shirt or shoes on the Internet."

Maclean's, October 27, 1997, p. 46. Reprinted with permission.

One company has developed "ad robots" that allow a company to, in effect, eavesdrop on chat room conversations while the user is on-line. If someone mentions, on-line, that they are having a problem with their car, for example, the robot would recognize the pattern of words in the discussion and send the person an ad for car repair.[22] But the future of direct consumer measurement on the Web is still uncertain and will become clearer only when the Web itself has further defined its direction.

The Future of New Media, On-line Media, and the Web

The future of media on-line is bound only by the interests of consumers and the imaginations of media developers, which are as diverse as the people who are on-line today and those going on-line tomorrow. The new media universe could become a purer reflection of the real universe than any medium yet created, with unprecedented potential, like all mass media, to both reflect and direct the culture.

Electronic game players are among the small number of people who are willing to pay for on-line media. Here, game enthusiasts check out the offerings at Electronic Entertainment Expo, a videogame trade show.

CP Picture Archive (Reed Saxon)

"The Internet is still in its infancy, and its potential is enormous," writes David Shaw. "As technology continues to improve and its audience continues to grow—as users and advertisers alike become more comfortable with it and knowledgeable about it—the Internet could ultimately attract the kind of audience and generate the kind of advertising revenue that would enable it to revolutionize human communication even more dramatically than Johann Gutenberg's first printing press did more than 500 years ago."[23]

In Focus

◎ The Internet is a combination of thousands of computer networks sending and receiving data from all over the world.

◎ Because of its global size and the absence of government controls, the Internet is completely different from traditional media.

◎ On-line media are the fastest growing type of media.

◎ Some examples of currently emerging new media technologies are immersive virtual reality systems, holographic theatres, personal channels, intelligent video agents, digital paper, portable tablets, line doublers and quadruplers for TV screens, and flat panel display screens.

◎ Information designer Roger Fidler coined the term *mediamorphosis* to describe the simultaneous evolution of several media industries at once.

◎ Nicholas Negroponte originated the concept of convergence in 1978 to describe the process by which the technologies of all the media industries are merging.

◎ The same collision of economics, technology, and creativity that drove the development of traditional media is behind today's race to develop new media.

◎ Electronic mail (e-mail) is the way most people first experience communicating in an electronic environment.

◎ Paul Saffo first defined the 30-year rule governing people's willingness to adopt new ideas.

◎ Tim Berners-Lee is the person most responsible for creating the World Wide Web.

◎ The free culture of the Web originated with its founders, who placed their discoveries in the public domain, which meant that anyone could use them for free.

◎ On the Web, any type of information—pictures, voice, graphics, and text—can travel virtually instantly to and from anyone with a computer and access to the Internet anywhere in the world.

◎ While a few Web sites, such as sexually explicit Web sites and on-line gaming sites, charge for their services, most people remain unwilling to pay for what's on the Web.

◎ What makes the Web different from traditional media is its capacity to combine information, entertainment, and commerce.

◎ Many Web sites now carry some form of advertising.

◎ Marketers are developing tracking software to monitor consumers' on-line habits.

◎ The future of media on-line is bound only by the interests of consumers and the imaginations of media developers, which are as diverse as the people who are on-line today and those going on-line tomorrow.

Review Questions

1. What characteristics set the World Wide Web apart from the traditional media?

2. Why is regulating new media so difficult?

Watching the Web

◎ **Electronic Frontier Foundation**

http://www.eff.org

◎ **Electronic Rights Defense Committee**

http://www.erights.qc.ca

◎ **Journal of Electronic Publishing**

http://www.press.umich.edu/jep

◎ **MIT Media Lab Project**

http://casr.www.media.mit.edu/groups/casr/papert.html

◎ **Associated Press Breaking News**

http://www.tampabayonline.net/news/apbreak.htm

ADVERTISING 10

What's Ahead

> THE ADVERTISING INDUSTRY
> CONTENDS THAT THE ULTIMATE
> TEST OF ANY PRODUCT IS THE
> MARKETPLACE, AND THAT
> ADVERTISING MAY STIMULATE
> CONSUMERS TO TRY A NEW
> PRODUCT OR A NEW BRAND, BUT
> CONSUMERS WILL NOT CONTINUE
> TO BUY AN UNSATISFYING
> PRODUCT.

Louis C. Kaufman, author,
Essentials of Advertising

Few dimensions of the media generate more heated controversy than advertising. It has, in connection with magazines, been the focus of a major and continuing trade dispute between Canada and the United States (see Chapter 3). It has also been contentious in its influence on children, in its role in political campaigns, in its promotion of consumerism, and in its deception and manipulation of consumers.

The American Marketing Association defines *advertising* as "any paid form of nonpersonal presentation and promotion of ideas, goods, or services by an identified sponsor." Consumers pay for most of their media (newspapers, magazines, radio, and television) by watching, listening to, and reading advertisements.

You pay directly for books, movies, and recordings, although these media use advertising to sell their products. But the broadcast programs you want to hear and see and the articles you want to read are surrounded by advertisements placed by advertising people who want to sell you products, ideas, political candidates, personal services, or merely a favourable image of their clients.

Paying for Our Pleasures: Advertising and the Media

Advertising is not a medium. Advertising carries the messages that come to you from the people who pay for the media. The price for all types of advertising (including billboards and direct mail, as well as print and broadcast advertising) exceeds $8 billion dollars in Canada each year (see Table 10.1).

Table 10.1

How Canadian Advertisers Spent Their Money in 1995—National and Local		
Medium	**Amount Spent Dollars (Cdn)**	**Percent**
Daily newspapers	1 900 000 000	25.5
Television	1 844 000 000	24.7
National	986 000 000	
Local	362 000 000	
Other	496 000 000	
Radio	754 000 000	10.1
National	169 109 000	
Local	579 000 000	
Weekly newspapers (semi, tri, etc., including controlled distribution)	579 000 000	7.8
National	58 000 000	
Local	521 000 000	
Magazines, general	265 000 000	3.6
Business papers	175 000 000	2.3
Yellow Pages	864 000 000	11.6
Other print	87 000 000	1.1
Catalogues and direct mail	991 000 000	13.3
Total	**7 459 000 000**	**100.0**

Source: Data from the Canadian Newspaper Association, "Canadian Advertising: All Media." On-line at the Newspaper Association of America website: http://www.naa.org/info/facts/24.html January 22, 1998.

There are two main advertising markets in Canada: anglophone and francophone. The difference goes well beyond the language of communication and involves deep-seated patterns of consumer behaviour that are rooted in the two founding cultures. A third smaller market, consists of allophones—those whose mother tongue and culture is neither English nor French. Allophones now number in the millions in Canada, and their tastes and cultures have affected the range of goods for sale, the manner in which they are advertised and sold, and the way brand loyalties are established.

Although the advertising industry itself is continental, advertising does not travel across borders well. Differences in accent, habits of consumption, the appearance of the paper money and coins, and the impact of celebrity endorsements all affect how a message is received within a culture. Advertising has to be crafted with the target culture in mind; it is not a generic good.

Early Advertising

In 1200 BC, the Phoenicians painted messages on stones near the paths where people often walked. In the sixth century BC, ships that came into port sent criers around town with signboards to announce their arrival. In the 13th century AD, the British began requiring trademarks to protect buyers and to identify faulty products. The first printed advertisement was prepared by printer William Caxton in England in 1478 to sell one of his books.

Advertising became part of the North American experience even before the settlers arrived. "Never was there a more outrageous or more unscrupulous or more ill-informed advertising campaign than that by which the promoters for the American colonies brought settlers here," writes historian Daniel Boorstin.

> Brochures published in England in the seventeenth century, some even earlier, were full of hopeful overstatements, half-truths, and downright lies, along with some facts which nowadays surely would be the basis for an action for misleading advertising. Gold and silver, fountains of youth, plenty of fish, venison without limit, all these were promised, and of course some of them were found.[1]

Advertising in Newspapers

North America's first newspaper advertisement appeared in *The Boston News-Letter*'s first issue in 1704 when the newspaper's editor included an ad for his own newspaper. The penny press of the 1800s counted on advertising to underwrite its costs. In 1833, the *New York Sun* candidly stated in its first issue: "The object of this paper is to lay before the public, at a price within the means of everyone, all the news of the day, and at the same time afford an advantageous medium for advertising."[2]

Three years later, the *Philadelphia Public Ledger* reported that "advertising is our revenue, and in a paper involving so many expenses as a penny paper, and especially our own, the only source of revenue."[3]

The first Canadian advertisement, an ad for butter, appeared in the *Halifax Gazette* in 1752. Advertisements grew in number and professionalism as the regional newspapers appeared.

Because they were so dependent on advertisers, newspapers in the 1800s accepted any ads they could get. Eventually they got complaints from customers, especially about the patent medicines that promised cures and often delivered hangovers. (Many of these medicines were mostly alcohol.)

Products like Anti-Corpulene pills claimed they would help someone lose 15 pounds a month. "They cause no sickness, contain no poison and never fail."[4] Dr. T. Felix Couraud's Oriental Cream guaranteed that it would "remove tan, pimples, freckles, moth patches, rash and skin diseases and every blemish on beauty."[5] Also heavily advertised were Carter's Little Liver Pills and Buckley's Cough Mixture (which is on the shelves of drugstores today, still advertising its bad taste as a sure sign of its effectiveness).

The newspaper publishers' response to complaints was to develop an open advertising policy, which allowed the publishers to continue accepting the ads. Then publishers criticized ads on their editorial pages. The *Public Ledger*'s policy was "Our advertising columns are open to the 'public, the whole public, and nothing but the public.' We admit any advertisement of any thing or any opinion, from any persons who will pay the price, excepting what is forbidden by the laws of the land, or what, in the opinion of all, is offensive to decency and morals."[6] But some editors did move their ads, which had been mingled with the copy, to a separate section.

Advertising historian Stephen Fox writes:

> Advertising was considered an embarrassment ... the wastrel relative, the unruly servant kept backstairs and never allowed into the front parlor.... A firm risked its credit rating by advertising; banks might take it as a confession of financial weakness.
>
> Everyone deplored advertising. Nobody—advertiser, agent, or medium—took responsibility for it. The advertiser only served as an errand boy, passing the advertiser's message along to the publisher: the medium printed it, but surely would not question the right of free speech by making a judgment on the veracity of the advertiser.[7]

Patent medicine ads in the 1800s often promised cures the products could not deliver. Advertising was not regulated, and claims were not restrained by common sense or scientific finding.

The Bettmann Archive

Advertising in Magazines

Until the 1880s, magazines remained wary of advertising. But Cyrus H.K. Curtis, who founded *The Ladies' Home Journal* in 1887, promoted advertising as the way for magazines to succeed. Once when he was asked what made him successful, he answered, "Advertising. That's what made me whatever I am. ... I use up my days trying to find men who can write an effective advertisement."[8]

When Curtis hired Edward Bok as editor, Bok began a campaign against patent medicine ads and joined with *Collier's* and the American Medical Association to seek government restraints. The U.S. Congress created the Federal Trade Commission in 1914, and part of its job was to monitor deceptive advertising.

Advertising on Radio

In the early days of Canadian radio, advertising was extensive, and much of it was imported along with U.S. programming. Radio advertising has been on the airwaves since WEAF in New York broadcast its first advertising in 1922, selling apartments in New Jersey. B.F. Goodrich, Palmolive, and Eveready commercials followed. In September 1928, the Lucky Strike Dance Orchestra premiered on NBC, and Lucky Strike sales went up 47 percent. More cigarette companies moved to radio, and Camel cigarettes sponsored weekly, then daily, programs. Much of this early radio advertising spilled over into Canada, either as a result of direct broadcasting, or through the rebroadcasting of U.S. programming in Canada. However, often the products advertised were not even for sale in Canada.

Canadians became familiar with ads such as those for Sir Walter Raleigh cigarettes, which sponsored the *Sir Walter Raleigh Revue*. In one hour, the sponsor squeezed in 70 references to the product, which was not available in Canada.

> The theme song ("rally round Sir Walter Raleigh") introduced the Raleigh Revue in the Raleigh Theater with the Raleigh Orchestra and the Raleigh Rovers; then would follow the adventures of Sir Walter in Virginia and at Queen Elizabeth's court, with ample mention of his cigarettes and smoking tobacco.[9]

In 1938, for the first time, radio collected more money from advertising than did magazines.

Advertising on Television

Television was born as an advertising medium. Never questioning how television would be financed, the networks assumed they would attract commercial support. They were right. Even by 1949 in the United States, television advertisers spent $12.3 million. In 1950, the total was $40.8 million and in 1951, $128 million.[10] In Canada, advertising expenditures on television did not reach $50 million until 1960, largely because of public funding and more stringent standards. In areas near the border, Canadian advertisers bought time on U.S. local stations in Detroit, Niagara Falls, and Buffalo, for example. The situation became more complicated in the 1960s, when Canadian cable systems were required to substitute Canadian advertising into broadcasts from the United States. Needless to say, this infuriated American broadcasters and advertisers, as did a related issue, the showing of U.S. television shows in earlier time slots on Canadian stations. These issues have left a legacy of mistrust.

In a practice adopted from radio, early television programs often carried **direct sponsorship**. Many shows, such as *Camel News Caravan*, carried the sponsor's name in the title and advertised a product (Camel cigarettes). Advertising agencies became television's programmers. "Given one advertiser and a show title often bearing its name, viewers associated a favorite show with its sponsor and—because of a 'gratitude factor'—would buy the products."[11]

Alfred Hitchcock became legendary for leading into his show's commercials with wry remarks about the sponsor: "Oh dear, I see the actors won't be ready for another sixty seconds. However, thanks to our sponsor's remarkable foresight, we have a message that will fill in here nicely."[12] But Hitchcock's sarcasm was the exception, and most programs welcomed advertising support without comment.

Catalogue retailers, here the Robert Simpson Company of Toronto, delivered all manner of goods throughout Canada. Customers ordered by mail from catalogues they received at home.

Courtesy of the Metropolitan Toronto Reference Library

Advertising in "Junk Mail"

Perhaps the most widespread form of early advertising was the department store catalogue distributed through the postal system. The post office distributed unaddressed bulk mailings of flyers and catalogues from its earliest days until 1997, when the Canadian government, under pressure from newspapers, ordered the cessation of bulk postal distribution of flyers and catalogues. This business largely shifted to newspapers as inserts. Addressed advertising continues to be carried by the postal system at favourable bulk mail rates.

How Advertisements Work

The word *advertise* originally meant to take note or to consider. By the 1700s, that meaning had changed. To advertise meant to persuade. "If we consider democracy not just a political system," says Daniel J. Boorstin, "but as a set of institutions which do aim to make everything available to everybody, it would not be an overstatement to describe advertising as the characteristic rhetoric of democracy."[13]

Advertising Shares Common Characteristics

Boorstin says that advertising shares three characteristics: repetition, style, and ubiquity.

Repetition. When Robert Bonner bought the *New York Ledger* in 1851, he wanted to advertise his newspaper in the competing *New York Herald*, owned by James Gordon Bennett. Bennett limited all of his advertisers to the same size typeface, so Bonner paid for an entire page of the Herald, across which he repeated the message "Bring home the *New York Ledger* tonight." This is an early example of the widespread practice of repeating a simple message for effect.

An Advertising Style. At first, advertising adopted a plain, direct style. Advertising pioneer Claude Hopkins, says Boorstin, claimed that "Brilliant writing has no place in advertising. A unique style takes attention from the subject.... One should be natural and simple ... in fishing for buyers, as in fishing for bass, one should not reveal the hook."[14]

The plain-talk tradition is a foundation of what advertisers call modern advertising. But advertising today often adopts a style of hyperbole, making large claims for products. Boorstin calls this "tall talk."

The tall-talk ad is in the P.T. Barnum tradition of advertising. Barnum was a carnival barker and, later, an impresario, who lured customers to his circus acts with fantastic claims. You may recognize this approach in some of the furniture and car ads on television, as an announcer screams at you that you have only a few days left until all the chairs or all of the cars will be gone.

Both plain talk and tall talk combine, Boorstin says, to create advertising's *new myth*:

> This is the world of the neither true nor false—of the statement that 60 percent of the physicians who expressed a choice said that our brand of aspirin would be more effective in curing a simple headache than any other brand.... It is not untrue, and yet, in its connotation it is not exactly true.[15]

Ubiquity. Advertising can be and is everywhere. Advertisers are always looking for new places to catch consumers' attention. Ads appear on shopping carts, on video screens at sports stadiums, atop parking meters.

> The ubiquity of advertising is, of course, just another effect of our uninhibited efforts to use all the media to get all sorts of information to everybody everywhere. Since the places to be filled are everywhere, the amount of advertising is not determined by the needs of advertising, but by the opportunities for advertising, which become unlimited.[16]

In some cases this ubiquity works to advertising's disadvantage. Many advertisers shy away from radio and TV because the ads are grouped so closely together. In 1986, in an attempt to attract more advertisers, TV began selling the "split-30" ad, which fits two 15-second ads into a 30-second spot. Even 10-second ads are available. Wherever these shorter commercials are sold, the station runs twice as many ads for different products, crowding the commercial time even more.

Grabbing Your Attention

To sell the products, advertisers must catch your eye, your ear, or your heart (preferably all three). With so many ads competing for attention, the advertiser must first get you to read, listen to, or watch one ad instead of another. "The immediate goal of advertising [is to] tug at our psychological shirt sleeves and slow us down long enough for a word or two about whatever is being sold."[17]

How Ads Appeal to Consumers

You make your buying decisions based on several other sources of information besides advertising: friends, family, and your own experience, for example. To influence your choices, the advertising message must appeal to you for some reason, as you sift through the ads to make judgments and choose products. Humanities and human sciences professor Jib Fowles, in his book *Mass Advertising as Social Forecast*, enumerated 15 appeals, which he calls an "inventory of human motives" that advertisers commonly use in their commercials.

1. *Need for sex.* Surprisingly, Fowles found that only 2 percent of the television ads he surveyed used this appeal. It may be too blatant, he concluded, and often detracts from the product.

2. *Need for affiliation.* The largest number of ads use this approach: You are looking for friendship. Advertisers can also use this negatively, to make you worry that you'll lose friends if you don't use a certain product.

3. *Need to nurture.* Every time you see a puppy or a kitten or a child, the appeal is to your maternal or paternal instincts.

4. *Need for guidance.* A father or mother figure can appeal to your desire for someone to care for you, so you won't have to worry. Betty Crocker is a good example.

5. *Need to aggress.* We all have had a desire to get even, and some ads give you this satisfaction.

6. *Need to achieve.* The ability to accomplish something difficult and succeed identifies the product with winning. Sports figures as spokespersons project this image.

7. *Need to dominate.* The power we lack is what we can look for in a commercial: "Master the possibilities."

8. *Need for prominence.* We want to be admired and respected, to have high social status. Tasteful china and classic diamonds offer this potential.

9. *Need for attention.* We want people to notice us; we want to be looked at. Cosmetics are a natural for this approach.

10. *Need for autonomy.* Within a crowded environment, we want to be singled out, to be "a breed apart." This can also be used negatively, by implying that you will be left out if you don't use a particular product.

11. *Need to escape.* Flight is very appealing; you can imagine adventures you cannot have. The idea of escape is pleasurable.

12. *Need to feel safe.* To be free from threats, to be secure is the appeal of many insurance and bank ads.

13. *Need for aesthetic sensations.* Beauty attracts us, and classic art or dance makes us feel creative, enhanced.

14. *Need to satisfy curiosity.* Facts support our belief that information is quantifiable and numbers and diagrams make our choices seem scientific.

15. *Physiological needs.* Fowles defines sex (item no. 1) as a biological need, and so he classifies our need to sleep, eat, and drink in this category. Advertisements for pizza are especially appealing late at night.[18]

IMPACT

Point of View

AD INFINITUM

By Steve Burgess

One Monday afternoon in February, 1997, in a little office with giant windows that look out on Coal Harbour, an argument is going on. The participants are all employees of the advertising agency BBDO Vancouver. More specifically, they are the people responsible for the Yellow Pages campaign.... "It was intentional," Greg Rowan says. "No way was it not intentional." "Coincidence," says Tony Lee. Helen Stutchbury weighs in next. "I'm with Greg. It had to be intentional." They are discussing the most recent episode of the Fox network's locally filmed series *Millennium*. In it, local actor Michael Sunczyk was seen giving a description to a police sketch artist. Talk about role reversal; Sunczyk is better known locally as the incompetent sketch artist from a now-famous Yellow Pages ad. In the award-winning

commercial, Suncyzk takes a detailed description from the mugging victim before turning his pad around with a flourish–"Is THIS the man who robbed you?"—only to reveal a green-eyed, gun-toting perpetrator who puts the stick back into stick-up man....

Other spots in the series include a bus-load of vegetarians getting the shock of their sanctimonious lives, and a thoroughly tasteless ad-within-an-ad for Happy Butt hemorrhoid cream. Each commercial concludes by showing which Yellow Pages section could have prevented catastrophe, along with the punch line, "Next time, think Yellow first."

The campaign has been a tremendous success. But now it's follow-up time. The BBDO team is gathered together on this late-winter afternoon to launch the process once again.... All they know

on this day are the difficult lessons that come with their trade. How hard it is for an ad to break through the media clutter. How each television-raised generation is more inclined to heckle those meticulously crafted plugs. And how a jaded public is used to having its intelligence insulted, its credulity stretched. People hardly blink when, in an ad seen by perhaps a billion viewers worldwide during the Super Bowl, an American Airlines employee proclaims, "You know, I don't say this to many people ..." They barely snicker when the Gillette ad explains that, for some reason never mentioned in physics class, a clear gel will go straight to your skin without getting caught in your underarm hair. And that, moreover, this is important.

But the team at BBDO appears to have some important advantages

Finding the Audience: Which Demographic Are You?

Advertisers target their messages to an audience according to the audience's needs. But an advertiser also seeks to determine the audience's characteristics. This analysis of observable audience characteristics is called **demographics**.

Demographics are composed of data about a target audience's sex, age, income level, marital status, geographic location, and occupation. These data are observable because they are available to advertising agencies through census data and other sources. Advertising agencies use demographic audience analysis to help advertisers target their messages.

A motorcycle dealer certainly wouldn't want to advertise in a baby magazine, for example, and a candy manufacturer probably wouldn't profit from advertising in a diet and exercise magazine. Advertising agencies try to match a client's product to a thoroughly defined audience so that each advertising dollar is well spent.

Defining the audience is important because the goal of advertising is to market a product to people who have the desire for the product and the ability to buy it. Audience analysis tells an advertiser whether there are enough people who can be targeted for a product to make the advertising worthwhile.

with the Yellow Pages project. They are setting out to create clever ommercials that people will genuinely appreciate. Since they are continuing a very successful campaign, they believe the client will grant them considerable leeway. And none of them actually believes that a clear gel will go straight through underarm hair. "That's one of those other agencies," Tony sniffs.

The "Next time, think Yellow" campaign was born because in the summer of 1995, Dominion Directory Ltd., publisher of the Yellow Pages, had some concerns. They were losing business customers to radio and television. Focus groups occasionally displayed an attitude toward the directory best summed up by the phrase sometimes used after a botched plumbing job has left the basement furniture floating:

"Where'd you find that guy? The Yellow Pages?"

Since the product is, itself, advertising, advertising it involved a unique problem. "Advertisers feel the Yellow Pages is very expensive," says BBDO account planner Georgia McIntosh. "So they're sensitive about how their money is being spent." In other words, TV ads designed purely to attract new clients only served to annoy existing clients, who felt their fees were being squandered. Businesses that bought space in the book wanted to see ads aimed at the public.

Thus, the new campaign would attempt a three-bird shot: one, convince the public that the directory was cool, thereby two, keeping existing advertisers happy, and three, ultimately attracting new ones. Heavy baggage for a few good gags to carry. But Tony and Greg

decided quickly that humour was the best approach: "We knew it would blow the dust off," Tony recalls.

Vancouver, *April 1998, p.53.*
Reprinted with permission from the author. Photo courtesy of Dominion Directory Information Services™.

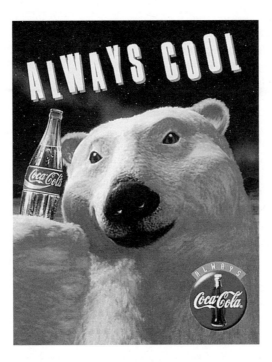

What's Wrong with Advertising?

The study of advertising provokes three main criticisms, according to Louis C. Kaufman, author of *Essentials of Advertising*.

1. *Advertising adds to the cost of products.* Critics of advertising maintain that advertising, like everything that is part of manufacturing a product, is a cost. Ultimately, the consumer pays for the cost of advertising. But the industry argues that advertising helps make more goods and services available to the consumer, and that the resulting competition keeps prices lower.

2. *Advertising causes people to buy products they do not need.* Says media scholar Michael Schudson:

   Most blame advertising for the sale of specific consumer goods, notably luxury goods (designer jeans), frivolous goods (pet rocks), dangerous goods (cigarettes), shoddy goods (some toys for children), expensive goods that do not differ at all from cheap goods (nongeneric over-the-counter drugs), marginally differentiated products that do not differ significantly from one another (laundry soaps), and wasteful goods (various unecological throw-away convenience goods).[19]

   The advertising industry contends that the ultimate test of any product is the marketplace and that advertising may stimulate consumers to try a new product or a new brand, but consumers will not continue to buy an unsatisfying product.

3. *Advertising reduces competition and thereby fosters monopolies.* Critics point to the rising cost of advertising, especially on television, which limits

which companies can afford to launch a new product or a new campaign. The industry argues that advertising is still a very expensive way to let people know about new products. "The cost of launching a nationwide advertising campaign may be formidable," writes Louis C. Kaufman, "but the cost of supporting larger, nationwide sales forces for mass-marketed goods would be greater still."[20]

To answer these and other criticisms, the American Association of Advertising Agencies (called the 4As) introduced—what else?—an advertising campaign to explain their point of view. The AAAA ads questioned the assumptions that many people make about advertising. Criticism of advertising also extends to the types of products sold in some ads. Advertising Standards Canada fulfills this critical role.

Does advertising work? According to Michael Schudson:

> Apologists are wrong that advertising is simply information that makes the market work more efficiently—but so too are the critics of advertising who believe in its overwhelming power to deceive and to deflect human minds to its ends. Evaluating its impact is more difficult than these simplicities of apology and critique will acknowledge.[21]

Working in Advertising

Advertising agencies buy time and space for the companies they represent. For this, they are usually paid a commission (commonly 15 percent). Many agencies also produce television and radio commercials and print advertising for their clients.

Depending on the size of the agency, the company may be divided into as many as six departments: marketing research, media selection, creative activity, account management, administration, and public relations.

Marketing research examines the product's potential, where it will be sold, and who will buy the product. Agency researchers may survey the market themselves or contract with an outside market research company to evaluate potential buyers.

Media selection suggests the best combination of buys for a client—television and newspapers, or magazines and billboards, for example.

Creative activity thinks up the ads. The "creatives" write the copy for TV, radio, and print. They design the graphic art and often produce the commercials. They also verify that the ad has run as many times as it was scheduled to run.

Account management is the liaison between the agency and the client. Account executives handle client complaints and suggestions and also manage the company team assigned to the account.

Administration pays the bills, including all the tabs for the account executives' lunches with clients.

Public relations is an extra service that some agencies offer for companies that don't have a separate public relations office.

All of these departments work together on an ad campaign. An advertising campaign is a planned effort that is coordinated for a specific time period. A campaign could last anywhere from a month to a year, and the objective is a coordinated strategy to sell a product or a service. Typically, the company assigns the account executive a team of people from the different departments to handle the account. The account executive answers to the people who control the agency, usually a board of directors.

The members of the campaign team coordinate all types of advertising—print and broadcast, for example—to make sure they share consistent content. After establishing a budget based on the client's needs, the campaign team creates a slogan, recommends a strategy for the best exposure for the client, approves the design of print and broadcast commercials, and then places the ads with the media outlets.

Advertising agencies tend to be clustered in big cities. In part, this is by tradition. The agencies may be near their clients in the city. They also have access to a larger pool of talent and facilities such as recording studios. But technology may enable greater flexibility.

The Business of Advertising

The advertising business and the media industries are interdependent—that is, what happens in the advertising business directly affects the media industries. And the advertising business is very dependent on the health of the economy. If the national economy is expanding, the advertising business and the media industries prosper. If the country (or a significant region) falls into a recession, advertisers typically reduce their ad budgets, which eventually leads to a decline in advertising revenue for the agencies and also for the media industries where the agencies place their ads. During a recession, advertisers also may change their advertising strategies—choosing radio over television because it is much less expensive, for example.

Advertising can also promote ideas. Canadian Heritage commissioned this poster to promote its anti-racism campaign.

Courtesy of Canadian Heritage and Scott Thornley & Company Inc.

The advertising industry today, therefore, must be sensitive to economic trends. The success of an ad agency is best measured by the results an ad campaign brings. The agency must analyze the benefits of different types of advertising and recommend the most efficient combination for their clients.

Commercials on Television

Even though the cost seems exorbitant, sponsors continue to line up to appear on network television. "Advertisers must use television on whatever terms they can get it, for television is the most potent merchandising vehicle ever devised," writes TV producer Bob Shanks in his book *The Cool Fire: How to Make It in Television*. Shanks is talking about national advertisers who buy network time—companies whose products can be advertised to the entire country at once.

"Of course, Brian, this victory wouldn't have been possible without fresh, white overalls."

Minutes in every network prime-time hour are divided into 10-, 15-, and 30-second ads. If an advertiser wants to reach the broad national market, television is an expensive choice because the average price for a 30-second TV commercial is $100 000. The price tag can go as high as $1.2 million for a widely watched program such as the Super Bowl.

Advertising on popular programs that are broadcast across North America is bought by national advertising agencies, which handle the biggest advertisers—Procter & Gamble and McDonald's, for example. These companies usually have in-house advertising and public relations departments, but most of the advertising strategy and production of commercials for these companies is handled by the agencies. Large agencies buy advertising space based on a careful formula, calculated on a cost-per-thousand (**CPM**) basis—the cost of an ad per one thousand people reached.

Making a TV commercial for North American broadcast is more expensive per minute than making a television program because each company wants its ads to look different from the rest. The price to produce a TV commercial can run as much as $1 million a minute. That may be why, as one producer said, "the commercials are the best things on TV."[22]

Network television commercials certainly are the most visible type of advertising, but not everyone needs the reach of network television. The goal of well-placed advertising is to deliver the best results to the client for the lowest cost, and this may mean looking to other media.

Using the Internet, Print, and Radio

Different types of media deliver different types of audiences. The Internet offers a large potential audience, but consumers can quickly click past ads on the Web, so no one is quite sure how effective Web ads are. Network television delivers a large, diverse audience, at a high price. Agencies also buy less expensive time and space in local television, radio, newspapers, and magazines to target a specific audience by demographics: age, education, gender, and income. Language also can be a targeting factor. A radio station with a rock format delivers for a different group than does an easy-listening station. The *Globe and Mail* targets a different reader from that of the *Vancouver Sun*.

The competition among different media for advertisers is heavy:

◎ The American Newspaper Publishers Association commissions a study that reveals that only one in five prime-time adult viewers could remember the last ad they had seen on television.

◎ Print advertisers claim that remote channel changers zap many TV ads, making TV commercials an unreliable way to deliver an audience.

◎ *Time* advertises that more airline customers read its magazine than read *Newsweek*.

◎ *Newsweek* advertises that it delivers more people for the money than *Time*.

◎ *Cosmopolitan* says that airline companies should advertise in its magazine because women who travel often don't watch daytime television.

◎ "Radio is the medium working women don't have to make time for," boasts the Radio Advertising Bureau (RAB). Whereas working women spend 15 percent of their daily media time reading a newspaper, they spend half of their media time with radio, says the RAB.[23]

Advertising agencies gather demographic information provided by A.C. Nielsen, Arbitron, and the Bureau for Broadcast Measurement (BBM) for broadcast and by the Audit Bureau of Circulations for print; the audience is converted into numbers. Based on these numbers, agencies advise advertisers about ways to reach buyers for their products. A Toronto company, COMPUSEARCH, sells repackaged Statistics Canada census data that focuses on small areas or neighbourhoods to advertisers. *Saturday Night* magazine, for example, is distributed free to some neighbourhoods, based on the census data, which allows the magazine to target the best audience for its advertisers.

Advertising Locally

Karen's Yogurt Shoppe, a small downtown business, does not need to advertise on *Home Improvement* or in the *Globe and Mail*. Karen and other local businesses only need to reach their neighbours. Businesses larger than the yogurt shop, such as a car dealer or a furniture store, may buy local television or radio time, but most of the local advertising dollar goes to newspapers.

A local advertising agency can design a campaign, produce the ad, and place the ad just like the national agencies, but on a much smaller scale. And some small companies design and place their own ads directly with the local media.

To attract customers, local media often help companies design their ads. Newspapers, for example, will help a small advertiser prepare an ad using ready-made art. A radio or television station may include the services of an announcer or access to a studio in the price for a series of spot ads. Broadcast stations sometimes trade ads for services offered by the advertiser—dinner for two at the local restaurant in return for two spot ads, for example. Then the station gives the dinners away on one of its programs.

IMPACT
on You

By Mia Stainsby
The Vancouver Sun

TINY MEDIA FOUNDATION, FOUNDER CHALLENGE ADVERTISING INDUSTRY GIANTS

Kalle Lasn is the force behind The Media Foundation, a small Vancouver organization devoted to sensitizing Canadians to advertising and how it shapes our culture and thinking.

The seven-year-old organization, which Mr. Lasn, 55, founded, primarily operates on profits from its successful magazine *Adbusters,* which challenges the messages of the advertising industry, and comments on economic and environmental issues.

The Foundation challenges the big three U.S. television networks and the largest magazines and is currently in a court battle with the CBC over public access to the airwaves.

Mrs. Lasn and his foundation want the same access to advertising that corporations have so they can counter what they deem to be some of the more destructive messages in the media today. Their central philosophy is that in a "free marketplace of ideas" consumers will have all the facts to make more informed decisions about where and how they spend their dollars.

The problem, they say, is a kind of collusion between some media organizations and advertisers in which the selling of harmful lifestyles and products goes unchallenged, largely because the union creates mutual financial benefits.

"I smell the blood," Mr. Lasn says, "when I deal with NBC and CBS and ABC and they refuse to air my messages and give me hocus-pocus reasons on why they can't.

"It was proven in the 1960s and '70s that anti-smoking ads against the giant tobacco industry were so true, so compelling, that eventually the industry had to back off TV because they could not compete with the free marketplace of ideas."

Mr. Lasn says his activism dates back to 1944 when his parents escaped from Estonia during the Soviet advance and made their way to Australia. They became "New Australians," or members of immigrant minorities who were, he says, "all made to feel second class."

It rankled, and as an adult, he emigrated to North America, which he viewed as the pillar of democracy.

As a documentary film-maker in the 1970s, he had his first inkling of the sanctity of commercial airwaves when he produced a commercial on how advertising increased the costs of the products they touted. CBC would not let him buy airtime. He was surprised, but left it at that.

By 1989, he was alarmed at how advertising was shaping our culture and thinking.

"My feeling is, if we lose the ability to buy 30 seconds of air time, we won't be able to steer into the future because corporations will do that for us. We want to re-invent the media culture, and advertising is just the tip of the spear," he says. "We'd like to de-commercialize it to some degree so instead of 12 minutes per hour of products ads, we have nine minutes of product messages and three minutes of idea ads."

That was the beginning of The Media Foundation. "We call ourselves the Greenpeace of the mental environment," Mr. Lasn says. And in Greenpeace style, the Media Foundation is brash, launching its attacks very publicly by "culture jamming," throwing a monkey wrench into the process of broadcast and magazine advertising.

It does that by developing its own ads, by promoting international events like "Buy Nothing Day" and "TV Turnoff Week," and by publishing *Adbusters: Journal of the Mental Environment,* a successful magazine about advertising and the media. *Adbusters,* a quarterly, is the breadwinner for The Media Foundation. It has newsstand sales of 32,000 copies, two-thirds of which are sold in the U.S.

"We're living in a media trance," says Mr. Lasn. "We're living a lie, where on the one hand, consumerism is killing the planet, yet we switch on the TV and get another dose of messages telling us to consume even more."

The Media Foundation raised "Buy Nothing Day" to an international level, involving nine countries. Last Nov. 29 (after the U.S. Thanksgiving and the beginning of Christmas spending), he had 50 international calls, including interviews with the BBC in London and ABC in Australia.

Another campaign is "TV Turnoff Week," where people across North America are challenged to wean themselves from television for a week.

Reprinted with permission.

Advertising Sales Representatives. What if you manufacture sunglasses in Burlington, Ontario, and you hire a local advertising agency to sell your product nationally? The agency tells you that they believe a good market for your product exists on the West Coast. How is the agency going to find out the most efficient way to sell your sunglasses in Vancouver?

In this situation, many advertising agencies would contact a **rep firm**—a company of advertising sales representatives who sell advertising time and space in their market to companies outside the area. In this case, the agency in Burlington would first decide who were the most likely customers for your sunglasses. If the agency decided that Vancouver-area males age 18–24 are the best potential customers, the agency would budget a certain amount of money for advertising in the Vancouver area and then call the ad reps there.

The rep firm, in return, takes a percentage (usually 15 percent) of the advertising dollars they place. Ad reps are, in effect, brokers for the media in their markets.

Each rep firm handles several clients. Some ad reps sell only broadcast advertising and some specialize in print ads, but many rep firms sell all types of media. In this case, each Vancouver ad rep would enter the demographics ("demos") for your product into a computer. Based on ratings, readership, and the price for the ads, each rep would come up with a CPM (cost per thousand people reached) for your product. The rep then would recommend the most efficient buy—how best to reach the people most likely to want your sunglasses. (M is the Roman numeral for 1000.)

Each rep then presents a Vancouver advertising plan for your product to the agency in Burlington. Usually the buy is based on price: The medium with the lowest CPM gets the customer. But a rep who cannot match the lowest CPM might offer incentives for you to choose his or her plan: If you agree to provide 50 pairs of sunglasses, for example, the rep's radio station will give away the glasses as prizes during a local program, each time mentioning the name of your product. So even though the ad time you buy will cost a little more, you will also get promotional announcements every time the station gives away a pair of sunglasses. Other ad reps might offer different packages.

The agency in Burlington then would decide which package is the most attractive and would present that proposal to you. This entire process can take as little as 24 hours for a simple buy such as the one for your sunglasses account, or as long as several weeks for a complicated campaign for a big advertiser.

Regulating Advertisers

The regulation of advertising is both extensive and demanding. In Canada, consumer protection agencies were not established until the mid-1960s. The Federal Department of Consumer and Corporate Affairs was established in 1967. It administers consumer protective legislation, ranging from old legislation that prevents the charging of usurious rates of interest on loans and ensuring fair weights and measures to laws regulating food, drugs, and automobile and tire safety. Health Canada monitors claims made about nonprescription health products, the source of much abusive advertising in the past.

The main piece of legislation governing corporate behaviour, the Competition Act (formerly the Combines Act), regulates a wide range of anticompetitive behaviour, including deceptive advertising. Provincial laws also govern deceptive advertising and shifty business practices, affecting what advertisers can and cannot do in making claims and offering inducements. The perpetual "closing sale" is one example of a deceptive advertising claim that can be challenged under provincial consumer protection laws.

All broadcasting stations are licensed by the CRTC, and their program content and advertising are subject to scrutiny and potential sanctions. Broadcasting advertising is subject to a voluntary code of behaviour, the Canadian Code of Advertising Standards, adopted by Advertising Standards Canada (ASC). The code specifically covers advertising directed toward children's, and food and cosmetic product promotions. ASC also maintains guidelines dealing with the portrayal of gender and diversity.

Any member of the public can lodge a complaint with ASC. If an advertiser declines to change or remove advertising judged by ASC to be inappropriate, it can recommend to member media that they not carry the offending material. The CBC also approves ads on its stations. It once required the removal of a television ad featuring Bill Cosby and the "Jello tree" because Bill appeared to encourage children to pick Jello from the tree without paying for it.

Government also regulates tobacco advertising. Ads for tobacco are now essentially banned, with the exception of limited outdoor advertising, and sponsorship of arts events by tobacco companies is soon to be phased out.

Yet another dimension of regulation has to do with the number and timing of both paid and free time political advertisements in political campaigns. These regulations tend to differ from province to province. Lawn signs during campaigns are also regulated, with penalties for defacement and unauthorized removal, posting advertising on public utility poles, and also with regard to who is obligated to remove signs after the election is over.

Advertising Liquor

The CRTC publishes stringent rules for radio and television advertising which, until the summer of 1998, might have been roughly summarized as no hard liquor, no people having fun with bottles in their hands, and no actual drinking shown. These limits have tended to reduce beer and wine advertising on television to entertaining interludes, punctuated with a brand label or the brand icon. As of the summer of 1998, however, hard-liquor advertising was allowed equal footing, as a result of a court case that overturned the ban in 1995.

Liquor advertising falls under provincial jurisdiction, usually of the provincial liquor board. Health Canada monitors any health claims made for the benefits of drinking alcoholic beverages. Print advertising of alcohol is allowed, subject to the scrutiny of ASC. Local signs and placards outside of stores and restaurants might also be regulated by municipalities under sign by-laws.

Regulations governing alcohol advertising in the United States are more relaxed than in Canada. Viewers regularly see advertisements on television for beer and wine, but the TV networks do not advertise hard liquor. For three decades, the Distilled Spirits Council of the United States, operating under a voluntary Code of Good Practice, did not run television ads. In 1996, some liquor companies decided to challenge the voluntary ban by placing ads on local television.

Montreal-based Seagram's (which, ironically, can trace its origins to 1920s bootlegging into the United States), became the first company to challenge the ban, by advertising Crown Royal whiskey on a local TV station in Texas. "We believe distilled spirits should have the same access to electronic media, just the same way beer and wine do," said Arthur Shapiro, executive vice president in charge of marketing and strategy for Seagram's in the United States.[24]

Technology Transforms the Future

The future of advertising will parallel changes in the media, in technology, and in demographics. As more products seek international markets, advertising must be designed to reach those markets. U.S. agencies today collect nearly half of the world's revenue from advertising. (See Figure 10.1 for the top ten U.S. agencies by gross worldwide income.)

International advertising campaigns are becoming more common for global products, such as Coca-Cola and McDonald's, and this has meant the creation of international advertising. Cable News Network (CNN) announced in 1991 that it would be selling advertising on CNN worldwide, so that any company in any nation with CNN's service could advertise its product to a worldwide audience.

Figure 10.1

The Top Ten U.S. Ad Agencies by Gross Income*
*1995 is the last year for which statistics are available.

Source: Data from *Advertising Age*, April 15, 1996.

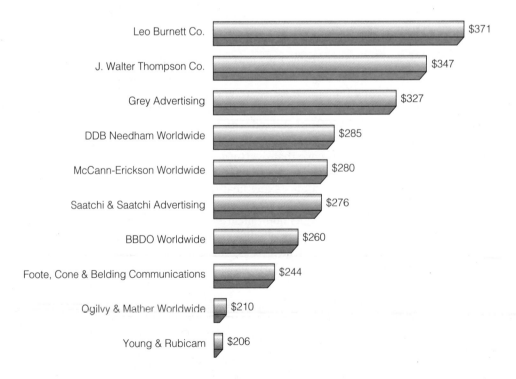

A second factor in the future of advertising is changing technology. As new media technologies create new outlets, the advertising community must adapt. Advertisers are trying to figure out how to reach consumers on their computer screens. Or a tennis instructional video could include advertising for tennis products. One company is using lasers to create advertising in the evening sky.

For all the publicity, very little money is being spent on advertising on the World Wide Web, especially in Canada. By one estimate, $180 million was spent on such advertising in the United States in 1996 but only $2 million in Canada in the same year.[25] Conservative hesitation may be partly to blame in Canada, combined with an inability to demonstrate a tangible impact on sales.

A third factor in the future of advertising is shifting demographic patterns. As the ethnicity of Canada evolves, marketing programs must adapt to reach new audiences. Future television ads could include dialogue in both English and Chinese. Some national ad campaigns already include multilingual versions of the same ad, targeted for different audiences.

The challenges for the advertising business are as great as for the media industries. The advertising industry will do what it has always done to adapt—follow the audience. The challenge for advertising in the 21st century will be to learn how to efficiently match the audience to the advertising messages the media deliver.

Figure 10.2

Advertising goes global: In 1998, the United States will account for 46 percent of the world's spending on advertising.

Source: Data from McCann-Erikson *Insider's Report,* December 1997.

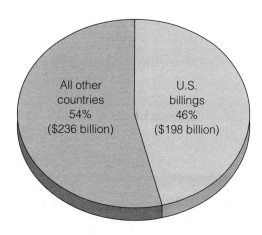

All other countries
54%
($236 billion)

U.S. billings
46%
($198 billion)

**Total worldwide ad spending
1998* ($434 billion)**

*projected

In Focus

◎ Advertising carries the messages that come to you from the sponsors who pay for the media.

◎ As early as 1200 BC, the Phoenicians painted messages on stones to advertise. In 600 BC, ship captains sent criers around to announce that their ships were in port. In the 13th century AD, the British began requiring trademarks to protect buyers.

◎ Newspapers were the first medium to use advertising, in 1704. Magazines, radio, and television followed.

◎ Daniel Boorstin says that advertising shares three characteristics: repetition, an advertising style, and ubiquity.

◎ Advertising can catch your attention, according to Jib Fowles, in 15 ways, including playing on your need to nurture, your need for attention, and your need to escape.

◎ Advertising provokes three main criticisms: advertising adds to the cost of products; advertising causes people to buy products they do not need; and advertising reduces competition and thereby fosters monopolies.

◎ Today's advertising agencies use sophisticated technology to track demographics to help deliver the audience the advertiser wants.

◎ The advertising business and the media industries are interdependent—what happens in the advertising business directly affects the media industries. And the advertising business is very dependent on national and provincial economic health.

◎ The industry is divided into national and local advertising. Advertising sales representatives broker local accounts to out-of-town advertisers.

◎ The media compete with each other for the advertising dollar, and some media are better than others for particular products.

◎ In 1996, the distilled spirits industry challenged the industrywide voluntary ban on liquor advertising on TV that has lasted for three decades. Although the TV networks still refuse to carry the ads, the liquor industry is placing the ads on local TV stations. Seagram's was the first company to break the ban, advertising on a local TV station in Texas.

◎ The future of advertising will parallel the development of international markets, the refinement and expansion of new media technologies, and changing demographics.

Review Questions

1. Why is advertising not a medium? What role does it play in the mass media industries?

2. What is the relationship between TV ratings and TV advertising?

3. What effect do you think consolidation will have on the advertising industry?

4. Explain four of Jib Fowles's 15 psychological appeals of advertising. Bring examples to class to represent each of the four appeals you choose.

5. Cite the major landmarks in the development of advertising. What did each development contribute to advertising's evolution?

Watching the Web

◎ **Advertising Council**

http://www.adcouncil.org

◎ **Canadian Advertising Agencies' Web site**

http://www.mhbizlink.com/cardlink/agencies.htm

◎ **Global Advertising Industry Overview**

http://www.newspage.com/browse/ [and choose *media and communications* link]

◎ **Advertising Standards Canada (ASC)**

http://www.screen.com/mnet/eng/indus/advert/caf.htm

PUBLIC RELATIONS

11

> **ABOVE ALL, TELL IT LIKE IT IS ... TELL THE TRUTH.**

Gerry Brown, former chairman
Canada News Wire

What's Ahead

You may think that the cash rebate program offered by many of today's car manufacturers is a new idea, but in 1914 Henry Ford announced that if he sold 300 000 Model Ts that year, each customer would receive a rebate. When the company reached its goal, Ford returned $50 to each buyer.[1] This was good business. It also was good public relations. Like Henry Ford, public relations people today work to create favourable images—for corporations, public officials, products, schools, hospitals, and associations.

Scholars have defined three methods to encourage people to do what you want them to do: power, patronage, and persuasion. Power involves ruling by law, but it can also mean ruling by peer pressure—someone does something because her or his friends do. Patronage is a polite term for bribery—paying someone with favours or money to do what you want.

The third method—persuasion—is the approach of public relations. Like advertising, public relations is not a mass medium. Public relations is a media support industry. In the classic definition, public relations involves creating an understanding for, or goodwill toward, a company, a person, or a product.

How Public Relations Grew

One of the first political leaders to realize the importance of public relations was Augustus Caesar, who commissioned statues of himself in the first century to be erected throughout the Roman Empire to enhance his image.[2] Many political leaders have ordered heroic images of themselves printed on coins and stamps.

Today's public relations approach can be traced to the late 19th century. Both government and journalists prompted the emergence of the public relations profession.

The Government and Public Relations

Seeking immigrants to populate the west, the Canadian government launched a public relations campaign in the United States and Europe to promote immigration, featuring offers of free land. The word *cold* was banished from these campaigns to avoid conveying the harsh realities of the prairie winter.

Clifford Sifton, the Minister of the Interior, oversaw the campaign. Pamphlets and paid advertising in local newspapers carried the message that farming in the prairies promised a good future. In a thoroughly modern twist—the media tour—newspaper editors from the United States were given free, guided junkets through the new settlement areas.

This campaign was successful in attracting several million people as immigrants to the Canadian west, providing continuing business for the Canadian Pacific Railway, and making previously unsettled border areas in southern Alberta and Saskatchewan more secure.

This public relations campaign created a legacy of bitterness in generations of immigrants, who found the reality of life in a sod hut on the bald prairie nothing like the romantic and rewarding "golden West" promised in British and European newspaper ads. However, the campaign stands as a highly successful model. It provoked millions of people to move over thousands of miles at very low cost to the government, which achieved its political goals of settlement.

The Press and Public Relations

Before 1900, business had felt that it could work alongside the press, or even ignore it. Many stories that appeared in the press promoted companies that bought advertising. Then the Industrial Revolution arrived in North America from Western Europe, and many industrialists exploited workers and collected enormous profits. Ida Tarbell and Lincoln Steffens began to make business people uncomfortable, writing stories for magazines like *McClure's* about the not-so-admirable characteristics of some companies (see Chapter 3).

> No longer could the railroads butter up the press by giving free passes to reporters. No longer would the public buy whitewashed statements like that of coal industrialist George F. Baer, who in 1902 told labor to put their trust in "the Christian men whom God in His infinite wisdom has given control of the property interests of the country."[3]

The Canadian government launched the first public relations campaign in Canada to promote immigration to the west.

National Archives of Canada/C-30621

Corporate and Institutional Public Relations

The first publicity firm, called the Publicity Bureau, opened in Boston in 1900 to head off the growing public criticism of the railroad companies. The best-known early practitioner of public relations was Ivy Lee, who began his PR career by opening an office in New York with George F. Parker. Lee and Parker represented coal magnate George F. Baer when coal workers went on strike. A former newspaper reporter, Lee issued a "Declaration of Principles" that he mailed to city editors. This declaration became a manifesto for early public relations companies to follow.

Reacting to criticism that the Publicity Bureau had worked secretly to promote the railroads, Lee wrote:

> This [the firm of Lee & Parker] is not a secret press bureau. All our work is done in the open. We aim to supply news.... In brief, our plan is, frankly and openly, on behalf of business concerns and public institutions, to supply to the press and public of the United States prompt and accurate information concerning subjects which it is of value and interest to the public to know about.[4]

Lee and Parker dissolved their firm in 1908 when Lee went to work as a publicity agent for the Pennsylvania Railroad. Eventually, John D. Rockefeller hired Lee to counteract the negative publicity that began with Tarbell's investigation of Standard Oil. (Lee worked for the Rockefellers until he died in 1934.) Also finding work with Rockefeller was Mackenzie King, future prime minister of Canada and creator of the modern Liberal Party of Canada. King worked for Rockefeller in his campaign to neutralize and accommodate trade union interests.

The idea of inhouse corporate public relations grew as Chicago Edison Company and American Telephone & Telegraph began promotional programs. The University of Pennsylvania and the University of Wisconsin opened publicity bureaus in 1904, and the Washington, D.C., YMCA hired a full-time publicist to oversee fundraising in 1905—the first time a publicist was hired for this job.[5]

In the 1920s, Sir Henry Thornton used public relations to rescue the Canadian National Railway, after construction was stopped during World War I. Thornton, the CNR's first president, was appointed after the government of Canada nationalized the incomplete transcontinental railway in the early 1920s. He inherited a debt of $1.3 billion dollars and a faltering operating system.

Thornton promoted the CNR as a valuable institution to Canadians. He appealed to CNR employees to focus on making the CNR a going concern, promoted the idea of service to small communities, and introduced travelling schools in railway cars, and medical teams to serve rural communities. Thornton also was instrumental in establishing public radio broadcasting in Canada through CNR radio stations across the country (this network eventually became the CBC). In demonstrating the value of the CNR to Canadians, Thornton ensured its long-term financial success.

Influencing Public Opinion

In 1923, Edward L. Bernays wrote the first book on public relations, *Crystallizing Public Opinion*, and taught the first course on the subject. Bernays was interested in mass psychology—how to influence the opinions of large groups of people. Procter & Gamble, General Motors, and the American Tobacco Company were among his clients. "Public relations," Bernays wrote in 1955, "is the attempt, by information, persuasion, and adjustment, to engineer public support for an activity, cause, movement, or institution."[6] In 1985, Bernays further defined public relations as "giving a client ethical advice, based on research of the public, that will win the social goals upon which the client depends for his livelihood."[7]

To sell the New Deal in the 1930s, President Franklin D. Roosevelt used every tactic he knew. Comfortable with the press and the public alike, and advised by PR expert Louis McHenry Howe, FDR

> projected an image of self-confidence and happiness—just what the American public wanted to believe in. He talked to them on the radio. He smiled for the cameras. He was mentioned in popular songs. He even allowed himself to be one of the main characters in a Rodgers and Hart musical comedy (played by George M. Cohan, a famous American music hall performer).[8]

During World War II, the Canadian government was faced with the problem of gaining public approval for conscription (compulsory enlistment in the armed forces). The Liberal Party, acutely aware of public opposition to conscription in Quebec, promised not to impose conscription for overseas service.

As the war progressed and the need for more soldiers became pressing, the government decided to resort to conscription, in spite of its earlier promise. To solve this public relations problem, Prime Minister W. L. Mackenzie King held a plebiscite in which Canadians would be asked to absolve the government from its promise. On April 17, 1942, 72.9 percent of Quebec residents voted no, whereas 80 percent of the rest of Canadians voted yes, producing a national result favourable to the government. Parliament then passed Bill 80, authorizing conscription for overseas service if it was deemed necessary.

"WHY DON'T THEY COME?"

WHY BE A MERE SPECTATOR HERE WHEN YOU SHOULD PLAY A MANS PART IN THE REAL GAME OVERSEAS!

JOIN THE 148th Battalion.

A.A. MAGEE LT COL
Headquarters

197, PEEL St MONTREAL.

To support Canadian involvement in the war the government mounted a massive public relations drive. The Wartime Information Board issued press releases, made short films, and distributed recruitment and Victory War Bond posters to promote the war effort.

The U.S. government also launched the largest public relations drive in its history, which centred on the Office of War Information, led by former newscaster Elmer Davis. Public relations boomed with the postwar economy, and more women began to enter the field.

Influencing Canadians to join the war effort.

Top: National Archives of Canada/ C-095730
Bottom: National Archives of Canada/PA-25180

Women in Public Relations

Doris E. Fleischman was among the first women in public relations when she joined her husband, Edward L. Bernays, in his PR firm. Fleischman was an equal partner with Bernays in their public relations business. An early advocate of public relations as a profession for women, Fleischman wrote in 1931 "one finds women working side by side with men in forming the traditions and rules that will govern the profession of the future."[9]

Two other women who were public relations pioneers were Leone Baxter and Anne Williams Wheaton. Baxter formed Baxter and Whitaker in San Francisco with her husband, Clem Whitaker—the first public relations agency to specialize in political campaigns. And in 1957, President Dwight Eisenhower appointed Anne Williams Wheaton as his associate press secretary.[10]

Development of Ethics Codes

In the 1930s, the requirements for someone to work in public relations were loose, and many people who said they worked in public relations were press agents who were not above tricks to get attention for their clients. Henry Rogers, cofounder of what was then the world's largest entertainment PR firm, Rogers & Cowan (based in Beverly Hills), admitted that in 1939 he created a "best-dressed" contest to promote little-known actress Rita Hayworth.

There had been no contest, but Rogers dubbed Hayworth the winner of this fictional event. *Look* magazine gave Hayworth a ten-page spread. "Press agents, and that's what we were, would dream up all sorts of phony stories," he said. "Journalists knew they were phony but printed them because they looked good in print."[11]

The Canadian Public Relations Society was established in 1948. In 1969, it introduced its first voluntary accreditation processes. Full accreditation is now contingent on five years' employment in the field, successful completion of an examination, and the promise to abide by the Society's code of professional standards. The Code of Professional Standards reads as follows:

Doris Fleischman, a public relations pioneer, began her career in the 1920s. Her husband, Edward L. Bernays, pictured below, wrote the first book on public relations, *Crystallizing Public Opinion.*

Top and bottom, UPI/ The Bettmann Archive

> Members of the Canadian Public Relations Society, Inc. are pledged to maintain the spirit and ideals of the following stated principles of conduct, and to consider these essential to the practice of public relations.
>
> 1. A member shall practice public relations according to the highest professional standards.
>
> 2. A member shall deal fairly and honestly with the communications media and the public.
>
> 3. A member shall practice the highest standards of honesty, accuracy, integrity and truth, and shall not knowingly disseminate false or misleading information.
>
> 4. A member shall deal fairly with past or present employers/clients, with fellow practitioners, and with members of other professions.
>
> 5. A member shall be prepared to disclose the name of their employer or client for whom public communications are made and refrain from associating themselves with anyone that would not respect such policy.
>
> 6. A member shall protect the confidences of present, former and prospective employers/clients.
>
> 7. A member shall not represent conflicting or competing interests without the express consent of those concerned, given after a full disclosure of the facts.
>
> 8. A member shall not guarantee specified results beyond the member's capacity to achieve.

9. Members shall personally accept no fees, commissions, gifts or any other considerations for professional services from anyone except employers or clients for whom the services were specifically performed.[12]

PR professionals continue to argue among themselves about the differences between the profession's beginnings as press agentry (which often meant fabricating stories) and the concept of ethically representing a client's business, as Edward L. Bernays described.

Public relations grew throughout the 1960s and 1970s with the encouragement of television, governments, and corporate interests.

How Public Relations Works

Public relations is an industry of specialties. The most familiar public relations areas are financial public relations, product public relations, and crisis public relations, but there are many other specialty areas.

Financial Public Relations

People in financial public relations provide information primarily to business reporters. "Business editors like a PR staff that can provide access to top management," wrote James K. Gentry in the *Washington Journalism Review*, "that knows its company well or can find needed information quickly, that demonstrates ethics and honesty and that knows and accepts the difference between news and fluff."

Gentry then listed comments gathered from editors about what makes a bad PR operation:

◎ "Companies that think they can hide the truth from the public or believe it's none of the public's business."

◎ "I despise it when a PR person intercepts our calls to a news source but then isn't capable of answering our questions."

◎ "When they hire an outside PR firm to handle the job."

◎ The 'no-comment' attitude. When they have little or no interest in going beyond the press release."

◎ "People who either get in the way of your doing your job, complain too much or are no help at all."[13]

Product Public Relations

Product PR uses public relations techniques to sell products and services. Many companies have learned that seeking publicity for a product often is less expensive than advertising the product. Public relations "is booming partly because of price," reports the *Wall Street Journal*. A PR budget of $500 000 is considered huge, whereas an ad budget that size is considered tiny.

PR can often reach more potential customers than advertising. Roots Canada Ltd., a manufacturer and retailer of clothing, has seen the direct benefits of effective PR in its sales figures.

The press clippings are piled three inches high on a table in Michael Budman's Toronto office. The co-owner of Roots Canada Ltd. strides into the sunny room, stops to survey the pile, plucks out a picture that features Prince William wearing the red Roots Olympic hat. "Didn't see that one," Budman mutters. "Huh." he brandishes the photo at two public relations assistants. "D'ya see that one? It's a great one. With the hat. Huh." Budman shakes his head in apparent amazement, puts the photo back atop the pile.

Instead of looking at the hat, he would like to talk about it—and the rest of the clothes Roots supplied to the Canadian Olympic team at the recent winter games in Japan.... "The way they felt in their clothes was part of the success of the team. This hat is a unifying piece of Canada."[14]

Athletes became free, walking advertisements during the 1998 Winter Olympics. Says *Maclean's* magazine, "The strategy boils down to this: get famous people to wear Roots clothes. Famous people have obliged, up to now, and the sales figures speak to the plan's success."[15]

Crisis Public Relations

The term *crisis public relations* has been used to describe the situation facing Johnson & Johnson after its product Tylenol was identified as the carrier of a poison that killed seven people in and near Chicago in 1982.

Johnson & Johnson and Burson-Marsteller, the company's PR agency, were credited with exceptional professionalism in handling the crisis. This is an example of responsible public relations in a crisis—when PR must counteract overwhelmingly negative information.

The poisonings called for immediate action to protect the consumer," explained Johnson & Johnson's Lawrence G. Foster, who was vice president of public relations at the time, "and there wasn't the slightest hesitation about being completely open with the news media. For the same reasons, Johnson & Johnson decided to recall two batches of the product, and later to withdraw it nationally. During the crisis phase of the Tylenol tragedy, virtually every public relations decision was based on sound, socially responsible business principles, which is when public relations is most effective.[16]

Johnson & Johnson sampled public opinion about its activities with nightly telephone surveys. Pulling the product from the shelves cost $100 million, but as soon as Tylenol was out of the stores, the company was viewed as acting responsibly. The challenge then was to rebuild the product's 37 percent share of the market.

The 2 500-member Johnson & Johnson sales force visited retailers and people in the medical community to rebuild confidence in Tylenol. Then Burson-Marsteller organized a televised 30-city satellite press conference for 600 journalists to give local media an equal chance at a nationwide story, which ensured broad coverage.

After relaunch of the product, Tylenol immediately regained a 24 percent share of the market and later regained its position as the top-selling brand.[17] The Tylenol case is often used as an example of very effective crisis public relations.

Not all PR campaigns are so successful, and some can even make the crisis seem worse (see Impact/Point of View, "Somalia Inquiry," pp. 246). The Somalia crisis and the Tylenol episode indicate how important specialization in crisis public relations can be within the public relations business.

The Business of Public Relations

Today, tens of thousands of people all over North America earn their livelihood working in public relations. There are thousands of PR firms and thousands of governments, which employ PR professionals. Several major corporations have 100 to 400 public relations specialists, but most public relations firms have fewer than four employees.[18]

Public relations people often deal with advertising agencies as part of their job, and because PR and advertising are so interrelated, several large public relations firms have joined several large advertising agencies. For example, J. Walter Thompson (advertising) bought Hill & Knowlton (public relations), and then in 1987 J. Walter Thompson Group was bought by a London firm, WPP Group PLC. Combined agencies can offer both public relations and advertising services to their clients, and the trend toward advertising/public relations combinations is continuing in the 1990s.[19] Hill & Knowlton is also involved in the sample survey

IMPACT

Point of View   *SOMALIA INQUIRY*

By David Pugliese

There was nothing wrong with deleting information from Somalia-related documents sent to a journalist under the Access to Information Act, an officer involved in the scheme told the Somalia inquiry Tuesday.

Lt.-Cmdr. Michael Considine testified that although the background portion of the documents was removed before being released under the access act, the essence of the records was not changed.

"I didn't think it changed the sense of what (the record) was," said Considine, a senior officer in the military's public relations section.

He said the portions deleted contained information that normally wouldn't be given out to a journalist "over the phone."

But Somalia inquiry chairman

Gilles Létourneau pointed out that the access act is not open to interpretation by military officers.

"It was not a phone call here," he said. "We're dealing with legislation called Access to Information."

The documents were pre-written answers Defence Department public relations officers could provide when asked questions about the Somalia mission. The background section, which included some information embarrassing to the Armed Forces, was deleted before being sent to a CBC Radio journalist.

The three-person civilian inquiry is investigating the Canadian Airborne Regiment's 1992–93 problem-filled mission to Somalia. It is also examining a military scheme to alter and destroy Somalia-related

documents to keep them out of the hands of journalists, contrary to the access act. Part of that investigation is to look at whether Canada's top soldier, Gen. Jean Boyle, knew of the plan.

The general has denied any wrongdoing.

Considine's testimony also contradicted earlier evidence from Lt. Joel Brayman, another military public relations officer. Brayman said he didn't originally know about the plan to alter the documents.

But Considine said Brayman was in on the scheme and even suggested using the computer to delete portions of the records in the fall of 1993.

Ottawa Citizen, May 29, 1996.
Reprinted with permission.

business through its acquisition of survey companies (such as Decima in Toronto), another interrelated business. Indeed, some survey firms now offer candidates for public office a comprehensive package of advice on campaign management and television advertising, in addition to their core business—survey collection and analysis.

The difference between public relations and advertising at the largest agencies can be difficult to discern. Advertising is an aspect of marketing that aims to sell products. People in advertising usually aren't involved in a company's policymaking. They implement the company's policies after company executives decide how to sell a product or a corporate image or an idea.

Public relations people, in comparison, usually *are* involved in policy. A PR person often contributes to decisions about how a company will deal with the public, the press, and its own employees.

Types of Clients

Public relations people work for several types of clients, including governments, nonprofit organizations, industry, and business.

Government. All levels of government hire people to handle PR. Related to government are PR people who work for political candidates and for lobbying organizations. Media consultants also are involved in political PR. These people counsel candidates and officeholders about how they should present themselves to the public through the media. The felicitous label *spin doctor* applies to the most accomplished of these public relations operators in the political arena.

Education. Universities, colleges, and school districts often hire public relations people to promote these educational institutions and to handle press attention to the consequences of decisions that educators make.

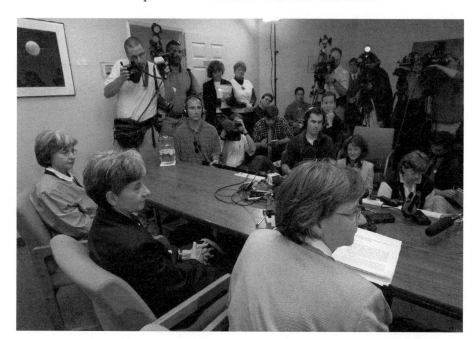

The surviving Dionne quintuplets give a press conference. Such events give the media a story—and the subjects media exposure—at low cost.

CP Picture Archive (Frank Gunn)

Nonprofit Organizations. This includes hospitals, churches, museums, and charities. Hospital PR is growing especially fast as different health care agencies compete with each other for donations and bequests.

Industry. AT&T's early use of public relations strategies was one type of industry PR. Many industries are government-regulated, so this often means that the industry PR person works with government agencies on government-related issues that affect the industry, such as utility rate increases or energy conservation programs.

Business. This is the best-known area of public relations. Large companies keep an inhouse staff of public relations people, and these companies also often hire outside PR firms to help on special projects. Product publicity is one of the fastest-growing aspects of business-related public relations.

Within many large businesses are people who handle corporate PR, sometimes called financial PR. They prepare annual reports and gather financial data on the company for use by the press. They also may be assigned directly to the executives of a corporation to help establish policy about the corporation's public image. And many companies sponsor charity events to increase their visibility in the community.

In an example of corporate public relations, Quickie Convenience Stores in Ottawa gave publicity and support for the annual fundraising bicycle marathon in Ottawa, Le Tour des Quickie. Thousands of cyclists took part in the 100-km ride through the streets of the city. In 1997, the marathon raised $300 000.

Athletic Teams and Entertainment Organizations. A professional sports team needs someone to travel with the team and handle the press requests that inevitably come at each stop. Sports information people also are responsible for the coaches', the owner's, and the team's relationship with the fans.

In 1939, Henry Rogers learned how to use press agentry to gather publicity for Rita Hayworth. Today, entertainment public relations agencies promote movies, and they also handle TV personalities and well-known athletes who appear on the lecture circuit.

International. As the consumer market broadens, more attention is being given to developing business in other countries. This means more opportunities in international PR. Hill & Knowlton and Burson-Marsteller, for example, are the two biggest foreign public relations firms now operating in Japan.[20]

What Do Public Relations People Do?

Responsibilities of PR people include the following. (For some insight on how public relations people make use of modern technology, see Impact/Technology, Communicators Brace for the Future.)

Writing. News releases, newsletters, correspondence, reports, speeches, booklet texts, radio and TV copy, film scripts, trade paper and magazine articles, institutional advertisements, product information, and technical materials.

Editing. Special publications, employee newsletters, shareholder reports, and other communications for employees and for the public.

Media Relations and Placement. Contacting news media, magazines, Sunday supplements, freelance writers, and trade publications with the intent of getting them to publish or broadcast news and features about or originated by the organization. Responding to media requests for information or spokespersons.

Special Events. Arranging and managing press conferences, convention exhibits, open houses, anniversary celebrations, fundraising events, special observances, contests, and award programs.

Speaking. Appearing before groups and arranging platforms for others before appropriate audiences by managing a speaker's bureau.

Production. Creating art, photography, and layout for brochures, booklets, reports, institutional advertisements, and periodicals; recording and editing audio- and videotapes; preparing audiovisual presentations.

Research. Gathering data to help an organization plan programs; monitoring the effectiveness of public relations programs. This is a fast-growing area of public relations that includes focus groups to test message concepts; research to target specific audiences; surveys of a company's reputation to use for improving the company's image; employee and public attitude surveys; and shareholder surveys to improve relations with investors.

Programming and Counselling. Establishing a program for effective public relations within the company.

Training. Working with executives and other people within the organization to prepare them to deal with the media.

Management. Overseeing the costs of running the public relations program and paying the bills.[21]

Public Relations and the Media

Public relations work often means finding ways to attract the attention of the press. Says Seymour Topping, managing editor of the *New York Times*,

> PR people do influence the news, but really more in a functional manner rather than in terms of giving new editorial direction. We get hundreds of press releases every day in each of our departments. We screen them very carefully for legitimate news, and very often there are legitimate news stories. Quite a lot of our business stories originate from press releases. It's impossible for us to cover all of these organizations ourselves.[22]

People in public relations provide **publicity**, which creates events and presents information so the press and the public will pay attention. Publicity and advertising differ: An *advertising* message *is paid for; publicity is free*. Advertising is a *controlled* use of media, because the message and where it will appear are governed by the person or company that places the ad. Publicity is considered an uncontrolled use of the media, because the public relations

IMPACT

Technology   *COMMUNICATORS BRACE FOR THE FUTURE*

By Colin Freeze

Public relations workers, consultants, and marketing executives take note—when the communications structure changes, so does the job. Doubters need only look at the downsized ranks of passenger pigeons and Pony Express riders.

For people who make their living at relaying information, reaction to the Internet is mixed. While some embrace the technology whole-heartedly, it causes only anxiety in others.

Yesterday, about 80 communications professionals, who ranged from the people who fax press releases to senior marketing executives, gathered at Hull's Museum of Civilization to explore just what new technology will mean for their work.

The conference was put on by two groups, the International Association of Business Communicators and the Canadian Public Relations Society, which represent about 400 public relations workers in Ottawa.

Many are already true believers in the Internet.

"The change we've experienced is nothing compared to what is about to come," said Joanne Pollack, who is a vice-president at Hill & Knowlton. "Without the Internet we would be completely ineffective."

Miss Pollack now said she connects with clients and co-workers in Helsinki and New York on a daily basis. The firm's work is global: one of Hill & Knowlton's clients is a Greek group making a bid for the 2004 Olympics; another is the Ontario government, which is seeking to attract investment from abroad.

Using the Internet widens a business's reach by cutting down on huge expenses that would have existed a generation ago, when the same work would have had to be done through travelling and long distance phone calls, she said.

Conference goers attended speeches and workshops, where executives from local high-tech companies spoke on the future of the Net.

"It is incumbent on everybody to get to know what the Web is all about, and how it is going to change everybody's lives," said Nortel's John Hewer, an international communications director.

Intranets, non-public Internets used only within firms, are growing and becoming important for internal communications.

"Our own Intranet is the glue that holds our company together," said Mr. Hewer, whose firm has 68,000 employees in over 250 locations worldwide.

To help co-ordinate work, Nortel employees access the more than 300,000 Web pages that exist on the company's Intranet, which sees over one million e-mails daily. Nevertheless, the company's publicly available Internet site remains important.

"More corporations will come to visit us through this window than will ever come visit us directly," said Mr. Hewer.

Today, moving sound and video files over the Net is slow and cumbersome. But once bandwidth increases, that will change. Jim Mackie, a marketing executive at Newbridge Networks, told a workshop that there are already

phenomenal rates of information transfer waiting to be tapped.

Mr. Mackie said that data, moving in underground fiberoptic cables, can now travel across the Atlantic at a rate of 40 gigabytes per second, a manner 143 times more cost effective than a decade ago. Once today's phone lines are replaced with quicker methods, the effects ought to be profound, he said.

"I'm saying to you that if the price of gas changed 143-fold, there would be a change in the economy," said a frustrated Mr. Mackie. "Would people understand then, that something significant is going on? People are failing to notice."

He maintains that much of the Internet, as it exists, is not so much a superhighway, but a barely beaten path.

Public relations workers, Mr. Mackie said, ought to recognize that bandwidth "is the great enabler," and start planning for when the data stream becomes a deluge.

Ottawa Citizen Online, March 21, 1997. http: //www.ottawacitizen .com/ business/970321/890113 .html
Reprinted with permission.

person provides information to the press but has no control over how the information will appear—the press writes the story. "We know how the media work," says David Resnicow of the PR firm Ruder Finn & Rotman, "and we make judgments on that, providing access to events as it becomes necessary."[23]

It is precisely because people in the media and people in PR know how each other work that they argue about the role of public relations in the news. The *Columbia Journalism Review* studied the relationship between corporate public relations and the *Wall Street Journal* by examining the stories in the *Journal* on a specific day and comparing the stories to press releases issued by PR people.

Specific companies were mentioned in 111 articles. Nearly half the news stories in the *Journal* that day, CJR reported in its analysis, were based solely on press releases. In 32 of the stories that were based on press releases, reporters paraphrased the releases almost verbatim; in the 21 remaining cases, only a small amount of additional reporting had been done.

The *Journal*'s executive director, Frederick Taylor, responded to *CJR*'s analysis by saying, "Ninety percent of daily coverage is started by a company making an announcement for the record. We're relaying this information to our readers."[24]

In a specific example of what is called press release journalism, *New York Times* reporter Douglas C. McGill published a story in the *Times* about the discovery of the original model that Michelangelo used to create his famous statue of David. McGill attributed the story to Professor Frederick Hartt, who had made the discovery.

Hartt had signed a contract with Abbeville Press to write a book about the Michelangelo discovery, and the book's photographer was David Finn, the chief executive officer of the public relations agency Ruder Finn & Rotman. In March 1987, two public relations people from Ruder Finn & Rotman had called McGill at the *Times* and offered him the story.

McGill added considerable research to the story, but when the connection was discovered, McGill told *Manhattan inc.* magazine that he felt uncomfortable. "I wasn't especially happy that the story was handed to me by a public relations agent. But once I heard about it, I thought it was an important story for *Times* readers no matter who it came from. The whole thing made me uneasy. It showed a high degree of sophistication from Ruder Finn."[25]

Public Relations Professionalism

Clever ways to attract attention are trademarks of today's successful public relations professional. According to Jeff and Marie Blyskal, who interviewed hundreds of PR people for their book *PR: How the Public Relations Industry Writes the News*:

> At the highest level of the profession, PR people are low-key, candid, creative, knowledgeable, warm, witty, charming, friendly, personable, self-confident. The best ones communicate as well as or better than some of the best journalists today; they are true communications technicians. We have found few hollow shells of human beings, bereft of moral conviction and marching in step with whatever "orders" their clients or employers bark out. Many were genuinely excited about their profession; some were swell-headed; only a few harkened back to their journalism days to assure us they were really "okay."

Then, too, we saw no cabals or international PR conspiracies to control the public's mind—though quietly controlling minds is, in fact, what PR people attempt to do on a case-by-case basis. PR people have chosen their profession, and most seem reasonably satisfied with being effective advocates for their clients.... Some will even admit that what they do is manipulation, but manipulation with a noble, higher goal in mind: defending or advancing the cause of their client. There are two sides to every story, goes the argument. They are, in a sense, the equivalent of attorneys in the court of public opinion.[26]

Technology Changes the Future

Like the future of advertising, the future of public relations is closely tied to the future of the media industries. The basic structure of the business will not change, but public relations practitioners will find themselves facing the same challenges as people in the advertising business.

Growing international markets will mean that, in the future, many public relations firms will expand overseas to the point that they will have no clear nationality or national base. Global communications will mean that public relations agencies will work internationally on some projects, and that the agencies will have to adjust to the cultural differences that global exposure brings.

New technologies, especially the Internet, will mean new ways to deliver public relations messages. Eventually, satellite technology may streamline all print, audio, and video, giving PR agencies the same access to distributing video to news organizations that the news organizations now possess themselves.

And, as in the advertising industry, shifting demographic patterns will mean growing potential markets for public relations services.

In Focus

◎ Modern public relations emerged at the beginning of the 20th century as a way for business to respond to the muckrakers and unfavourable treatment by governments.

◎ The promotion of immigration to Canada was the first full-scale public relations campaign in Canadian history.

◎ The best-known early practitioner of public relations was Ivy Lee, who wrote a "Declaration of Principles" to respond to the secret publicity activities of the Publicity Bureau.

◎ The Chicago Edison Company and American Telephone & Telegraph were the first companies to begin inhouse promotional programs.

◎ Edward L. Bernays wrote the first book on public relations, *Crystallizing Public Opinion*. Both Bernays and Ivy Lee have been called the father of public relations.

◎ Among the pioneering women who joined the public relations business were Doris E. Fleischman, Leone Baxter, and Anne Williams Wheaton. Doris Fleischman and Edward Bernays were equal partners in the Bernays public relations firm. Doris Fleischman was an early advocate of public relations as a career for women.

◎ The Canadian Public Relations Society was established in 1948 and introduced voluntary accreditation processes in 1969.

◎ Public relations expanded quickly in the 1960s and 1970s to accommodate television, governments, and corporate interests.

◎ Public relations people work in government, education, industry, business, nonprofit agencies, athletic teams, entertainment companies, and international business.

◎ Public relations people use persuasion and publicity to attract attention for their clients.

◎ The main difference between advertising and public relations is that advertising messages are controlled and public relations messages are uncontrolled.

◎ The trademark of today's public relations is a sophisticated approach to news. People who work in public relations have been called "attorneys in the court of public opinion."

◎ Public relations agencies face the same challenges as advertising agencies: expanding worldwide markets, the development of new technologies, and changing demographic patterns.

Review Questions

1. Cite the major landmarks in the development of public relations. What did each development contribute to the evolution of public relations?

2. How can crisis public relations be used by a company to diffuse a difficult situation? Give an example.

3. Discuss in some detail five of the qualities of a good, ethical PR person today. Offer three examples of unethical practices.

4. What are the advantages for public relations firms of "press release journalism" and the widespread use of video news releases? What are some of the disadvantages for media consumers?

Watching the Web

◎ **Directory of Public Relations Agencies and Resources on the Web**

http://www.webcom.com/impulse/prlist.html

◎ **Canadian Public Relations Society**

http://www.cprs.ca/newmemb.html

◎ **Online Public Relations**

http://www.connectingonline.com/anchors/online public relations.html

MASS MEDIA AND SOCIAL ISSUES

12

> THE MEDIA ARE EXTENSIONS OF
> THE HUMAN NERVOUS SYSTEM.

Marshall McLuhan

What's Ahead

How do the media affect what we do? The answers to this question are far from clear. For example, it is difficult to draw conclusions about the effect that violence shown in the media has on society. Clearly though, there is an impact of some sort.

In 1994, when O.J. Simpson was arrested after a "slow speed chase," televised worldwide, and charged with the murder of his former wife, calls to domestic violence hotlines in Los Angeles jumped 80 percent.[1] The graphic images of the Manitoba floods of 1997 and the great ice storm in Ontario and Quebec in 1998 stimulated Canadians all over the country to donate their time, their money, and even their personal possessions to victims of these natural disasters.

These examples of media effects are anecdotal insights—pieces of a very complex picture. Today, scholars understand that the media have different effects on various people, with differing results. Generalizations about the media's effects are easy to make but difficult to prove. "We do not fully understand at present what the media system is doing to individual behaviour, much less to American culture," according to William L. Rivers and Wilbur Schramm. "The media cannot simply be seen as stenciling images on a blank mind. That is too superficial a view of the communication process."[2]

Assessing the Impact: Early Media Studies

The concept that the media have different effects on different types of people is relatively new. Early media observers felt that an absolute one-to-one relationship existed between what people read, heard, and saw and what people did with that information. They also believed that the effects were the same for everyone.

The **magic bullet theory,** sometimes called the hypodermic needle theory, alleged that ideas from the media were in direct causal relationship to behaviour. The theory held that the media could inject ideas into someone the way liquids are injected through a needle. This early distrust of the media still pervades many people's thinking today, although the theory has been disproved.

Media research, like other social science research, is based on a continuum of thought, with each new study advancing slightly the knowledge from the studies that have come before. This is what has happened to the magic bullet theory. Eventually, the beliefs that audiences absorbed media messages uncritically and that all audiences reacted the same to each message were proven untrue. Research disclosed that analyzing media effects is a very complex task.

Some media research existed before television use became widespread in the mid-1950s, but TV prompted scholars to take an even closer look at media's effects. Two scholars made particularly provocative assertions about how the media influence people's lives. David M. Potter and Marshall McLuhan arrived at just the right moment—when the public and the scholarly community were anxiously trying to analyze media's effects on society.

In his book *People of Plenty*, published in 1954, Potter first articulated an important idea: that North America sustains a consumer society driven primarily by advertising. Potter, a historian, asserted that advertising is rooted in abundance.

> Advertising is not badly needed in an economy of scarcity, because total demand is usually equal to or in excess of total supply, and every producer can normally sell as much as he produces.... It is when potential supply outstrips demand—that is, when abundance prevails—that advertising begins to fulfill a really essential economic function.

Potter then warned about the dangers of advertising. "Advertising has in its dynamics no motivation to seek the improvement of the individual or to impart qualities of social usefulness.... It has no social goals and no social responsibility for what it does with its influence."[3] Potter's perspective was important in shaping the critical view of modern advertising. *People of Plenty* is still in print today.

In the 1960s, Canadian Marshall McLuhan piqued the public's interest with his phrase "the medium is the message," which he later parodied in the title of his book *The Medium Is the Massage*. One of his conclusions was that the widespread use of television was a landmark in the history of the world, "retribalizing" society and creating a "global village" of people who use media to communicate.

McLuhan suggested that electronic media messages are inherently different from print messages—to watch information on TV is different from reading the same information in a newspaper. McLuhan never attempted to offer systematic proof for his ideas, and his concepts are still widely debated. He was capable of mixing the commonplace, the banal, and the profound in striking rhetorical flourishes. His aphorisms about television, a medium he did not care for, will probably be repeated for as long as the medium exists.

Marshall McLuhan piqued the public's interest in media with his phrase "The medium is the message."

CP Picture Archive

Scholars who analyze the media today look for patterns in media effects, predictable results, and statistical evidence to document how the media affect us. Precisely because the media are ubiquitous, studies of their effects on society are far from conclusive. In this chapter you will learn about some of the major studies that have examined the media's effects and some of the recent assertions about the role that the media play in our lives.

Media research today includes media effects research and media content analysis. Effects research tries to analyze how people use the information they receive from the media—whether political advertising changes people's voting behaviour, for example. Content analysis examines what is presented by the media—how many children's programs portray violent behaviour, for example. (See the discussion of George Gerbner, page 259.) Sometimes these two types of analysis (effects research and content studies) are combined in an attempt to evaluate what effects certain content has on an audience.

Profile

MARSHALL MCLUHAN: THE MEDIA GURU OF WYCHWOOD PARK

Marshall McLuhan found fame late in life. Whether this recognition was as a result of a deliberate attempt on his part or merely an historical accident we shall never know. McLuhan was born in Edmonton in 1911. In the mid-1960s, he went from relative obscurity as a professor of English at the University of Toronto, with a Cambridge Ph.D. to being an instantly recognizable cultural icon, even appearing in the Woody Allen film *Annie Hall* in a cameo performance. Appearing on many television programs and speaker's podiums around the world, his long sentences and tortured expressions, delivered in a nasal drone, became commonplace.

McLuhan's ideas on the nature of the media and their influence on individuals and societies struck readers and listeners as novel and intriguing. He wrapped up complex ideas in aphorisms, which he constantly repeated in speeches and interviews, such as "the medium is the message," "television is a cool medium (as opposed to radio which is hot)," and "the media are extensions of the human nervous system." His ideas were seldom backed up with systematic evidence, and coming from a background in the humanities, he appeared uncomfortable with social science research techniques. He was, above all, concerned with the effects of the media on his fellow citizens. He left the impression that he thought the media were having seriously destructive effects on the developed world.

McLuhan lived in a large Victorian house overlooking downtown Toronto, in the affluent community of Wychwood Park. He virtually always appeared in suit and tie in the years of the Cultural Revolution of the 1960s, a time when formal dress was out of fashion. McLuhan was in most respects an Edwardian gentleman of moderate demeanour. It is hard to imagine a less likely individual to be known as a revolutionary. Still, his name will likely always be associated with the phrase "The Global Village," which he popularized.

His major works were *The Gutenberg Galaxy: The Making of Typographical Man* (1962) and *Understanding Media* (1964). He later published several other less influential books: *War and Peace in the Global Village* (with Quentin Fiore, 1968), *The Interior Landscape: the Literary Criticism of Marshall McLuhan* (collected, 1969), *Counterblast* (1969), *From Cliché to Archetype* (with Wilfred Watson, 1970), and *Take Today: The Executive as Dropout* (with Barrington Nevitt, 1972).

The Payne Fund Studies

The prestigious Payne Fund sponsored the first major study of media, conducted in 1929. The study contained 12 separate reports on media effects. One of these reports concentrated on the effects of movies on children. In his interviews, researcher Herbert Blumer simply asked teenagers what they remembered about the movies they had seen as children.

Using this unsystematic approach, he reported that the teenagers had been greatly influenced by the movies because they said they had been greatly influenced. Blumer's conclusion and other conclusions of the Payne Fund studies about the media's direct one-to-one effect on people were accepted without question, mainly because these were the first major studies of media effects, and the results were widely reported. This became known as the magic bullet theory.

The Payne Fund studies also contributed ammunition for the Motion Picture Producers and Distributors Association Production Code, adopted in 1930, which regulated movie content (see Chapter 8).

"Five thousand hours, and his vital signs are still strong."

The Cantril Study

The Martians who landed in New Jersey on the Mercury Theater "War of the Worlds" broadcast of October 30, 1939 (see Chapter 5), sparked the next major study of media effects, conducted by Hadley Cantril at Princeton University. The results of the Cantril study contradicted the findings of the Payne Fund studies and disputed the magic bullet theory.

The Cantril researchers wanted to find out why certain people believed the Mercury Theater broadcast and other people did not. After interviewing 135 people, Cantril concluded that a high level of critical thinking ability was the key. Better-educated people were much more likely to decide that the broadcast was a fake. This might seem to be a self-evident finding today, but the importance of the Cantril study is that it differentiated among listeners: People with different personality characteristics interpreted the broadcast differently.

The Lasswell Model

In 1948, Harold D. Lasswell designed a model to describe the process of communication that is still used today. Lasswell said that this process can be analyzed by answering five questions:

> Who?
> says what?
> on which channel?
> to whom?
> with what effect?

In other words, Lasswell said that the process of communication can be analyzed by determining who the sender is and what the sender says. Next, you must identify which channel—meaning the method—of communication the sender used. Then you must examine the audience and define the effect on that audience. Because Lasswell described the communication process so succinctly, most of the communications research that followed has attempted to answer his five questions.

Television and Children's Behaviour

The 1950s were a time of adjustment to the addition of the new medium of television, which was seen first as a novelty and then as a household necessity. Since 1960, four of the major studies of the effects of television have focused on children.

Television in the Lives of Our Children

Published in 1961 by Wilbur Schramm, Jack Lyle, and Edwin Parker, *Television in the Lives of Our Children* was the first major study of the effects of television on children. Researchers interviewed 6000 children and 1500 parents, as well as teachers and school officials.

Schramm and his associates reported that children were exposed to television more than to any other mass medium. On average, five-year-old children watched television two hours every weekday. TV viewing time reached three hours by the time these children were eight years old. In a finding that often was subsequently cited, Schramm said that from the ages of three to sixteen, children spent more time in front of the television set than they spent in school.

Children used television for fantasy, diversion, and instruction, Schramm said. Children who had troubled relationships with their parents and children who were classified as aggressive were more likely to turn to television for fantasy, but Schramm could find no serious problems related to television viewing. Schramm also found, in support of Cantril, that different children showed different effects.

Television and Social Behaviour

Television and Social Behavior, a six-volume study of the effects of television, was funded by $1 million appropriated by the U.S. Congress in 1969 after the discordant and violent decade of the 1960s. The U.S. Department of Health, Education, and Welfare, which sponsored the study, appointed a distinguished panel of social scientists to undertake the research.

The study's major findings, published in 1971, concerned the effects of television violence on children. A content analysis of one week of prime-time programming, conducted by George Gerbner of the University of Pennsylvania, reported that eight out of ten prime-time shows contained violence. The conclusions of *Television and Social Behavior* failed to make a direct connection between TV programming and violent behaviour, however. The report said only that there was a "tentative" indication that television viewing caused aggressive behaviour. According to the study, this connection between TV violence and aggressive behaviour affected only *some* children who were already classified as aggressive children and only in *some* environments.

Even though the report avoided a direct statement about violent behaviour in children as a result of television viewing, the U.S. Surgeon General called for immediate action against violence on television. The television industry dismissed the results as inconclusive.

The Early Window

Several subsequent studies since 1971 have suggested that television violence causes aggression among children. In their 1988 book *The Early Window: Effects of Television on Children and Youth*, psychologists Robert M. Liebert and Joyce Sprafkin urged caution in drawing broad conclusions about the subject:

Studies using various methods have supported the proposition that TV violence can induce aggressive and/or antisocial behaviour in children. Whether the effect will hold only for the most susceptible individuals (e.g., boys from disadvantaged homes) or whether it will hold for a wider range of youngsters obviously depends in part upon the measure being used.... The occurrence of serious violent or criminal acts results from several forces at once. Researchers have said that TV violence is a cause of aggressiveness, not that it is the cause of aggressiveness. There is no one, single cause of any social behaviour.[4]

Kathleen McConnell and Eugene D. Tate explain that violent behaviour may relate more to a person's environment than to the influence of television: violent content on TV or in other media will not move one to aggressive behaviour. People who dwell in violent or aggressive environments will experience the violent content as reinforcing that environment and lifestyle. Those living in nonviolent environments will dismiss violent media content because it is foreign to their understanding of the world in which they live.[5]

One of the major implications of this view is that clinical studies of the effects of the media will show different results from country to country and culture to culture.

Television Advertising to Children

The effects of advertising on adults have been widely analyzed, but in 1979 the advertising of children's products became an object of serious government attention with the release of the 340-page report *Television Advertising to Children* by the U.S. Federal Trade Commission.

The report, based on a two-year study, was designed to document the dangers of advertising sugar-based products to children, but embedded in the report was some provocative information about children's advertising. Children are an especially vulnerable audience, said the FTC. The report concluded:

◎ The average child sees 20 000 commercials a year, or about three hours of TV advertising a week.

◎ Many children regard advertising as just another form of programming and do not distinguish between programs and ads.

◎ Televised advertising for any product to children who do not understand the intent of the commercial is unfair and deceptive.

The report called for a ban on advertising to very young children, a ban on sugared products in advertising directed to children under age 12, and a requirement for counter-ads with dental and nutritional information to balance any ads for sugared products.[6]

This report and subsequent research about children's advertising suggest that younger children pay more attention to television advertising than older children. But by grade six, children adopt what has been called a "global distrust" of advertising.[7]

IMPACT

Point of View

CROSS BORDER GAWKING: WHY MTV AND MUCHMUSIC CAN'T COMPARE

More than gun control and bad exchange rates separate Canada and the U.S. Our video music stations are miles apart too. At least, that's the conclusion of York PhD music student Karen Pegley.

Pegley watched more MuchMusic and MTV videos than is probably healthy in her quest to understand these two disseminators of popular culture. "My goal is to determine how these two stations construct national, sexual and racial identities," Pegley says. As part of her doctoral studies, she's investigating how MTV and Much deal with issues of gender, race and national identity.

In 1995, she monitored both networks for an entire week, analysing musical and extra-musical genres, tempos, solos,

instrumentation, choreographic moves, filming and lighting techniques, lyrical content, race, sex, nationality of central performers, and the role of VJs. Differences in program scheduling and commercial content was also included.

In total, Pegley tracked 3,100 different "events," analysing them using techniques borrowed from popular music studies, feminist film theory, television criticism, gesture analysis, and recent theories of nationalism.

Her conclusion? "When you compare MuchMusic and MTV it's apparent they both have an agenda; both music stations are ideologically driven." That flies in the face of the common assumption that both stations are neutral, she adds.

She found MuchMusic played almost 50 percent more videos than MTV, and a significant number of these were from performers of different countries, many of whom sang in languages other than English. Much also named the home province or city of Canadian performers. MTV rarely identified musicians to the viewing audience by region.

Says Pegley: "The notion of Canada's cultural mosaic came through in Much's programming. MTV was insular. It reinforced the idea that the U.S. was the centre of the (musical) universe."

York University, Profiles, *vol. 8, iss. 3. August 1998, p.6.*

Television and Violence

Most of the latest studies of the media's role have continued to reinforce the concept that different people in different environments react to the media differently.

In Canada, the CRTC announced a new code on "gratuitous" TV violence in 1993. Broadcasters agreed to restrict television violence before 9 p.m. and provided a Broadcast Standards Council to which viewers could complain.

An extensive public examination of the effects of TV violence had been carried out by the Ontario Royal Commission on Violence in Communications (LaMarsh) in 1976. It reported complex and ambiguous chains of cause and effect. An interesting finding of the study is that the same shows containing explicit violence are shown to large audiences in Canada and the United States, but the rate of violent crimes is much lower in Canada. Therefore, either other factors are involved in some ill-understood way or there is no direct relationship between violent television programming and violent behaviour.

The V-Chip

The V-chip was invented by Tim Collings, an engineering professor at Simon Fraser University in Burnaby, B.C. The invention arose out of his concerns about the effect television violence seemed to have on his own children. The device, on instructions from its owner, simply blocks television signals according to the owner's criteria. The chip uses an industry rating system for programs (E for Exempt, G for General Audience, and R for Restricted, with a numerical rating for violence, sex, and language with 0 as the lowest level, and 5 as the highest). Set owners must set the chip to filter according to their personal choices.

One concern some people have with this device is that it may stifle innovation in television, by promoting the idea that bland is better. It remains to be seen whether many adults will take the trouble to use the device, given that many do not even program the date into their VCRs. As well, children might tape contentious programming on an unblocked TV and play the tape on a VCR. In general, in the wired world, censorship is extremely difficult both for technical and political reasons.

The Media and Politics

The media have transformed politics in ways that could never have been imagined when U.S. President Franklin D. Roosevelt introduced what were called Fireside Chats in 1933. Roosevelt was the first major politician in the West to use the media effectively to stimulate public support. The newest technology of Roosevelt's era—radio—gave him immediate access to a national audience. Roosevelt's media skill became an essential element in promoting his economic programs. Today, politics and the media seem irreversibly dependent on each other, one of the legacies of Roosevelt's presidency.

The Fireside Chats

In March 1933, just after he was inaugurated as president, Roosevelt looked for a way to avoid a financial panic after he announced that he was closing U.S. banks. For a week the country cooled off while politicians scrambled for a solution. On the Sunday night eight days after his inauguration, Roosevelt used radio to calm public anxiety before the banks began to reopen on Monday. He went down to the basement of the White House to give his first Fireside Chat.

There was a fireplace in the basement, but no fire was burning. The president could not find his script, so he borrowed a mimeographed copy from a reporter. In his first address to the U.S. populace as president, FDR gave a banking lesson to his audience of 60 million people: "I want to talk for a few minutes with the people of the United States about banking.... First of all, let me state the simple fact that when you deposit money in a bank, the bank does not put the money into a safe deposit vault. It invests your money in many different forms." When he finished, he turned to people in the room and asked, "Was I all right?"[8] The United States had its first media president, an elected leader talking directly to people through the media.

Roosevelt's chats are cited as a legendary example of media politics, yet he gave only eight of them in his first term of office. His reputation for press access also was enhanced by his other meetings with the press: In 13 years in office he held more than 900 press conferences.

The People's Choice

The first major study of the influence of media on politics was *The People's Choice*, undertaken precisely because Roosevelt seemed to be such a good media politician. This comprehensive examination of voter behaviour in the 1940 presidential election was quite systematic.

Researchers Paul Lazarsfeld, Bernard Berelson, and Hazel Gaudet followed 3000 people in rural Erie County, Ohio, from May to November 1940 to determine what influenced the way these people voted for president. The researchers tracked how people's minds changed over the six-month period and then attempted to determine why. (It is important to remember that this study was undertaken before television. Radio became the prevailing medium for political advertising in 1932, when the two parties spent more money for radio time than for any other item.[9])

What effect, the researchers wanted to know, did the media have on people's choosing one candidate over another? The results were provocative. Lazarsfeld and his colleagues found that only 8 percent of the voters in the study were actually *converted*. The majority of voters (53 percent) were *reinforced* in their beliefs by the media, and 14 percent were *activated* to vote. Mixed effects or no effects were shown by the remaining 25 percent of the people.

Lazarsfeld said that opinion leaders, who got their information from the media, shared this information with their friends. The study concluded that instead of changing people's beliefs, the media primarily activate people to vote and reinforce already-held opinions. *The People's Choice* also revealed that:

◎ Family and friends had more effect on people's decisions than the media did.

◎ The media had different effects on different people, reinforcing Cantril's findings.

◎ A major source of information about candidates was other people.

This finding that opinion leaders often provide and shape information for the general population was a bonus—the researchers hadn't set out specifically to learn this. This transmittal of information and ideas from mass media to opinion leaders to friends and acquaintances is called the **two-step flow** of communication.

The Unseeing Eye

In 1976, a second study of the media and presidential elections, called *The Unseeing Eye: The Myth of Television Power in National Elections*, revealed findings that paralleled those of *The People's Choice*. With a grant from the National Science Foundation, Thomas E. Patterson and Robert D. McClure supervised interviews with 2707 people from early September to just before Election Day in the November 1972 U.S. presidential race between George McGovern and Richard Nixon. The study did not discuss political media events, but it did analyze television campaign news and political advertising. (The role of journalists and news reporting is discussed in Chapter 13.)

The researchers concluded that, although 16 percent of the people they interviewed were influenced by political advertising, only 7 percent were manipulated by political ads. The researchers defined people who were influenced as those who decided to vote for a candidate based mostly on what they knew and only slightly on what the ads told them. The 7 percent of the people in the survey who were manipulated, according to Patterson and McClure, were people who cited political advertising as a major factor in their choices. Patterson and McClure concluded that political advertising on TV has little effect on most people.

> By projecting their political biases ... people see in candidates' commercials pretty much what they want to see. Ads sponsored by the candidate who shares their politics get a good response. They like what he has to say. And they like him. Ads sponsored by the opposing candidate are viewed negatively. They object to what he says. And they object to him.[10]

It is important to remember, however, that in some elections a difference of a few percentage points can decide the outcome. This is why political advertising continues to play such an important campaign role, and why such an effort is made to reach the percentage of the population that remains vulnerable.

Election Campaigns on Television

So far, no convincing systematic evidence has been presented to show that the media change the voting behaviour of large groups of people. Yet, since John F. Kennedy debated Richard Nixon during the 1960 presidential campaign, a deeply felt view has persisted among many people that the media—television in particular—have changed elections and electoral politics.

Kennedy's debate with Nixon in 1960 was the first televised debate of presidential candidates. Kennedy's performance in the debates often is credited for

his narrow victory in the election. In his book *Presidents and the Press*, media scholar Joseph C. Spear wrote:

> As the panel began asking questions, Nixon tended to go on the defensive, answering Kennedy point by point and ignoring his huge audience beyond the camera. Kennedy, by contrast, appeared rested, calm, informed, cocksure. Whatever the question, he aimed his answer at the millions of Americans viewing the program in their living rooms.
>
> It was an unmitigated disaster for Nixon. In the second, third, and fourth debates, he managed to recover somewhat from his initial poor performance, but it was too late. Surveys showed that an overwhelming percentage of the television audience had judged Kennedy the victor.[11]

One legacy of Kennedy's television victory is that today, national political campaigns everywhere in the Western world depend almost entirely on TV to promote leadership candidates.

Pierre Elliott Trudeau also used television to his advantage when he shot from obscurity in 1968 to become prime minister of Canada. His television persona was electric and conveyed a sense of intelligent optimism and the possibility of nondisruptive change. Trudeau's television persona overwhelmed that of his electoral opponent, Robert Stanfield, a balding, older man, who spoke in a halting and self-effacing manner and tended to be awkward physically, dropping a football on one televised occasion. It is hard to see how "Trudeaumania" could have happened without television.

Television is a very efficient way to reach large numbers of people quickly, but campaigning for television also distances the candidates from direct public contact. Television advertising also is very expensive.

Not all of the political money goes to television however. Television advertising in large markets delivers a bigger audience than candidates need, so they use direct mail or print advertising. But a candidate running in a rural area might use television because the entire district would be included in the local station's coverage.

In politics, the cost of radio and television advertising is rising quickly. In 1996, President Clinton and Republican challenger Bob Dole each spent $40 million for media advertising. The amount of money that each presidential candidate spends for media has doubled in the last 12 years.[12]

The rising cost of running for public office can exclude people without the means to raise huge sums of money. If people cannot easily participate in the political process, eventually they may choose not to participate at all, eroding the number of people who run for office, vote in elections, and work in political campaigns.

Canadian electoral campaigns are more severely limited in their media expenditures by law. Even independent, nonpartisan groups have had their advertising limited.

The proposed level of allowable campaign spending in 1998 in Ontario was about five dollars per voting citizen. The effect of these restrictions is somewhat offset by free television and radio slots for the advertising of established political parties. Some central party expenses are not covered by the limits.

Today, the media are essential to the political process, changing the behaviour of politicians as well as the electorate, raising important questions about governance and the conduct of elections.

Pierre Elliott Trudeau created an electric, intelligent television persona, which increased his popularity during the 1968 election campagn.

National Archives of Canada/C-27281

Mass Media Reflections on Cultural Values

Because media research is a continuing process, new ideas will emerge in the next decade from today's ideas and studies. Several provocative recent ideas and studies have extended the current boundaries of media research.

Silencing Opposing Viewpoints

Elisabeth Noelle-Neumann has asserted that because journalists in all media tend to concentrate on the same major news stories, the audience is assailed on many sides by similar information. Together, the media present the consensus; journalists reflect the prevailing climate of opinion. As this consensus spreads, people with divergent views, says Noelle-Neumann, may be less likely to voice disagreement with the prevailing point of view. Thus, the **"spiral of silence"** leads the media to gain more influence because opponents of the consensus tend to remain silent. The implication for future research will be to ask whether the media neutralize dissent and create a pattern of social and cultural conformity.

Losing a Sense of Place

In his book *No Sense of Place*, published in 1985, Joshua Meyrowitz provided new insight into television's possible effects on society. In the past, says Meyrowitz,

> parents did not know what their children knew, and children did not know what their parents knew they knew. Similarly, a person of one sex could never be certain of what a member of the other sex knew.... Television undermines such behavioural distinctions because it encompasses children and adults, men and women, and all other social groups in a single informational sphere or environment. Not only does it provide similar information to everyone but, even more significant, it provides it publicly and often simultaneously.[13]

This sharing of information, says Meyrowitz, means that subjects that were rarely discussed between men and women, for instance, and between children and adults, have become part of the public dialogue.

A second result of television viewing is the blurring of the distinction between childhood and adulthood, says Meyrowitz. When print dominated the society as a medium, children's access to adult information was limited. The only way to learn about "adult" concepts was to read about them, so typically a child was not exposed to adult ideas or problems, and taboo topics remained hidden from children.

In a video world, however, any topic that can be portrayed in pictures on television challenges the boundaries that print places around information. This, says Meyrowitz, causes an early loss of the naiveté of childhood.

> Television removes barriers that once divided people of different ages and reading abilities into different social situations. The widespread use of television is equivalent to a broad social decision to allow young children to be present at wars and funerals, courtships and seductions, criminal plots and cocktail parties.... Television thrusts children into a complex adult world, and it provides the impetus for children to ask the meanings of actions and words they would not yet have heard or read about without television.[14]

Meyrowitz concedes that movies offered similar information to children before television, but he says the pervasiveness of television today makes its effects more widespread. Television is blurring social distinction—between children and adults, and between men and women. And complicating the current study of media effects is the increase in the variety and number of available media sources.

Stereotyping Women

Journalists often use shorthand labels to characterize ethnic and other groups. In his 1922 book *Public Opinion,* political journalist Walter Lippmann first identified the tendency of journalists to generalize about other people based on fixed ideas.

> When we speak of the mind of a group of people, of the French mind, the militarist mind, the Bolshevik mind, we are liable to serious confusion unless we agree to separate the instinctive equipment from the stereotypes, the patterns, the formulae which play so decisive a part in building up the mental world to which the native character is adapted and responds.... Failure to make this distinction accounts for oceans of loose talk about collective minds, national souls, and race psychology.[15]

Calvin and Hobbes   by Bill Watterson

The image of women portrayed by the media has been a subject of significant contemporary study. Observers of the stereotyping of women point to past and current media showing very few women in professional roles and the lack of women shown as strong, major characters. The media's overall portrayal of women in mass culture is slowly improving, but in her book *Loving with a Vengeance: Mass-Produced Fantasies for Women*, Tania Modleski says that the portrayal in popular fiction of women in submissive roles began more than 250 years ago with the British novel *Pamela*, published in England in 1740.

Modleski analyzed the historical content of gothic novels, Harlequin Romances (published by the Canadian corporation Torstar and sold worldwide in the millions each year), and soap operas. Her study reveals:

> In Harlequin Romances, the need of women to find meaning and plea-sure in activities that are not wholly male-centered such as work or artistic creation is generally scoffed at.
>
> Soap operas also undercut, though in subtler fashion, the idea that a woman might obtain satisfaction from these activities [work or artistic creation].... Indeed, patriarchal myths and institutions are ... wholeheartedly embraced, although the anxieties and tensions they give rise to may be said to provoke the need for the texts in the first place.[16]

The implication in Modleski's research is that women who read romance novels will believe they should act like the women in the novels they read. A stereotype that has existed since 1740 is unlikely to change quickly.

Multiculturalism and the Mass Media

During the last century, selected media outlets, such as Chinese and Portuguese newspapers and magazines, have been able to cater to specific audiences. But the mainstream media, especially daily newspapers and the TV networks, have traditionally represented the interests of mainstream culture. Scores of media studies have documented stereotypical representation, and a lack of representa-tion, of ethnic minorities in all areas of culture.

Media scholar Carolyn Martindale, for example, in a content analysis of the *New York Times* from 1934 to 1994, found that most nonwhite groups were visible "only in glimpses."[17] According to Martindale, "The mainstream press in

The cast of CBC television's *North of 60* reflects an attempt by the network to present a diverse set of characters.

Courtesy the Canadian Broadcasting Corporation

the U.S. has presented minorities as outside, rather than a part of, American Society."[18]

The issue of accurate reflection by the media of a complex society invites analysis, as traditional media outlets struggle to reflect the evolving face of a society that is growing more diverse every day.

Alternative Lifestyles and the Mass Media

An understanding of media portrayals of diverse lifestyles received extra attention in 1997, when the television program *Ellen* portrayed two women exchanging a romantic kiss. Although promoted as the first female television kiss, the first romantic lesbian relationship actually had been shown on *L.A. Law* in 1991.

The subject of alternative lifestyles has remained primarily a subject for lesbian and gay newspapers and magazines. Bringing the issue to mainstream TV, as the *Ellen* program did, presents a dilemma for the TV networks because, when notified beforehand about the content of the program, some local TV stations refused to show the episode. The reluctance of television to portray alternative lifestyles is as much a reflection of the networks trying to protect their economic interests as it is of social values.

Understanding Mass Media and Social Issues

Scholars once thought that media effects were easy to measure, as a direct relationship between media messages and media effects. Contemporary scholars now know that the relationship between mass media and social issues is complex.

Communications scholar Neil Postman poses some of the questions that should be asked about media effects:

- What are the main psychic effects of each [media] form?
- What is the main relation between information and reason?
- What redefinitions of important cultural meanings do new sources, speeds, contexts, and forms of information require?
- How do different forms of information persuade?
- Is a newspaper's 'public' different from television's "public"?
- How do different information forms dictate the type of content that is expressed?[19]

These questions should be discussed, says Postman, because "no medium is excessively dangerous if its users understand what its dangers are.... This is an instance in which the asking of the questions is sufficient. To ask is to break the spell."[20]

In Focus

◎ Media scholars look for patterns in the effects of media, rather than anecdotal evidence.

◎ David Potter, in *People of Plenty*, described the United States as a consumer society driven by advertising.

◎ Canadian scholar Marshall McLuhan introduced the term *global village* to describe the way the media bring people together through shared experience.

◎ The magic bullet theory, developed in the 1929 Payne Fund studies, asserted that media content had a direct causal relationship to behaviour.

◎ Hadley Cantril challenged the magic bullet theory. Cantril found that better-educated people listening to "War of the Worlds" were more likely to detect that the broadcast was fiction. Today, scholars believe that the media have different effects on different people.

◎ In 1948, political scientist Harold D. Lasswell described the process of communication as: Who? says what? on which channel? to whom? with what effect?

◎ In 1961, Wilbur Schramm and his associates revealed that children used TV for fantasy, diversion, and instruction. Aggressive children were more likely to turn to TV for fantasy, said Schramm, but he could find no serious problems related to TV viewing.

◎ In 1976, the Ontario Royal Commission on Violence in Communications carried out an extensive study on the effects of TV violence on children.

◎ In 1993, the CRTC announced a new code on "gratuitous" TV violence.

◎ Several subsequent studies have suggested that TV violence causes aggression among children. Researchers caution, however, that TV violence is not *the* cause of aggressiveness, but only a contributing cause of aggressiveness.

◎ The U.S. Federal Trade Commission report, *Television Advertising to Children*, said that children see 20 000 commercials a year and that younger children are much more likely to pay attention to TV advertising than older ones.

◎ Although some studies find a connection between televised violence and aggressive behaviour, there is no way to predict who will be affected and why, and some researchers suggest that television only reinforces violence learned in one's environment.

◎ Media politics began in 1933 with President Franklin Roosevelt's Fireside Chats. John F. Kennedy broadened the tradition when he and Richard Nixon appeared in the first televised debate of U.S. presidential candidates in 1960.

◎ Pierre Elliott Trudeau was the first Canadian politician to use television to win public support, by creating a television persona.

◎ The first major study of politics and the media, *The People's Choice*, concluded that only 8 percent of the voters in the study were actually converted by media coverage of the 1940 campaign.

◎ The 1976 study *The Unseeing Eye* revealed that only 7 percent of the people in the study were manipulated by TV ads. The researchers concluded that political advertising has little effect on most people.

◎ Television is a very efficient way for political candidates to reach large numbers of people quickly, but campaigning for television also distances the candidates from direct public contact.

◎ Elisabeth Noelle-Newmann has asserted that, because of what she calls a "spiral of silence" supporting the consensus point of view, the media have more influence because opponents of the consensus tend to remain silent.

◎ Joshua Meyrowitz says that television viewing blurs the distinction between childhood and adulthood.

◎ Walter Lippmann first identified the tendency of journalists to generalize about groups of people and create stereotypes.

◎ Scholar Tania Modleski says that the media's inaccurate portrayals of women is not new but began in 1740 with publication of *Pamela*, the first novel.

◎ The mainstream media, especially newspapers and TV networks, have traditionally represented the interest of the mainstream culture.

Review Questions

1. Describe three studies involving children and TV and discuss the results. Why are children often the subject of television effects research?

2. How did Franklin D. Roosevelt's Fireside Chats and hundreds of press conferences change the way the media covered politicians?

3. Do you agree with Joshua Meyrowitz's conclusion that TV, by providing a single information environment, is blurring social distinctions, including those between men and women and between children and adults? Why or why not? Give specific examples.

4. Describe how prime ministers have used TV. Name several significant political events in which prime ministers have participated on television, and discuss the importance of these events.

Watching the Web

◎ **American Society of Newspaper Editors Minority Employment Report**

http://www.asne.org/kiosk/diversity/97minsrv.htm

◎ **An Appraisal of Technologies of Political Control**

http://jya.com/atpc.html

◎ **Association for Asian Studies**

http://www.easc.indiana.edu/~aas

◎ **Diversity in Electronic Media**

http://www.mediaaccess.org/program/diversity/index.html

MEDIA OWNERSHIP AND PRESS PERFORMANCE

13

LIKE SPIDERS THESE [MEDIA] COMPANIES COMPETE BY DEVOURING OTHERS OF THEIR KIND, AND BY SPINNING EVEN BIGGER WEBS—WEBS TO COVER ALL OF COMMUNICATIONS.

Ken Auletta,
The New Yorker

What's Ahead

In 1822, James Madison observed about the media's role in a democracy that "a popular government, without popular information, or the means of acquiring it, is but a prologue to a farce or a tragedy; or perhaps both."[1] One hundred years later, political columnist Walter Lippmann wrote, "The press is no substitute for institutions. It is like the beam of a searchlight that moves restlessly about, bringing one episode and then another out of darkness into vision."[2]

Because the media are the main source of information in all Western countries, it is important to examine who owns the media and how well journalists, working within that system of ownership, fulfill their responsibility of reporting on events. How well does today's system of media ownership with a high degree of concentration of ownership and control allow the media to bring the important and necessary "popular information" to the people? How well do journalists shine that searchlight to bring "one episode and then another out of darkness into vision," as Lippmann described? That is what this chapter is about.

Ownership: Who Controls the Messages?

In some media industries, ownership is distributed among more companies today than in the 1950s. There are six major movie studios located in the United States today, several of which are owned directly or indirectly by non-American corporations, compared to the Big Five of the 1940s; the number of companies that own broadcast stations has increased since the 1940s, and so has the number of magazine publishers. The number of companies that publish newspapers and the number of companies that produce records, however, have both declined—in the case of newspapers, dramatically so.

Overall, media ownership has been contracting rather than expanding since its heyday in the 1960s. The emergence of some new media, such as cable TV (and with it non-broadcast television specialty channels), is inviting more people into the media business, but the trend is for fewer companies to own more media businesses and for fewer companies to own more aspects of the media business. Neither the FCC in the United States nor the CRTC in Canada has shown much inclination to reverse the trend of corporate concentration. In Canada, this remains the case despite the fact that authoritative studies in the past—the Senate Committee on the Media, which issued *The Davey Report*, and the Kent Commission on Newspaper Ownership—suggested that corporate concentration in the mass media was a negative development.

Here is some media ownership information compiled from previous chapters, with some new facts added. (See also Table 13.1 and Impact/Point of View, "The Next Corporate Media Order" on page 275.)

◎ One conglomerate, Hollinger-Southam, controls 43 percent of all Canadian newspaper circulation. Adding the Thomson papers brings the proportion to 55 percent for these two corporate empires combined. In the United States, the top 10 corporations own only 20 percent of the dailies.

◎ Almost all of the movies shown on Canadian screens are distributed by one of the six large U.S. studios.

◎ The majority of recording company profits are collected from six major labels, two of which (MCA and Polygram) have recently combined.

◎ Nearly 9 out of 10 computers sold in 1997 used the Microsoft Windows operating system.[3]

T a b l e   1 3 . 1

Top 10 Canadian Media Companies in 1997		
Rank	**Company**	**1997 assets ($billion)**
1	Thomson*	US$13.3
2	Rogers***	US$6.0
3	Quebecor*	C$7.9
4	Hollinger**	US$3.0
5	Videotron*	C$2.9
6	Shaw*	C$2.5
7	CBC*	C$1.7
8	TorStar*	C$1.4
9	Southam*	C$1.1
10	WIC*	C$0.7

Note: Hollinger and Southam assets are both effectively controlled by the same management structure headed by Conrad Black.

Sources: *   annual report of the company
              **   U.S. Securities and Exchange Commission Form 10K public filings
              *** Standard and Poor's

Media Concentration

Media concentration involves four trends:

1. *Concentration of ownership* within one industry, such as print and broadcast chain ownership and broadcast network affiliation.

2. *Cross-media ownership*—companies that own more than one type of medium.

3. *Conglomerate ownership*—companies that own media properties and that are involved in businesses other than the media business.

4. *Vertical integration*—companies that control several aspects of a single media industry, such as production and distribution. (See Chapter 1 for more information about these categories.)

IMPACT

Point of View

THE NEXT CORPORATE MEDIA ORDER

By Ken Auletta

Consider the spider: a spider has four pairs of legs, as many as eight eyes, and jaws and a pair of pincers on the underside of the head; sometimes, after mating, female spiders devour their mates. The fluid from a spider's silk glands is spun into a web. When a spider moves, the entire web sways.

Now consider six of the world's most potent communications companies: Time Warner, the Walt Disney Company (which owns ABC), the News Corporation, Microsoft, General Electric (with its NBC unit), and Tele-Communications, Inc., or TCI (with its Liberty Media Group).

Like spiders, these companies compete by devouring others of their kind, and by spinning ever bigger webs—webs to cover all of communications, from owning ideas, through owning factories that manufacture the ideas as products, to owning the means of distributing those products, and on to owning their afterlife. While the companies continue to do battle with one another, however, they increasingly collaborate, and the result is a horizontal web of joint partnerships....

Competition & Collaboration

[The chart] shows how six major media companies often operate in the same areas of technology and entertainment, either directly or through companies in which they have investments. Normally, that would lead to competition among them, but these six companies are finding that one good way to do business is to collaborate.... The six giants often rely on one another.

Ken Auletta, "The Next Corporate Order: American Keiretsu," The New Yorker, October 20–27, 1997, pp. 225–227. Reprinted by permission of International Creative Management, Inc. Copyright © 1997 Ken Auletta.

	Microsoft	Disney/ABC	Time Warner	GE/NBC	TCI	News Corp.
Cable	■	■	■	■	■	■
TV and film production	■	■	■	■	■	■
Internet technology	■	■	■	■	■	■
Internet content	■	■	■	■	■	■
Home video, interactive programs, and games	■	■	■	■	■	■
Sports teams and venues	■	■	■	■	■	■
Satellite	■		■	■	■	■
Newspapers, magazines, and books	■	■	■	■		■
Telephone and wireless communications	■	■	■	■	■	
TV broadcasting and stations	■	■	■	■		■
Music and records	■	■	■		■	
Theme parks and stores	■	■				■

More than 30 years ago, *New Yorker* press critic A.J. Liebling warned about the danger of one-newspaper towns:

> As the number of cities … with only a single newspaper ownership increases, news becomes increasingly nonessential to the newspaper. In the mind of the average publisher, it is a costly and uneconomic frill, like the free lunch that saloons used to furnish to induce customers to buy beer.… With the years, the quantity of news in newspapers is bound to diminish from its present low. The proprietor, as Chairman of the Board, will increasingly often say that he would like to spend 75 cents now and then on news coverage but that he must be fair to his shareholders.[4]

Today, only about 2 percent of U.S. cities have competing newspapers. This is generally true of Canadian cities and towns, as well, though there may be "competing" papers published by the same company (i.e., *The Vancouver Sun* and the *Province*, both owned by Pacific Press). Gaps in local markets are filled by national newspapers such as the *Globe and Mail* or the new *National Post* in Canada, and *USAToday* in the United States. Toronto stands out in that it has five dailies.

Liebling's fears could apply to all forms of ownership concentration. The issue of concentration centres on one question, what former newspaper editor Norman E. Isaacs calls "the internal war between public purpose and making money" and what the book publishing industry calls the war between "culture and commerce."

"For an author, the increased concentration means decreased access to the market and fewer outlets for publication," write economists Michael J. Robinson and Ray Olszewski, summarizing statements made by the Authors Guild about concentration in the publishing industry. "Its impact on the marketplace for ideas … is to introduce the risk of corporate pressure being placed on editors and on the production process, pressure that would not be a problem with the existence of independent companies. Mergers and acquisitions reduce the number of diverse and antagonistic sources."[5]

In the advertising business, some executives are even more candid. "It's big for big's sake," said one advertising executive. "Advertising is really a personal service," said a second ad executive, "and the bigger it gets, the more impersonal it becomes."[6]

Competition and Convergence

Today's media companies are profit-centred. They are also driven by convergence (the melding of the communications, computer, and electronics industries described in Chapter 1) to seek business alliances that will help them compete in the next century. Media companies are owned by people who want to make money. As in all industries, there are people who want to make money quickly and people who take the long-term view about profits, but certainly none of them wants to lose money.

Traditionally, making money has been a goal supported by a clear majority of people. But the way these companies make money is the debate. Does the legacy of press freedom protection for news-gathering organizations mean that they have a special responsibility to provide the information people need in a democracy? Should entertainment-producing companies provide a diversity of cultural outlets for creativity? Will the adoption of corporate values benefit or harm the mass media industries?

Why Media Properties Are Selling

Turnover in ownership is highest in the newspaper and broadcast industries. Several factors have affected the market for these properties.

1. Newspaper and broadcast properties are attractive investments. Many report profits of 10 percent a year, which is about double the profit for the average manufacturing company, and some report much higher profits of up to 20 percent.

2. Newspapers, broadcast stations, and especially cable franchises are scarce commodities. Because the number of newspapers has been declining, the number of broadcast stations is government-regulated, and the number of cable franchises is essentially fixed, only so many properties are available. As with all limited commodities, this makes them attractive.

3. Many newspapers, especially, have gone through a cycle of family ownership. If the heirs to the founders of the business are not interested in joining the company, the only way for them to collect their inheritance is to sell the newspaper.

4. Newspapers and broadcast stations are easier to buy than to create. Because these businesses require huge investments in equipment, they are expensive to start up.

5. In broadcasting, the major factor that encouraged ownership changes in the 1980s was deregulation. This allowed companies that had never been in the broadcast business, or whose interests were purely regional before, to enter the industry using bank loans to pay for most of their investment. But deregulation had other effects, too. In the 1990s, the introduction of new technologies changed the economics of the industry.

Some new owners of media companies approach broadcast properties as they would any other business—hoping to invest the minimum amount necessary. They hope to hold onto the property until the market is favourable and then sell at a huge profit.

Advantages of Concentration

Supporters of concentrated ownership say that a large company can bring advantages that a small company could never afford—training for the employees, higher wages, and better working conditions. John C. Quinn, executive vice president for news for Gannett, says:

> A publisher's instinct for good or evil is not determined by the number of newspapers he owns. A group can attract top professional talent, offering training under a variety of editors, advancement through a variety of opportunities.... It can invest in research and

development and nuts-and-bolts experience necessary to translate the theories of new technology into the practical production of better newspapers.

Concentrated ownership can provide great resources; only independent, local judgment can use the resources to produce a responsible and responsive local newspaper. That measure cannot be inflated by competition nor can it be diluted by monopoly.[7]

William A. Henry III of *Time* magazine, who won a Pulitzer Prize at the *Boston Globe*, pointed out that several of the newspapers that are considered the best in the United States—*The New York Times*, the *Los Angeles Times*, and the *Washington Post*—are chain newspapers, although he acknowledged that these three are still dominated by family owners who hold the majority of stock. This is true, as well, of TorStar in Toronto, in which the Honderich family is still present.

The same arguments that are made against chain ownership can be made against independent ownership, Henry said.

Most independent owners run papers in ways that comfort them, their friends and their general social class.

A great many reporters have gotten into trouble over the years by going after buddies or business associates of the owners. And a great many more have compromised themselves by writing puffy, uncritical pieces about cultural institutions, department stores, restaurants or socialites favored by the owner or his spouse.[8]

Disadvantages of Concentration

The major arguments of those who support concentration are that a corporation can offer financial support to a small newspaper or broadcast station and that responsible, autonomous local management is the key to successful group ownership. Yet, chain newspapers seem more likely to support the favoured candidates in elections, and in major elections most if not all of the papers in a chain endorse the same candidate.

This is an example of the consequences of corporate control that forms the major argument against group ownership—that concentration limits the diversity of opinion and the quality of culture available to the public and reduces what scholars call **message pluralism**.

Former newspaper reporter Philip Weiss described what he says happens when corporate culture takes over journalism:

The problem with Gannett [newspapers] isn't simply its formula or its chairman, but the company's corporate culture. The product is the company—cheerful, superficial, self-promoting, suspicious of ideas, conformist, and implicitly authoritarian. But the Gannett story is more, too. For as many as 6 million daily readers, most of them in one-newspaper towns, Gannett serves as chief interpreter and informer about society—and does so unsustained by ideals of independence or thoroughness.[9]

The loss of message pluralism in television angers critics the most, since broadcasting still is licensed to serve the public interest. Broadcasters argue that this requirement is out of date because it was adopted when broadcast outlets were scarce. Today, broadcasters say many channels of information are available to the public.

But Ben H. Bagdikian, Dean Emeritus, Graduate School of Journalism at the University of California, Berkeley, describes how the loss of message pluralism can affect every aspect of communication:

> It has always been assumed that a newspaper article might be expanded to a magazine article which could become the basis for a hardcover book, which, in turn, could be a paperback, and then, perhaps a TV series and finally, a movie. At each step of change an author and other enterprises could compete for entry into this array of channels for reaching the public mind and pocketbook. But today several media giants own these arrays, not only closing off entry points for competition in different media, but influencing the choice of entry at the start.[10]

Press Performance: How Well Do Journalists Do Their Jobs?

Because the constitutional documents of most Western countries prescribe freedom of the press, it is important to examine how well the press uses that freedom to report on events. To understand how well the press performs, you must first understand who journalists are and how they work. Then you can examine how the public feels about the way members of the press do their job.

The latest study of just who journalists are comes from *The American Journalist in the 1990s*, by David H. Weaver and G. Cleveland Wilhoit, published in 1992 to update a similar study they conducted in 1986. In 1992, Weaver and Wilhoit surveyed 1400 U.S. journalists about their jobs. According to the 1992 study, today's "typical" journalist "is a white Protestant male who has a bachelor's degree from a public college, is married, 36 years old, earns about $31 000 a year, has worked in journalism about 12 years, does not belong to a journalism association, and works for a medium-sized (42 journalists), group-owned daily newspaper."[11]

Weaver and Wilhoit cautioned, however, that this typical portrait is misleading because there are:

> substantial numbers of women, non-Whites, non-Protestant, single, young and old, and relatively rich and poor journalists working in this country for a wide variety of small and large news media, both group and singly owned.

> Many of these journalists differ from this profile of the typical journalist. For example, Black and Asian journalists are more likely to be women than men, not to be married, to have higher incomes ($37,000–$42,000) than the typical journalist, to have worked in journalism 10 or 11 years, to be members of at least one journalism association, and to work for larger (100–150 journalists) daily newspapers.

> Hispanic journalists are more likely to be Catholic than Protestant, and to be more similar to Blacks and Asians than to the "typical" U.S. journalist on other characteristics. Aboriginal journalists are more likely to be of some other religion besides Protestant or

Getting the story and getting the story faster and better than the competition are major factors influencing journalistic values.

CP Picture Archive (Khue Bui)

Catholic, to make much less than the other groups (median income of $22,000) and to work for very small newspapers or television stations (3 or 4 journalists).

Following are some other important findings of the 1992 study:

1. *Employment growth stalls.* The substantial growth in the number of journalists working for the media that characterized the 1970s has stalled. The growth rate from 1982 to 1992 was 9 percent. Between 1971 and 1982, the growth rate was 60 percent.
2. *Minorities make some gains.* News organizations have made some progress in attracting minorities, despite the lack of growth in journalism jobs. The current minority news workforce of 8 percent is up from 4 percent in 1982–83.... Recent hires are 12 percent minorities.
3. *Mixed gains for women.* In spite of more women being hired in the 1980s, they remain at the same workforce percentage as a decade ago: 34 percent. The problem may be one of retention, as well as poor job growth. Salary equity with men has improved.
4. *Abandoning ship.* A serious retention problem in journalism may be just over the horizon. More than 20 percent of those surveyed said they plan to leave the field within five years. That's twice the figure in 1982–83. This is tied to a significant decline in job satisfaction, with complaints about pay and the need for a different challenge leading the list of major reasons for plans to leave journalism.
5. *Little shift in journalistic values.* Overall differences in ideas about journalistic roles and reporting practices are not great.... Two journalistic responsibilities seen as extremely important by a majority: getting information to the public quickly and investigating government claims.[12]

It has not been shown in any comprehensive survey of news gathering that people with liberal or conservative values insert their personal ideology directly into their reporting and that the audience unquestioningly accepts one point of view. The belief in a causal relationship between the media and the audience's behaviour is known as the magic bullet theory. This belief was disproved long ago (see Chapter 12).

But the assumption that journalists' personal beliefs directly influence their professional performance is common. Although the reporting by some journalists and columnists can certainly be cited to support this idea, the majority of journalists, says media scholar Herbert J. Gans, view themselves as detached observers of events:

> Journalists, like everyone else, have values, [and] the two that matter most in the newsroom are getting the story and getting it better and faster than their prime competitors—both among their colleagues and at rival news media. Personal political beliefs are left at home, not only because journalists are trained to be objective and detached, but also because their credibility and their paychecks depend on their remaining detached....
>
> The beliefs that actually make it into the news are professional values that are intrinsic to national journalism and that journalists learn on the job. However, the professional values that particularly antagonize conservatives (and liberals when they are in power) are neither liberal nor conservative but reformist, reflecting journalism's long adherence to good-government Progressivism.[13]

Some press critics, in fact, argue that journalists most often present establishment viewpoints and are unlikely to challenge prevailing political and social values.[14] In addition, the pressure to come up with instant analyses of news events may lead to conformity in reporting.

In mid-May 1989, for example, thousands of people gathered in Tiananmen Square to demonstrate against the Chinese government. Angered by the demonstrations, the government sent troops to clear the square, and hundreds of people were killed and injured, most of them students. In his analysis of the way the press reported on the violence, press critic David Shaw argued that journalists misread and misreported events as a pro-democracy uprising that could not be stopped. Shaw called this "consensus journalism"—the tendency among many journalists covering the same event to report similar conclusions about the event, rather than to report conflicting interpretations.

"Since you have already been convicted by the media, I imagine we can wrap this up pretty quickly."

Journalists' News Values

News organizations often are criticized for presenting a consistently slanted view of the news. But as Weaver and Wilhoit observed, news values often are shaped by the way news organizations are structured and the routines they follow. The press, it is generally agreed, don't tell you what to think but do tell you what and whom to think about. This is called **agenda-setting**.

There are two types of agenda-setting: the flow of information from one news organization to another and the agenda of information that flows from news organizations to their audiences.

In the first type of agenda-setting, the stories that appear in the widely circulated print media provide ideas to the other media. The print media, for example, often identify specific stories as important by giving them attention, so that widely circulated print media can set the news agenda on some national issues.

To analyze the second type of agenda-setting—the picture of the world that journalists give to their audiences—is to examine the social and cultural values that journalists present to the public. The most significant recent study of news values was offered by Herbert J. Gans in his book *Deciding What's News*.

Gans identified eight enduring values that emerged in his study of different types of news stories over a long period of time: **ethnocentrism** (the attitude that some cultural and social values are superior), altruistic democracy, responsible capitalism, small-town pastoralism, individualism, moderatism, order, and leadership. These values, said Gans, often help define what is considered news.

The news conveys the ideas of:

Ethnocentrism. The reporter's nation is to be valued above all others. "While the news contains many stories that are critical of domestic conditions, they are almost always treated as deviant cases, with the implication that American ideas, at least, remain viable," says Gans.

Altruistic democracy. Politics should be based on public service and the public interest. The news media expect all public officials to be scrupulously honest, efficient, and public-spirited.

The National Post: a new Canadian voice or just more of the same?

CP Picture Archive (Frank Gunn)

Responsible capitalism. Open competition will create increased prosperity for everyone. Business people should not seek unreasonable profits, and they should not exploit workers or customers.

Small-town pastoralism. Small agricultural or market towns are favoured over other settlements. Suburbs are usually overlooked as a place where news happens. Big cities are viewed as places with "urban" problems.

Individualism. A heroic individual is someone who struggles against difficulties and powerful forces. Self-made people are to be admired.

Moderatism. Moderation is valued, excesses and extremism are not.

Order. Importance is placed on political order. "The values in the news derive largely from reformers and reform movements, which are themselves elites. Still, the news is not simply a compliant support of elites, or the establishment, or the ruling class; rather, it views nation and society through its own set of values and with its own conception of the good social order."

Leadership. Attention is focused on leaders.[15]

These values exist throughout society and, indeed, come from historical assumptions derived from shared cultural experiences. As Gans suggests, this news ideology both supports and reflects elements of the social order.

Blurring Distinctions: News, Reality Shows, and Advertising

Today's TV reality shows, such as *Cops, Real Stories of the Highway Patrol,* and *America's Most Wanted* are blurring the distinction between what is news and what is re-created drama. These shows portray events and use interviews with crime victims and re-enactments of events in a documentary style that imitates news stories. These reality shows, or docudramas, can make it difficult for an audience to distinguish true news footage when they see it.

"Infomercials"—programs that pretend to give viewers information but that are really advertisements for the sponsors' products—also are making it harder to discern what is reporting and what is advertising. The line between news and entertainment on television becomes even more tricky when advertisers produce programs that look like news but are really advertisements.

In 1994, the Walt Disney Company produced an entertainment news segment that looked just like a TV newscast (see Impact on You, "News versus Advertising" on page 284). The effect of this merging of entertainment and news, as well as the entertaining graphics and the lighthearted presentation style of most local TV newscasts, are making it more difficult for viewers to separate fact from fiction, reality from re-enactment, and news from advertising. The result could be a decline in the audience's trust in television news to deliver accurate information.

The Public's Reception of the Press

Two astute observers of the press who have been critical of its performance are James Reston and Norman Corwin. "The truth is that most American newspaper people are really more interested in dramatic spot news, the splashy story, than in anything else," said *New York Times* columnist James Reston. "They want to be in on the big blowout, no matter how silly, and would rather write about what happened than whether it made any sense."[16]

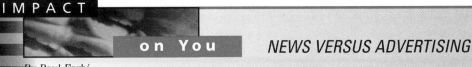

IMPACT

on You   *NEWS VERSUS ADVERTISING*

By Paul Farhi

Disney Blurs the Line Between Ballyhoo and Broadcasting

With its desk-bound anchorman and on-air celebrity interviews, *Movie News* looks just like the entertainment news segment of a TV newscast.

A recent installment, for example, took viewers behind the scenes in the making of three films, *The Lion King,* the Julia Roberts-Nick Nolte thriller *I Love Trouble,* and the Penny Marshall-directed comedy *Renaissance Man.*

The segment is so polished, in fact, that viewers might not realize that *Movie News* isn't really news—but a cleverly conceived commercial. *Movie News* was bought and paid for by Walt Disney Co. to promote the aforementioned releases from its Disney, Touchstone and Hollywood Pictures studios, respectively.

Like "advertorials" and "infomercials," Disney's new ads blur the lines between genuine news and corporate promotion. Such ads, in effect, hope to catch consumers with their guards down, adopting the urgent tone and implied journalistic detachment and credibility of news while down-playing or disguising the hard sell.

Movie News, for example, gives little hint of its true origins. Only at the end of the 60-second spot does a line flash briefly on the screen reading, "Paid for by Buena Vista." Say what? Buena Vista is Disney's distribution company.

For extra confusion, Disney is running the ads during breaks in late-night news, as well as other times.

The Disney ad "makes me uncomfortable" because of its potential to confuse viewers, said

David Bartlett, president of the Radio and Television News Directors Association. "Anytime I see an advertisement that is so slick that you can't figure out that it's actually a commercial makes me nervous." Even Bartlett said he needed two viewings of *Movie News* before he realized what he was seeing.

Disney declined to comment, saying it does not discuss marketing issues.

Washington Post, July 5, 1994, Dow//Quest ID#0000108771WP. © 1998, the Washington Post. Reprinted with permission.

Broadcast producer and writer Norman Corwin said about local television news people:

> The average local newscast, almost everywhere in the country, is a kind of succotash served in dollops and seasoned by bantering between anchorpersons, sportspersons, weatherpersons and person-persons. And these people had better be good-looking, sparkling or cute—weathermen with party charm, anchorladies with good teeth and smart coiffures, sportscasters with macho charisma. It doesn't matter if they have a news background or not.[17]

Reston and Corwin are members of the media who are critical of their own profession. The public's perception of how well members of the press perform their responsibility is equally important; only recently have the media begun to survey the public for their opinions about the news media.

Since 1986 Times Mirror has sponsored several ongoing studies of the public's feelings about the press conducted by the Gallup organization. For these surveys, Gallup has personally interviewed 1000 to 3021 people and then doubled back to ask the same respondents additional questions to clarify earlier findings.

Among the findings of these surveys, which Times Mirror calls *The People & the Press*, are the following:

◎ By a ratio of 4 to 1, the people who were surveyed said that the major news organizations—*The Wall Street Journal, CBS News, ABC News, NBC News, Newsweek*, and *Time*—are believable.

◎ 79 percent of the people surveyed said that news organizations "care about how good a job they do"; 72 percent said the press is "highly professional."

◎ In 1989, a majority (54 percent) said reporters get the facts straight; 44 percent said the press was often inaccurate. The inaccuracy rating has increased 10 percent since 1985 (see Figure 13.1).

◎ In 1989, more than two-thirds of the people (68 percent) said that journalists tend to favour one side, compared to 53 percent who felt the press were biased in 1985 (see Figure 13.1).

◎ The press is "pretty independent," according to 33 percent of the people, but 62 percent said the press is "often influenced by the powerful," including the federal government, big business, advertisers, and special-interest groups.

◎ 77 percent of the people interviewed in 1989 said that the press invades people's privacy. This was the most widely held criticism among the people surveyed.

◎ The people who have negative opinions about the press are those who consume the most news and are among the most vocal and powerful segments of society.[18]

Figure 13.1

The Public Rates the Press

Accuracy of News Organizations
Question: In general, do you think news organizations get the facts straight, or do you think that their stories and reports are often inaccurate?

Fairness of News Organizations
Question: In presenting the news dealing with political and social issues, do you think that news organizations deal fairly with all sides, or do they tend to favour one side?

Source: Data from *The People & the Press*, 1989.

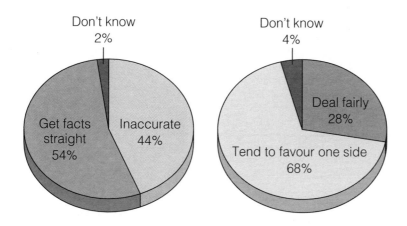

These surveys are the most comprehensive of their kind undertaken to date. They show that members of the public seem to support the press as an institution, but with specific misgivings about the way journalists do their job. It is also important to note that the people who pay the most attention to the news are the most critical about how the press performs.

After the first survey appeared, Times Mirror received nearly 8000 letters from people commenting on the results. One person wrote: "No question: No free press, no democracy. They go together like pie and ice cream." But a second person wrote, "Does a free press strengthen democracy? Absolutely, but it must be a *responsible press*. It must be *honest*. It must have *integrity*. And it must be willing to admit its mistakes as *loudly* as it claims its triumphs."[19]

IMPACT

Point of View

CANADA'S CULTURE CLASH

By John Geddes

Copps Fears That New Trade Rules May Threaten Homegrown Arts

On the afternoon before Canada Day, CBC president Perrin Beatty sat in his Ottawa office straining his voice to be heard over *Getting' Jiggy Wit It,* the infectious hit song by U.S. movie star and hip-hop recording artist Will Smith. The beat pulsating from Beatty's desktop computer was blasted out over the Internet by Radio VBC in Vladivostok. He makes a habit of checking out the growing number of stations around the world— including the CBC's own. An American song, on a Russian station, over a medium beyond the reach of Canadian regulators— what better background music for Beatty's musing on how technology is fast rendering old cultural protection policies obsolete?

He contends that even a public broadcaster must now rely on its ability to succeed in the marketplace if it is to survive and thrive. "If anybody wants to build an electronic wall around Canada," he said, "there is no wall high enough or thick enough that it can't be leapt by a satellite or pierced by a fibre-optic cable."

As Beatty spoke, Canadian Heritage Minister Sheila Copps was across town wrapping up two days of meetings on much the same theme with 20 culture ministers, representing countries from Brazil to Britain. Their common denominator: shared misgivings about the seductive onslaught of U.S. movies, television and music. No American politician was invited to attend. The ministers pledged to form a permanent network to try to prevent their national cultures from

being steamrolled by global trade and economic forces. Copps told *Maclean's* that she hopes the summit sowed the seeds for cultural institutions that will someday grow to parallel the powerful bodies, such as the World Trade Organization, that hold sway over global commerce.

"Globalization is a fact of life," she said. "But it has come on us so rapidly that on the cultural side we don't have any international instruments to deal with it."

Maclean's, July 13, 1998, 26–27.
Reprinted with permission.

Understanding Media Ownership and Press Performance

The media system described by Walter Lippmann and James Madison at the beginning of this chapter delivers a diversity of messages and opinions to an alert and informed public that uses this information to make intelligent decisions. The real question is, however, whether the present degree of corporate concentration is compatible with such a system. When concentration and activist management by the owners go hand in hand, the potential for oppressive manipulation of the customer is very real.

Media ownership that becomes concentrated in a few corporations can and does limit the society's access to "popular information, or the means of acquiring it" that Madison foresaw as an essential part of democratic government. A press that does not fulfill its public duty as "the beam of a search-light," which Lippmann described, risks losing the freedom that constitutional documents promise to protect.

To maintain the public's trust, the owners of media companies and members of the press must be willing to undergo constant scrutiny about whether they are meeting their responsibilities. A critical view of ownership issues and press performance issues is important because the media were founded in the belief that the press will perform conscientiously and that the public will have access to a variety of ideas and opinions through diverse media outlets.

In Focus

◎ Ownership issues centre around: (1) concentration; (2) cross-media ownership; (3) conglomerate ownership; and (4) vertical integration.

◎ Media properties are selling rapidly because they are attractive investments; they are scarce commodities; they are easier to buy than to launch; many newspapers have gone through a cycle of family ownership; and broadcast deregulation has lifted many restrictions.

◎ The major arguments of people who support concentration are that a corporation can offer financial support and that responsible local management is the key to successful group ownership.

◎ The major argument against group ownership is that concentration limits the diversity of opinion and the quality of culture available to the public—the loss of message pluralism.

◎ The *American Journalist* study (1992) indicates that today's "typical" journalist is a 36-year-old Protestant white male with a bachelor's degree, is married and has children, does not belong to a journalism association, and earns about $31 000 a year.

◎ Consensus journalism is the tendency of journalists covering the same event to report similar conclusions about the event, rather than to report conflicting interpretations.

◎ The press in North America doesn't tell you what to think. It *does* tell you what and whom to think *about*. This is called agenda-setting.

◎ There are two types of agenda-setting: the flow of information from one news organization to another (the broadcast media, for example, often develop stories that first appeared in the print media) and the flow of information from news organizations to their audiences.

◎ Herbert J. Gans, in his book *Deciding What's News*, identified eight enduring news values: ethnocentrism, altruistic democracy, responsible capitalism, small-town pastoralism, individualism, moderatism, order, and leadership.

◎ *The People & the Press* survey sponsored by the *Los Angeles Times* found that most people believe that news organizations care about how well they do their jobs; more than two-thirds of the people surveyed said journalists tend to favour one side; 62 percent felt that the press is influenced by special interests; 77 percent of the people felt the press invades people's privacy; people who consume the most news also are most critical of the press's performance.

◎ The merging of entertainment and news is making it more difficult for TV viewers to separate fact from fiction, reality from re-enactment, and news from advertising.

Review Questions

1. Define the following and give an example of each from the text:

   a. concentration of ownership

   b. cross-media ownership

   c. conglomerate ownership

   d. vertical integration

2. Discuss the ways that deregulation and re-regulation have affected broadcast programming.

3. List three of the major criticisms the public makes about the press, according to the Gallup survey *The People & the Press*. Do you agree or disagree? Why?

4. Define consensus journalism and explain some of the reasons that journalists practise it. Do they do this consciously? Why or why not?

5. Define the two types of "agenda-setting" and explain some of the problems associated with this practice.

Watching the Web

◎ **American Society of Newspaper Editors Minority Employment Report**

http:www.asne.org/kiosk/diversity/97minsrv.htm

◎ **An Appraisal of Technologies of Political Control**

http://jya.com/atpc.htm

◎ **Diversity in Electronic Media**

http://www.mediaaccess.org/program/diversity/index.html

◎ **Corporate Watch**

http://www.corpwatc.org/

◎ **Cross-Media Ownership Rules Campaign**

http://www.alliance.aust.com/CMOC/

◎ **FAIR-Fairness and Accuracy in Reporting**

http://www.fair.org/

◎ **Investigative Journalism on the Internet**

http://www.vir.com/~sher/julian.htm

LAW AND REGULATION

14

EVERYONE HAS THE FOLLOWING FUNDAMENTAL FREEDOMS: (A) FREEDOM OF CONSCIENCE AND RELIGION, (B) FREEDOM OF THOUGHT, BELIEF, OPINION, AND EXPRESSION, INCLUDING FREEDOM OF THE PRESS AND OTHER MEDIA OF COMMUNICATION; (C) FREEDOM OF PEACEFUL ASSEMBLY; AND (D) FREEDOM OF ASSOCIATION.

Section 2, Fundamental Freedoms, Constitution Act, 1982, Part I

The media are, with few exceptions, businesses operating to make a profit, but these businesses enjoy a special trust under the constitutional documents and legal practice of most Western countries. The legal and regulatory issues faced by the media are attempts by governments to balance this special trust with (1) the interests of individuals and community groups and (2) the interests of government.

Freedom of the Press

Freedom of the press as a legal concept has existed since the late 18th century, initially as part of the constitution of the United States (First Amendment, 1791), then as part of the French constitution (also in 1791), and subsequently in the laws of most Western countries, including Canada. In a sense, these guarantees remain philosophical since the press cannot publish what it does not know and need not publish what it does. The ability of governments, corporations, and individuals to withhold information from the press has, if anything, grown with the passing years. Privacy legislation, for instance, helps individuals to keep much personal information from the public.

There have also been important compromises in interpreting freedom of the press to exclude, for example, details of ongoing court cases (especially those involving juveniles) and matters of state security (in the United Kingdom the "D Notice" served on an editor was once enough to prohibit publication of information that the government deemed harmful to national security). Also exempt are information on members of the public (tax returns are confidential in most countries), statements that incite hatred, and certain types of pornography. The theory behind such cases is that freedom of speech and publication should be curtailed in the interests of higher community goals. Yet there has always been tension between privacy concerns, standards of public discourse, and the right to know.

Media Law and Policy in Canada

Media activities intersect with the law in a number of ways:

◎ The Canadian Charter of Rights and Freedoms asserts the freedom to communicate, to own media enterprises, and to collect, receive, and impart information.

◎ The courts, Parliament, and commissions of inquiry may compel Canadian journalists to disclose their sources.

◎ The media can publish the names of adults charged with a criminal offence but may not mention confessions until the trial is ended. Courts may also impose a ban on the reporting of evidence during the course of the trial. The ban is lifted after the trial has concluded.

◎ Access to information regulations exist at both federal and provincial levels, and the media may appeal refusals of access requests in court.

◎ To protect personal privacy, information collected for government purposes is confidential (e.g., census returns, tax returns).

◎ Civil defamation laws protect the reputation of individuals by giving legal recourse to those who feel their reputation has been damaged. Radio and television commentary might be considered slander since it is delivered verbally, albeit by broadcast, whereas libels are printed. Defamations include libel and slander—statements that derogate an individual's character but not that of a group or class..

◎ Communication of materials promoting hatred of groups or classes of individuals is subject to criminal prosecution.

◎ The Criminal Code restricts the production and dissemination of obscene materials, especially those involving children (where possession is an offence).

◎ Copyright, trademark, and patent registration and enforcement protects media products.

◎ Reporting requirements compel public companies, especially those whose shares trade publicly, to disclose corporate information. These requirements apply to the large media corporations. Even more rigorous requirements apply to Canadian corporations whose shares trade in the United States. They must file the Securities and Exchange Commission's form 10K.

◎ Employment laws protect most employees, including journalists, from unfair labour practices, including termination without cause.

◎ Canadian competition law seeks to prevent the abuse of monopoly powers by corporations.

◎ Specific regulatory bodies monitor the media (e.g., the CRTC).

◎ Crown corporations directly foster certain kinds of media activities (e.g., the National Film Board, Telefilm Canada, Telesat Canada, the Canadian Broadcasting Corporation, and provincially owned broadcast networks).

◎ Support is available for cultural industries, including publication subsidies and favourable tax treatment of cultural industries. These mechanisms seek to regulate the level of foreign cultural products in Canada and to promote Canadian culture.

Censorship

Various media industries historically have reacted differently to threats of **censorship**, the practice of suppressing material that is considered morally, politically, or otherwise objectionable. Most threats of censorship concern matters of morality, especially obscenity. Censorship is almost always an issue after the fact. Once the material is printed or displayed, it can be judged obscene and therefore censored. The motion picture and recording industries have accepted some form of self-regulation to avoid government intervention. The electronic media are governed by the criminal law in what they can and cannot transmit.

Print media have been the most vigorous defenders of the right to publish. The print media, of course, were the earliest media to be threatened with censorship, beginning with the philosopher Plato, who suggested in 387 BC that Homer's *Odyssey* be expurgated for immature readers.

Wartime Censorship

Wartime censorship applied to the press (through a special bureau of censorship) and to personal letters to and from military personnel. Letters were either cut up or lines blacked out to remove information of potential value to the enemy. This information could be as routine as the name of a geographic feature, which could allow a reader to deduce where the writer was located.

Censorship of Political Ideas

The publications of disfavoured political groups have also been subject to government censorship from time to time. For instance, the Quebec government of Maurice Duplessis passed legislation in 1937 that allowed it to shut down publications of the Communist Party. Before the legislation was repealed in 1957, the Quebec government used the "Padlock Law" to shut down left-wing newspapers and restrict the activities of the Jehovah's Witnesses religious group.

The government of Canada also censored the press during the FLQ crisis in 1970, when it enforced the War Measures Act and censored printing of the FLQ Manifesto. Although the government directed this action at the kidnappers of British consul James Cross and Quebec cabinet minister Pierre Laporte, it applied control of the press across the country and threatened student newspapers such as *the Varsity*, at the University of Toronto, with prosecution for disobeying the directive.

Several times in U.S. history before 1964, the federal government felt threatened enough by press freedom to attempt to restrict it. Probably the most memorable of these major moves challenging the First Amendment protection of free speech came in the late 1940s and early 1950s, culminating with the

Senator Joseph McCarthy explains his theory of communism during the Army–McCarthy hearings. Army counsel Joseph N. Welch, whose colleague had been declared subversive by McCarthy, is seated at the table.

The Bettmann Archive

actions of the House Un-American Activities Committee (HUAC) against the Hollywood Ten (see Chapter 8) and the Army–McCarthy hearings before the Permanent Subcommitee on Investigations, presided over by Senator Joseph R. McCarthy.

These congressional committees set a tone of aggressive Communist-hunting. When television broadcasts of McCarthy's investigation of Communist influence in the army and other reports eventually exposed his excesses, McCarthy's colleagues censured him by a vote of 67 to 22. But while the hearings were being held, they established a restrictive atmosphere that challenged free expression.

Customs Seizures

Sandra Bernstein has prepared a long chronicle of attempts to suppress the publication of information and artistic works in Canada which continues today in attempts to ban books as obscene.[1] The first incident on record was the banning of Balzac's *Droll Stories* by Canada Customs in 1914. For decades, Canada Customs had the right (and perhaps the obligation) to impound or turn back shipments of books and other publications that officers deemed to be obscene. Custom officers applied this practice in a seemingly haphazard manner over the years. At various times, both literature (e.g., D.H. Lawrence's *Lady Chatterley's Lover* and Norman Mailer's *The Naked and the Dead)* and pornographic magazines (e.g., *Penthouse*) have been seized by Customs. The same publications printed in Canada were exempt, since they were not subject to importation restrictions. James Joyce's *Ulysses* was on the prohibited importations list for 26 years. Companies or individuals might appeal to a tribunal of the Tariff Board to overturn Customs decisions, but this involved time and expense.

In Memorandum D9-1-1, distributed by Canada Customs in May 1985, all descriptions of gay and lesbian sexuality were deemed to be degrading and dehumanizing and therefore obscene. This directive has been subject to several "clarifications" over the years. In 1989, Canada Customs also attempted to ban Salmon Rushdie's *The Satanic Verses* for unspecified reasons, but it reversed the decision within 48 hours. Customs continues to maintain a "lookout list" of titles not permitted for importation. The focus has now shifted to child pornography.

IMPACT
Point of View

BETTER DEAD THAN READ? AN OPPOSING VIEW

In 1978, a committee in Huron County, Ontario, attempted to ban Margaret Laurence's The Diviners from school libraries. In a response to an article that supported the committee, Timothy Findley eloquently defended the right of authors to be free of censorship. Findley's words apply equally today, as debates over book censorship in schools continue in many parts of Canada.

By Timothy Findley

The whole of this current movement concerned with the censorship and banning of books, whether in schools or libraries or courts of law, is riddled with false moral indignation and fake concern for the hearts and minds of our children. It stems, in my opinion, from a truly evil manipulation of people's genuine fear and uncertainty about the world we live in. And the society we've created. And the children we've borne. The [censorship supporters] speak often of their children and of hopes for their moral and spiritual character. Well, those are the same concerns of the books these people want to ban and of the men and women who wrote them. Why are we so afraid of our own children that we want to close their hearts and minds to the fund of compassion they would find in these books? *Who Has Seen the Wind?*, *Lives of Girls and Women*, *The Diviners*, *One Day in the Life of Ivan Denisovitch*, *The Diary of Anne Frank*, *Huckleberry Finn*. The list goes on and on, and it grows and grows every year....

... Has nothing been learned? Of course, it has been argued that these books have "only been banned in the high schools. Anyone can read them after that." Wrong. Once banned in schools books will always be read without respect for their true qualitites. Even now children riffle the pages of these books wherever they may find them looking for "the dirty bits." This is not the book's fault. Nor the fault of its writer. It is the fault of those who have condemned the book as "obscene" or "pornographic" or "filled with profane language." Literature is being locked away with the truly obscene, as much as to imply that Margaret Laurence is an advocate of "child abuse." And this, of course, is nothing less than intellectual blasphemy.

It is an artist's privilege to see what others cannot see. Sometimes this is not a happy privilege. Sometimes what is seen is very hard to bear, and equally difficult to voice. But if it is the artist's privilege to see, it is also his job to tell what he sees. As W.H. Auden did, looking over his shoulder into Europe in 1939 and writing: "Intellectual disgrace stares from every human face, and the seas of pity lie locked and frozen in each eye."

These days, he wouldn't even have to look over his shoulder. But I don't want to close on that note, any more than Auden did. His poem, from which those lines are taken, was about the death of a poet, W.B. Yeats. Its last verse

makes a far better epigraph for the idea I have tried to express here, which is the idea that a false issue is being raised by people who, for motives of their own, want to prevent certain books from reaching the minds that most require them, minds that can make the future better than the present and infinitely better than the past. What Auden wrote is as fine a definition of the desired effect of an artist's work as anyone will ever give. And, like it or not Huron County, it applies to Margaret Laurence's *The Diviners*:

In the deserts of the heart,
Let the healing fountain start,
In the prison of his days
Teach the free man how to
    praise.

From Timothy Findley, "Better Dead Than Read? An Opposing View," Books in Canada (December 1978), pp. 3–5.

Photo courtesy HarperCollins Canada Ltd./Elizabeth Feryn

Censorship of Art and Film

Film censorship exists at the provincial level. Whole films have been denied an exhibition license (*I Am Curious Yellow* and Louis Malle's *Pretty Baby* in Ontario) or scenes were required to be cut before licensing (*The Tin Drum*).

There are ten different sets of provincial standards for the display of motion pictures. In practice, standards have been greatly relaxed in the last 20 years. However, the regulations remain in place.

Also subject to control are public exhibits of art, which might be charged as obscene under the Criminal Code or as exhibiting a disgusting object. Toronto police raided Eli Langer's exhibition at the Mercer Union gallery in 1993 and seized 35 drawings and 5 paintings. Langer and the gallery director were charged under the Criminal Code for exhibiting child pornography. These charges were ultimately dismissed, with the implication that this section of the Criminal Code would not withstand a constitutional rights challenge.

Prior Restraint

Prior restraint means censoring information before the information appears or is published. In an incident that never reached the courts but that was a type of prior restraint, the Reagan administration in 1983 kept reporters away from the island of Grenada, where the United States had launched a military offensive. This caused a press blackout beginning at 11 p.m. on October 24, 1983.

The administration didn't officially bar the press from covering the invasion, but the Pentagon refused to transport the press and then turned back press yachts and airplanes that attempted to enter the war zone. About a dozen print journalists and photographers were able to get in, but no television crews were allowed.

More than 400 journalists from 170 news organizations around the world who couldn't get to Grenada were left on Barbados, waiting for the news to get to them. Charles Lachman of the *New York Post* flew to Barbados, then to St. Vincent. Then he and some other reporters paid $6000 to charter a boat to Grenada. It was five days after the invasion when they arrived and discovered that one of the casualties of the military's action had been a hospital.[2]

News Blackouts and Press Pools

The Gulf War posed the toughest battleground yet for the rights of reporters versus the rights of the military to restrict access.

On Saturday, February 23, 1991, about three weeks into the Gulf War, the U.S. Defense Department announced the first total news blackout in U.S. military history. For 24 hours, defence leaders were told to issue no statements about the actions of U.S. troops. Military officials said that instantaneous transmission of information from the battlefield meant that live TV pictures could be picked up by Iraq. Press organizations protested the ban, but the military argued that modern communications technology necessitated the blackout.

Pentagon rules for war coverage, reached in cooperation with journalists, imposed stricter limits on reporting in the Persian Gulf than in any other U.S. war. Reporters had to travel in small "pools," escorted by public affairs officers. Every story produced by the pool was subject to military censorship. This system, called **pool reporting**, had been created in response to reporters' complaints about news blackouts during the Grenada incident. And an unprecedented number of journalists—1300 in Saudi Arabia alone—posed a challenge for military press officers.

In a commentary protesting the restrictions, *The New Yorker* magazine said, "The rules, it is clear, enable the Pentagon to promote coverage of subjects and events that it wishes publicized and to prevent reporting that might cast it, or the war, in a bad light."[3] Yet, in a *Los Angeles Times* poll of nearly 2000 people two weeks after the fighting started, 79 percent approved of the Pentagon's restrictions and 57 percent favoured even further limits.[4] When the war ended, many members of the U.S. press in the Middle East complained bitterly about their lack of access, but the military, and the public, seemed satisfied with the new rules for wartime coverage.

In Canada news blackouts are temporarily enforced in advance of the annual budget and during sensitive union bargaining sessions.

Libel Law

In Canada, the Criminal Code covers criminal libel, which includes seditious, blasphemous, and obscene libels that lower someone's reputation in the eyes of the public. In practice, criminal libel provisions are seldom, if ever, used. Most libels are dealt with as civil lawsuits under provincial legislation. Correctness in fact, fair comment, and privilege are acceptable defences against such a suit. Correctness is an absolute defence against a charge of libel in a civil suit for damages *except where malice is proven.*

In Quebec, the defendant in a libel suit must demonstrate the public benefit of the publication as well. Somewhat unusually, the burden of proof is placed on the accused, in what is called *reverse onus.* This means that the costs of defending a libel suit are imposed well in advance of a decision, as the defendant pays a steep "fine" in order to defend the suit. This has led to a climate of "libel chill"—authors and writers are hesitant to risk comments that might lead to a libel suit. The plaintiff hazards little in bringing a libel suit, since he or she is required only to demonstrate that the words were published, that they referred to the plaintiff, and that they could be considered defamatory (causing injury to the plaintiff's reputation). If a libel charge is upheld against a journalist, apologies and retractions can be substituted for a monetary award.

In the United States, true information, although sometimes damaging, cannot be considered libelous. Publishing true information, however, can still be an invasion of privacy. Furthermore, truth is a successful defense only if truth is proved to the satisfaction of a judge or jury. The U.S. press is free to report what is discussed during legislative and court proceedings, even though the information presented in the proceedings by witnesses and others may be untrue or damaging. This is called *qualified privilege.*

U.S. courts also have carefully protected freedom of the press to present opinions. Because opinions cannot be proved true or false, the press is free to comment on public issues and to laud a play or pan a movie, for example.

"The libel explosion does chill the courage of the press," says legal scholar Rodney A. Smolla, "and in that chill all of us suffer, for it threatens to make the press slavishly safe, pouring out a centrist, spiceless paste of consensus thought. All of us lose if we permit the trivialization of free speech."[5]

Masson v. *The New Yorker* Magazine

In 1991, the U.S. Supreme Court reinstated a $10 million libel suit brought against *The New Yorker* magazine by Toronto psychoanalyst Jeffrey M. Masson. Masson charged that author Janet Malcolm libelled him in two articles in *The New Yorker* and in a book when she deliberately misquoted him. Malcolm contended that the quotations she used were tape-recorded or were written in her notes.

Malcolm wrote, for example, that Mr. Masson said, "I was like an intellectual gigolo." However, this exact phrase was not in the tape-recorded transcript of her interview. Masson contended that he never used the phrase.

Issues in the case include whether quoted material must be verbatim and whether a journalist can change grammar and syntax. When the case was heard again in 1994, the court found that Malcolm had changed Masson's words but that the changes did not libel Masson. The Masson case is the most important recent example of a continuing interest in defining the limits of libel.

Successfully completed libel suits in Canada are few and far between. Most are resolved by an apology and a published retraction before a threatened suit is filed or are settled out of court before judgment. One example of a successfully completed libel suit is that of Robert Hodgson, who was regional engineer for York Region, north of Toronto, in 1991. On March 22, 1991, the *Globe and Mail* published the first in a series of articles that contained allegations of Hodgson's negligence and dishonesty.

Hodgson was fired from his job weeks later and brought a libel action against the *Globe* and reporter Jock Ferguson. After a lengthy trial, Mr. Justice Dennis Lane of the Ontario Court's General Division issued a judgment in favour of Hodgson and awarded him $400 000 in general damages, $100 000 in punitive damages, and $380 000 for lost income and pension benefits. Justice Lane held that there was "ample evidence of actual malice" on the part of the reporter, who, the Judge concluded, was trying to manufacture a sensational story.[6]

Privacy Law

The public seems to feel that invasion of privacy is one of the media's worst faults. As noted in Chapter 13, three out of four people interviewed in the Times Mirror survey said that news organizations invade people's privacy. The events following the death of Diana, Princess of Wales, were accompanied by a widespread outpouring of hostility toward the press. Many public figures clearly expect that their privacy will be respected; however, such respect is seldom required by law.

Privacy is an ethical issue. (See Chapter 15 for a discussion of the ethics of privacy.) Generally, the media can be guilty of invasion of privacy in three ways:

Satire is permissible and is protected from legal action. This picture of media mogul Conrad Black, altered digitally to make him look like a clown, would be considered satire.

Anonymously posted at
http://www.happyclown.com

1. By intruding on a person's physical or mental solitude.

2. By publishing or disclosing embarrassing personal facts.

3. By using someone's name or likeness for commercial benefit.

Physical or Mental Solitude

The courts in Western countries have recognized that a person has a right not to be pursued by the news media unnecessarily. A reporter can photograph or question someone on a public street or at a public event (but cannot now photograph persons on the street in Quebec without permission), but a person's home and office are private. For this reason, many photographers request that someone who is photographed in a private situation sign a release form, designating how the photograph can be used.

Celebrities like George Clooney become public objects of press attention. There are limits to the intrusion of their privacy, though these are ill-defined.

CP Picture Archive (Rob Schoenbaum)

One particularly notable case establishing this right of privacy is *Galella* v. *Onassis*. The late Jacqueline Onassis, widow of former president John F. Kennedy, charged that Ron Galella, a freelance photographer, was pursuing her unnecessarily. He had used a telephoto lens to photograph her on private property and he had pursued her children at private schools. Galella was ordered to stay 25 feet away from her and 30 feet away from her children.

Embarrassing Personal Facts

The personal facts the media use to report a story should be newsworthy. If a public official is caught travelling with her boyfriend on taxpayers' money while her husband stays at home, information about the boyfriend is essential to the story. If the public official is reported to have contracted AIDS from her contact with the boyfriend, the information probably is not relevant to the story and should not be covered.

In reality, however, public officials enjoy very little legal protection from reporting about their private lives. Information available from public records, such as court proceedings, is not considered private unless specifically sealed by the court. If the public official's husband testifies in court about his wife's disease, this information could be reported.

Fair Trial and the Right of Access

The answers to two other questions that bear on press freedoms and individual rights remain discretionary for the courts: When does media coverage influence a jury so much that a defendant's right to a fair trial is jeopardized? And how much access should the media be granted during a trial?

Fair Trial

The best-known decision affecting prejudicial press coverage of criminal cases is *Sheppard* v. *Maxwell*, the real-life basis for *The Fugitive* television series and a later movie of the same name. In 1954, Dr. Samuel Sheppard of Cleveland was sentenced to life imprisonment for murdering his wife. His conviction followed reams of newspaper stories, many of which proclaimed his guilt before the jury had decided the case. The jurors, who went home each evening, were told by the judge not to read newspapers or pay attention to broadcast reports, but no one monitored what the jurors did.

Twelve years later, lawyer F. Lee Bailey took Sheppard's trial to the U.S. Supreme Court, where the conviction was overturned on the premise that Sheppard had been a victim of a biased jury. In writing the decision, Justice Tom C. Clark prescribed several remedies. He said that the reporters should have been limited to certain areas in the courtroom, that the news media should not have been allowed to interview the witnesses, and that the court should have forbidden statements outside of the courtroom.

Courtroom Access

Publication bans are common in Canadian courts. These bans are intended to preserve the conditions necessary for a fair trial. The best-known of these bans were the restraints placed by Justice Kovacs in the Karla Homolka trial. Representatives of the press were allowed to be present while her plea of guilty was accepted and sentencing completed, but details of her plea were sealed pending the trial of her husband Paul Bernardo. Details of the case were distributed widely through the USENET newsgroups on the Internet anonymously, however, and reporters from U.S. border stations tended to disregard the publication ban. Some of their television reports were censored by Canadian cable TV systems in one of the more unfortunate and inglorious episodes of Canadian broadcasting.

The most widespread practices are restraining (publication bans and closed proceedings). With a publication ban, the judge limits what the press can report. Closed proceedings exclude the press from the courtroom. Closed proceedings are most commonly used in cases involving national security.

Cameras in the courtroom is a sticky issue between judges, who want to avoid the disruption that cameras present, and broadcast newspeople, who want to photograph what is going on. Cameras are seldom allowed in Canadian courtrooms (the Supreme Court being one exception), but many trials in the United States are televised. In selected cases, cameras have been allowed to record complete trials. In 1994, for example, Court TV broadcast the entire trial of O.J. Simpson. Cameras in the courtroom is a case by case and state by state decision in the United States. Some states allow cameras during civil but not criminal trials. Other states ban them altogether. The courts and the press are not yet completely comfortable partners.

Regulating Broadcasting

It goes without saying that all of the media are expected to abide by the laws of the country in which they are established. Regulation of the media comes from government agencies, such as the CRTC, that oversee almost all aspects of the media business. The print industry is not specifically regulated by any government agency, though as businesses, media companies have to obey taxation and corporate laws and deal fairly with customers. The largest area of media regulation in Canada is covered by the CRTC, which oversees broadcasting.

The concept behind broadcast regulation has been that the airwaves belong to the public, that they are a scarce resource that require public management, and that broadcasters are trustees operating in the public interest.

The CRTC

The regulation of broadcasting in Canada, both licensing and content aspects, is now carried out by the CRTC. Almost from the beginning of broadcasting in Canada, the government, acting through one agency or another, has regulated nearly all aspects of the broadcast media. Whereas older media such as newspaper and book publishing are not subject to this kind of regulation, the licensed use of a public asset—the electromagnetic spectrum—has meant much less freedom of action for broadcasters both public and private in Canada.

The modern era of broadcast regulation in Canada began in 1958 with the establishment of the Board of Broadcast Governors, supplanting the Canadian Broadcasting Corporation as the original regulator. It was succeeded in 1968 by the Canadian Radio-Television Commission. In 1976, the CRTC also acquired a regulatory mandate over the telecommunications sector. Commission members are appointed by the government of the day for terms of up to five years. Through its licensing function, it can stipulate performance criteria for licensees as a condition of obtaining or renewing a broadcast license. Conditions can relate directly to content (a certain percentage must be Canadian), to the amount and type of advertising allowed, and to the way the content is presented.

IMPACT

Point of View

STERN SAYS HE'S BEING "CRUCIFIED" BY REGULATORS

Canadian stations carrying show forced to air statement that it violates codes.

By Mike Boone

MONTREAL—The Howard Stern defence is taking shape, with the man at the centre of the controversy pleading both innocence and ignorance.

Yesterday morning, Montreal's CHOM–FM and Toronto's Q–107 broadcast a statement acknowledging that the station has "breached provisions of the (broadcast) industry's Code of Ethics and Sex Portrayal Code." The transgressions occurred during the first two weeks of September, when CHOM launched the syndicated Stern morning show.

In a decision Tuesday, the Canadian Broadcast Standards Council lambasted Stern's program for "abusive, discriminatory comments directed at French Canadians and other identifiable groups," for sexism and for "unsuitable language" and "description of

sexual activity" broadcast during a time of day when children listen to the radio.

Stern's response to the ruling was moderate by the standards of the New York-based "shock jock," whose stock in trade is over-the-top vitriol aimed at competitors, critics and multitudes of enemies, real and imagined.

"I am certainly not familiar with Canadian laws and rules," Stern told his listeners. "I don't have a clue how Canadian laws differ from American rules governing free speech. And I don't even really understand American laws."

Admitting that he is "too stupid to be a lawyer" (self-deprecation is another standard element of his routine), Stern said that he is an entertainer trying to make listeners laugh. He regrets that his humour is lost on Canadian broadcasting authorities.

"It's really odd for me to explain comedy," Stern said. "To dissect humour is truly unfunny. The show is spontaneous. It is satire. To try to explain what the jokes mean is mind-boggling to me.

"Sometimes it takes some people a little longer to get my brand of humour," Stern added.

CHOM and Q–107 are reserving comment on what could become an ugly battle with the Standards Council, which monitors compliance with the Canadian broadcast industry's codes, and with the Canadian Radio-television and Telecommunications Commission. The CRTC has an arsenal of regulatory weapons, including fines and the suspension of a broadcaster's licence. The council has the power of censure, and its chairman, Ron Cohen, has stated unequivocally that he expects CHOM and Q–107 to conform with the industry's rules.

The council considered whether Stern's excesses could be interpreted as comedy. The decision was emphatic. Stern's brand of "adolescent humour," it ruled, is "thoroughly in breach of Canadian codified broadcast standards."

Stern admitted yesterday that he didn't know much about Canada, a country he visited "once, for an hour when I was 16."

It is unusual for the CRTC to revoke a licence, but renewals can come at a heavy price of promises for future performance. Criticism of past results may also be rendered. Public comment is encouraged as part of the license renewal process.

Like the print media, broadcasters must follow the law and important court rulings on issues such as libel, obscenity, and the right of privacy. But broadcast stations also must follow the regulations that the CRTC establishes.

Violent Programming: TV Ratings and the V-Chip

Under pressure from politicians, television executives agreed to devise a voluntary ratings system for television programs. *Broadcasting and Cable* magazine called imposition of the ratings system a "stunning defeat" for the television industry, which had long resisted all content regulation.[7]

He protested that he was being "crucified" by the Broadcast Standards Council, which took some of his remarks out of context to buttress their argument that he consistently violates Canadian radio rules.

"There's only so much nonsense a radio station can put up with," he said. "I am fatigued from all this. I have so much *tsooris* (Yiddish for trouble) in Canada, I just can't believe it."

Stern told his radio audience that if such a reprimand had been issued in New York, people would take to the streets in anger.

Some in Canada share his concerns.

"If Howard Stern and the station he broadcasts over are legally free, as I think they should be, to say nasty things ... so should their colleagues be legally free to give them hell for it," said Alan Borovoy, general counsel to the Canadian Civil Liberties Association.

"The use of state coercion, however, creates an entirely different dimension."

Laws protecting freedom of speech are much mightier in the U.S. It's a civil liberty that "has been regrettably diluted" in Canada, Borovoy says.

One of the problems, he says, is that anti-hate laws here are too blunt to make a distinction between serious comments and satire.

The Montreal Gazette; *with files from the Canadian Press. Reprinted with permission.*

CP Picture Archive (Emile Wamsteker)

Courtesy of Don Wright, *The Palm Beach Post.*

Jack Valenti, president of the Motion Picture Association of America (MPAA), led the ratings task force (Valenti also helped establish the current system of movie ratings). In January 1997, the task force announced the new ratings system, which applies to all programming except sports, newsmagazines, and news shows.

Unlike movies, which are rated by an independent board, the TV shows will be rated by producers, networks, cable channels, syndicators, and other people who originate the programs.[8] These ratings evaluate violence and sexual content, and the results are displayed on the screen at the beginning of each program and coded into each TV program. The codes will be read by a so-called "V-chip." Beginning in 1998, this microchip device is scheduled to be included in all new television sets. The V-chip will allow parents to program the TV set to eliminate shows the parents find objectionable.

The Internet

The Internet offers the latest challenge to regulation. It is possible for an individual or a group to post anything at all on the World Wide Web in such a way to avoid the laws of his or her home jurisdiction. The technical means to do this are widely known and used. One upshot of this situation is that the Web now contains much information and opinion, which in previous eras would have resulted in prosecution, seizure of assets, and in many cases imprisonment. The case of Ernst Zundel and his holocaust denial Web site (which is maintained in California) has shown the difficulties in prosecuting the operator of a Web site that is housed in another country. It has proven impossible for Canadian authorities to stop Mr. Zundel from publishing his views on the holocaust on the Web.

Several countries have attempted to regulate the content of materials on the Internet. The most ambitious of these attempts was the Communications Decency Act in the United States. This law made it a felony to send indecent material over computer networks. The Act also "prohibited using a telecommunications device to:

◎ Make or initiate any communication that is obscene, lewd, lascivious, filthy or indecent with intent to annoy, abuse, threaten or harass another person;

◎ Make or make available obscene communication;

◎ Make or make available an indecent communication to minors;

◎ Transmit obscene material—including material concerning abortion—or for any indecent or immoral use."[9]

The Act relied on a very broad definition of the term "indecent." Under the Act's provisions, violators could be charged with a felony and fined up to $250 000. More than 50 opponents of the Act's indecency provision, including the American Library Association and the American Civil Liberties Union, went to court to challenge the law. A three-judge panel unanimously declared that the Internet indecency provision was unconstitutional, and the judges blocked enforcement of the law.

It is difficult both in principle and in practice to develop a technical means to censor or block any material on the Internet because the digital content moves freely across national borders. No single nation can establish jurisdiction to bring a prosecution, and the continuing absence of an international agreement to regulate content makes "electronic extradition" impossible.

Another aspect of the Web, low cost of operation, has meant that many electronic periodicals have sprung up that are available to any reader anywhere in the world. Freed of the necessity to print on paper, the cost barriers to publishing have been lowered dramatically. Again, anyone can now express views on the Web without much fear of prosecution, no matter what the substance of these views or presentations is. This new situation comes close to the philosophical ideal of freedom of speech, expression, and publication. What is lost, however, is the ability of nations to enforce community standards or to stifle the promotion of hatred.

In times of war, freedom of the press has routinely been restricted and formal censorship has been imposed. In Canada, the government used the War Measures Act for this purpose as late as 1970. However, today the threat of imminent war actually increases the volume of expression and sharing of information, as Web users post their ideas and take part in discussion groups. In the case of actual warfare, discussion reaches an even higher pitch. In addition, Web users have access to publications from other countries. This new arrangement would seem to preclude wartime censorship in the future.

Overall, the ability of nations to regulate the press through legislation has been severely curtailed in recent years. However, concentration of ownership has meant that the diversity of opinion you receive from the press has likewise been diminished, in the view of many. What prevents this situation from damaging the level of public knowledge is the World Wide Web. It has taken over as the place where breaking news, outrageous opinion, and "subversion" of the status quo takes place (witness the role of the "Drudge Report" site in the unfolding Clinton sex scandal of the spring 1998). Newspapers are now in many respects followers rather than leaders of the electronic publication of facts and interpretation. The diversity of sources, information, and opinion has flowered in the era of the Web. Since whatever is not expressly forbidden is both permitted and legal in the Western tradition of jurisprudence, an era of almost complete freedom of expression by individuals has begun in cyberspace.

In Focus

◎ Laws in Canada that restrict the media can be found at all levels of government: federal, provincial, and municipal.

◎ Canadian courts may compel reporters to divulge their sources.

◎ Materials that promote hatred are not protected under the Charter of Rights and Freedoms.

◎ Censorship of Canadian publications was routine in wartime and has been imposed under the War Measures Act as late as 1970.

◎ Canada Customs continues to have the right to seize "degrading" pornographic publications.

◎ Provinces retain the right to censor movies.

◎ Libel suits place the onus of disproof on the defendant.

◎ Publication bans are common in Canadian courts.

◎ The content of broadcasts is heavily regulated by the CRTC.

◎ There are no technical means available to regulate the content of the Internet.

Watching the Web

◎ **Copyright on the Net**

http://www.benedict.com

◎ **10 Big Myths about copyright explained**

http://www.templetons.com/brad/copymyths.html

◎ **Reporters Committee for Freedom of the Press**

http://www.rcpf.org/rcfp

◎ **A Chronicle of Freedom of Expression in Canada**

http://www.insight.mcmaster.ca/org/efc/pages/chronicle/chronicle.html

ETHICS

15

GOOD FAITH WITH THE PUBLIC
IS THE FOUNDATION OF ALL
WORTHY JOURNALISM.

*Society of Professional
Journalists Code of Ethics*

What's Ahead

ost of us would rather publish a story than not," explained journalist Anthony Brandt in an *Esquire* magazine article about ethics.

> We're in the business of reporting, after all; most of us believe the public should know what's going on, has a right to know, has, indeed, a responsibility to know, and that this right, this responsibility, transcends the right to privacy, excuses our own pushiness, our arrogance, and therefore ought to protect us from lawsuits even when we are wrong.
>
> But most reporters also know there are times when publishing can harm or ruin people's lives. Members of the press sometimes print gossip as truth, disregard the impact they have on people's lives, and are ready to believe the worst about people because the worst sells.... We in the media have much to answer for.[1]

Origin of Ethical Concepts in Journalism

Discussions about how journalists answer for what they do centre on *ethics*. The word derives from the Greek word *ethos*, meaning the traditions or guiding spirit that govern a culture. Part of the British common law heritage are the hard-won freedoms of expression. Sometimes these are embedded in bills of rights such as the Canadian Charter of Rights and Freedoms or the unique First Amendment protection in the United States. But any discussion of ethics and the media acknowledges the cultural belief that the right to publish freely carries with it special obligations. Among these obligations are professional ethics.

Journalists are probably no more likely to exploit their positions than people in other professions; but when journalists make the wrong ethical choices, the consequences can be very visible and damaging. "It may well be that if journalism loses touch with ethical values, it will then cease to be of use to society, and cease to have any real reason for being," writes media ethics scholar John Hulteng. "But that, for the sake of all of us, must never be allowed to happen."[2]

Journalists sometimes make poor ethical judgments because they work quickly and their actions can be haphazard; because the lust to be first with a story can override the desire to be right; because they sometimes don't know enough to question the truthfulness of what they're told; because they can win attention and professional success quickly by ignoring ethical standards; and because journalists sometimes are insensitive to the consequences of their stories for the people they cover. Consider these actual situations:

1. *Creating composite characters*. A journalist for a prestigious magazine admitted that he sometimes embroidered the events he wrote about or created composite characters in his articles without telling his readers. Was the journalist presenting fiction as fact, or was he simply using journalistic licence?

2. *Insider friendships*. A syndicated political columnist coached a candidate for political office before a televised debate and then praised the candidate's performance on a nationwide TV program. Did the columnist get too close to a news source, or did he simply help a friend?

3. *Reporting personal information*. A reporter verified that a well-known public figure was dying of AIDS, although the news figure would not admit his illness. Did the reporter infringe on the person's privacy, or did the readers deserve to know about the extent of this growing health hazard?

4. *Staging sensational events*. A television newsmagazine program showed a Chevrolet truck exploding when struck near the gas tank. But the explosion was staged to closely resemble real accidents, and the collision did not in fact cause the explosion shown to viewers. Did the network exploit a story for its shock value, or will the public understand this type of tragedy better by viewing the staged demonstration?

Defining Ethical Dilemmas

Ethical dilemmas faced by the media can be described using four categories: truthfulness, fairness, privacy, and responsibility. Falsehood is the issue for the journalist who embroidered characters in example 1. Bias is the question for the columnist who coached the political candidate in example 2. Invasion of privacy is the debate facing the reporter who published the AIDS information in example 3. And the television network that staged the explosion in example 4 could be criticized for acting irresponsibly.

Some ethical debates are easier to resolve than others. These four incidents and several other examples are described here to demonstrate how vulnerable the media can be to ethical lapses.

Truthfulness

Truthfulness in reporting means more than accuracy and telling the truth to get a story. Truthfulness also means not misrepresenting the people or the situations in the story to readers or viewers. Another aspect of truthfulness is the responsibility of government officials to not manipulate the media for their own ends, a process often called **disinformation**.

Misrepresentation

The journalist described in example 1 was *New Yorker* magazine writer Alistair Reid, who acknowledged in 1984 that in more than 20 years as a writer for *The New Yorker*, he had modified facts five separate times. In "Letter from

Barcelona," Reid had described some Spaniards sitting in "a small, flyblown bar" jeering at a televised speech by Spanish dictator Francisco Franco. In fact, Reid said that he watched the speech at the home of a one-time bartender and that two of the main characters were composites. This was particularly surprising because *The New Yorker* prides itself on its fact-checking department. Reid said that he created the fictional environment and characters to protect his sources from retribution by the government.

A more celebrated case of a journalist embroidering the facts is Janet Cooke, who was a reporter for the *Washington Post* in 1980 when she wrote "Jimmy's World," a story about an eight-year-old heroin addict. After she was awarded the Pulitzer Prize for the story in April 1981, reporters began to check up on her background, and the *Post* learned that she had lied on her résumé. The editors then questioned her for several hours about the story. She was allowed to resign.

"'Jimmy's World' was in essence a fabrication," she wrote in her resignation letter. "I never encountered or interviewed an 8-year-old heroin addict. The September 19, 1980, article in the *Washington Post* was a serious misrepresentation which I deeply regret. I apologize to my newspaper, my profession, the Pulitzer board and all seekers of truth."[3]

A month later, columnist Michael Daly of the New York *Daily News* resigned, admitting that he had invented a British soldier in a story about Ireland. He said he had re-created the adventures of "Christopher Spell" from a description given to him by another soldier, who had witnessed the events. "The question of reconstruction and using a pseudonym—I've done it a lot," said Daly. "No one has ever said anything."[4]

Misrepresenting people by creating composite characters, as in these three cases, causes readers to question the facts in all stories: Which are actual people and which are composites? Is the story fiction or fact?

Disinformation

In October 1986, the press learned that in August 1986 the Reagan administration had launched a disinformation campaign to scare Libyan leader Moammar Qadhafi. Selected U.S. government sources had planted stories with reporters that U.S. forces were preparing to strike Libya. The first report of the bogus preparations appeared in the August 25, 1986, *Wall Street Journal.*

On the basis of this story and a statement by White House spokesman Larry Speakes that the article was "authoritative," other newspapers, including the *Washington Post*, carried the story. This brings up the ethical question of a government's responsibility not to use the press for its own ends. The planted Qadhafi story raises the ethical question: How is the public to differentiate between true stories and those that are planted by the government?

Fairness

Fairness implies impartiality—that the journalist has nothing personal to gain from a report, that there are no hidden benefits to the reporter or to the source from the story being presented. Criticism of the press for unfairness results from debates over close ties that sometimes develop between reporters and the

I M P A C T

Point of View   *THE CONFLICTS OF JOURNALISTS*

By Anthony Wilson-Smith

Perhaps you have already had this experience: you engaged in an activity you would rather keep confidential. Now, you are prepared to discuss it with an acquaintance—but only if that person promises not to tell anyone else. A short while later, everyone knows the story. Your supposed friend is clearly the culprit. When you confront him or her, the defense is that the story was too interesting to keep private.

That, in essence, is what happened to Brian Mulroney earlier this year. The former prime minister met with Quebec author and journalist André Pratte to assist him with a biography Pratte was writing on Jean Charest. The interview was given on condition that it be "on background," meaning that Mulroney would not be quoted and Pratte would not cite the interview as the source of his information. He agreed. But when Pratte's book was published in June, he quoted Mulroney, relating how he helped to persuade Charest to quit as leader of the Progressive Conservatives to lead the Quebec Liberal party. Although Mulroney never said he could break the agreement, Pratte did so, he explained, because the information was "significant."

A friend who broke such a promise would not be considered trustworthy, or a friend, any more. In the case of journalists, recourse is more complex. There was no formal agreement, so Mulroney probably cannot take legal action. Moreover, there is no indication that he was misquoted, slandered, or that his reputation suffered. But Mulroney was burned for trusting the word of a journalist, and the only certainty is that it will be a long time before he gives anyone a similar opportunity.

The incident aroused only fleeting attention outside Quebec, but the issues it raises deserve greater resonance. Journalism, despite frequent claims to the contrary, is not a profession. A true professional, by comparison, is a doctor or lawyer, both of whom must pass rigorous tests and

can be barred from practising if they violate rules regarding their conduct. Journalism has no universal code of conduct, although most organizations establish guidelines of acceptable behavior. And while most journalists today have attended university, there are no specific requirements to become a reporter.

That lack of standards and, sometimes, ethics has been evident recently in some highly publicized cases in the United States. A columnist at *The Boston Globe* was fired for fabricating quotes, a contributing editor to *The New Republic* and *George* magazines was sacked after admitting making up quotes and incidents, and *CNN* and *Time* magazine apologized for a joint report that suggested the United States military used poison gas in Viet Nam in the 1960s. A follow-up investigation concluded that could not be proven.

A less-publicized problem is the ethical netherworld that exists for media institutions and the people who work for them. True, there will never be a way to regulate against bad taste—such as the disgraceful story that appeared on the front page of *The Globe and Mail* recently about Bank of Montreal CEO Matthew Barrett: it suggested, without evidence beyond unnamed sources and snickering reference to the gossip magazine *Frank*, that Barrett's effectiveness has been compromised because of his delight in his glamorous new wife, Anne-Marie Sten. In that case, the story was more damaging to the newspaper printing it than the subject of the story.

But some problems are more hidden: it is understandable if people who listen to television and radio news and read newspapers and magazines attach equal credibility to all. But the standards attached to each institution can be quite different. Major print institutions, for example, such as the *Globe* or *The Financial Post*, forbid reporters from investing in stocks they cover. But no such stricture exists at some television and radio stations, so that

people who report business—and give investment advice—may have a vested, undeclared interest of their own. Similarly, many radio talk-show hosts also do commercials as part of their programs. When such people write freelance columns for newspapers, as is the case in several markets, should their conflicts be noted, and are their opinions as credible as those of journalists who do not shill products?

Then, there are the conditions by which interviews take place, and some stories are published. In the United States, some celebrities give interviews only if they are guaranteed a cover story, and approval over the photographs that appear. Many interviews take place with the proviso that the person being interviewed will discuss only certain subjects. And every year, the major television and movie studios sponsor junkets in which they pay for journalists' travel and accommodations and arrange interviews with stars—with the understanding that only soft questions will be asked, and the ensuring stories will be favorable. (*Maclean's* pays for all travel expenses by reporters on assignment.) Some institutions explain the practice to their readers; most do not.

Everyone in journalism will benefit if media institutions put aside their differences long enough to agree on new industry-wide standards of behavior. For now that is about as likely as, say, a blanket editorial endorsement of the New Democratic Party by Conrad Black's Southam newspapers. Journalists argue that the business already effectively polices itself— and that the overwhelming majority of people involved are decent and honorable.... In both cases, it is true—and in neither case is it an acceptable excuse for doing nothing about existing problems.

Maclean's, *August 3, 1998, p. 11.*
Reprinted with permission.

people they write about (called *insider friendships*); reporters who accept personal or financial benefits from sources, sponsors, or advertisers (called *conflicts of interest*); and reporters who pay their sources for stories (called *chequebook journalism*).

Insider Friendships

The columnist in example 2 was ABC News commentator George Will; the candidate was Ronald Reagan. In 1980, Will coached Reagan before he faced President Jimmy Carter for a televised debate. On the ABC program *Nightline*, after the debate, Will compared Reagan's performance to that of a "thoroughbred." In 1983, when Will's actions were reported, Will admitted that he would not do the same thing again.

In 1987, *The Wall Street Journal* reported that in December 1986, ABC's Barbara Walters had carried a private message from arms merchant Manucher Ghorbanifar to President Reagan after she conducted an exclusive interview with Ghorbanifar for an ABC story. Ghorbanifar was a central figure in the arrangements during 1985 and 1986 between the White House and the Iranian government to send arms to Iran in exchange for American hostages. Walters did not report on ABC that she had delivered a message to the president.

"After the interviews, Mr. Ghorbanifar asked to speak with Ms. Walters again and asked that she send his views to the president," stated network spokesman Tom Goodman. "Believing that her information could be of assistance to the remaining hostages (held in Lebanon), and before informing her management, Ms. Walters did that and also gave her information to the appropriate editors" at the network.[5]

New York Times reporter Judith Miller, who covered the Middle East for three years, criticized Walters for becoming a participant in a story she covered. "We're in the business of publishing what we know.... We don't deliver messages," said Miller.[6]

Part of the job of being a reporter is learning to be friendly with many different types of people. In both the Walters and Will examples, the reporters became part of the stories they were supposed to be covering. How can the public trust a reporter who becomes more than an outside observer of events and instead takes part in the story? Insider friendships can remove a reporter's necessary detachment.

Conflicts of Interest

Reporters with conflicts of interest are divided between at least two loyalties, and the ethical question is: How will the stories the reporters write and the integrity of the organizations for which they work be affected?

In 1984, *The Wall Street Journal* fired stock tip columnist R. Foster Winans for allegedly leaking stories in advance to a group of friends who paid Winans for his help and then used the information to make profitable stock market investments. An investigation by the Securities and Exchange Commission had prompted the *Journal* to question Winans.

In 1985, Winans was found guilty of 59 counts of fraud and conspiracy. "What made the conduct here a fraud was that Winans knew he was not supposed to leak the timing or contents of his articles or trade on that knowledge," wrote

Judge Charles E. Stewart in his decision on the case. "Here, the fraudulent taking and misuse of confidential information stolen from *The Wall Street Journal* placed immediately in jeopardy probably its most valuable asset—its reputation for fairness and integrity."[7] Winans was sentenced to 18 months in jail, $5000 in fines, five years' probation, and 400 hours of community service.

A different type of conflict of interest happens when reporters accept free meals and passes to entertainment events (freebies) and free trips (junkets). In a 1986 survey of 34 newspapers, nearly half said they accepted free tickets to athletic events, and nearly two-thirds accepted free tickets to artistic events.[8]

In 1986, Walt Disney World invited journalists from all over the world to attend its 15th anniversary celebration in Orlando, Florida, and more than 10 000 journalists and their guests accepted the invitation. Most of the press guests let Disney pay for the hotel, transportation, and meals. *Variety* called the event "one of the biggest junkets in showbiz history," at an estimated cost to Disney, the airlines, hotels, and tourism agencies of $8 million. In an editorial about the junket, *The New York Times* said: "Accepting junkets and boondoggles does not necessarily mean that a reporter is being bought—but it inescapably creates the appearance of being bought."[9]

Chequebook Journalism

In 1994, U.S. Olympic skater Tonya Harding reportedly received $600 000 for appearing on *Inside Edition* after she was charged with participating in an attack on her opponent, Nancy Kerrigan.[10]

After New York's "Son of Sam" serial killer David Berkowitz signed a lucrative film and book deal, the state passed a law to prohibit criminals from profiting from such contracts. But on December 10, 1991, the U.S. Supreme Court overturned the law as an infringement on free speech.

Public figures such as Gennifer Flowers sometimes try to use their celebrity status to earn money.

Agence France Presse/Corbis-Bettmann

Various attempts to introduce similar legislation in Canada have been unsuccessful. The most recent attempt was a private member's bill introduced in the House of Commons by Tom Wappel in 1998. It failed to pass. Several convicts have written books in prison and received payment for their writing, such as Roger Caron, who wrote *Go Boy*.

New language for a draft bill that the provinces would enact to distribute the profits of such books to victims of crime was provided by the minister of justice in September 1997. The draft bill rests on the same shaky ground with respect to the Charter of Rights as previously proposed legislation.

Besides the ethical questions about whether journalists and criminals should profit from crime, there are other hazards in any kind of chequebook journalism. One danger is that a paid interviewee will sensationalize the information to bring a higher price, so the interviewee's veracity cannot always be trusted. The second hazard is that such interviews often become the exclusive property of the highest bidder, shutting out smaller news organizations and independent journalists from the information. A third possibility is that the person who is paid by the news organization to comment could possibly carry a hidden agenda.

Privacy

Reporting on AIDS and on rape are the most visible examples of a complex ethical dilemma: How does the press balance the goals of truthfulness and fact-finding with the need for personal privacy? Is the private grief that such a report may cause worth the public good that can result from publishing the information?

Reporting on AIDS

Because many people who die from AIDS are homosexual, announcing that a person's illness is AIDS may reflect on the person's private sexual behaviour. One argument in favour of the press reporting the nature of the illness in these cases is that covering up the information means that the public won't understand the widespread extent of the public health problem that AIDS represents.

"Covering up the truth, by doctors or journalists, stigmatizes other sufferers—the less widely the disease is acknowledged, the less easily they can be accepted. And it shields communities and industries from understanding the full, devastating effect of AIDS," argued *Newsweek* in a story called "AIDS and the Right to Know."[11] The counterargument is that a person's illness and death is strictly a private matter and that publishing the information will harm the person's reputation.

The case of the public figure with AIDS in example 3 describes two recent situations. In 1986, New York lawyer Roy Cohn died of AIDS without acknowledging before his death that he suffered from the disease. Entertainer Liberace also withheld information about his illness before he died in 1987.

Roy Cohn became a public figure in the 1950s during the McCarthy hearings (see Chapter 14), as counsel for the Senate committee investigating Communist activity in the 1950s. As a lawyer in the 1980s, he defended many organized-crime figures, and he lived a high-profile existence in New York City. A week before Cohn died, columnists Jack Anderson and Dale Van Atta published a story saying that Cohn was being treated with azidothymidine (AZT), a drug used exclusively for AIDS patients.

Journalist William Safire criticized Anderson and Van Atta in *The New York Times*, saying "Doctors with some sense of ethics and journalists with some regard for a core of human privacy are shamed by [this] investigative excess."[12] After Cohn's death, *Harper's* magazine published copies of the hospital records on which Van Atta had based his column.

Liberace's illness was first revealed in the *Las Vegas Sun* about two weeks before he died. *Sun* publisher Brian Greenspun appeared on ABC's *Nightline* to defend publishing the information before the entertainer's death. Because only the *Sun* had access to the documentation, other members of the media who wrote about Liberace's illness attributed the information to the *Sun*. After Liberace died, the Riverside County coroner confirmed that Liberace suffered from a disease caused by AIDS.

A third example of a story about someone dying of AIDS represents one journalist's answer to the debate. *Honolulu Star-Bulletin* Managing Editor Bill Cox announced in a column published September 1, 1986, that he was going on disability leave because he had AIDS. "As a journalist," he wrote, "I have spent my career trying to shed light in dark corners. AIDS is surely one of our darkest corners. It can use some light."[13]

Reporting on Rape

Privacy also is an important issue in reporting on rape cases. Common newsroom practice forbids the naming of rape victims in stories. In 1989, editor Geneva Overholser of the *Des Moines Register* startled the press community when she wrote an editorial arguing that newspapers contribute to the public's misunderstanding of the crime by withholding not only the woman's name, but also an explicit description of what happened.

The *Des Moines Register* series about the rape of Nancy Ziegenmeyer focused attention on the ethics of publishing the names of rape victims with their consent.

© 1990 Des Moines Register and Tribune Company. Reprinted with permission.

IT COULDN'T HAPPEN TO ME: ONE WOMAN'S STORY

In 1990, the *Register* published a five-part series about the rape of Nancy Ziegenmeyer, with Ziegenmeyer's full cooperation. Ziegenmeyer had contacted the *Register* after Overholser's column appeared, volunteering to tell her story. The Ziegenmeyer series has provoked wide-ranging debate among editors about this aspect of privacy.

Is there more benefit to society by printing the victim's name, with the victim's permission, than by withholding it? Should the press explicitly describe sexual crimes, or is that merely sensationalism, preying on the public's salacious curiosity?

The Cohn, Liberace, and Ziegenmeyer cases demonstrate how complex privacy issues in today's society have become. When is it in the public interest to divulge personal information about individuals? Who should decide?

Responsibility

The events that journalists choose to report and the way they use the information they gather reflect on the profession's sense of public responsibility. Most reporters realize that often they change the character of an event by covering that event. The mere presence of the media magnifies the importance of what happens.

The media can be exploited by people in trouble or by people who covet the notoriety that media coverage brings. And the media can exploit an event for its shock value to try to attract an audience. The following two specific examples demonstrate how differently individual media organizations and individual members of the media interpret their responsibility to the public.

A Staged Accident Demonstration

In 1992, *Dateline NBC* broadcast a story questioning the safety of General Motors trucks. To demonstrate the alleged problems with the trucks, NBC hired a company to stage an accident. In the news footage of the accident used in the broadcast, the truck's gas tank appeared to explode on impact. General Motors threatened to sue NBC, saying the footage had been edited to give the appearance of an explosion, but that the company hired by NBC to stage the crash used spark igniters to cause the fire, and that the staff of *Dateline NBC* knowingly aired footage that was an inaccurate portrayal of a staged event. This is example 4.

After a month-long NBC-commissioned investigation, NBC President Robert Wright admitted that NBC News employees made "'seriously flawed judgments' and violated numerous (news) division guidelines in putting together a much-criticized story." The president of NBC News, who originally denied the GM charges, was forced to resign, as were three staff members directly involved with the story. The reporter on the story, who said she had argued against using the footage, was reassigned.[14]

The NBC incident demonstrates the important responsibility that reporters share for the information they present to the public. The credibility of any news organization rests on the truthfulness of the information the reporters present, and slanting the information, or conveying inaccurate information, even in just one story, ultimately can cause readers and viewers to doubt the truth of all stories presented by that organization.

A Live TV Raid

In 1993, three Cable News Network reporters accompanied U.S. Department of Fish and Wildlife agents in Jordan, Montana, on an investigation of a ranch owned by Paul Berger, who was 72. Dressed in street clothes, like the Fish and Wildlife agents, the reporters spent 10 hours searching the ranch, along with the agents. The agents targeted Berger because they said they had reason to believe he was poisoning eagles who were preying on his sheep. During the aerial and ground search, agents wore recording devices that documented the raid for CNN.

"This was a case where government agents became reporters and reporters became government agents," asserted Berger's attorney, Henry Rossbacher. Eventually a jury found that Mr. Berger was not guilty of poisoning eagles, mainly because the search of the ranch did not turn up any poisoned eagles, although Berger was found guilty of lacing two sheep carcasses with poison, a misdemeanour. CNN aired the video of the raid in a 12-minute program called "Ring of Death," which portrayed the search as a complete success for the agents. Mr. Berger then sued CNN, claiming that the network violated his rights against unreasonable search and seizure. CNN admitted no wrongdoing.

This case "raises ethical issues for the press, particularly at a time when new shows profiling law enforcement are proliferating, and reporters are increasingly eager to ride along on the execution of search warrants," reported the *Wall Street Journal*. "While a reporter's presence could work to a suspect's benefit—by keeping investigators from becoming abusive or bearing witness to a police failure to find incriminating evidence—critics worry that it more often than not inspires uncivil police theatrics. The allure of access often tempts the media into deals that give the authorities substantial power to shape both the content and timing of stories."[15]

Are members of the media, as CNN contends, merely conduits for information? Or do they have a responsibility to protect the interests of the people they cover?

Found Guilty Before Proven Innocent

Canadian breaches of ethical standards are seldom as stark and straightforward as those in the U.S. media. The striking cases discussed to this point serve as clearcut examples of what journalists should not do. Often though, the situation is not clear-cut.

Consider, for instance, the treatment accorded former prime minister Brian Mulroney in the Airbus affair. The RCMP began a criminal probe into allegations that Mulroney pocketed millions of dollars in kickbacks from the sale of Airbus jets to Air Canada. The innuendoes in the media were such that Mulroney's already flagging reputation was damaged not by facts, but by the publicity itself. The former prime minister was eventually exonerated and received a large cash settlement in his civil lawsuit. In addition, the lead RCMP investigator, Fraser Fiegenwald, was the subject of an inquiry and was forced to resign for allegedly leaking investigation material to a journalist. In this case, the Canadian media failed to offer Mulroney the presumption of innocence, and his reputation suffered as a result.

Another example of ethical misconduct, which was discussed in Chapter 14, is the case of Robert Hodgson who received a libel judgement against the *Globe and Mail*, which misstated the facts about his job performance for the purposes of making a story more sensational.

Frank magazine also routinely carries false, misleading, and just plain vengeful articles about public figures, makes fun of their physical appearance, and has developed a special vocabulary for alleging that figures are alcoholics without actually saying so ("overly refreshed"). In all probability, no readers of *Frank* take all that appears in the magazine as the truth, but some victims of its treatments are hurt and insulted, and some have sued. Although there must always be a place for satire, routinely making fun of the physical characteristics of public figures does raise ethical questions.

Philosophical Principles of Journalistic Ethics

Scholars can only suggest guidelines for moral decisions, because each situation presents its own special dilemmas. First, it is important to understand the basic principles that underlie these philosophical discussions.

In their book *Media Ethics*, Clifford G. Christians, Kim B. Rotzoll, and Mark Fackler identify five major philosophical principles underlying today's ethical decisions: Aristotle's golden mean, Kant's categorical imperative, Mill's principle of utility, Rawls's veil of ignorance, and the Judeo-Christian view of persons as ends in themselves.

◎ *Aristotle's golden mean.* "Moral virtue is appropriate location between two extremes." This is a philosophy of moderation and compromise, often called the *golden mean*. The journalistic concept of fairness reflects this idea.

◎ *Kant's categorical imperative.* "Act on that maxim which you will to become a universal law." Eighteenth-century philosopher Immanuel Kant developed this idea, an extension of Aristotle's golden mean. Kant's test—that you make decisions based on principles that you want to be universally applied—is called the *categorical imperative.* This means you would act by asking yourself the question, "What if everyone acted this way?"

◎ *Mill's principle of utility.* "Seek the greatest happiness for the greatest number." In the 19th century, John Stuart Mill taught that the best decision is the one with the biggest overall benefit for the most human beings.

◎ *Rawls's veil of ignorance.* "Justice emerges when negotiating without social differentiations." John Rawls's theory, devised in the 20th-century, supports an egalitarian society that asks everyone to work from a sense of liberty and basic respect for everyone, regardless of social position.

◎ *Judeo-Christian view of persons as ends in themselves.* "Love your neighbour as yourself." Under this long-standing ethic of religious heritage, people should care for one another—friends as well as enemies—equally and without favour. Trust in people and they will trust in you.[16]

None of these five philosophies operates independently. Ethical choices in many journalistic situations are seldom simple. What is predictable about journalistic ethics is their unpredictability. Therefore, journalists generally adopt a philosophy of "situational" ethics: Because each circumstance is different, individual journalists must decide what is best in each situation.

Should the press adopt Rawls's idea of social equality and cover each person equally, or should public officials receive more scrutiny than others because they maintain a public trust? Is it a loving act in the Judeo-Christian tradition to allow bereaved parents the private sorrow of their child's death by drowning, or is the journalist contributing to society's greater good by warning others about the dangers of leaving a child unattended? Questions like these leave the press in a continually bubbling cauldron of ethical quandaries.

How the Media Define Ethics

Ethical dilemmas might seem easier to solve with a rule book nearby, and schools of journalism and many professional media organizations have tried to codify ethical judgments to ensure the outcomes in difficult situations. Codes of ethics can be very general ("Truth is our ultimate goal"—Society of Professional Journalists in the United States); some are very specific ("We will no longer accept any complimentary tickets, dinners, junkets, gifts or favors of any kind" —*The San Bernardino* [California] *Sun*); and some are very personal ("I will try to tell people what they ought to know and avoid telling them what they want to hear, except when the two coincide, which isn't often"—CBS commentator Andy Rooney).[17]

Some ethical decisions carry legal consequences—for example, when a journalist reports embarrassing facts and invades someone's privacy (see Chapter 14). In most cases, however, a reporter or a news organization that makes an ethical mistake will not face a lawsuit. The consequences of bad ethical judgments usually involve damage to the newsmakers who are involved and to the individual journalist, damage to the reputation of the news organization where the journalist works, and damage to the profession in general.

Professional Ethics Codes

Professional codes of ethics set a leadership tone for a profession, an organization, or an individual. Several groups have attempted to write rules governing how the media should operate.

Today, codes of ethics for both print and broadcast are voluntary, with no absolute penalties for people who violate the rules. Many media organizations, such as the CBC, maintain their own detailed standards and may actually hire people to oversee ethical conduct. Other organizations use guidelines from professional groups as a basis to develop their own philosophies. Advertising and public relations organizations also have issued ethical codes.

Ethics and Professional Standards for the School of Journalism and Communication at Carleton University

In Canada, there are no national codes of journalistic ethics. However, the code of ethics published by the School of Journalism and Communication at Carleton University may be taken as representative. The following list quotes directly from the code's major points:

Fundamental Principles

◎ In a democracy, **all** people must be encouraged to exert influence and be involved.

◎ A free society offers choices. Information and understanding is essential for meaningful participation and informed decision-making.

◎ The role of journalism and of the journalist is to collect and disseminate information and opinion, to foster understanding, so that people may enjoy the rights and discharge the responsibilities of full citizenship.

◎ The public trust implicit in journalism calls for a high degree of independence and impartiality. This public trust is not a right. It is a privilege to be earned and sustained through daily practice. Never compromise your independence. The journalist's mandate calls for the highest degree of ethical behaviour, professionalism and judgment.

Guidelines

1. Journalists constantly have to balance the individual's right to privacy against the public's need for information. Where an individual's need for privacy is an issue, **do** weigh it against the value of the information to the audience. If the weight is clearly on the side of the individual or the audience, the decision is easy. When the balance seems even, the journalist's first obligation is to the audience. If in doubt, consult your instructor.

2. **Do** identify yourself as a journalist. On investigative assignments, if doing so is likely to result in the withholding of information essential to the story, exceptions may be made with the approval of the instructor.

3. Keep professional promises to sources who have been honest with you.

4. **Don't** solicit or accept information from sources on the understanding that you are a student and it will not be published. That's not journalism. Identify yourself as a student, but state that, if at all possible, you hope to publish the article.

5. **Don't** solicit or accept information on the understanding that the source will have any right of approval or control over what is written or broadcast, or the right to see or hear, in advance, what will be published or broadcast.

6. **Do** inform interviewees about the general subject matter, and explain what may be done with their answers. **Don't** provide a list of questions in advance, either for information or approval, without the approval of the instructor. In such a case, **do** make it clear that you will not be limited in the interview to the questions on the list.

7. **Don't** pay sources or give gifts or favours to sources nor accept special treatment, money, favours or gifts of value from sources. Use your common sense. A cup of coffee is not a bribe. But a free trip, lavish entertainment or a bottle of liquor may be seen as one. Not only should you not be bought, but you should not be seen as having been bought.

8. Unless approved by your instructor, **don't** tape or videotape a source for broadcast without first having explained that you will do so.

9. Reporting without direct attribution is sometimes essential to go beyond the apparent and superficial in covering public affairs. **Do**, however, identify sources and attribute information as a general rule. Journalists making a commitment of confidentiality should be aware that, in law, they have no legal privilege with sources and may be convicted of contempt of court, a criminal offence, for honouring their commitment.

10. **Do** confirm with sources exactly what is meant when they provide information on the understanding that it is "off the record," "background" or "not for attribution." **Do** ask if "off the record" information may be used to get it on the record.

11. Many people are not accustomed to dealing with the media, to the point of being naive and extremely vulnerable. In many cases, they find themselves "in the news" through no actions of their own. **Don't** take advantage of such naiveté or vulnerability, or manipulate such a person.

12. **Do** quote sources precisely, and fairly reflect the context of conversations. While some instructors may impose a stricter standard, there may be no harm in altering a quote to:
    ◎ correct grammar that could make the statement confusing or make the speaker look foolish.
    ◎ avoid dialect that is not essential to the story.

13. **Don't** fabricate or plagiarize. (This includes faking on-location actuality, film/video or photographs; or fabricating sound bytes, or clips, in any way.) Both may result in disciplinary action up to and including suspension from the journalism program. Faculty members must report to the director of the school, as quickly as possible, allegations of fabrication or plagiarism.

14 Second-hand information, beyond that which is general background and uncontroversial, must be checked independently. The basic principle: **do** your own research.

15. If erroneous information is disseminated, **do** admit and correct the error(s) as soon as possible.

16. Opinion, interpretative or analytical pieces should be clearly labelled in a way that is easily understood by the audience.

17. Offensive language, including profanity and insulting comment, should be included only when clearly relevant to the story.

Conflict of Interest

1. **Do** avoid direct conflicts of interest and be aware that the appearance of conflict should also be considered.
2. **Don't** interview your friends and family unless you make the relationship clear to the audience. Where, because of personal or family relationships, your objectivity or impartiality may be called into question, **don't** undertake a reporting or editing assignment. The integrity of the journalist-source relationship varies inversely with their personal closeness.
3. Journalists should not be denied the rights of citizenship, but exercising these rights in a partisan way may conflict with journalistic integrity. The journalist is disqualified from writing or editing news about matters in which he/she is specifically involved.
4. **Don't** abuse your journalistic role for personal benefit or gain or for the benefit or gain of a family member, friend or acquaintance.

The Media's Responses to Criticism

Prescriptive codes of ethics are helpful in describing what journalists should do, and informal guidelines can supplement professional codes (see Point of View "Do Canadians Want to Know?"). Moreover, most journalists use good judgment. But what happens when they don't? People with serious complaints against broadcasters sometimes appeal to the CRTC (see "Regulating Broadcast," Chapter 14), but what about complaints that must be handled more quickly? The press has offered three solutions: press councils, readers' representatives, and correction boxes.

News Councils

News councils originated in Great Britain. They are composed of people who formerly worked or currently work in the news business, as well as some laypeople. The council reviews complaints from the public, and when the members determine that a mistake has been made, the council reports its findings to the offending news organization.

Media ethics scholar John Hulteng writes:

> It would seem that—as with the [ethical] codes—the great impact of the press councils is likely to be on the responsible editors, publishers and broadcasters who for the most part were already attempting to behave ethically.... An additional value of the councils may be the mutual understanding that grows out of the exchange across the council table between the members of the public and the managers of the media. These values should not be dismissed as insignificant, of course. But neither should too much be expected of them.[18]

I M P A C T

Point of View   *DO CANADIANS WANT TO KNOW?*

By Anthony Wilson-Smith

When it comes to scandal, intrigue and wrongdoing in Ottawa, any journalist can identify obvious potential culprits. Prime Minister Jean Chrétien routinely violates established rules of grammar. Deputy Prime Minister Herb Gray, a rock 'n' roll aficionado, is believed guilty of playing Hootie and the Blowfish on his stereo at unacceptably high decibel levels. Reform Leader Preston Manning, during visits to Quebec, systematically assaults the French language. All members of the Bloc Québécois commit verbal abuse of English Canada. The New Democratic Party has kidnapped the 1960s and holds them hostage in its political program. The Progressive Conservatives, who first reported all their ideas stolen by the Liberals, are now believed missing themselves.

In short, for better *and* worse, the history of political scandals reported by the Canadian media is small beer compared to that of the United States. That is mostly cause for satisfaction: the prospect of the Prime Minister or Manning engaging in an extramarital dalliance seems as unlikely as it is unappealing. Ottawa's dull air of probity allows Canadians to peer south at President Bill Clinton's alleged sexual follies, secure (or wistful) in the knowledge that such things Could Never Happen Here.

In fact, there is no reason why they could not, although the volume of allegations against Clinton bears a typically American grandness of scale. But even before considering the possibility of similar scandal in Ottawa, two questions arise: do Canadians want to know salacious details about their leaders—and, if so, would the media tell them? The answer to the first is maybe; to the second, probably not.

When it comes to controversies involving the personal lives of politicians, members of the parliamentary press gallery traditionally operate on two levels; there is the shortlist of scandals they publicly cover, and the much longer list of those that they privately speculate on. Sir Wilfrid Laurier had a mistress who bore him a child—but it was not until recent years that Laurier biographers mentioned that fact. William Lyon Mackenzie King's fascination with prostitutes was not written about until the publication of his diaries long after his death.

In the 1970s, Canadians learned about Margaret Trudeau's indiscretions only after they appeared in the American media; until then, Canadian journalists were aware, but silent. That restraint is the rule, not the exception; most journalists in Ottawa can, without breaking a sweat, recount rumours involving high-ranking cabinet members of every government of the past three decades. In the late 1970s, it was widely known that one member of the Progressive Conservative caucus came home to find another member in bed with his wife. At least one member of a Liberal cabinet had a public affair while married. Both the Tories and the present Liberal administration have had cabinet ministers believed to have serious drinking problems. All such cases were virtually ignored.

There are a variety of reasons for that. Journalists can be reluctant to print information damaging to a confidential source. Reporters, MPs and their political aides often interact in the most personal ways—including times when one or both are married to others. And, although some politicians would be astonished by the idea, many journalists do not relish heaping embarrassment on them.

Another reason for silence is the explanation that the alleged scandals are impossible to verify; often, however, this is because reporters only make half-hearted attempts at verification. Then, there is the notion that Canadians do not share Americans' appetite for gossip and intrigue—and are, in fact, repelled by same. But journalist Stevie Cameron's *On the Take*, a muckraking attack on Brian Mulroney and his government, has sold more than 250,000 copies. The satirical gossip magazine *Frank* sells a respectable average of 20,000 copies of each issue, despite the fact it spends next to nothing on promotion, is only available in a few cities, and carries content that even its publisher Michael Bate, admits may be only half-true.

The strongest argument for keeping silent is this: private lives should remain so unless they affect the politician's performance as a public figure. Someone who is, say, secretly homosexual should be allowed to stay in the closet—unless he or she publicly supports anti-gay actions and legislation. A politician with an alcohol problem is left alone until it appears that it is affecting his or her public performance. And a politician's sexual affairs go unreported—unless he or she is vigorously espousing family values.

That is changing. In Washington, *Newsweek*—which had the original allegations against Clinton—delayed publication because of concerns about their veracity. But when details were released on the Internet in *The Drudge Report*—whose author had no additional means of determining if they were true—they immediately entered the public domain. *Frank*, in Canada, routinely does the same. One principle cited is "the public's right to know." The question is whether that should encompass things that are unproven, unsourced or untrue. Another justification is the age-old vow to "publish and be damned." It sounds rather noble—except that the one most damned by gossip is almost never the publisher. Should journalists be expected to publicly declare all the speculation they make in private to one another? If so, the obvious answer is either to investigate a lot more—or talk a lot less.

Maclean's, *February 9, 1998*, p. 13. *Reprinted with permission.*

Readers' Representatives

The *readers' representative* (also called an ombudsperson) is a go-between at a newspaper who responds to complaints from the public and regularly publishes answers to criticism in the newspaper. However, most newspapers still funnel complaints directly to the editor.

Correction Boxes

The *correction box* is a device that often is handled by a readers' representative but that also has been adopted by many papers without a readers' representative. The box is published in the same place, usually a prominent one, in the newspaper every day. As a permanent feature of the newspaper, the correction box leads readers to notice when the newspaper retracts or modifies a statement. It is used to counter criticism that corrections sometimes receive less attention from readers than the original stories.

Readers' representatives and correction boxes are used by many papers to help handle criticism of the newspapers and to avert possible legal problems that some stories foster. But these solutions address only a small percentage of issues. In newsrooms every day, reporters face the same ethical decisions that all people face in their daily lives—whether to be honest, how to be fair, how to be sensitive, and how to be responsible.

The difference is that, unlike personal ethical dilemmas that other people can debate privately, reporters and editors publish and broadcast the results of their ethical judgments and those judgments become public knowledge—in newspapers, magazines, books, and on radio and television. So potentially, the media's ethical decisions can broadly affect society.

The Importance of Professional Ethics

A profession that accepts ethical behaviour as a standard helps guarantee a future for that profession. The major commodity that the press has to offer is information, and when the presentation of that information is weakened by untruth, bias, intrusiveness, or irresponsibility, the press gains few advocates and acquires more enemies. Writes John Hulteng:

> The primary objective of the press and those who work with it is to bring readers, listeners, and viewers as honest, accurate, and complete an account of the day's events as possible.... The need to be informed is so great that the Constitution provides the press with a First Amendment standing that is unique among business enterprises. But as with most grants of power, there is an accompanying responsibility, not constitutionally mandated but nonetheless well understood: that the power of the press must be used responsibly and compassionately.[19]

In Focus

◎ The word *ethics* derives from the Greek word *ethos*, which means the traditions or guiding spirit that govern a culture.

◎ Journalists' ethical dilemmas can be discussed using four categories: truthfulness, fairness, privacy, and responsibility.

◎ Truthfulness means more than telling the truth to get a story. Truthfulness also means not misrepresenting the people or the situations in the story to readers or viewers.

◎ Truthfulness means that government agencies should not knowingly provide disinformation to the press.

◎ Fairness implies impartiality. Criticism of the press for unfairness results from insider friendships, conflicts of interest, and chequebook journalism.

◎ Two important invasion-of-privacy issues are the publication of the names of AIDS victims and the publication of the names of rape victims.

◎ Responsibility means that reporters and editors must be very careful about the way they use the information they gather.

◎ Staged events, such as the GM truck explosion, and live events, such as the raid broadcast by CNN, offer especially perilous ethical situations.

◎ Five philosophical principles underlying the practical application of ethical decisions are: Aristotle's golden mean, Immanuel Kant's categorical imperative, John Stuart Mill's principle of utility, John Rawls's veil of ignorance, and the Judeo-Christian view of persons as ends in themselves.

◎ Many media schools and professional associations have adopted ethical codes to guide their conduct, such as the guidelines adopted by Carleton University's School of Journalism and Communications.

◎ Three responses by the press to criticism have been to create press councils, to employ readers' representatives, and to publish correction boxes. These solutions address only a small percentage of the issues.

Review Questions

1. How can chequebook journalism affect the quality of reporting?

2. Do TV and print differ in their coverage of live news events? Why? Why not?

3. What effect do you believe that ethical codes have on the professionals for whom they have been adopted?

4. How effective have the use of press councils, readers' representatives, and correction boxes been in overcoming ethical abuses and erroneous reporting? What are their limitations? Explain.

Watching the Web

◎ **Drudge Report**

http://www.drudgereport.com/

◎ **Freedom Forum**

http://www.freedomforum.org/

◎ **The New Media Monitor**

http://www.gpnet.it/dallomo/

◎ **Radio-Television News Directors Ethics Codes**

http://www.missouri.edu/~jourvs

A GLOBAL MEDIA MARKETPLACE

16

What's Ahead

AS THE UNIVERSE BEHIND THE SCREEN EXPANDS, IT WILL BE THE PEOPLE IN FRONT WHO SHAPE THE SOUL OF THE NEW MACHINE.

The Economist, *"Wired Planet," February 1994*

- Differing Standards of Practice
- Political Theories and the Press
- Defining Global Media Systems
- Looking at Similarities and Differences among World Media Systems
- Western Europe
- Eastern Europe
- The Middle East and North Africa
- Africa
- Asia and the Pacific
- Latin America and the Caribbean
- News and Information Flow
- Global Media Open New Markets
- Chasing International Consumers
- Opening New Pathways for Ideas

We often assume that the media in most countries around the world operate like the media we know well. But media industries in different countries are as varied as the countries they serve. Can you identify the countries in the following media situations?

1. Citizens of this country woke up one morning to find that, overnight, their leader had shut down several independent newspapers and broadcast stations. Heavily armed police raided the media outlets and shut them down.

2. In this country, contestants on a weekly TV game show eat overly spicy foods, and the champion is dubbed Super Spiciness King.

3. In this country, a program called *Youth TV* broadcasts racy rock videos, professional wrestling from Madison Square Garden, and Oliver Stone's epic *J.F.K.* The station is run by the son of the government's leader.

4. This country's TV Licence Police tour neighbourhoods with television set detectors. If they find an unregistered set, they can knock on the door of someone's house, fine the owner, and threaten him or her with jail if the person doesn't pay the annual TV licence fee.[1]

Differing Standards of Practice

The armed police raid (example 1) took place in Nigeria in 1993, when the country's ruler, General Ibrahim Babangida, raided newspapers and magazines owned by his primary rival, millionaire business tycoon Moshood Abiola. One year later, the Nigerian government closed newspapers that were critical of the military government.

The TV game show with the spicy cast (example 2) is very popular in Japan, where *TV Champion* is one of several shows in which contestants vie for modest prizes and national attention by showing *gaman*, or endurance.

The manager of the station where *Youth TV* appears (example 3) is Uday Hussein, Saddam Hussein's son. His station, Channel 2, began broadcasting the new format in Iraq in 1993. Iraq's culture minister Hamid Youssel Hammadi told the *Los Angeles Times*, "We don't want our youth to be more or less split from what is going on outside."

British householders are responsible for paying a yearly TV licence fee, which is about $200 (example 4). The fee is due at the post office each year. The collectors are employees of the post office who rove the streets with special detection equipment installed in vans. The government collects more than $2.5 billion

a year from the fees, which allows the British Broadcasting Corporation (BBC) to operate several TV channels without advertising, aside from promotion of the networks' own programming.

These examples help demonstrate the complexity of defining today's international media marketplace, which clearly is a marketplace in rapid transition. To discuss global media, this chapter is divided into four sections: (1) the media and government, (2) world media systems, (3) news and information flow, and (4) global media markets.

Political Theories and the Press

No institutions as sizable and influential as the mass media can escape involvement with government and politics. The media are not only channels for the transmission of political information and debate, but also significant players with a direct stake in government's regulatory and economic policies, as well as government's attitude toward free speech and dissent. Remember that *the way a country's political system is organized affects the way the media within that country operate.* Media systems can be broadly divided into those systems that allow effective dissent and those that do not.

Defining Global Media Systems

To categorize the political organization of media systems, scholars often begin with the 1956 book *Four Theories of the Press*, by Fred S. Siebert, Theodore Peterson, and Wilbur Schramm. These four theories described the political systems under which media operated in different countries: (1) the Soviet theory, (2) the authoritarian theory, (3) the libertarian theory, and (4) the social responsibility theory. A fifth description, the more modern *developmental theory*, updates the original categories.

The Soviet Theory

In the now-defunct Soviet Union (now the Commonwealth of Independent States), the government owned and operated the mass media. All media employees were government employees, expected to serve the government's interests.

Top media executives also served as leaders in the Communist party. Even when the press controls loosened in the 1980s, the mass media were part of the government's policy. Government control came *before* the media published or broadcast; people who controlled the media could exercise *prior restraint*. They could review copy and look at programs *before* they appeared.

This description of the Soviet press system applied before the events of the 1990s challenged the basic assumptions of Soviet government. Many Eastern bloc countries, such as Romania and Czechoslovakia, which once operated under Soviet influence, based their media systems on the communist model. Today, the media systems in these countries are in transition.

The Authoritarian Theory

Media that operate under the authoritarian theory can be either publicly or privately owned. This concept of the press developed in Europe after Gutenberg. Until the 1850s, presses in Europe were privately owned, and aristocracies (which governed the countries) required some sort of control over what was printed about them. The aristocracies had the financial and political power necessary to make the rules about what would be printed.

Their first idea was to license everyone who owned a press so the licence could be revoked if someone published something unfavourable about the government. The first colonial newspapers in North America, for example, were licensed by the British government. This system was unsuccessful, however, because many people who owned presses didn't apply for licences.

The next authoritarian attempt to control the press was to review material after it was published. A printer who was discovered publishing material that strongly challenged the government could be heavily fined or even put to death.

Today, many governments still maintain this type of rigid control over the media. Many monarchies and totalitarian dictatorships, for example, operate in an authoritarian tradition, which tolerates very little dissent. Media systems that serve at the government's pleasure and with the government's approval are common.

"And, finally, after a day of record trading on Wall Street, the entire world was owned by Mickey Mouse."

The Libertarian Theory

The concept of a libertarian press evolved from the idea that people who are given all of the information on an issue will be able to discern what is true and what is false and will make good choices. This is an idea embraced by democratic governments.

This theory assumes, of course, that the media's main goal is to convey the truth and that the media will not cave in to outside pressures, such as from advertisers or corporate owners. This theory also assumes that people with opposing viewpoints will be heard—that the media will present all points of view, in what is commonly referred to as a free marketplace of ideas.

The constitutions (written and unwritten) in most Western countries advocate the idea of freedom of the press. Most Western countries today operate under the libertarian theory, although this ideal has been challenged often by changes in the media industries and may not work well in practice when ownership of media industries is heavily concentrated.

The Social Responsibility Theory

This theory accepts the concept of a libertarian press but prescribes what the media should do. Someone who believes in the social responsibility theory believes that members of the press will do their jobs well only if they are periodically reminded about their duties.

This theory grew out of the 1947 Hutchins Commission Report on the Free and Responsible Press, published in the United States. The commission listed five goals for the press, including the need for truthful and complete reporting of all sides of an issue. The commission concluded that the press's privileged constitutional position means that the press must always work to be responsible to society.[2]

If the media fail to meet their responsibilities to society, the social responsibility theory holds that the government should encourage the media to comply. In this way the libertarian and the social responsibility theories differ. The libertarian theory assumes the media will work well without government interference; the social responsibility theory advocates government involvement with the media to ensure that they act in society's best interest.

Since 1956, when the four theories first were used to describe media systems, critics have contended that these theories are too limiting and that the categories cannot neatly describe all of the world's media. In fact, many countries today combine elements of one or more types of media systems.

The Developmental Theory

A fifth description of media systems that can be added to describe today's media has been called the developmental or Third World theory. Under this system, named for the developing nations where it is most often found, the media can be privately owned, but they usually are owned by the government. The government uses the media to promote the country's social and economic goals, and to direct a sense of national purpose. For example, a developmental media system might be used to promote birth control or to encourage children to attend school. The media become an outlet for some types of government propaganda, then, but in the name of economic and social progress for the country.

Although the theory that best describes most Western media is the libertarian theory, throughout their history the media have struggled with both authoritarian and social responsibility debates: Should the press be free to print secret government documents, for example? What responsibility do the networks have to provide worthwhile programming to their audiences? The media, the government, and the public continually adjust their interpretations of just how the media should operate.

Looking at Similarities and Differences among World Media Systems

It has been four decades since scholars began using the four theories of the press to define the world's press systems. At today's transitional period in global history, even the recent addition of the developmental theory of the press still leaves many press systems beyond convenient categorization.

The print media form the basis for press development in North America, Australia, Western Europe, and Eastern Europe, where two-thirds of the world's newspapers are published.[3] Many developing countries matured after broadcast media were introduced in the 1920s, and newsprint in these countries often is scarce or government-controlled, making radio their dominant communications medium. Radio receivers are inexpensive, and many people can share one radio.

Television, which relies on expensive equipment, is in widespread use in prosperous nations and in urban areas of developing countries. Yet, many countries still have only one television service, usually run by the government.[4] In most developing countries, all broadcasting—television and radio—is owned and controlled by the government.

What follows is a description of today's press systems by region: Western Europe, Eastern Europe, the Middle East and North Africa, Africa, Asia and the Pacific, and Latin America and the Caribbean.

Western Europe

Western European media operate under guarantees of freedom of expression of one sort or another, but each nation has modified the idea to reflect differing values. For example, in Great Britain the media are prohibited from commenting on a trial until the trial is finished. France and Greece, unlike other countries, give more libel protection to public figures than to private citizens.

Scandinavian journalists enjoy the widest press freedoms of all of Western Europe, including almost unlimited access to public documents.

Print Media

Johannes Gutenberg's invention of movable type rooted the print media in Western Europe. Today, Western European media companies produce many newspapers. *The Times* of London, *Frankfurter Allgemeine* of Germany, *Le Monde* of France, and *Corriere della Sera* of Milan enjoy healthy circulations. Western European newspapers tend to be much more partisan than the North American press, and newspapers (and journalists) are expected to reflect strong political points of view. British newspapers, for instance, are widely known to follow a political line.

Audio and Video Media

As elsewhere, the print media in Western Europe are losing audiences to broadcast and cable. (See Figure 16.1.) Governments originally controlled most of Western Europe's broadcast stations. A board of 12 governors, appointed by the government, supervises the British Broadcasting Corporation (BBC), for example. To finance the government-run broadcast media, countries tax the sale of radios and TVs or charge users an annual fee. Broadcasting in Western Europe is slowly evolving to private ownership and commercial sponsorship, with much more choice available now as a result of the introduction of cable TV, direct-to-home satellite broadcasting, and multiple public broadcaster channels. Channels from other countries and in other languages are now being made available, as well.

Western Europeans have watched less than half as much television as people in the United States as a rule—an average of 3 hours a day per household in Europe. One reason for the difference in viewing time may be that many Western European TV stations don't operate 24 hours a day. In the majority of countries, commercials are shown back-to-back at the beginning or the end of a program.[5]

In Western Europe, direct-to-home satellite viewing is more advanced than in North America. Signals are delivered by satellite 24 hours a day (often including the CNN International channel). This service is rapidly changing the television viewing environment in Western Europe; choice is the dominant feature.

Figure 16.1

Switching On

Source: Data from *The Economist.*

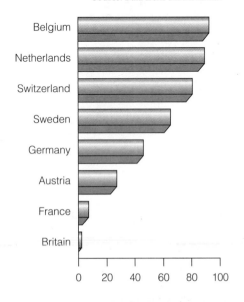

Percentages of households with televisions connected to cable

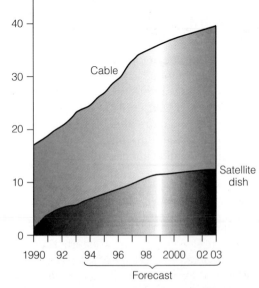

Current and projected percentages of European households with cable and satellite

Europe, however, still gets much of its programming from the United States. Of 125 000 hours of TV broadcast in Western Europe each year, only 20 000 hours are produced in Europe. Most of the programming comes from the United States, with a few shows imported from Canada, Australia, and Japan.[6] U.S. imports are attractive because programs such as *L.A. Law*, which is very popular in Western Europe, are cheaper to buy than to produce. In terms of quality, however, domestically produced programs, especially dramas, are generally superior.

The European Community (EC) created a single, unified European market. The policy adopted by the EC establishes "Television Without Frontiers" to promote an open marketplace for television programs among countries in the EC, as well as between EC countries and Canada and the United States.

Some members of the EC (especially France) have proposed quotas to limit imported TV programs, charging that U.S. imports are an example of "cultural imperialism." Countries that favour quotas fear that the importation of U.S. programs imposes a concentration of U.S. values on their viewers. The United States opposes such quotas, of course, because Western European commercial broadcasting offers a seemingly insatiable market for recycled U.S. programs. In general, cultural industries such as television have been excluded from international free trade agreements.

Eastern Europe

The democratization of Eastern Europe is transforming the media in these countries at an unprecedented pace. Some examples:

◎ In the six months after the Berlin Wall came down in 1990, circulation of East Germany's national newspapers *Neues Deutschland* and *Junge Welt* dropped 55 percent as the East German population, hungry for news from the West, embraced the flashy West German mass circulation daily *Bild*.[7]

◎ In Poland, Eastern Europe's first private television station, Echo, went on the air in February 1990, with a total cash investment of $15 000. The station broadcast programs from the windowless janitor's room of a student dormitory.[8]

◎ One week after the 1991 failed coup in the Soviet Union, President Mikhail Gorbachev fired the directors of the Soviet news agency, TASS, who had supported the coup.[9] Then, on December 25, 1991, Gorbachev resigned. Within 24 hours, President Boris N. Yeltsin of Russia announced that the government would maintain control of the broadcast media. TASS moved away from government control and was renamed RITA (Russian Information Telegraph Agency).

Everette E. Dennis, executive director of the Gannett Center for Media Studies, and Jon Vanden Heuvel described the Eastern European challenges in a report issued after a Gannett-sponsored 1990 fact-finding trip:

> Mass communication in the several countries of the region was reinventing itself. While grassroots newspapers and magazines struggled for survival, new press laws were being debated and enacted; elements of a market economy were coming into view; the media

Point of View — MEXICAN TV GETS "PERSONAL"

*Soap operas have always been pop-
ular on Mexican TV, but three years
ago, the government allowed a private
network to compete with the government-run Televisa. The new network,
TV Azteca, produced programs that
reflected many real-life problems,
such as drug dealers and corrupt government officials. In this article from
the* Washington Post, *reporter Molly
Moore describes how this change in
programming is transforming the role
that TV plays in Mexican life.*

MEXICO CITY—High-level assassina-
tions. Narco-corruption. Embarrassing
political scandals. The usual fodder for
Mexico's daily newspapers.

But wait. This is not the news.
This is a prime-time soap, where the
biggest scandals are supposed to be
in the bedroom, where poor-but-sexy
housemaid lures rich-but-unfulfilled
business exec to the altar and both
live blissfully ever after in their newly
refurbished hacienda, oblivious to
peso crashes and political upheaval.

To be sure, "Nada Personal," or
"Nothing Personal," the nightly soap
opera that aspires to rewrite the script
of Mexican television, comes with
more than its share of steamy sex,
boudoir intrigue and petty jealousies.

But the producers of a major
"telenovela" finally figured out what
most Mexicans have known all along:
This country's real-life soap operas
are far more entertaining. And with
relaxed government control over television, they're able to leave no plot
unturned.

Three years ago, for the first time
in Mexican history, the government
allowed a private network to compete
with its staid, nationalistic, government-run Televisa. And thus TV
Azteca was born.

It was punchier, irreverent and,
most important, not subject to the
strict self-imposed censorship of the
official voice of the government and
the nation. To wean the audience from
the only network Mexicans have ever
known required bold experiments.

"Nothing Personal" is one. The
name comes from a scene in the
opening episode, which aired May 20,
[1996] in which the chief of intelligence for the city police (who is
bought and paid for by the drug car-
tels) stands beside the bullet-riddled
van containing the bloodied and very
dead body of the attorney general he
had ordered killed. He mutters, "It's
nothing personal, compadre."

"This is the first time a 'novela' has
presented the realities of what drives
our country," said Silvia Navarrete, an
avid soap fan and 34-year-old special-
education teacher.

Breaking TV Taboos
The show has also broken long-held
television taboos and so both titil-
lated and shocked viewers here.
("Nothing Personal" is shown in 17
other countries, including the United
States.)

Telling It Like It Is
The show portrayed a lesbian relationship for the first time on Mexican
television. And it gave the first
televised glimpse of a naked man.
It has a leading character who is in a
wheelchair but has an active sex life.
Its characters throw around foul
language with unprecedented force
and regularity.

The show that thrives on scandal
is now contending with a scandal of
its own.

Twenty-six episodes before the
climactic final chapter of the 200-
show serial, the star quit in a very
public huff. Ana Colchero, who at age
27 was paid nearly $500,000 to desert
Televisa this year for the leading role
on TV Azteca's premier soap, said it
was a matter of principle.

An Unrealistic Turn
"This was supposed to be a different
type of soap opera, a realistic story
that talks about things that really
happened," Colchero said in an
interview at the colonial-style house
she rents in one of Mexico City's
most charming neighborhoods. "My

character was a very active woman,
very courageous, very honest."

She played Camila, recent law-
school grad and doting daughter of
the assassinated attorney general.
In the first episode the blue-eyed,
pouty-lipped actress proves her
macho mettle by leaping into the ring
to distract a bleeding bull about to
gore the matador.

Then, in Colchero's favorite scene,
Camila calls the crooked cops crooks
at a gutsy news conference after her
father's murder and vows to launch
her own investigation. Alas, she's
sidelined by those same crooked
cops, who plant a fat packet of coke
in her purse and throw her in jail on
drug charges.

"That was OK, she had to go to
jail," Colchero said of her character.

What she didn't like is what happened when she got out of jail. The
writers, according to Colchero, turned
her into a whimpering, lying, two-
timing begins-with-a-B.

"She started to become the same
type of character as in all the other
soap operas," Colchero said.

A brief translation: Camila falls in
love with and gets pregnant by the
TV camerman who took her to the
hospital after her dad's murder, but
marries his brother (Demian Bichir),
who also happens to be the cop
investigating her dad's murder. She
lies to the cameraman and tells him
the baby is the cop's. Hardly the
scenario that independent, straight-
talking Camila would have written for
herself, according to Colchero.

"Nothing Personal" writers and
producers are scrambling to deal with
the Colchero debacle. The game plan
is simply to replace the actress and
follow the script as planned, Ibarra
said.

No matter how popular the show,
a serial on Mexican television runs no
more than one season. The final
episode of "Nothing Personal" [aired]
in February [1997].

system itself and its role in the state and society were being redefined, as was the very nature of journalism and the job description of the journalist, who was no longer a propagandist for the state.[10]

Eastern Europe in transition is defining a new balance between the desire for free expression and the indigenous remnants of a system of government control.

In many of these countries, the media played a central role in upsetting the established power structure. Often one of the first targets of the revolutionary movements was the broadcast facilities.

For example, in Romania in 1989, opposition leaders of the National Salvation Committee and sympathetic employees barricaded themselves in a Bucharest TV station, rallying the audience to action. "Romania was governed from a hectic studio littered with empty bottles, cracked coffee mugs and half-eaten sandwiches, and run by people who had not slept in days," the Associated Press reported.[11]

Audio and Video Media

Television in the Eastern bloc countries developed under government direction because the Communists were in power before TV use was widespread. Radio broadcasting also was tightly controlled, although foreign broadcasts directed across Eastern European borders, such as *Voice of America* and *Radio Free Europe*, usually evaded jamming attempts by Radio Moscow. These short-wave broadcasts were regarded by many as counter-propaganda in their own right.

Print Media

Print media were strictly controlled in the East Bloc, with high-ranking party officials forming the core of media management. Because paper supplies were limited, newspapers rarely exceeded 12 pages. *Pravda*, the Soviet Union's oldest newspaper, was founded in 1912 by revolutionary leader Vladimir Lenin, who said that a newspaper should be a "collective propagandist," a "collective agitator," and a "collective organizer."[12] The Eastern European nations developed their press policies following the Soviet model.

In the late 1980s, President Mikhail Gorbachev relaxed media controls as part of his policy of *glasnost*. In 1988, the first paid commercials (for Pepsi-Cola, Sony, and Visa credit cards) appeared on Soviet TV, and in 1989, the Soviet daily newspaper *Izvestia* published its first Western ads (including ads for perfume, for wines from the French firm Pechiney, and for Dresdner, a German bank).

In 1990, the Supreme Soviet outlawed media censorship and gave every citizen the right to publish a newspaper.[13] Within five months, more than 100 newspapers began publication. Then, showing how quickly government positions can change, in early 1991 Gorbachev asked the Supreme Soviet to suspend these press freedoms, but they refused.[14] Less than a year later, the Soviet Union had been replaced by the Commonwealth of Independent States, and Gorbachev's successor in the new country of Russia, President Boris Yeltsin, continued to relax government control of the press.

As the Eastern European governments change and realign themselves, the adjustments facing Eastern European media are unprecedented. According to Dennis and Vanden Heuvel:

Lenin's journalistic legacy: *Pravda*.

CP Picture Archive (Sergei Karpukhin)

Once the revolution came, among the first acts of new government was to take (they would say liberate) electronic media and open up the print press. Permitting free and eventually independent media was a vital beginning for democracy in several countries and a clear break with the past. The freeing up of the media system, speedily in some countries and incrementally in others, was the lifting of an ideological veil without saying just what would replace it.[15]

The Middle East and North Africa

Press history in the Middle East and North Africa begins with the newspaper *Al-Iraq*, first published in 1817, although the first daily newspaper didn't begin until 1873. With one exception, development of the printed press throughout this region follows the same pattern as in most developing countries: More newspapers and magazines are published in regions with high literacy rates than in regions with low literacy rates. The exception is Egypt, where less than half the people are literate. Yet, Cairo is the Arab world's publishing centre.[16] *Al Ahram* and *Al Akhbar* are Egypt's leading dailies.

Print Media

The Middle Eastern press is tightly controlled by government restrictions, through ownership and licensing, and it is not uncommon for opposition newspapers to disappear and for journalists to be jailed or to leave the country following political upheaval.

Following the revolution in Iran, all opposition and some moderate newspapers were closed, and according to the National Union of Iranian Journalists (now an illegal organization), more than 75 percent of all journalists left the country, were jailed, or no longer work in journalism.[17]

The Palestinian press, for example, was subject to censorship by the Israeli government, and all Palestinian newspapers and magazines once required permission from the Israeli government to be published.[18]

Audio and Video Media

The foreign-language press is especially strong in the Middle East because of the large number of immigrants in the area. And foreign radio is very popular. Radio and television are almost completely controlled by the governments within each country, and television broadcasts for only a few hours each night. So radio signals beamed from Europe have become the region's alternative affordable source of news.

Because of tight censorship, newspapers and television stations in the Arab world frequently reflect the biases or outright propaganda of their governments. But radio broadcasts from outside the region travel easily across borders and long distances, and many Arabs regard those stations as the most reliable sources of unbiased news.[19]

The BBC World Service (based in London) and Radio Monte Carlo (based in Paris) are the main across-the-border program sources. Also, because of careful government control of television programming, another alternative medium has emerged—the VCR.

> Saudi Arabia and some of the Gulf countries have the highest VCR penetration levels in the world, in spite of the high cost of the equipment. And since only Egypt, Turkey, Lebanon, and Israel [of the Gulf countries] have copyright laws, pirated films from Europe, the United States, India, and Egypt circulate widely in most countries.... The widespread availability of content that cannot be viewed on television or at the cinema (Saudi Arabia even forbids the construction of cinemas) has reduced the popularity of broadcast programming.[20]

In the Middle East, as in other developing regions, the government-owned media are perceived as instruments of each country's social and political programs. The rapid spread of technological developments such as the VCR, however, demonstrates new challenges to the insulated Middle Eastern media cocoon.

IMPACT

Point of View

ERNIE USES HEBREW, BERT SPEAKS ARABIC; MOSES, HE'S A GROUCH

On Middle East "Sesame Street" the Rules Are Different: No Hugs or Kisses Please

By Amy Dockser Marcus

TEL AVIV—Can you tell me how to get, how to get to Sesame Street? In the Middle East, the directions are downright confusing.

If you want the Israeli Sesame Street, look for a boardwalk with an ice-cream parlor and a view of the Mediterranean. For the Palestinian version of the same episode, head for a street with a water well, a shop selling Arab sweets and a backdrop of West Bank-style hills and olive trees.

And if you want Muppets from both streets to get together, call in the American mediators.

In fact, Americans have been involved in this peace process from the beginning. A few years ago, producers at Children's Television Workshop, creators of the original "Sesame Street," came up with the idea of a joint Israeli-Palestinian version of the popular children's show. If former enemies like Yitzhak Rabin and Yasser Arafat could shake hands, they figured, then why not Israeli and Palestinian Muppets?

Both sides loved the idea, but with changes. After so many years of conflict, the Israelis and Palestinians didn't want to live together, even on Sesame Street. "They each insisted on having their own street," says Lewis J. Bernstein, the show's executive producer.

This isn't the first time the program has been tailored for a foreign audience. Seventeen foreign versions of "Sesame Street" are broadcast around the globe, and each has its own idiosyncrasies. The Russians came up with plot lines more appropriate for a Tolstoy novel, arguing that their children aren't used to more lighthearted fare. The French, Mr. Bernstein says, insisted on giving Big Bird a face lift so he has a profile akin to Charles Degaulle's. But the Israeli-Palestinian show is unique, the only one made by former enemies. In uncanny ways, the production mirrors the difficulties of the peace process itself.

The Wall Street Journal, *June 5, 1997, p. A–1. Reprinted by permission of* The Wall Street Journal, © *1997 Dow Jones & Co., Inc. All Rights Reserved Worldwide.*

Africa

Most of the new nations of Africa were born after 1960. African history is a record of colonialism, primarily by the British, French, Dutch, Belgian, and Portuguese, and the early print media were created to serve the colonists, not the native population.

Print Media

The first English-language newspaper in sub-Saharan Africa, the *Capetown Gazette and African Advertiser*, appeared in 1800; a year later, the first black newspaper, the *Royal Gazette and Sierra Leone Advertiser*, appeared in Sierra Leone.

French settlement in Africa is reflected in the pages of *Fraternité-Matin*, the only major daily in French Africa. A Portuguese settler founded *Noticias*, published in Mozambique. In Kenya, three tabloid newspapers enjoy wide circulations with relative independence: the English-language *Daily Nation* and *The Standard* and the Swahili daily *Taifa Leo*.

Media scholar L. John Martin describes the African media landscape:

> Africans have never had an information press. Theirs has always been an opinion press. Advocacy journalism comes naturally to them. To the extent that they feel a need for hard news, that need is satisfied by the minimal coverage of the mass media, especially of radio. Soft news—human interest news or what [media scholar Wilbur] Schramm has called immediate-reward news—is equally well transmitted through the folk media, such as the "bush telegraph" or drum; the "grapevine," or word-of-mouth and gossip; town criers and drummers; traditional dances, plays; and song.[21]

Martin points out that African cultures are very diverse, with an estimated 800 to 2000 language dialects, making it impossible to create a mass circulation newspaper that can appeal to a wide readership. The widest circulating publication is a magazine called *Drum*, published in South Africa but also distributed in West Africa and East Africa.

Today, most newspapers in South Africa, for example, are owned and edited by whites, who publish newspapers in English and in Afrikaans, a language that evolved from South Africa's 17th century Dutch settlers. South Africa's first Afrikaans newspaper, *Di Patriot*, began publishing in 1875.

South Africa's highest circulation newspaper is the *Star*, which belongs to the Argus Group, South Africa's largest newspaper publisher. The Argus Group also publishes the *Sowetan*, a newspaper based in Johannesburg, with colour graphics, an appealing design, and a healthy circulation of about 120 000. Many of the Argus Group's editors spent time in jail for speaking out against apartheid. As South Africa's largest newspaper publisher, the Argus Group owns a total of nine major papers, six of them dailies, in several African states.

From 1985 to 1990, the South African government demonstrated its distaste for dissident speech when it instituted strict limits on domestic and international news coverage in the region. Because of violent demonstrations supporting the opposition African National Congress, President P.W. Botha declared

In Africa, radio is a much more widely used medium than television, but new technology may change that. Here, villagers watch a solar-powered TV in Niger.

John Chaisson/Liaison International

a state of emergency in the country in 1985. In 1988, the government suspended the *New Nation* and four other alternative publications.[22] These suspensions and the regulations that prevented journalists from covering unrest show the power of government to limit reporting on dissent.

Audio and Video Media

Broadcasting and African independence emerged at about the same time; the result is that today, radio is a much more important medium in Africa than print or television. Because literacy rates are lower in Africa than in many other regions of the world, radio is the most accessible and cheapest way for people to follow the news.

Some governments charge licence fees for radio sets, which are supposed to be registered, but many radios go unregistered. Most stations accept advertising, but the majority of funding for radio comes from government subsidies.[23]

Less than 2 percent of the African public owns a TV set.[24] Television in the region is concentrated in the urban areas, and TV broadcasts last only a few hours each evening. Says L. John Martin, "TV remains a medium of wealthy countries."[25]

Asia and the Pacific

The development of media in this region centres primarily in four countries: Japan's prosperous mix of public and private ownership; Australia's media barons with their entrepreneurial fervour; India's phenomenal media growth; and the People's Republic of China, with its sustained, government-controlled media monopoly.

Japan

Japan boasts more newspaper readers than any other nation in the world. Japan's three national daily newspapers are based in Tokyo—*Asahi Shimbun, Yomiuri Shimbun,* and *Mainichi Shimbun.* These three papers, each of them more than 100 years old, account for almost half of the newspaper circulation.

Broadcast media in Japan developed as a public corporation called the Japanese Broadcasting Corporation (NHK). During World War II, NHK became a propaganda arm of the government. After its surrender, Japan created a licensing board similar to the U.S. Federal Communications Commission, but with an operating board similar to that of Great Britain's BBC. Japan also decided to allow private broadcast ownership.

As a result of this, Japan today has a mixed system of privately owned and publicly held broadcast media and NHK continues to prosper. According to broadcast scholar Sydney W. Head,

> NHK enjoys more autonomy than any other major public broadcasting corporation. In a rather literal sense, the general public "owns" it by virtue of paying receiver fees. The government cannot veto any program or demand that any program be aired. It leaves the NHK free to set the level of license fees and to do its own fee collecting (which may be why it rates as the richest of the world's fee-supported broadcasting organizations).[26]

Private ownership is an important element in the Japanese media, and many broadcasting operations are owned by newspaper publishers. NHK owns many more radio properties than do private broadcasters; NHK shares television ownership about equally with private investors.[27] However, Japan has very few cable systems (see Figure 16.2), which will hinder access to global communications networks.

Australia

In Australia, acquisitions by media magnates skyrocketed in the 1980s, and today Rupert Murdoch controls an astounding 60 percent of Australia's newspaper circulation, which includes the *Daily Telegraph Mirror* in Sydney and *The Herald-Sun* in Melbourne.

Figure 16.2

Cable TV Subscribers in the United States, Canada, and Japan

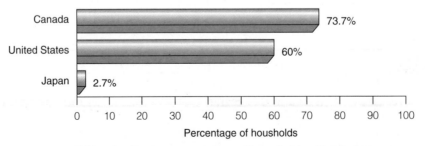

Cable subscribers as a percentage of households with televisions
(Excludes hookups that provide only improved reception)

Source: Data from Statistics Canada, Household Facilities and Equipment survey, and The New York Times. © 1993 by The New York Times Company. Reprinted by permission.

Murdoch, although somewhat burdened with debt because of his binge of acquisitions in the 1980s (see Impact/Profile, "Four Moguls of the Media," Chapter 1), emerged in the 1990s as Australia's uncontested print media baron after the other major Australian media family, the Fairfaxes, fell into bankruptcy in December 1990.

Broadcasting in Australia is dominated by the Australian Broadcasting Corporation (ABC), modelled on the BBC. Three nationwide commercial networks operate in the country, but all three were suffering financial difficulty in the early 1990s, a legacy "of the heydays of the 1980s, when aspiring buyers, backed by eager bank lenders, paid heady prices for broadcast and print assets," reported *The Wall Street Journal*.[28]

India

Entrepreneurship is an important element in the print media of India, which gained independence from Britain in 1947. Forty years following independence, Indian print media had multiplied 1000 times—from 200 publications in 1947 to nearly 25 000 publications in 1987.[29]

Broadcasting in India follows its British colonial beginnings, with radio operating under the name All India Radio (AIR) and TV as Doordarshan ("distance view"). Doordarshan uses satellite service to reach remote locations, bringing network TV to four out of five people. As in most developing countries, the network regularly broadcasts programs aimed at improving public life, about subjects such as family planning, health, and hygiene.

People's Republic of China

Social responsibility is an important element of media development in the People's Republic of China, where a media monopoly gives government the power to influence change. At the centre of Chinese media are the two party information sources, the newspaper *People's Daily* and Xinhua, the Chinese news agency. These two sources set the tone for the print media throughout China, where self-censorship maintains the government's direction.

Broadcasting in China, as in India, offers important potential for social change in a vast land of rural villages. China's three-tier system for radio includes a central national station; 100 regional, provincial, and municipal networks; and grassroots stations that send local announcements and bulletins by wire to loudspeakers in outdoor markets and other public gathering places.[30]

A television set is a prized possession in China, where the Chinese have bought some U.S. programs and accepted some U.S. commercials, but generally produce the programming themselves. The 1989 demonstrations in Tiananmen Square cooled official enthusiasm for relationships with the West, and Chinese media today sometimes use information and entertainment programming from the West to show the dangers of Western influence, proving the power and the reach of a government media monopoly. While nominally illegal, home satellite receiving dishes have proliferated, and Western programming is often available in larger communities. Rupert Murdoch, who operates a direct-to-home service in Asia, has cooperated with the Chinese government by removing the BBC World Service signal from his package, much to the chagrin of civil libertarians.

In the new market economy in China, there are ten times as many newspapers and magazines today as there were in 1978. The number of newspapers has

Public billboard advertising for motion pictures in China.

CP Picture Archive (Greg Baker)

jumped from 186 in 1978 to 2200 today. The number of magazines increased from 930 to 8100. With the increased competition for readers, some of the print media are beginning to look like Western tabloids, running some sensationalist stories.

This sensationalism has angered Party officials, who are trying to maintain control on what is published. In 1996, the president of the popular newspaper *Beijing Youth Daily* was disciplined after the paper ran a story about a poisoning case involving a state-run business. "The leadership of the news media must be tightly held in the hands of those who are loyal to Marxism, the party and the people," said President Jiang Zemin.[31] News of the outbreak of the mysterious avian flu in Hong Kong in 1997 (which presumably originated in mainland China) was vigorously suppressed, as well.

Latin America and the Caribbean

In Latin America, where hectic political change is the norm, the media have been as volatile as the region. The media are part of the same power structure that controls politics, business, and industry; family dynasties often characterize Latin American media ownership.

Romulo O'Farrill, Jr., chairman of the board of Televisa in Mexico, owns more than 150 TV stations and 8 newspapers. Mario Vásquez Raña owns more than 50 Mexican newspapers. His name became familiar in North America in 1986 when he bought a controlling interest in United Press International. A year later he sold his interest.

Print Media

In Santiago, Chile, the Edwards family has owned *El Mercurio* since 1880; the *El Mercurio* newspapers now total at least 14. *O Estado de São Paulo* in Brazil, owned by the Mesquita family, has represented editorial independence in the region for more than 50 years, and often is mentioned as one of the country's best newspapers. Argentina's *La Prensa* refuses government subsidies and has survived great conflicts with people like former dictator Juan Perón, who shut down the newspaper from 1951 to 1955.[32]

Home delivery for newspapers and magazines is uncommon in Latin America; the centres of print media merchandising are street-corner kiosks, where vendors offer a variety of publications. *Manchete*, published in Brazil, is one of the most widely circulated national magazines, similar in size and content to *Life* magazine.[33]

Audio and Video Media

Broadcasting operates in a mix of government and private control, with governments often owning a few key stations and regulating the stations that are privately owned. But the pattern is varied.

Cuba's broadcast media are totally controlled by the government, for example. In Costa Rica and Ecuador, almost all of the broadcast media are privately owned. In Brazil, private owners hold most of the radio stations and television networks, including TV Globo Network, which claims to be the world's fourth largest network (after the United States' three TV networks).[34]

As in many other developing regions, Latin American media often are targets for political and terrorist threats, and being a journalist can be very hazardous.

> Threats to journalists come not only from governments but from revolutionary groups, drug lords, and quasi-government hit squads as well. Numerous news organizations have been bombed, ransacked, and destroyed by opponents. Dozens of Latin American journalists have been murdered for their beliefs or for writing articles that contain those beliefs.[35]

Journalists face danger in this region because the media represent potential opposition to the political power of a country's oligarchy. Perhaps more than in any other part of the world, the Latin American media are woven into the fibre of revolutionary history.

News and Information Flow

Countries in Latin America and in many other developing nations have criticized what they believe is a Western bias in the flow of information throughout the world. These countries charge that this practice imposes cultural imperialism, centred in Western ideology.

The reason for this criticism is that most of the major international news services are based in the West. The Associated Press, United Press International, Reuters (Great Britain), Agence France-Presse (France), Deutsche Presse-Agentur (Germany), and Agencia Efe (Spain) supply news to the print and broadcast media. Visnews, based in Great Britain, and the U.S.-based Cable News Network (CNN) and World International Network (WIN) offer international video services. Rupert Murdoch's Sky TV in Europe and Star TV in Asia deliver programs by satellite.

Despite Western dominance of global news organizations, many regions of the world support information services within their own countries and even within their regions. For example, Middle East News Agency (MENA), based in Egypt, serves all of the countries of the Middle East, and News Agency of Nigeria (NAN) limits services to Nigeria.

Within the past 40 years, news services outside the Western orbit have been created, including Russian Information Telegraph Agency (RITA); Asian-Pacific News Network in Japan; Caribbean News Agency (CANA); Pan-African News Agency (PANA); Non-Aligned News Agency (NANA), linking the non-aligned nations with the national news agencies, based in Yugoslavia; and Inter Press Service (IPS), based in Rome as an "information bridge" between Europe and Latin America.[36] In 1991, Japan Broadcasting Corporation announced, and then cancelled, plans for a worldwide news network, citing a projected start-up cost of more than $1 billion.

New World Information and Communications Order

Even with the creation of these added sources of information, Western news services dominate. Critics of the present system of news and information flow have labelled this issue the New World Information and Communications Order (NWICO), saying that the current system is **ethnocentric**, that is, it promotes the superiority of one political formation (in this case, the Western world) over any other.

> Developing world media and newly independent governments (and cultural sovereignists in many of the Western countries themselves) have been highly critical of this situation, arguing that coverage from the major services contains ethnocentric occidental values that affect its content and presentation. Coverage from these media most often include political, economic, Judeo-Christian religious, and other social values that are not universal.... In addition, developing world media and governments have argued that Western ethnocentrism creates an unequal flow of information by providing a large stream of information about events in the developed world but only a very small flow from the developing world.[37]

UNESCO's 1978 Declaration

The United Nations organization UNESCO adopted a declaration in 1978 supporting the principles of self-reliant communications and self-determination for countries as they establish their own communications policies. Critics of the statement, especially journalists, felt that some aspects of the declaration supported government control of the flow of information out of a country, because some news services are official government mouthpieces.

The MacBride Report

Four years later, UNESCO, which had appointed a 16-member commission headed by Irish statesman Sean MacBride, received its recommendations at the general conference of UNESCO in Belgrade, Yugoslavia. These recommendations became known as the MacBride Report. The report listed 82 ways to help achieve the New World Information and Communications Order, but after the report was issued neither critics of the current status of communications nor those who opposed the report's recommendations were satisfied:

The West objected to the report's skepticism about a free market in communication, including its opposition to advertising, for example; many NWICO supporters objected to its downplaying of government controls (for example, its advocacy of self-imposed rather than government codes of ethics for journalists).[38]

The Belgrade conference passed a general resolution supporting NWICO, but in 1983, citing opposition to some of the principles outlined in the MacBride Report, the U.S. government withdrew its $50 million in financial support for UNESCO, seriously crippling the organization, as the United States had been its largest contributor.

UNESCO has since turned to other issues. The NWICO still remains a theoretical idea that scholars of global media continue to debate because of its implications for the international media community.

Global Media Open New Markets

Today's media markets are increasingly global. Ted Turner, Conrad Black, and Rupert Murdoch are just three examples of media moguls who are moving into the global media marketplace. Large international media companies are looking for markets worldwide at the same time that overseas media companies are purchasing pieces of media industries in the domestic media marketplace. MTV, for example, is available 24 hours a day in St. Petersburg in the Commonwealth of Independent States. Here are some more examples:

◎ ABC and the British Broadcasting Corporation (BBC) have formed a news-gathering partnership to share television and radio news coverage worldwide. This service will compete with CNN to deliver news by satellite.[39]

Domestic television newscasts from the BBC in London are now available to viewers around the world on the World Wide Web, soon after they are broadcast domestically. Other networks, such as the CBC, make radio programming available in much the same way.

CP Picture Archive (Eraldo Peres)

◎ Rupert Murdoch expanded his Hong Kong-based satellite TV network, British Sky Network, into India. Murdoch said he planned to offer more than just TV coverage in India. "Our plan is not just to beam signals into India but also to take part in Indian films, make television programs, and broadcast them."[40]

◎ Jun Murai, who has been called the father of Japan's Internet, created a nonprofit network to connect all of Japan's universities to the Internet, without government approval. Ultimately, he says, he "wants to connect all the computers in this world."[41]

◎ U.S./British advertising and public relations partnerships are on the rise. The British firm Shandwick is the largest agency in the United Kingdom and the second largest agency in the United States. More than half of Shandwick's business comes from the United States.[42]

All of these companies are positioning themselves to manage the emerging global media marketplace. This media marketplace includes news and information services, programming, films, and recordings, as well as products and the advertising to sell those products.

Fuelling the move to global marketing is the decision by the European countries to eliminate all trade barriers among countries. A further sign of the times is the shrinking proportion of worldwide advertising expenditures accounted for by the United States, which has long been the world's advertising colossus. In recent years, advertising spending by companies outside the United States has overtaken the amount spent by companies in the United States (see Figure 16.3).

Figure 16.3

The Growth in Worldwide Advertising

Source: McCann-Erickson *Insider's Report,* December 1997.

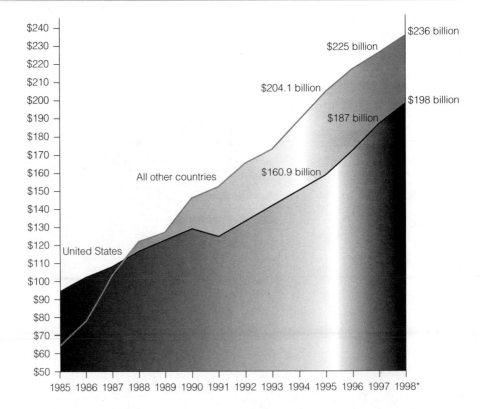

U.S. and non-U.S. advertising spending (billions of dollars)

*projected

Chasing International Consumers

International communication on the Internet (see Chapter 1) is now flowering with the easy, affordable, accessible transfer of information and entertainment back and forth between Western countries. The full editorial content of most major world newspapers is available on the World Wide Web, which means that national status of the quality press is in the process of blurring. Furthermore, since access to this material on the Web is generally free of direct charges, an interesting split is occurring between paying subscribers, who receive a paper copy complete with advertising, and nonpaying Web readers, who only get the "meat" of the publication.

Media companies in Western countries also are looking longingly at the large populations in other countries that are just beginning to acquire the tools of communication, making millions of people instantly available for all types of products.

The number of TV sets in the world has jumped to more than 1 billion—a 50 percent jump in the past five years. "TV sets are more common in Japanese homes than flush toilets. Virtually every Mexican household has a TV, but only half have phones. Thai consumers will buy a TV before an electric fan or even a refrigerator....Vans roam Bogotá streets with miniature satellite dishes on the roof and a megaphone blaring promises of hookups for $150. In New Delhi, 'dish wallahs' nail satellite receivers to crowded apartment buildings."[43]

Workers watching Hindi movies in New Delhi.

CP Picture Archive (Saurabh Das)

Opening New Pathways for Ideas

Along with the transfer of information in the new global communications future, however, comes the transfer of ideas.

Historically, empowered elites have usually sought to suppress the wider distribution of ideas, wealth, rights and, most of all, knowledge. This is as true today as it was 536 years ago, when the German printer Gutenberg invented movable type to print the Bible. For two centuries afterward, government tightly controlled what people could read through the widespread use of "prior restraint...."

Just as blanket censorship of the printed word could not continue with the emergence of democracy in 17th-century Britain and 18th-century America, so today suppression of the electronic media is thwarted by technology and rapidly growing economies around the world."[44]

IMPACT

Technology

JAPAN'S NEWEST HEARTTHROBS ARE SEXY, TALENTED, AND VIRTUAL

The newest media sweethearts in Japan are virtual creations. Video game characters are becoming celebrities. What makes the Japanese characters appealing is that they are interactive, explains Andrew Pollack in The New York Times, *and the object of these video games is to capture the character's affection.*

TOKYO—Shiori Fujisaki is a 17-year-old high school junior with long reddish hair and dreamy eyes who is about to release her first record. Shingo Hagiwara is a 21-year-old college sophomore who idolizes her. He goes to nearly every event at which she appears and has bought calendars, posters, watches and mugs with her picture on them.

"Shiori does everything perfectly," he sighed.

Perfect she might be, but Shiori Fujisaki is not real. She is a character in a video game called Tokimeki Memorial, the goal of which is to get Shiori or one of her friends to date you and fall in love.

Shingo Hagiwara, on the other hand, is quite real. He is one of the growing legion of young Japanese men who have given their hearts to a virtual girl.

So-called "love simulation" games, normally sold on CD-ROMS, have become one of the hottest categories in Japan's home video game industry.

The girls in such games are animated characters that have only a limited ability to converse. Players cannot type in whatever they want

to say; rather, they use the video game controller merely to pick a topic of conversation or a multiple-choice reply. In most games, the text of the conversation is also printed on the bottom of the screen.

Some players become so absorbed in their pursuit that the girls become real to them. Some young men send love letters and birthday cards to their favorite characters.

"Everybody has one character for whom he could sacrifice his life," said Mr. Hagiwara, the college student.

The New York Times, November 25, 1996, C–5. Copyright © 1996 by The New York Times. Reprinted by permission. Images © 1996 Konami. All rights reserved.

It was so much fun today. Please take me out again.

朝日奈「今日は超楽しかったね。
また何処か誘ってね。

I like it... My heart is throbbing.

美樹原「私、好きなんです…。
どきどきしますね。

Ho ho ho ho (Snobbish laughter) Of course.

鏡「ほーほほほ。
当たり前ですわ。

Governments that are accustomed to controlling the information that crosses their borders face unprecedented access within their borders to global information sources.

According to media theorist Ithiel de Sola Pool:

> International communications is often considered a mixed blessing by rulers. Usually they want technical progress. They want computers. They want satellites. They want efficient telephones. They want television. But at the same time they do not want the ideas that come with them.[45]

Many governments that attempt to control the media, especially broadcast media, expected to continue to control the messages as long as they could supervise access to newsprint and satellites. But this is becoming increasingly difficult.

In 1994, the Chinese government passed regulations to ban satellite dishes and prohibit people from watching foreign broadcasts. Factories that own dishes were required to broadcast only approved programs. But many Chinese simply refused to abide by the edict.[46]

Videos can travel in a suitcase across borders, and video signals can travel unseen to pirated satellite dishes, assembled without government knowledge. The airwaves are truly "borderless." Reports the *Los Angeles Times*, "Asked once what had caused the stunning collapse of communism in Eastern Europe, Polish leader Lech Walesa pointed to a nearby TV set, 'It all came from there.'"[47]

As more and more national media boundaries open up throughout the world, news, information, and entertainment will be able to move instantly from each home country to become part of the global media dialogue. At the dawn of the new millennium, the media industries are entering a media marketplace without boundaries, a global marketplace that is truly "transnational."

> Optimists declare that the world is headed unstoppably for an electronic Renaissance. How arrogant; how naive. The essence of a technology of freedom is that it endows its users with the freedom to fail. But pessimists are equally wrong to think that failure is inevitable. Nothing is inevitable about this technology except its advance.... As the universe behind the screen expands, it will be the people in front who shape the soul of the new machine.[48]

In Focus

◎ The four theories of the press (the Soviet theory, the authoritarian theory, the libertarian theory, and the social responsibility theory), plus the developmental theory, still leave many press systems beyond categorization.

◎ The print media form the basis for press development in North America, Australia, Western Europe, and Eastern Europe.

◎ Radio is often the dominant medium in developing countries; television is in widespread use in prosperous nations and in urban areas of developing countries. Yet, most countries still have only one TV service, usually run by the government.

◎ Western European media today prosper under guarantees of freedom of expression similar to North American ideals, although each nation has modified the idea to reflect differing values.

◎ Scandinavian journalists enjoy the widest press freedoms of all of Western Europe, including almost unlimited access to public documents.

◎ Western European newspapers tend to be much more overtly partisan than North American newspapers.

◎ Western Europeans watch less than half as much TV as people in the United States; most TV stations in Europe don't go on the air until late afternoon.

◎ Most of Western European programming comes from the United States. U.S. programs are attractive to European broadcasters because it is cheaper to buy them than to produce their own.

◎ Some members of the European Community have proposed quotas on the importation of U.S. programs.

◎ Eastern Europe in transition is defining a new balance between the desire for free expression and the remnants of government control.

◎ In many Eastern European countries, the media played a central role in upsetting the established power structure.

◎ Television in the Eastern bloc countries developed under Communist direction because the Communist governments were in power before TV use was widespread; radio broadcasting also was tightly controlled.

◎ The Eastern European nations developed their press policies following the Soviet model.

◎ In the Middle East and North Africa, more newspapers and magazines are published in regions with high literacy rates than in regions with low literacy rates; the one exception is Cairo, Egypt, which is the Arab world's publishing centre.

◎ The Middle Eastern press is tightly controlled by government restrictions, through ownership and licensing.

◎ Radio Monte Carlo and the BBC offer alternative radio programming across Middle Eastern borders. VCRs also are very popular.

◎ In the Middle East, as in other developing regions, the media are perceived as instruments of each country's social and political programs.

◎ African culture is very diverse, making it impossible to create a mass circulation newspaper that can appeal to a wide readership.

◎ Suspension of five publications in South Africa during the state of emergency from 1985 to 1990 demonstrates the power of government to limit reporting on dissent.

◎ In Africa, radio is a much more important medium than print because it is an inexpensive way for people to follow the news.

◎ The three major Japanese national dailies account for almost half of the newspaper circulation.

◎ Japan today has a mixed system of privately owned and publicly held broadcast media.

◎ Entrepreneurs, including Rupert Murdoch, control large segments of Australia's media; broadcasting in Australia is dominated by the Australian Broadcasting Corporation (ABC).

◎ Since India's independence in 1947, the number of publications has increased 1000 times; broadcasting in India follows its British colonial beginnings.

◎ Chinese media operate under a government monopoly, supported by a belief in the media's social responsibility.

◎ Media in Latin America are part of the power structure, and media often are owned by family dynasties.

◎ Journalists in Latin America face danger because the media represent a challenge to political power.

◎ The New World Information and Communications Order (NWICO), supported by UNESCO, advocated parity for the media in all countries.

◎ U.S. media companies are looking for markets overseas at the same time that overseas media companies are purchasing pieces of media industries in the United States and other countries.

◎ Along with the transfer of information in the new global communications future comes the transfer of ideas. Governments that are accustomed to controlling the information that crosses their borders face unprecedented access within their borders to global information sources.

Review Questions

1. In what ways might a media system be shaped by the government's political philosophy? Cite some specific examples.

2. Compare and contrast the role of radio within developed and developing countries. Cite specific examples.

3. Discuss the persuasive role of the media in Japan. What role do NHK and the three major daily newspapers play in Japanese media?

4. Name the media baron who holds the monopoly over Australian media. Discuss his role in his country's media, as well as the role of the Australian Broadcasting Corporation.

5. What do you think the term "borderless media" means? Describe the consequences of borderless media in the global marketplace.

Watching the Web

◎ **BBC News**

http://news.bbc.co.uk/default/htm

◎ **CBC Newsworld**

http://www.newsworld.cbc.ca

◎ **The Electronic Telegraph**
(The "best Internet newspaper" for the second year in a row)

http://www.telegraph.co.uk/

◎ **The Exile (from Moscow)**

http://www.exile.ru/index.htm

◎ **Jerusalem Post**

http://www.jpost.co.il

◎ **Mediapolis**

http://mediapolis.es/

◎ **World Net Daily**

http://www.WorldNetDaily.com

STUDENT
RESOURCE
GUIDE

GLOSSARY OF MEDIA TERMS

MEDIA RESEARCH DIRECTORY

END NOTES

GLOSSARY

OF MEDIA TERMS

accreditation

certification by the government of members of the press to cover wartime action or other official government business.

affiliates

broadcast stations that use broadcast network programming but that are owned by companies other than the broadcast networks.

agenda-setting

the principle that members of the press do not tell people what to think but do tell people what and whom to think about.

alternative press

newspapers that become outlets for the voices of social protest; also called the dissident press.

analog

in mass communications, a type of technology used in broadcasting, whereby video or audio information is sent as continuous signals through the air on specific airwave frequencies.

ancillary-rights market

the revenue opportunity for a movie beyond its theatre audience, including television and video-cassette sales.

blanket licensing agreement

an arrangement whereby radio stations become authorized to use recorded music for broadcast by paying a fee.

blind booking

the practice of renting out films to exhibitors without showing the films to the exhibitors first.

block booking

the practice of scheduling a large number of movies for a theatre, combining a few good movies with many second-rate features.

browser

software that allows people to search electronically among many documents to find what they want on-line.

Canadian Broadcasting Corporation (CBC)

the principal public broadcaster in Canada.

CANCON

Canadian content regulations for radio music programming administered by the CRTC.

Canadian Radio/Television and Telecommunications Commission (CRTC)

the federal commission charged with regulating the telecommunications sector in Canada.

censorship

the practice of suppressing material that is considered morally, politically, or otherwise objectionable.

channel

in mass communication, the medium that delivers the message.

concentration of ownership

the trend among the media industries to cluster together in groups.

consumer magazines

all magazines sold by subscription or at newsstands, supermarkets, and bookstores.

content

the multimedia term for information sources and programs that can be digitized for the new communications network.

convergence

the blurring of lines between the publishing industry, the communications industry, consumer electronics, and computers because of advances in technology.

cooperative news gathering

a practice first used by the New York Associated Press, whereby member newspapers share the expenses of acquiring news and returning any profits to the members.

CPM

in advertising, cost-per-thousand, which is the cost of an ad per one thousand people reached. (M is the Roman numeral for 1000.)

cross-ownership

used to describe a company that owns television and radio stations in the same broadcast market.

data compression

a process that uses software and hardware to squeeze information into a tiny electronic package.

demand programming

request radio that is controlled completely by the listener.

demographics

the analysis of data used by advertising agencies to target an audience by sex, age, income level, marital status, geographic location, and occupation.

deregulation

the process of ending government monitoring of an industry.

digital

a way to store and transmit data by reducing it to electronic signals—digits—and then reassembling them for an exact reproduction.

digital audio broadcast (DAB)

a technology that uses computer codes to send music and information, which eliminates the static and hiss of current broadcast signals.

digital audiotape (DAT)

a new type of audiotape that uses computer codes to produce recordings.

digital film

the electronic manipulation of film images.

direct sponsorship

feature of early radio and television programming in which the advertiser sponsored an entire show, which often bore the name of the product or company in the title.

disinformation

the planting by government sources of inaccurate information.

dissident press

see *alternative press*.

drive-time audiences

term coined by Gerlad Bartell in 1957 to describe people who listened to the radio between 6 and 9 a.m. and between 4 and 7 p.m.

e-mail

electronic messages delivered on-line.

ethnocentric

characterized by the attitude that one's own culture is superior to those of others.

ethnocentrism

the attitude that some cultural and social values, especially North American values, are the only correct ones.

FCC (Federal Communications Commission)

five-member commission in the United States responsible for administering the provisions of the Telecommunications Act of 1996.

feedback

in mass communication, a response sent back to the sender (source) from the receiver.

freelancers

in magazine or newspaper publishing, journalists who write for more than one pubication and are paid separately for each article they write.

free media

used to describe over-the-air broadcast media.

high-definition television (HDTV)

a type of television that provides a picture with a clearer resolution than do normal television sets.

home page

the first page of a Web site that welcomes the user.

HTML (hypertext markup language)

a computer programming language developed by Tim Berners-Lee that allows people to send text and pictures on the Web.

HTTP (hypertext transfer protocol)

a computer programming language developed by Tim Berners-Lee that allows people to create "links" on the Web from one source of information to another.

IMAX films

a large-screen movie format developed in Canada.

interactive

a two-way, viewer-controlled electronic process that allows the consumer to select among a variety of services.

Internet

a web of interconected computer networks that sprang from a U.S. government effort to connect government and academic locations. It currently links about 15 million people.

libel

a false statement that damages a person's character or reputation by exposing that person to public ridicule or contempt.

line doublers/line quadruplers

devices that can double and quadruple the number of lines scanning the TV screen to make the picture sharper.

links

electronic connections from one source of information to another.

magic bullet theory

a belief that ideas from the media create a direct causal relationship to behaviour.

mass communication

communication from one person or group of persons through a transmitting device (a medium) to a large audience or market.

mass media industries

used in *Media/Impact* to describe the seven types of media businesses: newspapers, magazines, radio, television, movies, recordings, and books.

media

plural for *medium.*

mediamorphosis

a term coined by information designer Roger Fidler to describe the intense rate of change that occurs when all media change simultaneously.

medium

in mass communication, the transmitting device by which a message is carried.

message pluralism

a broad and diverse representation of opinion and culture by the media.

muckrakers

turn-of-the-century magazine journalists who wrote articles to expose big business and corrupt government.

multimedia

the blending of different types of media—audio, video, and data—into a single product or service.

narrowcasting

in broadcasting, identifying a specific audience segment and specifically programming for that segment.

National Film Board of Canada (NFB)

federal government film production agency originally set up to produce government films in wartime. It now produces short, animated films and a small number of feature films, in addition to made-for-television programming.

Navigator

a software program that allows one to browse easily through program services.

network

a collection of radio or television stations that offer programs, usually simultaneously, throughout the country, during designated program times.

new media

all emerging communications media that combine text, graphics, sound, and video, using computer technology.

news services

originally called wire services, agencies formed to provide information to print and broadcast news operations from locations throughout the world.

O & O's

broadcast stations that are *o*wned and *o*perated by a broadcast network.

pass-along readership

an audience of readers who share a magazine with its original owner.

payola

a contraction of the words *pay* and *Victrola* (an early record player), used to describe the payment of a fee to a disc jockey in exchange for playing a recording on the air.

penny paper

first popularized by Benjamin Day of the *New York Sun* in 1833, a newspaper produced by dropping the price of each copy to a penny and supporting the production cost through advertising.

photojournalism

the use of photographs and text to tell a better story than either could tell alone.

pool reporting

a system in which a group of reporters is approved by the government to cover a specific event. This device often limits journalists' access to cover an event.

prime time

in broadcasting, the hours between 7 p.m. and 11 p.m., when more people watch television than during any other period.

prior restraint

the power of government to stop information from being published or broadcast.

program blocking

the use of a "lock-box" to block out cable channels.

publicity

uncontrolled use of media by a public relations firm to create events and present information to capture press and public attention.

publishing

used to denote items placed on the Web.

rating

the percentage of audience for a program, based on the total number of households with receivers.

rep firm

a company of advertising sales representatives who sell advertising time and space in their market to advertisers outside their geographic area.

resolution

clarity of the picture on the screen.

search engine

the tool used to locate information in an on-line computer database.

selective perception

the concept that people perceive messages differently.

sender (*or* source)

the agency that puts a message on a channel (for example, a local cable company).

server

a computerized storage system used to send programs and data to consumers, using cable, phone lines, or other networks.

set-top box

the device that sits on top of a TV set and links viewers to cable systems (and, in the future, to the new communications network).

share

an abbreviation for *share-of-audience*, which compares the audience for one show with the audience for another. *Share* means the percentage of the audience with TV sets on that is watching each program.

situation comedy

a television program that establishes a fixed set of characters in either a home or work situation.

small presses

book publishers with fewer than ten employees.

spiral of silence

a phenomenon in which people are unlikely to voice disagreement with the prevailing climate of opinion embraced by the media.

split-run editions

magazines that are published in several countries with the same editorial content, but with local advertisements.

studio system

the system of movie industry ownership in the 1930s that allowed the studios to control production, distribution, and exhibition.

subsidiary rights

the rights to market a book for other uses—to make a movie, for example, or to print a character from the book on T-shirts.

syndicates

agencies and news organizations that sell articles for publication to appear in many different outlets simultaneously.

syndicators

services that sell programming to broadcast stations and cable.

tabloid

a small-format newspaper that features large photographs and illustrations along with sensational stories.

tabloid journalism (*or* jazz journalism)

a newspaper format style that combines large pictures and headlines to emphasize sex and violence.

telco

an abbreviation for *tele*phone *co*mpany.

30-year rule

a theory about how long people take to completely adopt a new technology, developed by futurist Paul Saffo.

time-shifting

the practice of taping a television program using a VCR, so that someone can watch it later.

two-step flow

the transmittal of information and ideas from mass media to opinion leaders and then to their friends and acquaintances.

V-chip

a microchip device that allows parents to program TV sets to eliminate objectionable programs.

vertical integration

the process by which one company controls several related aspects of the media business simultaneously.

World Intellectual Property Organization (WIPO)

an organization that develops international treaties for the protection of copyright.

World Trade Organization (WTO)

an organization that administers the rules of international trade; the successor to GATT.

yellow journalism

highly emotional, often exaggerated or inaccurate reporting that emphasizes crime, sex, and violence.

MEDIA RESEARCH
DIRECTORY

This directory is designed to familiarize you with some of the publications that will help you find background and current information about the media. Also included is a list of associations that can provide information about specific media businesses.

The study of the media covers many areas of scholarship besides journalism and mass communications. Historians, psychologists, economists, political scientists, and sociologists, for example, often contribute ideas to media studies. This directory therefore includes a variety of information sources from academic and industry publications, as well as from popular periodicals.

General Media Sources You Should Know

The *Toronto Star* (www.thestar.com/thestar/index.html), the *Globe and Mail* (www.theglobeandmail.com), and the *Financial Post* (www.canoe.ca/FP/home .html) are the best daily sources of information about the business of the media in Canada. The *Toronto Star* has an excellent Web site, which contains most of the editorial content of the newspaper each day, as well as free access to an archive of past issues. The *Globe and Mail* Web site provides selected content from the daily newspaper and more limited archives. Partial content of the *Financial Post* is now available on the Sun newspaper Web site CANOE.

For U.S. media news and information, the *Wall Street Journal* (wsj.com) is the best daily source of information, though access to its Web site involves payment. The *Los Angeles Times* (www.latimes.com) daily section "Calendar" follows the media business very closely, especially television and movies, because many such companies are based in Los Angeles. The *LA Times* Web site is very complete and available free of charge (though searching its archives involves a fee). Of the other major U.S. dailies, the *Washington Post* (www.washingtonpost.com) is fully available on the Web at about midnight EST for the following day's edition, seven days a week. The site also provides access to recent past issues. The *New York Times* (www.nytimes.com) charges users who reside outside of the United States for access to its generally excellent Web site. Of the British newspapers, perhaps the best site is mounted by *The Telegraph* (www.telegraph.co.uk), a Hollinger group newspaper. It is considered by many to be the best newspaper Web site in the world.

Another good source is the *Statistics Canada Daily*, which releases new data and information every business day. It appears at about 8 a.m. EST. Its archives can be searched and links followed to more detailed information contained on various subjects on the main Statistics Canada site (www.statcan.ca). Statistics Canada collects information on many aspects of media businesses and consumer use of the media. Although Stats Can paper publications are diminishing in number and tend to be prohibitively expensive, most university and college libraries carry them. However, they are increasingly being replaced with electronic products.

Canadian academic journals of interest are the *Canadian Journal of Communication,* the *Ryerson Review of Journalism,* and the *Canadian Journal of Educational Communications.* Canadian scholarship is best searched for electronically using *Sociofile* or *Current Contents* CD-ROMs in the reference section of a university or college library.

Many U.S. trade and academic publications can be of use to students. *Advertising Age* publishes special issues throughout the year focusing on newspapers, magazines, and broadcasting. *Communications Arts* publishes a monthly glossy magazine devoted to design issues in the advertising and magazine businesses.

Columbia Journalism Review and *American Journalism Review* regularly critique developments in the print and broadcast industries. *Columbia Journalism Review* is published by New York's Columbia University Graduate School of Journalism. The University of Maryland College of Journalism publishes *American Journalism Review.* Other professional journals that carry articles of potential interest include *Communications Abstracts, Communications Research, Journal of Communication, Journalism Quarterly, Journalism History, Journal of Advertising Research, Newspaper Research Journal,* and *Public Relations Review.*

Since 1973, the brokerage firm of Paine Webber in New York has sponsored an annual conference on upcoming media issues. The results are published in an annual report, *Outlook for the Media,* issued each June.

Broadcasting & Cable Yearbook is an annual compilation of material about the broadcasting industry. Also listed are syndicators, brokers, advertising agencies, and associations.

For basic facts and figures on the Canadian newspaper business, the best place to look is the Web site of the Canadian Newspaper Association (www.cna-acj.ca). *Ulrich's International Periodicals Directory* lists magazines alphabetically and by subject. *The Micromedia Canadian News and Periodicals Index* (www.micromedia.on.ca) lists more Canadian periodicals in print.

Working the Web

Thousands of Web sites on the Internet offer useful material. What follows is an alphabetical list of the specific Web sites listed at the end of each chapter. Because Web site addresses change daily, some of these addresses may be different from those listed previously. If you can't reach the Web site at the address listed, search using the site's name, listed in **bold type.** Also, if you can't find a Web site as listed, try changing the search engine you are using. Common search engines are AltaVista, Yahoo!, and Lycos.

Media Web Sites

Advertising Council
http://www.adcouncil.org
Advertising Standards Canada
http://www.screen.com/mnet/eng/indus/advert/caf.htm

All Media E-mail Directory (e-mail addresses for key editors, columnists, correspondents, and executives in magazines, newspapers, radio, TV, and news syndicates across Canada and the United States)
http://www.owt.com/dircon
Amazon Books Online
http://www.amazon.com
American Society of Newspaper Editors Minority Employment Report
http://www.asne.org/kiosk/diversity/97minsrv.htm
An Appraisal of Technologies of Political Control
http://jya.com/atpc.html
Associated Press Breaking News
http://www.tampabayonline.net/news/apbreak.htm
Associated Press Wire
http://www.latimes.com/HOME/NEWS/AUTOAP/ICBTOPAP.html
Association for Asian Studies
http://www.easc.indiana.edu/~aas
BBC News (text, audio, and video)
http://news.bbc.co.uk/default.htm
Bureau of Broadcast Measurement
http://www.bbm.ca/
Canadian Advertising Agencies' Web Sites
http://www.mhbizlink.com/cardlink/agencies/htm
Canadian Association of Broadcasters Hall of Fame
http://www.rcc.ryerson.ca/schools/rta/ccf/personal/hof/hof.html
Canadian Broadcasting Corporation Radio (audio and text)
http://www.radio.cbc.ca/radio/programs/news/headline-news/
Canadian News and Information
http://wwwcanada~acsus.plattsburgh.edu/cannews/paper.htm
Canadian Public Relations Society
http://www.cprs.ca/newmemb.html
CBC Newsworld
http://www.newsworld.cbc.ca
CBC Television
http://www.tv.cbc.ca/
CD Now (CD sales)
http://www.cdnow.com
Chatelaine **Magazine**
http://www.chatelaine.com
A Chronicle of Freedom of Expression in Canada
http://insight/mcmaster.ca/org/efc/pages/chronicle/chronicle.html
CNN Audioselect (audio tracks of all CNN channels)
http://www.cnn.com/audioselect
Communications Topics Web-site
http://www.syr.edu/~bcfought
Computer Assisted Reporting
http://www.home.att.net/~bdedman/index.html
Copyright on the Net
http://www.benedict.com
Corporate Watch
http://www.corpwatc.org/

Cross Media Ownership Rules Campaign
http://www.alliance.aust.com/CMOC/
David Letterman
http://www.cbs.com/lateshow
Dilbert (Scott Adams's comic)
http://www.unitedmedia.com/comics/dilbert
Directory of Public Relations Agencies and Resources on the Web
http://www.webcom.com/impulse/prlist.html
Diversity in Electronic Media
http://www.mediaaccess.org/program/diversity/index.html
Drudge Report
http://www.drudgereport.com/
Duthie's Books
http://www.literascape.com
Editing for Magazines
http://www.well.com/user/mmcadams/copy.editing.html
Editor & Publisher Interactive
http://www.mediainfo.com
Electronic Frontier Foundation
http://www.eff.org
Electronic Rights Defense Committee
http://www.erights.qc.ca
The Electronic Telegraph
http://www.telegraph.co.uk/
The Exile
http://www.exile.ru/index.htm
Freedom Forum
http://www.freedomforum.org/
Global Advertising Industry Overview
http://www.newspage.com/browse
Grateful Dead Concerts Online
http://www.deadradio.com
Internet Movie Database
http://us.imdb.org/Movies/credits.html
ITP Nelson
http://www.nelson.com
Jerusalem Post
http://www.jpost.co.il
Journal of Electronic Publishing
http://www.press.umich.edu/jep
Lilith Fair
http://lilithfair.excite.com/
***Maclean's* Magazine**
http://www.macleans.ca
Market Guide to the Motion Picture Industry
http://www.marketguide.com/MGI/INDUSTRY/movies.htm
McClelland & Stewart
http://www.mcclelland.com
Media Awareness Network
http://www.screen.com/mnet/eng/issues/stats/stats.htm

Media History Project on the Web
http://www.mediahistory.com
Mediapolis
http://mediapolis.es/
MIT Media Lab Project
http://casr.www.media.mit.edu/groups/casr/papert.html
Motion Picture Industry: Behind the Scenes
http://library.advanced.org/10015
Motion Picture Industry Book
http://www.studentcenter.com/where/industry/IN7822.htm
National Public Radio
http://www.realaudio.com/content/nrp.html
The New Media Monitor
http://www.gpnet.it/dallomo/
Newslink to Most Major Newspapers, Magazines, and Broadcasts
http://www.newslink.org
Newspapers on the Web
http://www.naa.org/hotlinks.index.asp
North American Television Listings
http://www.clicktv.com/
Online Public Relations
http://www.connectingonline.com/anchors/online public relations.html
Pauley Report on Broadcast Journalism
http://www.spj.org/pauleyreport/index.htm
PBS
http://www.pbs.org/Welcome.html
Radio-Television News Directors Ethics Codes
http://www.missouri.edu/~jourvs
Real Networks
http://www.real.com
Recording Industry Association of America
http://www.riaa.com/
Reporters Committee for Freedom of the Press
http://www.rcpf.org/rcpf
Ryerson Review of Journalism On-line
http://www.ryerson.ca/rrj/
Salon Magazine
http://www.salonmagazine.com
Society for the History of Authorship, Reading and Publishing
http://www.indiana.edu/~sharp
Sony
http://www.sony.com
Statistics Canada
http://www.statcan.ca
Surfing the Aether: Radio and Technology History
http://www.the-bridge.net/~bchris/index.htm
Ten Big Myths about Copyright Explained
http://www.templetons.com/brad/copymyths.html
TSN Sports Scoreboard
http://www.tsn.ca/scoreboard/

Women in Film
   http://www.cinema.ucla,edu/women/
World Net Daily
   http://www.WorldNetDaily.com

Using On-line Search Services

In addition to print indexes, several on-line services and electronic databases offer access to information about the media. However, keep in mind the following when using electronic databases for research:

1. Some libraries charge fees for on-line searches based on the computer time required. To avoid unnecessary costs, define your subject as specifically as possible.

2. Many of the listings are duplicates. Reprinted articles may appear in several different publications under different titles.

3. On-line searches are best for current information only. Most electronic databases contain information from only the preceding five to ten years. For the best historical information, you may have to return to print indexes.

Several electronic databases are useful for mass media research:

◎ Biography Master Index—information on where prominent individuals are cited in various biographical sources.

◎ Com Index—a new microcomputer-based retrieval system that includes selected journals in the communications field.

◎ Dissertation Abstracts Online—access to citations on doctoral dissertations accepted at North American universities since 1861.

◎ Dow Jones News Retrieval—access to eight news wires, including Dow Jones, *Los Angeles Times*, *Washington Post*, and many regional newspapers.

◎ Newsearch—a daily index to 2000 news stories and features from the National Newspaper Index and from popular magazines, trade and industry journals, legal periodicals, and press releases from PR Newswire.

◎ PR Newswire—complete text of news releases prepared by a variety of companies, public relations agencies, and governments.

Uncovering Media History

A History of Journalism in Canada by Wilfred Kesterton (Toronto: McClelland & Stewart) is a comprehensive source for the history of Canadian print journalism. *The Law and the Press in Canada*, also by Kesterton (Toronto: McClelland & Stewart, 1976), provides further research on the topic.

   Additional sources for Canadian newspaper history include *A Victorian Authority: The Daily Press in Late Nineteenth Century Canada* by Paul Rutherford (Toronto: University of Toronto Press, 1990) and *The Canadian Illustrated News 1869–1883* by Peter Desbarats (Toronto: McClelland &

Stewart, 1970). In his memoir *A Funny Way to Run a Country* (Edmonton: Hurtig, 1986), Charles Lynch recounts his experiences as a journalist from World War II to the 1980s.

An overview of television history is provided by Paul Rutherford in his book *When Television Was Young: Primetime Canada 1952–67* (Toronto: University of Toronto Press, 1990). Robert Babe's *Canadian Television Broadcasting Structure, Performance and Regulation* (Ottawa: Supply and Services, 1986) describes the regulation of the industry. Also of interest are *Closed Circuits: The Sellout of Canadian Television* by Herschel Hardin (Toronto: Douglas & McIntyre, 1985); *The Politics of Canadian Broadcasting 1920–1951* by Frank W. Peers (Toronto: University of Toronto Press, 1969); and *The Public Eye: Television and the Politics of Canadian Broadcasting 1952–1968*, also by Frank W. Peers (Toronto: University of Toronto Press, 1979).

Canadian National Theatre on the Air, 1925–1961: A Descriptive Bibliography by Howard Fink with Brian Morrison (Toronto: University of Toronto Press, 1983) lists numerous sources of information on Canadian drama broadcasting.

For interesting reading on the movie business in Canada, you might turn to Martin Knelman's *Home Movies: Tales from the Canadian Film World* (Toronto: Key Porter, 1987). Knelman was the film reviewer for the *Globe and Mail* in the early 1970s. Other good sources include D.B. Jones's *Movies and Memoranda: An Interpretive History of the National Film Board of Canada* (Ottawa: Canadian Film Institute, 1981) and Peter Harcourt's *Movies and Mythologies: Towards a National Cinema* (Toronto: Canadian Broadcasting Corp., 1977). Good introductions to the U.S. film industry are provided by *A History of Films* by John L. Fell (New York: Holt, Rinehart & Winston, 1979) and *Movie-Made America* by Robert Sklar (New York: Random House, 1975).

Sterling and Kittross's *Stay Tuned: A Concise History of American Broadcasting*, 2nd ed. (Belmont, Calif.: Wadsworth, 1990) provides some information about the recording industry. *This Business of Music* by Sidney Shemel and M. William Krasilovsky (New York: Billboard Publications, 1985) explains the way the recording industry works.

A direct source on the book publishing industry in Canada is the Royal Commission on Book Publishing report *Canadian Publishers and Canadian Publishing* (Toronto: Queen's Printer for Ontario, 1973). A recommended source of statistics on the book trade is *The Book Publishing and Manufacturing Industry in Canada: A Statistical and Economic Analysis*, provided by the federal Department of Industry, Trade and Commerce (Ottawa: Information Canada, 1970).

Keith J. Tuckwell provides an overview of advertising in *Canadian Advertising in Action* (Scarborough, Ont: Prentice-Hall Canada, 1995). Information on advertising in the United States can be found in *The Making of Modern Advertising* by Daniel Pope (New York: Basic Books, 1983) and *The Mirror Makers: A History of Twentieth Century American Advertising* by Stephen Fox (New York: Morrow, 1984).

In 1923, Edward L. Bernays wrote the first book specifically about public relations, *The Engineering of Consent* (Norman: University of Oklahoma Press, reprinted in 1955). For an understanding of today's public relations business, you can read *This is PR: The Realities of Public Relations* by Doug Newsom, Alan Scott, and Judy VanSlyke Turk (Belmont, Calif.: Wadsworth, 1993).

For information about historical events and people in the media who often are omitted from other histories, you can refer to *Up from the Footnote: A History of Women Journalists* by Marion Marzolf (New York: Hastings House, 1977); *Great Women of the Press* by Madelon Golden Schilpp and Sharon M. Murphy (Carbondale: Southern Illinois University Press, 1983); *Minorities and Media: Diversity and the End of Mass Communication* by Clint C. Wilson and Felix Gutiérrez (Newbury Park, Calif.: Sage, 1985); *Gender, Race and Class in Media* by Gail Dines and Jean M. Humez (Newbury Park, Calif.: Sage, 1994); and *Facing Difference: Race, Gender and Mass Media* by Shirley Biagi and Marilyn Kern-Foxworth (Newbury Park, Calif.: Pine Forge Press, 1997).

For an overview of the media in Canada, you might turn to *Canada's Cultural Industries: Broadcasting, Publishing, Records and Film* by Paul Audley (Toronto: Lorimer, 1983). Benjamin D. Singer's *Communications in Canadian Society*, 4th ed. (Toronto: Nelson Canada, 1995) is a collection of important readings on the history of media development and activities in Canada.

Finding the Best Index

Another good place to begin specific mass media research is with an index. Indexes provide quick, comprehensive access to listings of articles about the mass media industries. Pick a subject heading about your topic, then check the most likely index from the following print index list that catalogues information about your topic. You may have to check two or more indexes to locate all of the citations you need.

Print Indexes

Access: The Supplementary Index to Periodicals

Arts and Humanities Citation Index

Business Index

Business Periodicals Index

Communication Abstracts

Current Contents

Film Literature Index

Graphic Arts Literature Abstracts

Humanities Index

Index to Legal Periodicals

Journalism Monographs

Library Literature

Popular Periodicals Index

Readers' Guide

Sociofile

Trade and Industry Index

Ulrich's Periodicals Index

Magazines for Media Research

Many magazines publish information about the mass media industries and support industries. The following is an alphabetical listing of the major magazines in each subject area. If a periodical is indexed, the name of the index appears in parentheses.

Advertising

Advertising Age (Business Periodicals Index)
Adweek/Adweek: National Marketing Edition (Business Periodicals Index)
Affiliated Advertising Agencies International (Ulrich's Periodicals Index)
Journal of Advertising (Business Periodicals Index)
International Journal of Advertising (Ulrich's Periodicals Index)
Marketing Magazine (Canadian Periodical Index)
Marketing Online (Canadian Periodical Index)

Broadcasting

Broadcasting & Cable (Business Periodicals Index)
Broadcast Weekly (Broadcasting & Cable Yearbook)
Cable and Satellite Europe (Broadcasting & Cable Yearbook)
Cablecaster (Canadian Periodical Index)
Cablevision (Ulrich's Periodicals Index)
Eastern European & Soviet Telecon Report (Broadcasting & Cable Yearbook)
Electronic Media (Ulrich's Periodicals Index)
Emmy, published by the Academy of Television Arts and Sciences (Access: The Supplementary Index to Periodicals)
Journal of Broadcasting and Electronic Media, published by Broadcast Education Association (Communications Abstracts)
Television Digest
TV Guide (Access: The Supplementary Index to Periodicals)
Video Week (Ulrich's Periodicals Index)

Magazine and Book Publishing

Books in Canada (Canadian Periodical Index)
Canadian Author (Canadian Periodical Index)
Canadian Bookseller (Canadian Periodical Index)
Folio, the magazine for magazine management (Trade and Industry Index)
Masthead (Canadian Periodical Index)
Publishers Weekly (Business Periodicals Index)
Quill & Quire (Canadian Periodical Index)

Media-Related Topics

Canadian Journal of Communication (Canadian Periodical Index)
Canadian Journal of Educational Communications (Canadian Periodical Index)

Censorship News, published by the (U.S.) National Coalition Against Censorship

Communication Research (Communication Abstracts)

Communications and the Law (Index to Legal Periodicals)

Entertainment Law Reporter, covers motion pictures, radio, TV, and music (Index to Legal Periodicals)

NewMedia Canada Magazine (Canadian Periodical Index)

Wired (Business Periodicals Index)

Movies

American Film (Arts and Humanities Citation Index)

Film Comment (Arts and Humanities Citation Index)

Hollywood Reporter

Variety (Business Index)

Video Review, covers video for home viewing

Newspapers

Editor & Publisher: The Fourth Estate (Business Periodicals Index)

Journalism Monographs, published by the Association for Education in Journalism and Mass Communication (Communication Abstracts)

International Media Guide, Newspapers Worldwide

Newspaper Financial Executive Journal, published by International Newspaper Financial Executives (Encyclopedia of Business Information Sources)

Newspaper Research Journal, published by the Association for Education in Journalism and Mass Communication (Communication Abstracts)

Presstime, published by the Newspaper Association of America (Graphic Arts Literature Abstracts)

Quill, published by the Society of Professional Journalists (Humanities Index)

Ryerson Review of Journalism (Canadian Periodical Index)

Periodicals

InterMedia (Broadcasting & Cable Yearbook)

Public Relations

Public Relations Journal (Business Periodicals Index)

Public Relations Quarterly (Business Periodicals Index)

Public Relations Review (Communication Abstracts)

Recordings

Billboard (Business Periodicals Index)

Cash Box (Encyclopedia of Business Information Sources)

Down Beat (Readers' Guide)

Music Index, a separate index that covers articles on the music industry
Music Review (Ulrich's Periodicals Index)
Rolling Stone (Popular Periodicals Index)

Other

World Press Review
Media International (Ulrich's Periodicals Index)
OPMA Overseas Media Guide (Ulrich's Periodicals Index)

END NOTES

Chapter 1 You in the New Information Age

1. George Gilder, "Life After Television, Updated," *Forbes*, Feb. 28, 1994, Dow//Quest ID#0000385340ZF.
2. Ibid.
3. Melvin L. DeFleur and Everette E. Dennis, *Understanding Mass Communication*, 2nd ed. (Boston: Houghton Mifflin, 1986), p. 5. This is an abbreviated and modified version of DeFleur and Dennis's definition.
4. Gilder.
5. Thomas R. King, "News Corp's Twentieth-Century Fox Forms Unit to Make 'Mainstream' Films," *The Wall Street Journal*, Aug. 23, 1994, p. B-5.
6. Ibid.
7. From the Conclusion of *The Road to the Future: Preparing Canada for a Digital World, the Final Report of the Information Highway Advisory Council*. On-line: http://strategis.ic.gc.ca/SSG/ih01647.e.html
8. Bart Ziegler, "Building the Highway: New Obstacles, New Solutions," *The Wall Street Journal*, May 18, 1994, p. B-1.
9. Ibid.
10. Philip Elmer Dewitt, "Electronic Superhighway," *Time*, April 12, 1993, p. 53.
11. Ziegler.
12. Ibid.
13. "It's the End of the World As We Know It ... And I Feel Fine." *The Economist 330*, no. 7850 (Feb. 12, 1994): 17.
14. Special calculations, General Social Survey, Cycle 7, 1992.
15. This is a projected estimate based on *The Veronis, Suhler & Associates Communications Industry Forecast 1997–2001*.
16. National Rates. On-line: http://www.tcp.ca/Ad/top-adrates-98/rates-national.htm
17. Ken Auletta, "The Pirate," *The New Yorker*, November 13, 1995, pp. 80–93.
18. John Seabrook, "Why Is the Force Still With Us?" *The New Yorker*, January 6, 1997, pp. 40–53.
19. View Desk (Bob Sipchen and John Lindsay), "Bill Gates Charts 'The Road Ahead,'" *Los Angeles Times*, December 5, 1996, Dow/Quest LATM9634000484.
20. Anthony Smith, *Goodbye Gutenberg* (New York: Oxford University Press, 1980), p. 6.
21. Plato, *Collected Works* (Princeton, N.J.: Phaedrus, 1961), pp. 520–21.
22. Smith, p. 5.
23 Ibid., p. 8.
24. Edupage, 26, October 1997. On-line: www.educom.edu

Chapter 2 Newspapers

1. Marion Marzoff, *Up from the Footnote* (New York: Hastings House, 1977), p. 2.
2. Ibid., pp. 1–11.
3. The National Library of Canada, National Bibliography. On-line. Available: www.hlc-bnc.ca
4. Lauren Kessler, *The Dissident Press* (Beverly Hills: Sage, 1984), p. 21.

5. Edwin Emery and Michael Emery, *The Press and America*, 6th ed. (Englewood Cliffs, N.J.: Prentice-Hall, 1988), p. 36.
6. W.A. Swanberg, *Citizen Hearst* (New York: Bantam Books, 1971), p. 68.
7. Emery and Emery, p. 241.
8. Emery and Emery, p. 35.
9. James N. Dertouzos and Timothy H. Quinn, "Bargaining Responses to the Technology Revolution: The Case of the Newspaper Industry," *Labor Management Cooperation Brief*, U.S. Department of Labor, September 1985, p. 7.
10. James Winter, *Democracy's Oxygen: How Corporate News Media Smother the Facts* (Montreal: Black Rose Books, 1996).
11. Anthony Smith, *Goodbye Gutenberg* (New York: Oxford University Press, 1980), p. 52
12. Patrick M. Reilly, "Newspapers Are Paging Young Readers," *The Wall Street Journal*, May 6, 1991, p. B-1.
13. Karen Jurgenson, "Diversity: A Report from the Battlefield," *Newspaper Research Journal* 14, no. 2 (Spring 1993): 92.
14. Reilly.

Chapter 3 Magazines

1. Madelon Golden Schilpp and Sharon M. Murphy, *Great Women of the Press* (Carbondale: Southern Illinois University Press, 1983), p. 44.
2. W.A. Swanberg, *Luce and His Empire* (New York: Scribner's, 1972) p. 57.
3. Deidre Carmody, "A Guide to New Magazines Shows Widespread Vitality," *The New York Times*, Feb. 25, 1991, p. C-1.
4. Ibid.
5. *The Magazine Hand Book* 1992–1993. Magazine Publishers of America, p. 39.
6. James B. Kobak, "1984: A Billion-Dollar Year for Acquisitions," *Folio* 14, no. 4 (April 1985): 82–95.
7. Karlene Lukovitz, "The Next 10 Years: 24 Predictions for the Future," *Folio* 11, no. 9 (September 1982): 103.

Chapter 4 Books

1. E.B. White, *Letters of E.B. White*, ed. Dorothy Lobrano Guth (New York: Harper & Row, 1976), p. 571.
2. Lewis A. Coser, Charles Kadushin, and Walter W. Powell, *Books: The Culture & Commerce of Publishing* (New York: Basic Books, 1982), p. 7.
3. Ibid.
4. James D. Hart, *The Popular Book* (Berkeley: University of California Press, 1950), p. 9.
5. Ibid., p. 57.
6. Ibid., p. 138.
7. Ibid., p. 151.
8. Ibid., p. 185.
9. Ibid., p. 274.
10. Kenneth C. Davis, *Two-Bit Culture: The Paperbacking of America* (Boston: Houghton Mifflin, 1984), p. xii.
11. Ibid., p. 316.
12. John P. Dessauer, *Book Publishing: What It Is, What It Does* (New York: R.R. Bowker, 1974), p. 8.
13. Coser, Kadushin, and Powell, p. 7.
14. [to come]
15. U.S. Department of Commerce: *The Veronis, Suhler & Associates Communications Industry Forecast 1997–2001*, pp. 27–29.
16. Coser, Kadushin, and Powell, p. 14.
17. Ibid., p. 43.
18. Laura Lanaro, "Publishers' Thirst for Blockbusters Sparks Big Advances and Big Risks," *The Wall Street Journal*, Feb. 3, 1986, p. 21.
19. Coser, Kadushin, and Powell, p. 35.

Chapter 5 Radio

1. A.M. Sperber, *Murrow: His Life and Times* (New York: Freundlich, 1986), p. 168.
2. Erik Barnouw, *Tube of Plenty* (New York: Oxford University Press, 1978), p. 9.
3. Ibid., p. 13.
4. Ibid., p. 15.
5. Irving Settel, *A Pictorial History of Radio* (New York: Citadel Press, 1960), p. 32.
6. Ibid., p. 39.
7. Barnouw, p. 145.
8. Peter Fornatale and Joshua E. Mills, *Radio in the Television Age* (New York: Overlook Press, 1980), p. 20.
9. David R. MacFarland, *The Development of the Top 40 Radio Format* (New York: Arno Press, 1979), p. 46.
10. Ibid., p. 44.
11. Ibid., p. 53.
12. *The Veronis, Suhler & Associates Communications Industry Forecast*, June 1992, p. 86.
13. On-line. Available: http://www.bbm.ca/radio/math/terms.htm
14. Eric Zorn, "Radio Lives!" reprinted from *Esquire* in *Readings in Mass Communication*, 6th ed., eds. Michael Emery and Ted Curtis Smythe (Dubuque, Iowa: Wm. C. Brown, 1986), pp. 340–41.
15. Ibid., p. 339.

Chapter 6 Recordings

1. R. Serge Denisoff, *Solid Gold* (New Brunswick, N.J.: Transaction Books, 1975), p. 1.
2. Robert Metz, *CBS: Reflections in a Bloodshot Eye* (Chicago: Playboy Press, 1975), pp. 147–48.
3. Ibid., p. 153.
4. James D. Harless, *Mass Communication: An Introductory Survey* (Dubuque, Iowa: Wm. C. Brown, 1985), p. 201.
5. David Pauly, "A Compact Sonic Boom," *Newsweek*, Dec. 6, 1985, p. 47; *U.S. Industrial Outlook* 1991, pp. 32–33.
6. *Billboard* 52, no. 104 (Dec. 26, 1992):14, 99.
7. Jeffrey Zaslow, "New Rock Economics Make It Harder to Sing Your Way to Wealth," *The Wall Street Journal*, May 21, 1985, p. 1.
8. Ibid.
9. Stephen Dreider Yoder, "Digital Tape Is Inevitable: So Why the Delay?" *The Wall Street Journal*, Aug. 12, 1986, p. 29.
10. *Revving Fast Forward*. Recording Industry Association, 1995, p. 34.
11. Robert Epstein, "Now It's the Recording Industry's Turn to Face the Music," *Los Angeles Times*, Nov. 22, 1990, p. F-1.
12. John Rockwell, "Compact Disks Are Here to Conquer," *The New York Times*, Feb. 9, 1986, p. H-1.
13. James R. Smart, *A Wonderful Invention: A Brief History of the Phonograph from Tinfoil to the LP* (Washington: Library of Congress, 1977) p. 6.
14. Metz, p. 146.

Chapter 7 Television

1. Doug Saunders, "Why Canadian TV will soon be more Canadian." *The Globe and Mail*, July 25, 1998.
2. Statistics Canada Daily, "Television and Radio Audiences," Feb. 5, 1998, p. 1.
3. Jeff Greenfield, *Television: The First Fifty Years* (New York: Abrams, 1977), pp. 52–53.
4. Erik Barnouw, *Tube of Plenty* (New York: Oxford University Press, 1975), p. 17.
5. Les Brown, *The Television: The Business Behind the Box* (New York: Harcourt Brace Jovanovich, 1971), p. 43.
6. Shirley Biagi, *NewsTalk II* (Belmont Calif.: Wadsworth, 1987), p. 140.
7. Ibid.
8. Saunders.
9. Newton Minow, *Equal Time: The Private Broadcaster and the Public Interest* (New York: Atheneum, 1964), p. 51.

10. Ibid., p. 317.
11. Greenfield, p. 234.
12. Christopher H. Sterling and John M. Kittross, *Stay Tuned: A Concise History of American Broadcasting*, 2nd ed. (Belmont, Calif.: Wadsworth, 1990), p. 414.
13. Statistics Canada, *Cable Television Statistics*, 1996, Catalogue 56-001-XPB, October 1997, p. 1.
14. John Lippman, "Southwestern Looks to Enter Cable Race," *Los Angeles Times*, Nov. 5, 1993, p. D-1.
15. Julie Amparano Lopez and Mary Lu Carnevale, "Fiber Optics Promises a Revolution of Sorts, If the Sharks Don't Bite," *The Wall Street Journal*, July 10, 1990, p. A-1.
16. Ibid.

Chapter 8 Movies

1. Jason E. Squire, ed., *The Movie Business Book* (New York: Simon & Schuster, 1983), p. 3.
2. Ibid., p. 2.
3. Robert Sklar, *Movie-Made America* (New York: Random House, 1975), p. 9.
4. Tino Balio, *The American Film Industry* (Madison: University of Wisconsin Press, 1976), p. 27.
5. Sklar, p. 16.
6. Ibid., p. 36.
7. Ibid., p. 40.
8. Balio, p. 75.
9. Jack C. Ellis, *A History of American Film*, 2nd ed. (Englewood Cliffs, N.J.: Prentice-Hall, 1985), p. 43.
10. Balio, p. 112.
11. *Moving Picture World*, Feb. 1, 1919, p. 619.
12. Motion Picture Association of America, *Motion Picture Production Code*, 1954, p. 2.
13. Ibid., pp. 2–5.
14. Balio, p. 209.
15. Ibid., p. 213.
16. Dalton Trumbo, *Additional Dialogue: Letters of Dalton Trumbo: 1942–1962* (New York: M. Evans, 1970), p. 301.
17. Balio, p. 372.
18. Ibid., p. 315.
19. Sklar, p. 389.
20. David J. Jefferson, "Movie-Making Cost Record $28.8 Million in '92, Valenti Tells U.S. Theatre Owners," *The Wall Street Journal*, March 10, 1993, p. B-5.
21. Michael Cieply and Peter W. Barnes, "Movie and TV Mergers Point to Concentration of Power to Entertain," *The Wall Street Journal*, Aug. 21, 1986, p. 1.
22. Squire, p. 155.
23. Ibid., p. 150.
24. Statistics Canada, *Canada's Culture, Heritage and Identity: A Statistical Perspective*, 1997 edition. Catalogue 87-211-XPB. Table 4.1a, p. 56.
25. Ibid., Table 4.1.1a, p. 57.
26. Ibid., p. 57.
27. Ibid., p. 58.
28. Ibid., p. 61.
29. *The Globe and Mail*, May 15, 1997.
30. "Interactive Video Games," *Mediascope*, June 1996.
31. Squire, p. 298.
32. Thomas R. King, "Theatre Chain Has Plans to Jolt Movie Viewers," *The Wall Street Journal*, Aug. 18, 1994, p. B-1.
33. "The World Is Hollywood's Oyster," *Business Week* 3195 (Jan. 14, 1991): 97.
34. Cieply and Barnes.
35. Ibid.

Chapter 9 New Media, On-line Media, and the Web

1. Roger Fidler, *Mediamorphosis* (Thousand Oaks, Calif.: Pine Forge Press, 1997), 100–101.
2. Ibid, 103.
3. EMA Global Internet Statistics. On-line: http://www.euroktg.com/globstats/

4. Fidler, 209.
5. "The Book of the Future," *Frames* (January 1996: 51), 1.
6. Mick LaSalle, "Get a Really Good Picture—for Only $250,000," *San Francisco Chronicle*, January 13, 1998, E1.
7. Fidler, 180, 233.
8. Fidler, 22–23.
9. Ibid.
10. Ibid., 26.
11. Ibid., 373.
12. Ibid.
13. "Paul Saffo and the 30-year Rule," *Design World*, 24 (1992): 18.
14. "Net Numbers," *The Financial Post*, August 29, 1998, R27. Full results on-line: http://www.commerce.net/research/gideon
15. Robert Wright, "The Man Who Invented the Web," *Time*, May 19, 1997, p. 68.
16. David Shaw, "Internet Gold Rush Hasn't Panned Out Yet for Most," *Los Angeles Times*, June 19, 1997, A-1.
17. Ibid.
18. Ibid.
19. Julia Angwin, "Now You Got to Pay to Play Online," *San Francisco Chronicle*, June 20, 1997, B-1.
20. Ibid.
21. Ibid.
22. Shaw.
23. Ibid.

Chapter 10 Advertising

1. Daniel J. Boorstin, "The Rhetoric of Democracy," in *American Mass Media: Industries and Issues*, 3rd ed., eds. Robert Atwan, Barry Orton, and William Vesterman (New York: Random House, 1986), p. 37.
2. Ibid.
3. Robert Atwan, "Newspapers and the Foundations of Modern Advertising," in *The Commercial Connection*, ed. John W. Wright (New York: Doubleday, 1979), p. 16.
4. Edgar R. Jones, *Those Were the Good Old Days* (New York: Simon & Schuster, 1979), p. 35.
5. Ibid., p. 44.
6. Atwan.
7. Stephen Fox, *The Mirror Makers: A History of American Advertising and Its Creators* (New York: Morrow, 1984), p. 15.
8. Ibid., p. 32.
9. Ibid., p. 155.
10. Ibid., p. 210.
11. Ibid., p. 212.
12. Ibid.
13. Boorstin.
14. Ibid.
15. Ibid.
16. Ibid.
17. Jib Fowles, "Advertising's Fifteen Basic Appeals," in *American Mass Media: Industries and Issues*, p. 43.
18. Ibid., pp. 46–52.
19. Michael Schudson, *Advertising: The Uneasy Persuasion* (New York: Basic Books, 1984), p. 13.
20. Louis C. Kaufman, *Essentials of Advertising*, 2nd ed. (New York: Harcourt Brace Jovanovich, 1987), p. 510.
21. Schudson, p. 13.
22. Jonathan Price, "Now a Few Words About Commercials..." in *American Mass Media: Industries and Issues*, p. 63.
23. Radio Advertising Bureau, *Radio Facts for Advertisers 1989–1990* (New York: Radio Advertising Bureau), p. 28.
24. Sally Goll Beatty, "Seagram Flouts Ban on TV Ads Pitching Liquor," *The Wall Street Journal*, June 11, 1996, p. B-6.
25. *Globe and Mail*, "Doing Business on the Web," August 29, 1997.

Chapter 11 Public Relations

1. Fraser P. Seitel, *The Practice of Public Relations*, 2nd ed. (Columbus, Ohio: Charles E. Merrill, 1984), p. 40.
2. Theodore Lustig, "Great Caesar's Ghost," *Public Relations Journal*, March 1986, pp. 17–19.
3. Doug Newsom and Alan Scott, *This is PR: The Realities of Public Relations*, 3rd ed. (Belmont, Calif.: Wadsworth, 1986), p. 40.
4. Quoted in Sherman Morse, "An Awakening on Wall Street," *American Magazine* 62 (Sept. 1906): 460.
5. Scott Cutlip, Allen H. Center, and Glen M. Broom, *Effective Public Relations*, 3rd ed. (Belmont, Calif.: Wadsworth, 1986), p. 39.
6. Edward L. Bernays, *The Engineering of Consent* (Norman: University of Oklahoma Press, 1955), pp. 3–4.
7. Craig Randall, "The Father of Public Relations: Edward Bernays, 93, Is Still Saucy," *United* 30, no. 11 (November 1985): 50.
8. Newsom and Scott, p. 47.
9. Doris E. Fleischman, "Public Relations—A New Field for Women," *Independent Woman*, February 1931, p. 58, as quoted in Susan Henry, "In Her Own Name?: Public Relations Pioneer Doris Fleischman Bernays," a paper presented to the Committee on the Status of Women Research Session, Association for Education in Journalism and Mass Communication, Portland, Oregon, July 1988.
10. Doug Newsom and Alan Scott in *This Is PR* are especially dilligent about chronicling women's contributions to public relations. This specific information appears on p. 49.
11. "Interview: Henry Rogers," *PSA* 21, no. 10 (October 1986): 70.
12. Canadian Public Relations Society Code of Professional Ethics. On-line: http://www.cprs.ca/cprscode.html
13. James K. Gentry, "The Best and Worst Corporate PR," *Washington Journalism Review* 8, no. 7 (July 1986): 38–40.
14. Stephanie Nolen, "Fame, Friends, Fortune," *Maclean's*, April 13, 1998, p. 40
15. Ibid.
16. Lawrence G. Foster, "The Role of Public Relations in the Tylenol Crisis," *Public Relations Journal*, March 1983, p. 13.
17. Jeff Blyskal and Marie Blyskal, "Making the Best of Bad News," *Washington Journalism Review* 7, no.12 (December 1985): 52.
18. *County Business Patterns 1989*, U.S. Bureau of the Census, December 1991.
19. *Public Relations Journal* 49, no. 3, March 1993; Newsom and Scott, p. 69.
20. "Japanese Said Lagging in PR," *Los Angeles Times*, reprinted in *The Sacramento Bee*, Dec. 8, 1986, p. C-3.
21. Summarized from a list of work assignments listed in Cutlip, Center, and Broom, p. 64.
22. Jeff Blyskal and Marie Blyskal, PR: *How the Public Relations Industry Writes the News* (New York: Morrow, 1985), p. 46.
23. Craig Bromberg, "Goliath Pitch Behind Times. 'David Story,'" *Manhattan, inc.* 4, no. 4 (April 1987): 18.
24. Joanne Angela Ambrosio, "It's in the Journal, But This Is Reporting?" *Columbia Journalism Review 18*, no. 6 (March/April 1980): 35.
25. Bromberg.
26. Blyskal and Blyskal, *PR*, p. 82.

Chapter 12 Mass Media and Social Issues

1. Lynn Smith, "Calls to L.A. Domestic Abuse Lines Jump 80%," *Los Angeles Times*, June 24, 1994, Dow//Quest.
2. William L. Rivers and Wilbur Schramm, "The Impact of Mass Communications," in *American Mass Media: Industries and Issues*, 3rd ed., eds. Robert Atwan, Barry Orton, and William Vesterman (New York: Random House, 1986), pp. 11–12.
3. David M. Potter, *People of Plenty* (Chicago: University of Chicago Press, 1954), p. 167.
4. Robert M. Liebert and Joyce Sprafkin, *The Early Window*, 3rd ed. (New York: Pergamon Press, 1988), p. 161.
5. Kathleen McConnell and Eugene D. Tate, "The Mass Media and Violence," in *Communications in Canadian Society*, 4th ed., ed. Benjamin Singer (Scarborough, Ont.: ITP Nelson, 1995).

6. "Synopsis of FTC Staff Report on Television Advertising to Children," in *The Commercial Connection*, ed. John W. Wright (New York: Dell, 1979), pp. 340–42.

7. Scott Ward, cited in George Comstock et al., *Television and Human Behavior* (New York: Columbia University Press, 1978), p. 199.

8. James David Barber, *The Pulse of Politics: Electing Presidents in the Media Age* (New York: Norton, 1986), p. 150.

9. Ibid., p. 246.

10. Thomas E. Patterson and Robert D. McClure, *The Unseeing Eye: The Myth of Television Power in National Elections* (New York: Putnam, 1976), p. 113.

11. Joseph C. Spear, *Presidents and the Press* (Cambridge, Mass.: MIT Press, 1984), p. 52.

12. Herbert E. Alexander, *Financing the 1980 Election* (Lexington, Mass.: D.C. Heath, 1983); Herbert E. Alexander and Brian A. Haggerty, *Financing the 1984 Election* (Lexington, Mass.; D.C. Heath, 1987).

13. Joshua Meyrowitz, *No Sense of Place* (New York: Oxford University Press, 1985), p. 92.

14. Ibid., p. 242.

15. Walter Lippman, *Public Opinion* (New York: Free Press, 1965), p. 61.

16. Tania Modleski, *Loving with a Vengeance: Mass-Produced Fantasies for Women* (New York: Methuen, 1982), p. 113.

17. Carolyn Marindale, "Only in Glimpses: Portrayal of America's Largest Minority Groups by *The New York Times* 1934–1994," a paper presented at the Association for Education in Journalism and Mass Communication Annual Convention, Washington, D.C., August 1995.

18. Ibid.

19. Neil Postman, *Amusing Ourselves to Death* (New York: Viking Penguin, 1985), pp. 160–61.

20. Ibid.

Chapter 13 Media Ownership and Press Performance

1. James Madison, letter to W.T. Barry, Aug. 4, 1822, in *Letters and Other Writings of James Madison, Fourth President of the United States, Vol. 3, 1816–1818* (Philadelphia: J.B. Lippincott, 1854), p. 276.

2. Walter Lippmann, *Public Opinion* (New York: Free Press, 1965), p. 229.

3. Additional information that has not appeared in preceding chapters is from Ben H. Bagdikian, *The Media Monopoly* (Boston: Beacon Press, 1983); Newspaper Association of America: *Broadcasting & Cable Yearbook 1993* (New Providence, N.J.: Reed Reference Publishing Co., 1993); *U.S. Industrial Outlook 1993*, section 24, p. 11; *Advertising Age*, April 15, 1996, p. 520; Steven Levy, "A Blow to the Empire," *Newsweek*, December 29, 1997/January 5, 1998, 58–60.

4. A.J. Liebling, *The Press* (New York: Ballantine, 1961), pp. 4–5.

5. Michael J. Robinson and Ray Olszewski, "Books in the Marketplace of Ideas," *Journal of Communication 30*, no. 2 (Sping 1980): 82.

6. Joanne Lipman, "Ad Agencies Feverishly Ride a Merger Wave," *The Wall Street Journal*, March 9, 1986, p. 6.

7. Benjamin M. Compaine, *Who Owns the Media?* (White Plains, N.Y.: Knowledge Industry Publications, 1979) p. 26.

8. William A. Henry III, "Learning to Love the Chains," *Washington Journalism Review* 8, no. 9 (September 1986): 16.

9. Philip Weiss, "Invasion of the Gannettoids," *The New Republic*, Feb. 2, 1987, p. 18.

10. Ben H. Bagdikian, "Conglomeration, Concentration, and the Media," *Journal of Communication* 30, no. 2 (Spring 1980): 60.

11. David H. Weaver and G. Cleveland Wilhoit, *The American Journalist in the 1990s, Preliminary Report* (New York: The Freedom Forum, 1992), pp. 1, 2, 7.

12. Ibid.

13. Herbert J. Gans, "Are U.S. Journalists Dangerously Liberal?" *Columbia Journalism Review 24*, no. 4 (November/December 1985): 32–33.

14. See William A. Dorman, "Peripheral Vision: U.S. Journalism and the Third World," *World Policy Journal*, Summer 1986, pp. 419–46.

15. Herbert J. Gans, "The Messages Behind the News," in *Readings in Mass Communication*, 6th ed., eds. Michael Emery and Ted Curtis Smythe (Dubuque, Iowa: Wm. C. Brown, 1986), pp. 161–69.

16. James Reston, *The Artillery of the Press* (New York: Harper & Row, 1966), p. 49.

17. Norman Corwin, *Trivializing America: The Triumph of Mediocrity* (Secaucus, N.J.: Lyle Stuart, 1986), p. 33.
18. Times Mirror, *The People & The Press* (Los Angeles: Times Mirror, 1986), p. 30; Times Mirror, *The People & The Press* (Los Angeles: Times Mirror, 1989), pp. 25-26.
19. Times Mirror, *We're Interested in What You Think* (Los Angeles: Times Mirror, 1987), p. 8.

Chapter 14 Law and Regulation

1. The full document (*A Chronicle of Freedom of Expression in Canada*, Parts 1 and 2), is available on-line at http://insight.mcmaster.ca/org/efc/pages/chronicle/chronicle.html
2. Jeff Blyskal and Marie Blyskal, PR: *How the Public Relations Industry Writes the News* (New York: Morrow, 1985), p. 15.
3. "Notes and Comment," *The New Yorker* LXVI, no. 51 (Feb. 4, 1991): 21.
4. Thomas B. Rosenstiel, "The Media Take a Pounding," *Los Angeles Times*, Feb. 20, 1991, p. A1.
5. Rodney A. Smolla, *Suing the Press* (New York: Oxford University Press, 1986), p. 257.
6. Donn Downey, "Globe loses libel case," *Globe and Mail*, July 4, 1998, p. A5.
7. Christopher Stern, "The V-chip: First Amendment Infringement vs. Empowerment Tool," *Broadcasting & Cable*, February 12, 1996 (Dow Jones News Retrieval).
8. Sylvia Rubin, "New TV Ratings Unveiled—To Renewed Criticism," *San Francisco Chronicle*, December 20, 1996, p. A-1.
9. Benton Foundation, *The Telecommunications Act of 1996 and the Changing Communications Landscape* (Washington, D.C.: Benton Foundation, 1996), pp. 7–8.

Chapter 15 Ethics

1. Anthony Brandt, "Truth and Consequences," *Esquire* 102, no. 4 (October 1984): 27.
2. John Hulteng, *The Messenger's Motives: Ethical Problems of the News Media* (Englewood Cliffs, N.J.: Prentice-Hall, 1985), p. 221.
3. Tom Goldstein, *The News at Any Cost* (New York: Simon & Schuster, 1985), p. 217.
4. Ibid., p. 218.
5. "ABC: Walters Wrong to Be Iran Messenger," *The Sacramento Bee*, March 17, 1987, p. 1.
6. Ibid.
7. "Federal Judge Finds Winans, Two Others Guilty," *The Wall Street Journal*, June 25, 1985, p. 2.
8. M.L. Stein, "Survey on Freebies," *Editor & Publisher*, May 31, 1986, p. 11.
9. Alan Prendergast, "Mickey Mouse Journalism," *Washington Journalism Review* 9, no. 1 (January/February 1987): 32.
10. Richard Harwood, "What Is This Thing Called 'News'?" *Washington Post*, March 12, 1994 Dow//Quest ID#0000096451WP.
11. Jonathon Alter with Peter McKillop, "AIDS and the Right to Know," *Newsweek*, Aug. 18, 1986, p. 46.
12. Dale Van Atta, "Faint Light, Dark Print," *Harper's* 273, no. 1,638 (November 1986): 57.
13. Ibid.
14. Elizabeth Jensen, "NBC-Sponsored Inquiry Calls GM Crash on News Program a Lapse in Judgment," *The Wall Street Journal*, March 23, 1993, p. B10.
15. Kevin Helliker, "CNN Got Its Story About Poisoned Eagles, But Rancher Cries Foul," *The Wall Street Journal*, November 25, 1997, p. A-1.
16. Clifford G. Christians, Kim B. Rozoll, and Mark Fackler, *Media Ethics*, 2nd ed. (New York: Longman, 1987), pp. 9–17.
17. Andy Rooney, "The Journalist's Code of Ethics," in *Pieces of My Mind* (New York: Atheneum, 1984), pp. 59–60.
18. Hulteng, pp. 215–16.
19. John Hulteng, "Get It While It's Hot," *feed/back* 12, nos. 1 and 2 (Fall 1985/Winter 1986): 16.

Chapter 16 A Global Media Marketplace

1. "Nigeria Cracks Down on Media," *San Francisco Chronicle*, July 24, 1993, p. A-18; Michael Williams, "'Gaman' Adds Spice to Japanese Life and Its TV Fare," *The Wall Street Journal*, March 5, 1993, p. A-1; Mark Fineman, "Iraqis Plugging In to Youth TV," *Los Angeles Times*, Aug. 3, 1993, p. H-2; Kevin Helliker, "Drop That Remote! In Britain, Watching TV Can Be a Crime," *The Wall Street Journal*, Sept. 27, 1993, p. A-1.
2. Fred S. Siebert, Theodore Peterson, and Wilbur Schramm, *Four Theories of the Press* (Urbana: University of Illinois Press, 1963), p. 135.
3. Lowndes F. Stephens, "The World's Media Systems: An Overview," *Global Journalism: Survey of International Communication*, 2nd ed. (New York: Longman, 1991), p. 62.
4. Ibid., p. 680.
5. Ibid., p. 96.
6. Philip Revzin and Mark M. Nelson, "European TV Industry Goes Hollywood," *The Wall Street Journal*, Oct. 3, 1989, p. A-18.
7. Marshall.
8. Blaine Harden, "'Maniacs on TV Wake Up Poland," *Washington Post*, March 11, 1990, p. A-20.
9. Associated Press, "Media Chiefs Fired; Allegedly Backed Coup," *The Sacramento Bee*, Aug. 27, 1991, p. A-11.
10. Everette E. Dennis and Jon Vanden Heuvel, *Emerging Voices: East European Media in Transition* (New York: Gannett Center for Media Studies, October 1990), p. 2.
11. Mort Rosenblum, "TV Takes the Center Stage in Romanian Revolution," *The Sacramento Bee*, Dec. 17, 1989, p. A-11.
12. Manny Paraschos, "Europe," *Global Journalism: Survey of International Communications*, 2nd ed. (New York: Longman, 1991), p. 124.
13. The Associated Press, "Ads for Comrades: Soviets Run U.S. Commercials," *The Sacramento Bee*, May 18, 1988, p. E-1; Mark J. Porubcansky, "Soviet Paper Finally Prints Capitalist Ads," *The Sacramento Bee*, Jan. 4, 1989, p. C-4; *Baltimore Sun*, "Censorship Outlawed in the U.S.S.R.," *The Sacramento Bee*, June 13, 1990, p. A-8.
14. Laurie Hays and Andrea Rutherford, "Gorbachev Bids to Crack Down on Soviet Press," *The Wall Street Journal*, Jan. 17, 1991, p. A-8.
15. Dennis and Vanden Heuvel.
16. Christine Ogan, "Middle East and North Africa," *Global Journalism: Survey of International Communication*, 2nd ed. (New York: Longman, 1991), p. 130.
17. Ibid., p. 135.
18. Ibid.
19. Charles P. Wallace, "Radio: Town Crier of the Arab World," *Los Angeles Times*, Jan. 7, 1988, p. 1.
20. Ogan, pp. 139–40.
21. L. John Martin, "Africa," *Global Journalism: Survey of International Communication*, 2nd ed. (New York: Longman, 1991), p. 161.
22. Mike Wallace, "The Press Needs a National Monitor," *The Wall Street Journal*, December 18, 1996, DW/Quest J9635300131.
23. Martin.
24. Ibid., p. 190.
25. Ibid.
26. Sydney W. Head, *World Broadcasting Systems* (Belmont, Calif.: Wadsworth, 1985), p. 89.
27. Ibid., p. 90.
28. S. Karene Witcher, "Fairfax Group to Be Placed in Receivership," *The Wall Street Journal*, Dec. 11, 1990, p. A-4.
29. Anne Cooper Chen and Anju Grover Chaudhary, "Asia and the Pacific," *Global Journalism: Survey of International Communication*, 2nd ed. (New York: Longman, 1991), p. 214.
30. Ibid., p. 240.
31. "Publish and Be Ideologically Damned," *The Economist*, October 26, 1996, p. 41.
32. Michael B. Salwen, Bruce Garrison, and Robert T. Buckman, "Latin America and the Caribbean," *Global Journalism: Survey of International Communication*, 2nd ed. (New York: Longman, 1991), pp. 274–85.
33. Ibid.

34. Head, p. 27.
35. Salwen, Garrison, and Buckman, p. 305.
36. Ibid., p. 302.
37. Robert G. Picard, "Global Communications Controversies," *Global Journalism: Survey of International Communication*, 2nd ed. (New York: Longman, 1991), p. 74.
38. Head, p. 381.
39. Elizabeth Hensen, "ABC and BBC to Pool Their Radio-TV News Coverage," *The Wall Street Journal*, March 26, 1993, p. B-1.
40. "Murdoch to Expand Television in India," *Dow Jones International News*, Feb. 15, 1994, Dow//Quest.
41. Andrew Pollack, "Japan's Master Maverick of the Internet," *The New York Times*, Nov. 21, 1993, section 3, p. 3.
42. Ray Josephs and Juanita Josephs, "Public Relations the U.K. Way," *Public Relations Journal*, April 1, 1994, Dow//Quest ID#0000403889ZF.
43. John Lippman, "Tuning In the Global Village," *Los Angeles Times*, Oct. 20, 1992, p. H-2.
44. Ibid.
45. "Wired Planet," *The Economist* 330, no. 7850 (Feb. 12, 1994): 12.
46. "China Refuses to Switch Off," *The Economist* 332, no. 7870 (July 2, 1994): 35.
47. Lippman, p. H-1.
48. "Wired Planet," *The Economist*, p. 18.

INDEX

To the owner of this book

We hope that you have enjoyed *Media/Impact*, and we would like to know as much about your experiences with this text as you would care to offer. Only through your comments and those of others can we learn how to make this a better text for future readers.

School _____ Your instructor's name _____

Course _____ Was the text required? _____ Recommended? _____

1. What did you like the most about *Media/Impact*?

_____

_____

_____

2. How useful was this text for your course?

_____

_____

_____

3. Do you have any recommendations for ways to improve the next edition of this text?

_____

_____

_____

4. In the space below or in a separate letter, please write any other comments you have about the book. (For example, please feel free to comment on reading level, writing style, terminology, design features, and learning aids.)

_____

_____

_____

_____

Optional

Your name _____ Date

_____

May ITP Nelson quote you, either in promotion for *Media/Impact* or in future publishing ventures?

Yes _____ No _____

You can also send your comments to us via e-mail at
college_arts_hum@nelson.com

PLEASE TAPE SHUT. DO NOT STAPLE.

TAPE SHUT

TAPE SHUT

FOLD HERE

Nelson

MAIL ⇒ POSTE

Canada Post Corporation
Société canadienne des postes

Postage paid   Port payé
if mailed in Canada   si posté au Canada
Business Reply   **Réponse d'affaires**

0066102399   **01**

TAPE SHUT

TAPE SHUT

0066102399-M1K5G4-BR01

ITP NELSON
MARKET AND PRODUCT DEVELOPMENT
PO BOX 60225 STN BRM B
TORONTO ON M7Y 2H1